THE GOLDEN AGE
OF SCIENCE

*Thirty Portraits of
the Giants of 19th - Century Science
by Their Scientific Contemporaries*

Edited by BESSIE ZABAN JONES
with an Introduction by
EVERETT MENDELSOHN, Harvard University

Published by
SIMON AND SCHUSTER, NEW YORK
in cooperation with the
SMITHSONIAN INSTITUTION,
WASHINGTON, D.C.

CONTENTS

ALPHABETICAL LISTING

The Context of Nineteenth-Century Science

EVERETT MENDELSOHN
Harvard University

It was during the nineteenth century that science came of age. It was during the same century that the word *scientist* first came into common usage. The context in which the new word was first used by William Whewell is worth examining, for it is illustrative of many of the changes which were taking place during this age when science reached its maturity. "We need very much a word to describe a cultivator of science in general," wrote Whewell. "I should incline to call him a *scientist*. Thus we might say, that as an artist is a musician, painter or poet, a scientist is a mathematician, physicist or naturalist."

Science had moved up and out at the same time. The cultivators of science were moving up from the status of amateur experimenter to that of professional investigator, and as such had become increasingly conscious of their public image. Science was also fragmenting into many specialties, each engaging the whole of a man's energies. Thus, a man was a student of chemistry, of physics, of astronomy, and at the same time a member of a larger group whose general interests transcended the special field of science. In the middle decades of the nineteenth century, *scientist* came to replace the older *natural philosopher* as the descriptive term for men involved in the study of nature.

If the new term *scientist* took several years in gaining full acceptance, this was no less the case for the ideas and institutional forms which make up the activity called science. A series of strong new generalizations were proposed which guided the work of several generations of scientists. The social institution that is science underwent a radical rebuilding, during the course of which the relationship of science to education, to government and to industry was significantly altered. The relevance of science to modern industrial society became more apparent with each passing year and, in turn, added a new set of pressures and demands.

These developments are reflected in this enthralling collection of biographies. That each of the authors was himself a scientist, and that these lives were written primarily as a means of sharing with the whole scientific community the achievements of one of their number, gives these sketches their special quality.

AN AGE OF SYNTHESIS

Charles Darwin was born in 1809, the same year in which Jean Baptiste Lamarck published his *Philosophie Zoologique*. Fifty years later, in 1859, Darwin's *Origin of Species* put forward a theory of organic evolution which had superficial resemblances to the evolutionary proposal advanced by Lamarck in the almost-forgotten treatise of 1809. The importance and widespread influence of Darwin's theory, when contrasted with the virtual obscurity of Lamarck's earlier proposal, give us an insight into what happened to the sciences during the course of the nineteenth century.

Lamarck, on the basis of his own insight and a limited amount of data, had outlined a theory of gradual organic change, depending upon a combination of an innate will to change and the direct environmental influence, to explain the mutability of species. In the years prior to 1859, Lamarckian evolution received scant attention or outright rejection. In Darwin's hands, by contrast, evolution became one of the major generalizations in biology. Others extended evolutionary hypotheses to a host of different scientific fields and, indeed, into the study of society itself. Calling upon a great mass of evidence and providing the mechanism of natural selection to explain organic change, Darwin's theory won attention and widespread acceptance. But then, by the mid-century, strong generalizations, which explained and linked broad classes of previously unconnected phenomena, were becoming the order of the day in science. Darwin may have prided himself on his fact-gathering, and there is little doubt that he ransacked the biological literature looking for evidence of the mutability of species, but it was the simplicity and great range of his theory which made the impact on his contemporaries.

One of the paradoxes surrounding Charles Darwin was, in many ways, of his own making; Darwin seemed intent on appearing before the world in the guise of the amateur involved in science. The moment one looks at his career, however, the lie is given to this self-made myth. Darwin epitomized the thorough professional; he was a scientist's scientist. And in this he represents another of those changes which were becoming apparent in the science of the nineteenth century. Darwin was no lone worker developing a theory and conducting his examinations wholly upon his own. He may not yet have had a university post, and, in this sense, the private income left to him by his family has often added to the evidence of his "amateur status." One look at his voluminous correspondence, beginning immediately after his five years of scientific exploration aboard the H.M.S. *Beagle,* however, suggests the magnitude of his contacts with the scientific community. There is hardly a major figure in natural history on either side of the Atlantic Ocean with whom Darwin did not exchange letters. His detailed contacts with the leading figures of English geology, botany and zoology give every indication of a man who knew how to use the accumulated knowledge of the scientific community. The library of books and reprints and the enormous collection of notes that Darwin took upon his readings give further evidence of a well-trained, if largely self-educated, scientist at work. Darwin's own pattern of public communication and sensitivity to his critics, real and potential, show a scientist thoroughly engaged in the activities of the fraternity. Science was for Darwin a full-time occupation, and his enormous productivity in the many fields of natural history, both observational and experimental, provide an epitome of what the nineteenth-century scientist was expected to be.

Another of the major synthetic statements which characterize mid-nineteenth-century science was the principle of the conservation of energy, proposed by Hermann von Helmholtz in 1847. Conservation, like evolution, was a bold theory, and, as with evolution, there had been men prior to its major statement who had talked in terms not wholly incompatible with those which were to be used by Helmholtz. In fact, both theories have within them that quality of "generalizing" which one is likely to find in the writings of the romantic philosophers turned to science. One reason, indeed, why both evolution and conservation seem suspect at first was the similarity that some saw in the works of Darwin and Helmholtz to the earlier writings of the German *Naturphilosophen.* We know, for example, that Poggendorff refused to publish the paper by Helmholtz in the *Annalen der Physik und Chemie,* because of its affinity to the ideas of the "romantic scientists" who had been so recently discredited. But once the idea of conservation had been stated and provided with the kind of spare and elegant proof that Helmholtz gave, it came to seem almost self-evident. Indeed, it was rapidly adopted as a built-in assumption in many fields of science.

Darwin had waited until his fiftieth year to publish his theory of evolution, and even then, only because of the news that Alfred Russel Wallace had also come up with a theory of natural selection. Helmholtz, on the other hand, had just completed his formal studies and was still in his mid-twenties when his famous paper, *Die Erhaltung der Kraft,* went to press. He was, moreover, not even a physicist, but a physician and physiologist, who had moved to this enunciation of one of the major principles of physics from his studies of the physiology of heat production in animals. But if he represented traditions of the past by entering science through medicine and making his major contribution in one field while doing work in another, Helmholtz in almost every other way went on to become an example of the "modern" professional scientist. While Darwin had worked as the unaffiliated scientist (one of the last to be found in this category), Helmholtz held professorships in several of the major German universities. I suspect it is more a testimony to Helmholtz's enormous capacity and brilliance than a reflection on the state of the sciences at the time, that in mid-career he was able to leave the field of physiology, which had occupied fully half his life, and move to physics and a professorship at Berlin.

These were only two of the important generalizations in science that made the nineteenth century seem the period in which nature would finally be mastered by man. One need only mention the atomic theory of matter, the germ theory of disease, the field theory of forces and the cell theory of the organism, to get some sense of the new and potent statements which were organizing scientific activities during the century. But even as we look at these synthetic statements, which seem now so representative of nineteenth-century science, it is important to remember that this was also a period of scientific specialization, during which there was much effort at reducing complex things to their simpler and, hopefully, experimentally understandable parts. The optimism which abounds in the work of nineteenth-century scientists reflects, I believe, the balance achieved between detailed specificity and theoretical broadness.

THE PROFESSIONALIZATION OF SCIENCE

A similar balance is reflected in the social structure of nineteenth-century science, a period which saw the development and growth both of broadly scientific societies and of specialized organizations drawing members from specific disciplines within science. In the first half of the century, a sharp upswing in scientific activity—in new periodicals published and in the formation of new societies—occurred. It is necessary to look in detail at some of the social innovations that took place in science during this period if one is to understand the fine structure which underlies and makes possible the major and obvious changes.

Throughout the nineteenth century, science underwent what might well be called a "second scientific revolution," this one most involved with changes in the social institution within which science was practiced. By the beginning of the century, the scientist was already a different man from his seventeenth-century counterpart. In the earlier period, most scientists were amateurs, men who either made their living in another profession, such as medicine, or came from the landed gentry and aristocracy, supporting their scientific activities with inherited wealth. Some few others were indebted to important and wealthy patrons. The nineteenth-century scientist was no longer from society's upper classes. More often than not, he came from the middle or even lower middle class, and in consequence of his social origin, the nineteenth-century scientist had to look for support for his scientific activity in the practice of science itself. The scientific community became conscious of the vocational needs of its members, and a good deal of time was spent seeking recognition of and support for scientists. "Science is not yet a profession," Charles Babbage could complain in 1830. Its members were not yet being given the kind of recognition which he and many others felt they deserved; scientific societies still had to convince universities, government and industry to create the jobs which scientists should fill. By the close of the nineteenth century, however, almost everything that had been asked for earlier had been gained, and the position of science within society seemed secure.

One of the major steps to professionalization involved changes in the pattern of training the next generation of scientists—in short, the development of scientific education. A single institution, the Ecole Polytechnique, reflects in its founding and early years fulfillment of the highest aspirations for scientific education. A child of the French Revolution, the Ecole Polytechnique came into being in 1794, the creation of a group of scientists led by the chemist Fourcroy, who saw, as the basis of all the industries needed for waging the war, a sound training in "the geometrical and physical sciences." In many of its educational reforms, the Revolution had given recognition to the necessity for training in the sciences, but in the Ecole Polytechnique were innovations which were to have a lasting and widespread influence. First, the student body itself represented the desire of the Revolution in France, and indeed of reform movements in many parts of Europe, to democratize education. Students gained their place in the Ecole Polytechnique through competitive examinations held simultaneously in twenty-two cities. The 386 men chosen for the first class were selected by a professor of mathematics, a professor of physics, and a citizen revolutionary. Many of them were from poorer families, and a stipend was given to each to pay for room and board with a family in Paris. Thus, in a single stroke, this remarkable new institution substituted ability for social position as the major qualification for candidacy, changing the educational practices of centuries.

The school pioneered in other areas as well. The faculty, called together from all France, had among its members the most notable scientists of the day. Among the first generation of teachers were Berthollet, Fourcroy, Vauquelin, Monge, Fourier, Lagrange, Laplace, Prony and Poinsot—mathematicians, physicists and chemists, all of them productive scientists. The second generation of teachers, many of them former students at the Ecole Polytechnique themselves, included Ampère, Gay-Lussac, Poisson, Arago, and Cauchy. These men were still active scientists, conducting experiments and publishing papers, and it can rightly be claimed that students in the first years of the Ecole Polytechnique were taught by the leadership of French science, the most productive scientists of the day. The example set for scientific education throughout the world was a potent one, and in succeeding decades, many institutions attempted to emulate the establishment in Paris by hiring eminent scientists.

The pattern of active participation in science, however, was not limited to members of the distinguished faculty. It was at the Ecole Polytechnique that the practice of involving students in laboratory activities was first developed. In both chemistry and physics, students were assigned research problems which were carried out in rooms designated as student research laboratories. The students, working in small groups, were directed by a more advanced member of the student body who, in turn, received direction from one of the faculty. The pattern of the teaching laboratory, wherein students were expected to become as familiar with techniques as with theories, was a conscious invention of the early nineteenth century, which was widely adopted in the training of scientists elsewhere. Justus von Liebig, for example, went to Paris at the suggestion of Alexander von Humboldt to study in the laboratories of Gay-Lussac at the Ecole Polytechnique. Upon his return, Liebig immediately set about adapting the idea, which had so impressed him by its success, and established at the University of Giessen the teaching laboratory through which most of the great men of chemistry of the nineteenth century passed. Other German scientists, also impressed with the French model, established a host of new institutions in Germany, the *Polytechnikum,* later renamed *Technisches Hochschulen,* as a means of providing a scientific and technical education for a wider portion of the public.

The pattern of innovation and change in scientific education took place, at first, outside the traditional and established schools and universities. The Ecole Polytechnique and the *Technisches Hochschulen* were independent of the university system, and among the universities themselves, it was the new foundations, the Universities of Berlin and London, which first introduced science as an important part of the curriculum, while the ancient foundations, medieval Oxbridge and their German counterparts, fell far behind, not undergoing serious reform until the closing decades of the nineteenth century.

An important impetus for change in the scientific scene was the industrial revolution and the demands of the new industries for greater scientific participation. This was explicitly recognized by Fourcroy and his associates as they founded the Ecole Polytechnique. It can be identified in the support which the German industries, particularly the chemical industry, gave to the *Technisches Hochschulen,* which sprouted in a host of German cities. There can be no doubt of the industrial motivation behind the founding of the Royal College of Chemistry and the Royal School of Mines in England.

Another sign of industrial influence can be discovered in the formation, in the last two decades of the eighteenth century and in the first few decades of the nineteenth, of new scientific societies, located in the newly formed industrial centers of England and the continent. This growth was particularly noticeable in England, where a series of scientific societies were founded in such provincial cities as Leeds, Birmingham, Manchester, Newcastle and Bristol, during the 1780's and 1790's. What gave these groups their distinctive character was the new tone and the new tasks which were set. Sons of artisans and manufacturers, the members of these provincial scientific and philosophical societies were anxious to bring to industry the benefits they recognized in science.

The Manchester Literary and Philosophical Society, for example, established during its first year a gold medal which was to be given "to the author of the best experimental paper on any subject relevant to the Arts and Manufactures." As the President said in making the first award, "We have established a Society which, in its views, combines practice with speculation; and unites with the culture of science, the improvement of the arts." The democratization of science, then, took this second form of movement away from the capital cities and into the provincial centers, where the sons of the new industrial middle classes became the active cultivators of science.

The development of general scientific societies was accompanied by the growth of specialized organizations. A geological society, an astronomical society, a botanical society, a chemical society: each of these, and more, came into being in all the major European countries during the opening two or three decades of the nineteenth century. The membership of each of these groups swelled, and a stream of new journals and periodical publications were brought into being. What the practitioners of science seemed to be saying was that each of the branches of science was reaching that degree of depth and complexity which requires the scientist to take to one field with the whole of his energy. They were also implying that, in their eyes, the only competent judges of scientific advance were their fellow specialists who shared a detailed understanding of the specific questions under investigation. When charted numerically, the new specialized scientific societies together with the provincial scientific academies represent the figures which underlay the sharp rise in the number of scientific organizations.

Another mark of the conscious attempt of the scientific community to increase its stature can be seen in the formation of a series of new national scientific organizations in each of the major European countries and in the United States. The model for these new societies was the German Gesellschaft Deutscher Naturforscher und Ärzte, which came into being in 1822. Its practices were copied wherever similar new organizations were founded. First was the peripatetic nature of the group, meeting annually in a different city within the country. Coupled with this was the annual election of a new president. And the German scientific society imposed one new, important restriction: "The actual members of this assembly may only be those who have published a scientific paper." Membership was dependent upon a display of real dedication to science as evidenced by independent research and publication. The society grew rapidly and, within a decade, was serving as an example to the many foreign visitors who attended its annual meetings.

The British Association for the Advancement of Science was founded in 1831, in a direct attempt to emulate the successful German society and to transfer to England the gains for the scientific community which Englishmen saw accruing to their German colleagues. British scientists, mindful of the low level to which the Royal Society had fallen and of what they considered the too extensive influence of non-scientific Fellows of the Royal Society, followed their German colleagues in ruling that officers of the BAAS had to be practicing scientists, that is to say, men who had published scientific papers.

Similar groups were founded in France (the Congrès Scientifique de France, 1833), in Italy, and finally in the United States (the American Association for the Advancement of Science, 1848). As one reads the proceedings of many of these new scientific societies, it becomes clear that the phrase "advancement of science" meant not only the development of new scientific knowledge and technique, but quite clearly referred to the advancement of scientists as well. As one spokesman for the BAAS put it: "There is a service of science to be rendered to the state, with which it cannot dispense. . . . All, I think, must allow that it is neither liberal nor politic to keep those who employ the rarest intellectual endowments in the direct service of the country upon a kind of *parish allowance*." The "cultivators of science" had found a spokesman in these new organizations: the profession had added one more important institutional form.

THE REVOLUTION OF APPLIED SCIENCE

At the very same time that science was adopting all the institutional forms which we have come to associate uniquely with science, it was achieving a new relevance to society at large, which in earlier generations even the staunchest advocates of the utility of science had hardly dreamed of. Although scientists had, from time immemorial, used their wit and ingenuity to aid technological and industrial practices, most of what they had produced had been irrelevant to the needs of industry. The nineteenth century witnessed a change—applied science came into being. The synthetic, organic chemical industry and the electrical industry could not have existed except for the success of scientific discoveries made in scientific laboratories. The translation of new scientific discoveries into successful industrial tools depended, moreover, on the developments in scientific and technical education and training that we have described above.

The synthetic dye industry was born in the year 1856, when William Henry Perkin, an eighteen-year-old student at the Royal College of Chemistry in London, synthesized a strong mauve dye from coal tar. Within one year, Perkin and his father exploited the discovery in launching a new industry. The synthesis was made in a scientific laboratory at a technical college, and the ability to put the new science to work depended upon the fact that there were a large number of trained chemists, graduates of the Royal College of Chemistry and of the *Technisches Hochschulen* in Germany, or disciples of Liebig, who knew how to manipulate and control the many processes involved in the making of organic dyes. By 1862, just five years after Perkin began manufacturing, a total of five colors were being synthetically produced—all of them were important for industry. Synthetic mauve, fuchsia, aniline blue, yellow and imperial purple were being widely produced, changing the economy of the several nations which had previously manufactured the natural analogues of these colors. Within five years of Perkin's original discovery, twenty-nine firms in Europe and England were engaged in the manufacture of synthetic dyes. Indeed, August Hofmann, the director of the Royal College of Chemistry and the man who had supervised Perkin's work, himself a student of Liebig, was quite carried away when he saw the extent to which the organic dye industry was growing as he surveyed the exhibition in 1862; he predicted the day when England "would become the greatest color producer in the world; nay, by the strangest of revolutions, she may ere long send her coal-derived blues to indigo-growing India, her tar-distilled crimson to cochineal-producing Mexico and her fossil-substitutes for quercitron and safflower to China and Japan." We know that Hofmann's optimism was correct in all but one point, the name of the country involved. Within a short time, Germany had outstripped England as a producer of organic dyes, and by the end of the nineteenth century, Germany was exporting synthetic dyes to England. The reasons for this reversal can be traced to the great differential in opportunities for scientific and technical training in the two countries: Germany had moved quickly to develop wide-scale training for technicians, the second- and third-level scientists, while England had lagged behind, still depending upon her few great men of science.

The long association between chemistry (and chemists) and industry, an association dating back through the eighteenth century, had provided the kind of facilities and tools, as well as the manpower, necessary for the application of this science to industrial activities. In contrast, a much greater lag existed between discoveries in electrical science and the development of an electrical industry. Hans Christian Oersted made the first of several important discoveries in 1820 when he recognized the magnetic effects of an electric current and, essentially, set out the principles of the electric motor. Some eleven years later, Michael Faraday (in 1831) demonstrated the principle of electromagnetic induction, showing that one electric current can generate a second, and thereby linked magnetism and mechanical motion to an electric current. Faraday had discovered the principle of the electric dynamo. By the end of the nineteenth century, electricity came to be used for communication, light and power, in that order. The development, however, was very slow. Except for the telegraph, more than fifty years were needed until electricity's full potential could be grasped by industry. And yet, everything needed was implicit in the works of Oersted and Faraday, and indeed, Faraday himself pointed out the utility of his own discovery. Others, however, were slow to see the relationship. Isambard Kingdom Brunel, the great inventor, industrialist, railroad- and ship-builder, for example, commented in mid-century that electricity was a toy, even though it was in use in telegraphy on some of the railroads he himself had built.

The difference between the experience in electricity and that in organic chemistry can be traced to the difference in the number of men and the amount of material available for manipulation and experimentation. The long history of inorganic chemistry and its applications had provided this for chemistry; telegraphy finally served the same function in the development of the applied science of electricity.

The telegraph raised questions which interested a number of important scientists, among them William Thomson, Lord Kelvin, and brought into existence a whole series of new, and soon readily available, products. Batteries, insulated wire, terminals, switches, coils, and simple galvanometers were the nursery equipment for the fledgling electrical scientist. But it took close to two generations to produce in the technical schools and colleges sufficient numbers of working scientists and trained technicians who could carry into new areas applications of discoveries in the electrical sciences. The nineteenth century, then, can be understood as a century of applied science when we recognize that its achievements depended not alone upon the great scientific discoveries made by the great men of science, but required the development of the institutional underpinnings—the educational facilities, the research laboratories, the instrumentation and the equipment—which permitted the application of the new discoveries.

AN ENIGMA: SCIENCE IN THE UNITED STATES

Just as the application of electricity repeated the pattern set by the application of chemistry, although fifty years later, scientific activity in general in the United States followed the pattern set in Europe, though a generation later. Looking backward from the vantage point of mid-twentieth century and asking what we should expect when examining science in the United States prior to 1900, the almost universal answer is "more than has been found." Americans made few notable contributions to science during the first century of the republic, and many explanations have been offered to account for what appears to be a lack of intellectual vigor. Tocqueville blamed it on democracy. Others attributed it to the pastoral nature of American society. A major part of the answer can be found by examining the institutional underpinnings which are necessary to support science as a profession, and by asking when these arose in the United States and under what conditions.

Science in America through the Revolutionary War was derivative. America was a colonial country, and its scientists were part of the British scientific community. No indigenous scientific tradition developed, and very few of the institutional forms then growing up to support science in Europe came into being. European discoveries were transmitted across the ocean, and although there was some active discussion, there was very little in the way of original contributions made on this side of the Atlantic. Each generation had to import its science anew; there was nothing like a continuous tradition, handed down through schools and colleges. Most Americans who did make discoveries or describe new finds in the fauna and flora of the new continent sent their original works for publication to London or Edinburgh; very seldom did they announce their discoveries in literature published in the United States. During the eighteenth century, America was an underdeveloped colony, and its intellectual activities were, by and large, an extension of those of the English motherland. During the nineteenth century, America was an independent developing nation, and it took time to find or create its own traditions and to develop its own institutions.

In one way, the practitioners of science in the United States during the nineteenth century were more fortunate than many who have been in colonial status. Having carried out their successful revolution, they were free to accept cultural and intellectual influences from continental Europe and not restricted to the mother country alone. Americans went to France to study during the early nineteenth century and flocked to Germany for university and advanced training during the latter decades of the century.

The building of the indigenous institutions, however, was slow, and although there were two prominent eighteenth-century scientific societies, one in Philadelphia and another in Boston, there were a total of only twenty-three different scientific organizations in the entire United States by 1825. The first new well-established scientific society, the American Association of Geologists and Naturalists, was founded in 1840; considering the importance of field geology and natural history in American scientific history, 1840 is a late date for a national group of this sort to come into being. By 1848, this same society had reorganized to become the American Association for the Advancement of Science. From this point on, the growth of specialized groups and local academies in the United States followed the pattern set in Europe some thirty to forty years earlier.

The first scientific periodical in the United States, the *American Journal of Science and Arts,* published in New Haven by Benjamin Silliman, and widely known as Silliman's Journal, came into being in 1818. Its purpose, as spelled out in an early number, gives further indication of what most Americans thought science to be in the early years of the century:

It is designed as a deposit for original communication, but will contain also occasional selections from foreign journals. Within its plan are embraced: natural history, in its three great departments of mineralogy, botany and zoology. Chemistry and natural philosophy, in their various branches; mathematics, pure and applied. It will be a leading part to illustrate American natural history and especially our mineralogy and geology.

The earth sciences and natural history provided the focus for what scientific activity there was in the first half of the nineteenth century. Silliman himself charted the progress of American science, and as he looked back in 1847 over some thirty years of publication, noted "a very gratifying change." The number of scientists had grown, and the number of societies and associations had grown with them. He still pointed, however, to the overbearing role of natural history and collection as distinct from experimentation. Certainly the first areas to gain federal and state support in the sciences were those of exploration and survey, both cross-country and within states. The local environment was being explored, and the possibility of its economic exploitation continually examined.

As young American scholars went to study abroad, something of the ferment of the radical functional changes which European universities were undergoing was transmitted to them. Even the best of the American colleges suffered by comparison with universities in nineteenth-century Europe. As the young Henry Wadsworth Longfellow acidly wrote from Göttingen in 1829:

What has heretofore been the idea of an University with us? The answer is a simple one:—Two or three large brick buildings—with a chapel and a President to pray in it!

The research tradition which lured men to study in the European schools came into being with the shift of the role of the university from that of a mere transmitter of tradition to that of a producer of new knowledge. It was not until the centennial year of American independence, however, that Johns Hopkins University, the "Göttingen of Baltimore," was founded. Its first faculty, almost to a man, had studied in Germany, and their idea of a university was clear: teaching was conducted at the graduate level and time was provided and incentives given for faculty and student research. The impact of the new institution is hard to overestimate, for it served as an example and a spur to American institutions of higher education throughout the country. Among the first crop of graduate students were Henry A. Rowland, Thorstein Veblen, John Dewey, James J. Sylvester, Herbert B. Adams, Woodrow Wilson, Richard T. Ely, Henry C. Adams and Josiah Royce. The pattern of graduate education was widely copied, and by the close of the century, the United States could boast of fifteen major graduate schools. Within a period of two decades, American universities developed from producing under two hundred Ph.D.'s per year to graduating well over two thousand.

American science, going through its period of apprenticeship, lagged a generation or so behind England and the continent in development. However, the pattern of scientific growth and the institutional forms necessary for growth mirrored the European pattern. Academies and periodicals, schools and laboratories, were all brought into existence as part of the effort to achieve an indigenous American scientific community.

Even as we have been able to recognize the interaction of science with its surrounding society, we can also appreciate the inner logic that ties together all scientific activity. The pattern of advance in scientific ideas and experiments is intimately tied to the mode in which scientists have come to live and work. To understand both is to appreciate the life of science.

PREFACE

IN 1858 the Smithsonian Institution began to publish in its Annual Reports a remarkable series of biographical memoirs of great scientists, written by distinguished scientists who as contemporaries could both vividly evoke the personalities and times and authoritatively estimate the achievements of their subjects. A large number, though by no means all, were translated for the Institution from the famous *Éloges* of the French Academy of Sciences, whose perpetual secretaries during their tenure were required to prepare extended essays on the lives and labors of deceased colleagues. Other memoirs were drawn from the learned journals of England, Germany, Italy, Switzerland, Belgium, and our own country as these were established. The introduction to the first memoir published, on Joseph Priestley, read originally before the National Institute of France on June 27, 1805, explained the nature and purpose of the proposed series:

The discourses by which the French Academy of Sciences is accustomed to commemorate its deceased members, whether native or foreign, constitute, it is known, a body of highly interesting biographical and scientific literature. Far from being limited to encomium, as the title of "Éloges" by which they are usually called might suggest, they maintain a tone of candid criticism, and in dispensing justice to scientific discoverers deal in enlarged and original views of science itself. The names of their authors—of Delambre, Fourier, Cuvier, Arago and others—would teach us to expect no less.

Those delivered by Arago, late perpetual secretary of the Academy, have been recently translated and published in England among the works of that distinguished and lamented individual. A few others may be found dispersed through the volumes of scientific periodicals of Great Britain, but as these are little accessible to the general reader, and as many have not been translated which well deserved to be so. it has been thought that a more extended collection than has yet appeared would not be unacceptable to the literary public.

In this view, a translation, not indeed of the whole series, but of such as, having not been already published in this country, may serve to give a connected and popular exposition of the progress of science, has been undertaken at the suggestion of the Secretary of the Smithsonian Institution; and the proposed work will appear under the auspices of the Institution, in so far, at least, as to guarantee the correctness of its views and the fidelity of its execution.

As a specimen of the work, as well as for its own intrinsic interest, the following memoir of one of the most original and ingenious promoters of modern science, who closed his eventful life in our own country, is appended to the present report.

The complete roster of memoirs reveals at once how staunchly the Smithsonian for years thereafter—indeed, even into the third decade of our century—maintained its policy of "diffusing knowledge" as it increased through the genius of men in every branch of science—astronomy, biology, botany, chemistry, geology, geography, meteorology, natural science, paleontology, physics, physiology, zoology. Between 1858, when they began, and 1931, when they ended, more than a hundred biographies enriched the Annual Reports. As might be expected, they varied in language, style, emphasis, length—no other writers, for example, enjoyed the scope or developed the magnificent sweep of the great French academicians, whose essays (and translations!) often ran to sixty or seventy pages —but a standard of excellence, of both subject and treatment, generally prevailed. Only in the course of time as other media, especially the learned journals, increasingly published their own *éloges* did the Smithsonian resort first to briefer more routine notices, then cease altogether to assume the responsibility.

Unfortunately, however desirable and however in most instances justified by their comparable significance and interest for the history of science, inclusion of even a portion of those here omitted would have required another volume of equal or greater length. On what basis then, the specialist in any one of the sciences may reasonably inquire, were some preferred to the exclusion of others no less influential? In the chemistry and physics of electrical phenomena, for example, if Faraday, Oersted, Henry, Volta belong, where is Ohm and where the mighty Ampère? In the natural sciences, why Cuvier, anti-evolutionist, but not Geoffroy Saint-

Hilaire, who refuted him before Darwin? And so in other areas—why Bunsen but not his great collaborator Kirchhoff, why Ludwig rather than the more familiar Virchow, why David Gill but not Delambre, or Encke or John Herschel? For that matter, why so few Americans?

Without presuming to rank scientists in order of genius—a hazardous business at best—the present editor (not a professional scientist but a "general reader" belonging to the "literary public" for whom the series was originally intended) has selected thirty memoirs for this collection. These seem to her to follow most closely the spirit of the first memoir published, in subject to cover the widest possible range of theories advanced by "original and ingenious promoters of modern science," and in authorship to show "enlarged and original views of science itself." Yet length is a factor that has also operated: the essay on Ampère alone covers sixty closely packed pages that elude feasible condensation, but since his contribution is touched upon elsewhere, especially by Élie de Beaumont in his memoir on Oersted, the omission can be forgiven. A few memoirs from German sources (on Kirchhoff and Virchow) proved less happy in their translators.

As for the scarcity of Americans, it is enough to quote from the Smithsonian's *Annual Report* of 1853, in which the first secretary of the Institution, dean of American science of the period, and initiator of the biographical series, wrote:

While we rejoice that in our country . . . so much attention is paid to the diffusion of knowledge, truth compels me to say that comparatively little encouragement is given to its increase. . . . As soon as any branch of science can be brought to bear on the necessities, conveniences, or luxuries of life, it meets with encouragement and reward. Not so with the discovery of the incipient principles of science; the investigations which lead to those receive no fostering care from the government and are considered trifles unworthy the attention of those who place the supreme good in that which immediately administers to the physical needs. . . . But he who loves truth for its own sake, feels that its higher aims are lowered and its moral influence marred by being continually summoned to the bar of immediate and palpable utility.

And almost twenty years later, in 1870, Henry still lamented the emphasis this country placed on applied rather than "theoretical science," and the continued dependence on European leadership in scientific research.

Although this collection concentrates essentially on distinguished men of nineteenth-century science, the memoirs should properly be regarded less as a coherent history of that science than as suggestive of it. The modern reader who turns from the earlier to the later selections (they are arranged in order of birth dates rather than by the dates of the most important individual discoveries) will note in addition to the expanded areas of science an actual change in the style of describing them. Rhetorical manner for the most part gives way to restraint, the generalized vocabulary of "natural philosophy" yields to the greater precision of technical specialism. The difference is not merely verbal. It marks a shift in the attitude not only toward science, but toward the role of the scientist and the data considered appropriate to biographical information about him. In France, where the eulogistic art achieved an elegant literary form of its own, the demand for more austere treatment manifested itself early enough for Arago to oppose it. Addressing his fellow-academicians on Gay-Lussac, he found it necessary to express the hope that he would not offend "the dignity of this assembly" by narrating an anecdote about their deceased associate, and in a digression (omitted in the present version for lack of space) he sharply refuted those who "allege that details of private life (they call them anecdotes with a desire to stigmatize them with absolute censure) ought not to be preserved in our academic archives." When he reminded his critics of the "interesting portraitures contained in the [earlier] admirable eulogies of Fontenelle and Condorcet, they replied that everything is good in its time, that the progress of knowledge has rendered the modifications they demand indispensable." They would "limit these biographies," Arago objected, "to purely technical analysis; they would discard everything which concerns the sentiments of the man and the citizen."

Fortunately for the purposes of this collection, though the period saw the natural philosopher (who, it was said, "thought God's thoughts after Him") become increasingly the specialist who regarded scientific inquiry as an end in itself, the writers of these memoirs in the main held to the larger view of Arago: "I regard as an essential part of the mission I have to fulfill," he declared, "an investigation into whether the associates whom we have had the misfortune to lose have caused the worship of science and that of integrity to keep pace with each other; whether they have, as the poet expresses it, allied fine talents to a fine character." For the scientist over most of this period was still a man speaking to men. His biographer presents him in these sketches not as mechanized intellect, but as a human being, a member of society at large, a responsible citizen not less than as a genius, a discoverer, a pathfinder. (In this connection note especially Nordmann's comments on Poincaré as philosopher and mathematician.) Possibly one of the chief values of the memoirs, one that more than justifies their reissue, is the diffused sense they convey of the social and political responsibility that shaped the lives and informed the thinking of so many great geniuses of the age. Their successors look out today on dazzling new vistas, but perhaps a backward glance may recall to them the famous acknowledgment of debt voiced by an earlier genius: "If I have seen farther it is by standing on the shoulders of giants."

For assistance in the preparation of this collection it is a pleasure to name, first, members of the Smithsonian Astrophysical Observatory in Cambridge—Mr. Leon Campbell, Jr., and Mr. James Cornell, Jr., who provided exact copies of all original texts, Mrs. Jane Petschaft, who answered various queries, Dr. Edward Fineman and Dr. Luigi Jacchia, who clarified certain technical obscurities. Professor Donald Fleming, of Harvard University, generously gave advice about certain selections and called attention to flaws in translations needing amendment. Mr. Paul Oehser, formerly editor-in-chief of Smithsonian publications in Washington, encouraged the project and arranged for publication, and Miss Sue Colby, of the Archives Division of the Institution, heroically assembled the illustrations from several sources. Finally, the publishers, especially Mr. Michael Korda, greatly eased the entire task by paying perhaps too ready deference to the judgments of the editor.

B.Z.J.

A NOTE ON THE TEXT

SINCE the language and tone are as much a part of the history as the facts themselves, the original texts have been preserved wherever possible. For the convenience of the modern reader, however, it has seemed desirable to eliminate excessive punctuation, to modify paragraphing, to correct typographical errors, and to regularize the setting of such details as extracts and titles of works. Where translations of some phrases and terms seemed either too unidiomatic or imprecise, they have been slightly amended, though it must be admitted that care for adherence to the texts has left obvious infelicities, especially in the earlier memoirs. It could not have been easy at the time to find in this country that happy combination, rare at all times, of the linguist, the prose stylist, and the scientist. Finally, in order to include as many memoirs as possible, those of excessive length and those from which certain passages could be spared have been condensed, and only a few of the original footnotes are retained.

THE GOLDEN AGE
OF SCIENCE

William Herschel *

1738–1822

———◆———

DOMINIQUE FRANCOIS ARAGO †

WILLIAM HERSCHEL, one of the greatest astronomers that ever
lived in any age or country, was born at Hanover on the 15th of
November, 1738. The name of Herschel has become too illustrious
for the world to neglect searching back, along the stream of time,
to learn the social position of the families that have borne it. Yet
pardonable curiosity on this subject has not been entirely satisfied.
We only know that Abraham Herschel, great-grandfather of the
astronomer, resided at Mähren, whence he was expelled on account of his strong attachment to the Protestant faith; that Abraham's son Isaac was a farmer in the vicinity of Leipzig; that Isaac's
eldest son Jacob Herschel disappointed his father's earnest desire
to see him devote himself to agriculture, that he determined on being a musician, and settled at Hanover.

Jacob Herschel, father of William, the astronomer, was an eminent musician, not less remarkable for the good qualities of his
heart than for those of his mind. His very limited means did not
enable him to bestow a complete education on his family, consisting of six boys and four girls, although by his care his ten children
all became excellent musicians. The eldest, Jacob, even acquired a
rare degree of skill, which procured for him the appointment of
master of the band in a Hanoverian regiment, which he accompanied to England. The third son, William, remained under his
father's roof and, without neglecting the fine arts, took lessons in

* Smithsonian *Annual Report,* 1870, pp. 197–222 (hereafter, *A.R.*).
† French astronomer and physicist (1786–1853), perpetual secretary of the
French Academy of Sciences, author of many scientific works and a number
of brilliant eulogies, especially of scientists in mathematics, physics, and
astronomy.

1

the French language and devoted himself to the study of metaphysics, for which he retained a taste to his latest day.

In 1759 William Herschel, then about twenty-one years of age, went over to England, not with his father, as has been erroneously stated, but with his brother Jacob, whose connections in that country seemed likely to favor the young man's opening prospects in life. But neither London nor the country towns afforded him any resource in the beginning, and the first two or three years after his expatriation were marked with cruel privations which were, however, manfully endured. A fortunate chance finally raised the young Hanoverian to a better position; Lord Durham engaged him as master of the band in an English regiment which was quartered on the borders of Scotland. From this moment he began to acquire a reputation as a musician that was gradually extended, until in 1766 he was appointed organist at Halifax (Yorkshire). The emoluments of this situation, together with those of giving private lessons both in the town and the counry around, afforded him the means to remedy, or rather to complete, his early education. It was then that he learned Latin and Italian, though without any other help than a grammar and a dictionary, and that he also acquired some knowledge of Greek. So great was the desire for knowledge with which he was inspired that while residing at Halifax he found means to continue his philological exercises and at the same time to study deeply the learned but very obscure mathematical work of Smith on the theory of music. This treatise either explicitly or implicitly supposed the reader to have a knowledge of algebra and geometry, which Herschel did not possess, but of which he made himself master in a very short time.

In 1766 Herschel obtained the appointment of organist to the Octagon Chapel at Bath. This was a more lucrative post than that at Halifax, but it also devolved on him new obligations. He had to play incessantly either at the oratorios or in the rooms at the baths, at the theater, and in the pubic concerts. Besides this, from among his patrons in the most fashionable circle of England he could not refuse to take numerous pupils who wished to be instructed in his art. It is difficult to imagine how among so many duties, so many distractions of various kinds, Herschel could continue the studies, which even at Halifax had required so much resolution and perseverance, with a very uncommon degree of talent. We have seen that it was by music that Herschel was led to mathematics; mathematics in their turn led him to optics, the principal and fertile source of his illustrious career. The time finally arrived when his theoretic knowledge was to guide the young musician into a laborious application of principles quite foreign to his habits; and of which the brilliant success, as well as the excessive temerity, must excite reasonable astonishment.

A telescope—a simple reflector, only two English feet in length —falls into the hands of Herschel during his residence at Bath. This instrument, however imperfect, shows him a multitude of stars in the sky that the naked eye cannot discern; shows him also enlarged known objects, under their true dimensions; reveals forms to him that the richest imaginations of antiquity had never suspected. He is transported with enthusiasm and resolves without delay to have a similar instrument but of larger size. The answer from London is delayed for some days. These few days appear to him as years. When the answer arrives, the price that the optician demands proves to be much beyond the pecuniary resources of a mere organist. To any other man this would have been an unsurmountable obstacle. This unexpected difficulty, on the contrary, inspired Herschel with fresh energy. He cannot buy a telescope; then he will construct one with his own hands. The musician of the Octagon Chapel rushes immediately into a multitude of experiments, on metallic alloys that reflect light with the greatest intensity, on the means of giving the parabolic figure to the mirrors, on the causes that in the operation of polishing affect the regularity of the reflection, etc. So rare a degree of perseverance at last receives its reward. In 1774 Herschel has the happiness of being able to examine the heavens with a Newtonian telescope of five English feet focus, entirely made by himself. This success tempts him to undertake still more difficult enterprises. Other telescopes of seven, of eight, of ten, and even of twenty feet focal distance, crown his efforts. As if to answer in advance those critics who would have accused him of a superfluity of apparatus, of unnecessary luxury in the large size of the new instruments and the extreme *minutiæ* in their execution, nature granted to the astronomical musician, on the 13th of March, 1781, the unprecedented honor of commencing his career of observation with the discovery of a new planet, situated on the confines of our solar system. Dating from that moment, Herschel's reputation, no longer in his character of musician but as a constructor of telescopes and as an astronomer, spread throughout the world. George III, a lover of science, and much inclined besides to protect and patronize both men and things of Hanoverian origin had Herschel presented to him. He was charmed with the simple yet lucid and modest account that the astronomer gave of his repeated endeavors; he caught a glimpse of the glory that such an observer might reflect on his reign; granted him a pension of three hundred guineas a year and furnished him with a residence near Windsor Castle, first at Clay Hall and then at Slough. The anticipations of George III were completely realized. We may confidently assert, relative to the little house at Slough, that it is the place of all the world where the greatest number of astronomical discoveries have been made. The name of that village will never perish. Science will transmit it religiously to our latest posterity.

I shall avail myself of this opportunity to rectify a mistake, of which ignorance and idleness wish to make a triumphant handle, or, at all events, to wield in their cause as an irresistible justification. It has been repeated to satiety that at the time when Herschel entered on his astronomical career he knew nothing of mathematics. But I have already said that during his residence at Bath the organist of the Octagon Chapel had familiarized himself with the principles of geometry and algebra; and a still more positive proof of this is that a difficult question on the vibration of strings loaded with small weights having been proposed for discussion in 1779, Herschel gave it a solution which was thought worthy to be inserted in several scientific periodicals of the year 1780. The adventurous life of Herschel is here closed. The great astronomer will not quit his observatory any more, except to submit the sublime results of his laborious vigils to the Royal Society of London. These results are contained in his memoirs; they constitute one of the principal riches of the celebrated collection known under the title of *Philosophical Transactions*.

Herschel was even elected as a member of the principal academies of Europe, and about 1816 he was named a Knight of the Guelphic Order of Hanover. According to the English custom, from the time of that nomination the title of Sir William took the place on all his memoirs, already honored with so much celebrity, of the former appellation of Doctor William. He had been named a doctor of laws in the University of Oxford in 1786. This dignity, by special favor, was conferred on him without any of the obligatory formalities of examination, disputation, or pecuniary contribution usual in that learned corporation.

I should wound the elevated sentiments that Herschel professed all his life if I were not here to mention two indefatigable assistants that this fortunate astronomer found in his own family. The one was Alexander Herschel, endowed with a remarkable talent for mechanism, always at his brother's service, and who enabled him to realize without delay any ideas that he had conceived; the other was Miss Caroline Herschel, who deserves a still more particular and detailed mention.

Miss Caroline Lucretia Herschel went to England as soon as her brother became special astronomer to the King. She received the appellation there of Assistant Astronomer, with a moderate salary. From that moment she unreservedly devoted herself to the service of her brother, happy in contributing night and day to his rapidly increasing scientific reputation. Miss Caroline shared in all the night watches of her brother, with her eye constantly on the clock and the pencil in her hand; without exception she recorded all the observations; she afterward made three or four copies in separate registers; coordinated, classed, and analyzed them. If the scientific world saw with astonishment how Herschel's works succeeded each other with unexampled rapidity during so many years, they were specially indebted for it to the ardor of Miss Caroline. Astronomy, moreover, has been directly enriched with several comets [observed] by this excellent and respectable lady. After the death of her illustrious brother she retired to Hanover, to the house of Jahn Dietrich Herschel, a musician of high reputation and the only surviving brother of the astronomer.

William Herschel died without pain on the 23rd of August, 1822, aged eighty-three. Neither fame nor fortune ever changed in him the fund of childlike candor, inexhaustible benevolence, and sweetness of character with which nature had endowed him. He preserved to the last both his brightness of mind and vigor of intellect. For some years before his death he enjoyed with delight the distinguished success of his only son, Sir John Herschel.* At his last hour he sank to rest with the pleasing conviction that his beloved son, heir of a great name, would not allow it to fall into oblivion, but would adorn it with fresh luster, and that great discoveries would also honor his career. No prediction of the illustrious astronomer has been more completely verified.

In the English journals an account is given of the interesting means adopted by the family of Sir William Herschel for preserving the remains of the great telescope of thirty-nine feet focus constructed by that celebrated astronomer. The metal tube of the instrument, carrying at one end the recently cleaned mirror of four feet

---

* Sir William had married Mary, the widow of John Pitt, Esq., possessed of a considerable jointure, and the union proved a remarkable accession of domestic happiness. This lady survived Sir William by several years. They had but this son. [TRANSLATOR'S NOTE.] See N. S. Dodge, "Memoir of Sir John Frederick William Herschel," *A.R.*, 1871, pp. 109–135.

ten inches in diameter, was placed horizontally in the meridian on
solid piers of masonry, in the midst of the circle where formerly
stood the mechanism requisite for maneuvering the telescope. The
first of January 1840, Sir John Herschel, his wife, their children,
seven in number, and some old family servants assembled at Slough.
Exactly at noon the party walked several times in procession
around the instrument; they then entered the tube of the telescope,
seated themselves on benches that had been prepared for the
purpose, and sang a requiem with English words composed by Sir
John Herschel himself. After their exit the illustrious family ranged
themselves around the great tube, the opening of which was then
hermetically sealed. The day concluded with a party of intimate
friends.

I know not whether those persons who can only appreciate
things from the peculiar point of view from which they have been
accustomed to look may think there was something strange in
several of the details of the ceremony that I have just described. I
affirm, however, that the whole world will applaud the pious feeling
which actuated Sir John Herschel, and that all the friends of
science will thank him for having consecrated the humble garden,
where his father achieved such immortal labors, by a monument
more expressive in its simplicity than pyramids or statues.

The chronological and detailed analysis of [his] many labors*
would involve numerous repetitions. A systematic order will be
preferable, since it more distinctly fixes the the eminent place that
Herschel will never cease to occupy in the small group of contemporary men of genius, while his name will re-echo to the most
distant posterity. The variety and splendor of Herschel's labors
vie with their extent. The more we study them the more we must
admire them. It is with great men as it is with great movements
in the arts: we cannot understand them without studying them
from various points of view. . . . The life of Herschel had the rare
advantage of forming an epoch in an extensive branch of astronomy; it would require us almost to write a special treatise on
astronomy to show thoroughly the importance of all the researches
that are due to him.

The improvements that Herschel made in the construction and
management of telescopes have contributed so directly to the discoveries with which that observer enriched astronomy that we
cannot hesitate to bring them forward at once. I find the following passage in a memoir by Lalande, printed in 1783, and forming

* The Chronological Table of the Memoirs of Herschel in the original essay
(*A.R.,* pp. 201–204) is omitted.

part of the preface to Volume III of the *Ephemerides of the Celestial Motions:*

Each time that Herschel undertakes to polish a mirror (of a telescope) he condemns himself to ten, or twelve, or even fourteen hours of constant work. He does not quit his workshop for a minute, not even to eat, but receives from the hands of his sister that nourishment without which one could not undergo such prolonged fatigue. Nothing could induce Herschel to leave his work; for, according to him, if he did so it would be to spoil it.

The advantages that Herschel found in 1783, 1784, and 1785 in employing telescopes of twenty feet and with large apertures made him desire to construct one much larger still. The expense would be considerable; the King provided for it. The work, begun about the close of 1785, was finished in August 1789. This instrument had an iron cylindrical tube thirty-nine feet four inches in length and four feet ten inches in diameter. Such dimensions are enormous as compared with those of telescopes previously made. They will appear but small, however, to persons who have heard the report of a pretended ball given in the Slough telescope. The propagators of this popular rumor must have confounded the astronomer Herschel with the brewer Meux, and the cylinder, in which a man of the smallest stature could scarcely stand upright, with divers wooden vats as large as a house, in which beer is made in London. Herschel's telescope, forty English feet* in length, allowed the realization of an idea, the advantages of which would not be sufficiently appreciated if I did not here recall to mind some facts.

In any telescope, whether refracting or reflecting, there are two principal parts: the part that forms the aerial images of the distant objects and the small lens by the aid of which these images are magnified just as if they consisted of radiating matter. When the image is produced by means of a lenticular glass, the place it occupies will be found on the prolongation of the line that extends from the object to the center of the lens. The astronomer, furnished with an eyepiece and wishing to examine that image, must necessarily place himself *beyond* the point where the rays that form it have crossed each other; *beyond,* let us carefully remark, means *farther off* from the object-glass. The observer's head can-

---

* Conforming to general usage, and to Sir W. Herschel himself, we shall allude to this instrument as the *forty-foot* telescope, though M. Arago adheres to thirty-nine feet and drops the inches, probably because the Parisian foot is rather longer than the English. [TRANSLATOR'S NOTE.]

not then interfere with the formation or the brightness of the image, however small may be the distance from which he may have to study it. But it is no longer thus with the image formed by means of reflection. For the image is now placed between the object and the reflecting mirror, and when the astronomer approaches in order to examine it, he inevitably intercepts, if not the totality at least a very considerable portion of the luminous rays, which would otherwise have contributed to give it great distinctness. It will now be understood why in optical instruments where the images of distant objects are formed by the reflection of light it has been necessary to carry the images by the aid of a second reflection out of the tube that contains and sustains the principal mirror. When the small mirror on the surface of which the second reflection is effected is plane and inclined at an angle of 45° to the axis of the telescope; when the image is reflected laterally through an opening made near the edge of the tube and furnished with an eyepiece; when, in a word, the astronomer looks definitively in a direction perpendicular to the line described by the luminous rays coming from the object and falling on the center of the great mirror, then the telescope is called *Newtonian*. But in the *Gregorian* telescope the image formed by the principal mirror falls on a second mirror, which is very small, slightly curved, and parallel to the first. The small mirror reflects the first image and throws it beyond the large mirror through an opening made in the middle of that mirror. Both in the one and in the other of these two telescopes the small mirror interposed between the object and the great mirror forms relative to the latter a sort of screen which prevents its entire surface from contributing toward forming the image. The small mirror also, in regard to intensity, gives some trouble.

Let us suppose, in order to clear up our ideas, that the material of which the two mirrors are made reflects only half of the incident light. In the course of the first reflection, the immense number of rays that the aperture of the telescope had received may be considered as reduced to half. Nor is the diminution less on the small mirror. Now half of a half is a quarter. Therefore the instrument will send to the eye of the observer only a quarter of the incident light that its aperture had received. If these two causes of diminished light did not exist in a refracting telescope, it would give, under a parity of dimensions, four times more* light than a Newtonian or Gregorian telescope gives.

* It will be more correct to say four times *as much* light. [TRANSLATOR'S NOTE.]

Herschel did away with the small mirror in his large telescope by placing the large mirror obliquely in the tube. This causes the images to be formed, not in the axis of the tube, but very near the circumference or edge of the outer mouth, as we may call it. The observer might therefore look at them directly merely by means of an eyepiece. A small portion of the astronomer's head, it is true, encroaches on the tube, forms a screen, and interrupts some incident rays. Still, in a large telescope this loss does not amount to half as much as it would inevitably do if the small mirror were there.

Those telescopes in which the observer, standing at the anterior extremity of the tube, looks directly into it, turning his back to the objects, were called by Herschel *front-view telescopes*. In Volume LXXVI of the *Philosophical Transactions* he says that the idea of this construction occurred to him in 1776 and that he then applied it unsuccessfully to a ten-foot telescope; that during the year 1784 he again made a fruitless trial of it in a twenty-foot telescope. Yet I find that on the 7th of September 1784 he recurred to *a front view* in observing some nebulæ and groups of stars. However discordant these dates may be, we cannot without injustice neglect to remark that a front-view telescope was already described in 1732, in Volume VI of the collection entitled *Machines and Inventions approved by the Academy of Sciences*. The author of this innovation is Jacques Lemaire, who has been unduly confounded with the English Jesuit, Christopher Maire, assistant to Boscovitch in measuring the meridian comprised between Rome and Rimini. Jacques Lemaire, having only telescopes of moderate dimensions in view, was obliged, in order not to sacrifice any of the light, to place the great mirror so obliquely that the image formed by its surface should fall entirely outside the tube of the instrument. So great a degree of inclination would certainly distort the image. The *front-view* construction is admissible only in very large telescopes.

I find in the *Transactions* for 1803 that in solar observations Herschel sometimes employed telescopes the great mirror of which was made of glass. It was with a telescope of this kind, seven feet long and six inches and three-tenths in diameter, that he observed the transit of Mercury on the 9th of November, 1802.

Practical astronomers know how much the mounting of a telescope contributes to produce correct observations. The difficulty of a solid yet very movable mounting increases rapidly with the dimensions and weight of an instrument. We may then conceive that Herschel had to surmount many obstacles in mounting a telescope suitably of which the mirror alone weighed upward of 1,000 kilograms (a ton). But he solved this problem to his entire satisfaction by the aid of a combination of spars, pulleys, and ropes, of which a correct idea may be formed by referring to the woodcut given in Arago's *Treatise on Popular Astronomy* (Vol. I). This apparatus and the different stands that Herschel devised for telescopes of smaller dimensions assign to that illustrious observer a distinguished place among the most ingenious mechanics of our age.

The public in general—I may even say the greater part of astronomers—know not what was the effect that the great forty-foot telescope had in the labors and discoveries of Herschel. Still, we are not less mistaken when we suppose that the observer of Slough always used this telescope than in imagining with Baron von Zach (see *Monatliche Correspondenz,* January 1802) that the colossal instrument was of no use at all; that it did not contribute to any new discovery; that it must be considered as a mere object of curiosity. These assertions are distinctly contradicted by Herschel's own words. In the volume of *Philosophical Transactions* for the year 1795 (p. 350) I read, for example: "On the 28th of August, 1789, having directed my telescope (of forty feet) to the heavens, I discovered the sixth satellite of Saturn, and I perceived the spots on that planet better than I had been able to do before." (See also relative to this sixth satellite the *Philosophical Transacions* for 1790, p. 10.) In that same volume of 1790 (p. 11) I find: "The great light of my forty-foot telescope was so useful that on the 17th of September, 1789, I remarked the seventh satellite, then situated at its greatest western elongation." On the 10th of October, 1791, Herschel, looking in at the mirror of his forty-foot telescope with his naked eye, without any kind of eyepiece, saw the ring of Saturn and the fourth satellite.

Let us acknowledge the true motives that prevented Herschel from oftener using his forty-foot telescope. Nothwithstanding the excellence of the mechanism, the maneuvering of that instrument required the constant aid of two laborers and that of another person charged with noting the time at the clock. Besides this, during nights when the variation of temperature was considerable, this telescope, on account of its great mass, was always behind the atmosphere in thermometric changes, giving rise to a difference of density in the air within and without the tube very injurious to the distinctness of the images.

Herchel found that in England there are not above a hundred hours in a year during which the heavens can be advantageously observed with a telescope of forty feet, furnished with a magnifying power of a thousand. This observation led the celebrated astronomer to the conclusion that to take a complete survey of the heavens with his large instrument, though each successive field should remain only for an instant under inspection, would not require less than eight hundred years. He explains very clearly the rare occurrence of the circumstances in which it is possible to make good use of a telescope of forty feet and of very large aperture. A telescope does not magnify real objects only, but magnifies also the apparent irregularities arising from atmospheric refractions; now, all other things being equal, these irregularities of refraction must be so much the greater, so much the more frequent, as the stratum of air is thicker through which the rays have passed in going to form the image.

Astronomers expressed extreme surprise when in 1782, they learned that Herschel had applied linear magnifying powers of a thousand, of twelve hundred, of two thousand two hundred, of two thousand six hundred, and even of six thousand times, to a reflecting telescope of seven feet in length. The Royal Society of London participated in this surprise and officially requested Herschel to give publicity to the means he had adopted for using such amounts of magnifying power in his telescopes. Such was the object of a memoir that he inserted in Volume LXXII of the *Philosophical Transactions;* and it dissipated all doubts. No one will be surprised that magnifying powers, which it would seem ought to have shown the lunar mountains as the chain of Mont Blanc is seen from Mâcon, from Lyons, and even from Geneva, were not easily believed in. They did not know that Herschel had never used magnifying powers of three thousand and six thousand times, except in observing brilliant stars; they had not remembered that light reflected by planetary bodies is too feeble to continue as distinct under the same degree of magnifying power as the direct light of the fixed stars does.

Opticians had given up, more from theory than from careful experiments, attempting high magnifying powers, even for reflecting telescopes. They thought that the image of a small circle cannot be distinct, cannot be sharp at the edges, unless the pencil of rays coming from the object in nearly parallel lines and entering the eye after having passed through the eyepiece, be sufficiently broad. This being once granted, the inference followed that an image ceases to be well defined when it does not strike at least two of the nervous filaments of the retina with which that organ is supposed to be overspread. These gratuitous conditions, grafted on each other, vanished in presence of Herschel's observations. After having put himself on his guard against the effects of diffraction—that is to say, against the scattering that light undergoes when it passes the terminal angles of bodies—the illustrious astronomer proved in 1786 that objects can be seen well defined by means of pencils of light whose diameter does not equal five-tenths of a millimeter.

Herschel considered the almost unanimous opinion of the double-lens eyepiece being preferable to the single-lens eyepiece as a very injurious prejudice to science, since experience proved to him, notwithstanding all theoretic deductions, that, with equal magnifying powers, in reflecting telescopes at least (and this restriction is of some consequence) the images were brighter and better-defined with single than with double eyepieces. On one occasion this latter eyepiece could not show him the bands of Saturn while by the aid of a single lens they were perfectly visible. Herschel said: "The double eyepiece must be left to amateurs and to those who, for some particular object, require a large field of vision." (*Philosophical Transactions,* 1782, pp. 94–95.)

It is not only relative to the comparative merits of single or double eyepieces that Herschel differs in opinion from opticians generally. He thinks, moreover, that he has proved by decisive experiments that concave eyepieces (like that used by Galileo) surpass convex eyepieces, as regards both clearness and definition. Herschel assigns the date of 1776 to the experiments which he made to decide this question. (*Philosophical Transactions,* 1815, p. 297.) Plano-concave and double-concave lenses produce similar effects. In what did these lenses differ from the double-convex lenses? In one particular only: the latter received the rays reflected by the large mirror of the telescope after their union at the focus, whereas the concave lenses received the same rays before that union. When the observer made use of a convex lens, the rays that went to the back of the eye to form an image on the retina had previously crossed each other in the air, but no crossing of this kind took place when the observer used a concave lens. Holding the double advantage of this latter sort of lens over the other as quite proved, one would be inclined, like Herschel, to admit "that a certain mechanical effect, injurious to clearness and definition, would accompany the focal crossing of the rays of light."

This idea of the crossing of the rays suggested an experiment, the result of which deserves to be recorded. A telescope of ten English feet was directed toward an advertisement covered with very small printing and placed at a sufficient distance. The convex lens of the eyepiece was carried not by a tube, properly so called, but by four fine rigid wires, placed at right angles; this arrangement left the focus open in almost every direction. A concave mirror was then placed so that it threw a very condensed image of the sun laterally on the very spot where the image of the advertisement was formed. The solar rays, after having crossed each other, finding nothing on their route, went on and lost themselves in space. A screen, however, allowed the rays to be intercepted at will before they united. This done, having applied his eye to the eyepiece and directed all his attention to the telescopic image of the advertisement, Herschel did not perceive that taking away and then replacing the screen made the least change in the brightness or definition of the letters. It was therefore of no consequence in this instance as well as in the other whether the immense quantity of solar rays crossed each other at the very place where, *in another direction,* the rays united that formed the image of the letters. I have marked in italics the words that especially show in what this curious experiment differs from the previous experiments and yet does not entirely contradict them. In this instance the rays were of different origin, those coming from the advertisement and those from the sun crossed each other, respectively, in an almost rectangular direction; while in the comparative examination of the stars with convex and with concave eyepieces, the rays that seemed to have a mutual influence had a common origin and crossed each other at very acute angles. There seems to be nothing then in the results at which we need to be much surprised.

Herschel increased the catalogue, already so extensive, of the mysteries of vision when he explained in what manner we must endeavor to distinguish separately the two members of certain double stars very close to each other. He said, "If you wish to assure yourself that η Coronæ is a double star, first direct your telescope to α Geminorum, to ζ Aquarii, to μ Draconis, to ρ Herculis, to α Piscium, to ε Lyræ. Look at those stars for a long time, so as to acquire the habit of observing such objects; then pass on to ξ Ursæ majoris, where the closeness of the two members is still greater. In a third essay select ι Boötis (marked *44* by Flamsteed and *i* in Harris's maps), the star that precedes α Orionis *n* of the same constellation, and you will then be prepared for the more difficult observation of η Coronæ. Indeed, η Coronæ is a sort of miniature of *i* Boötis, which may itself be considered as a miniature of α Geminorum." (*Philosophical Transactions,* 1782, p. 100.)

As soon as Piazzi, Olbers, and Harding had discovered three of the numerous telescopic planets now known, Herschel proposed to himself to determine their real magnitudes; but telescopes not having then been applied to the measurement of excessively small angles, it became requisite, in order to avoid any illusion, to try some experiments adapted to giving a scale of the powers of those instruments. Of the labor of our indefatigable astronomer in this line I am going to give a condensed account.

The author relates first that in 1774 he endeavored to ascertain experimentally with the naked eye, and at the distance of distinct vision, what angle a circle must subtend to be distinguished by its form from a square of similar dimensions. The angle was never smaller than 2′ 17″; therefore at its maximum it was about one-fourteenth of the angle subtended by the diameter of the moon. Herschel did not say of what nature the circles and squares of paper were that he used, nor on what background they were projected. It is an omission to be regretted, since in those phenomena the intensity of light must be an important feature. However it may have been, the scrupulous observer, not daring to extend to telescopic vision what he had discovered relative to vision with the naked eye, undertook to do away with all doubt by direct observations. On examining some heads of pins, placed at a distance in the open air, with a three-foot telescope, Herschel could easily discern that those bodies were round when the subtended angles became, after being magnified, 2′ 19″. This is almost exactly the result obtained with the naked eye. When the globules were darker— when, instead of pins' heads, small globules of sealing wax were used—their spherical form did not begin to be distinctly visible till the moment when the subtended magnified angle—that is, the moment when the natural angle multiplied by the magnifying power—amounted to five minutes. In a subsequent series of experiments some globules of silver, placed very far from the observer, allowed their globular form to be perceived even when the magnified angle remained below two minutes. Under equality of subtended angle, then, the telescopic vision with strong magnifying powers showed itself superior to the naked-eye vision. This result is not unimportant.

If we take notice of the magnifying powers used by Herschel in these laborious researches—powers that often exceeded five hundred times—it will appear to be established that the telescopes possessed by modern astronomers may serve to verify the round form of distant objects, the form of celestial bodies, even when the diameters of those bodies do not subtend naturally, to the naked eye, angles of above three-tenths of a second; and 500 multiplied by three-tenths of a second give 2′ 30″.

Much still remained to be learned in regard to refracting telescopes; even when they already served to reveal brilliant astronomical phenomena the result was due rather to chance than to definite theory. Their theory, as far as it depended on geometry and optics, had made rapid progress. These two early phases of the problem leave but little more to be wished for; it is not so with a third phase, hitherto a good deal neglected, connected with physiology, and with the action of light on the nervous system. Therefore we should search in vain in old treatises on optics and on astronomy for a strict and complete discussion on the comparative effect that the size and intensity of the images, the magnifying power and the aperture of a telescope may have, by night and by day, on the visibility of the faintest stars. This lacuna Herschel tried to fill up in 1799; such was the aim of the memoir entitled "On the Space-penetrating Power of Telescopes."

This memoir contains excellent things; still it is far from exhausting the subject. The author, for instance, entirely overlooks the observations made by day. I also find that the hypothetical part of the discussion is not perhaps as distinctly separated from the rigorous part as it might be; that doubtful numbers, though given with a degree of precision down to the smallest decimals, do not contrast well as terms of comparison with those which, on the contrary, rest on observations bearing mathematical evidence of correctness. Whatever may be thought of these remarks, the astronomer or the physicist who would like again to undertake the question of visibility with telescopes will find some important facts in Herschel's memoir and some ingenious observations well adapted to serve them as guides.

The curious phenomenon of a periodical change of intensity in certain stars very early excited the earnest attention of Herschel. The first memoir by that illustrious observer, presented to the Royal Society of London, and inserted in the *Philosophical Transactions,* treats especially of the changes of intensity of the star *o* in the neck of the Whale. This memoir was dated from Bath, May 1780. Eleven years afterward, in the month of December 1791, Herschel communicated a second time to that celebrated English society the observations that he had made by occasionally directing his telescopes to this mysterious star. At both those epochs the observer's attention was chiefly directed to the absolute values of the *maxima* and *minima* of intensity.

The changeable star in the Whale was not the only periodical star with which Herschel occupied himself. His observations of

1795 and of 1796 proved that α Herculis also belongs to the category of variable stars, and that the time requisite for the accomplishment of all the changes of intensity, and for the star's return to any given state, was sixty days and a quarter. When Herschel obtained this result, about ten changeable stars were already known; but they were all either of very long or very short periods. The illustrious astronomer considered that by introducing between the two groups that exhibited very short and very long periods a star of somewhat intermediate conditions—for instance, one requiring sixty days to accomplish all its variations of intensity—he had advanced the theory of these phenomena by an essential step, the theory at least that attributes all to a movement of rotation which the stars may undergo round their centers.

Sir William Herschel's catalogues of double stars offer a considerable number to which he ascribes a decided green or blue tint. In binary combinations, when the small star appears very blue or very green, the large one is usually yellow or red. It does not appear that the great astronomer took sufficient interest in this circumstance. I do not find, indeed, that the almost constant association of two complementary colors (of yellow and blue, or of red and green) ever led him to suspect that one of those colors might not have anything real in it, that it often might be a mere illusion, a mere result of contrast. It was only in 1825 that I showed that there are stars whose contrast really explains their apparent color; but I have proved besides that blue is incontestably the color of certain insulated stars, or stars that have only white or other blue stars in their vicinity. Red is the only color that the ancients ever distinguished from white in their catalogues.

Herschel also endeavored to introduce numbers in the classification of stars as to magnitude; he endeavored, by means of these, to show the comparative intensity of a star of the first magnitude with one of second, or one of third magnitude, etc.

In one of the earliest of Herschel's memoirs we find that the apparent sidereal diameters are proved to be for the great part factitious, even when the best telescopes are used. Diameters estimated by the seconds—that is to say, reduced according to the magnifying power—diminish in certainty as the magnifying power is increased. These results are of the greatest importance.

In the course of his investigation of sidereal parallax, though without finding it, Herschel made an important discovery—that of the proper motion of our system. To show distinctly the direction of the motion of the solar system, not only was a displacement of the sidereal perspective required, but profound mathematical knowledge and a peculiar tact. This peculiar tact Herschel possessed in an eminent degree. Moreover, the result deduced from the very small number of proper motions known at the beginning of 1783 has been found almost to agree with that found recently by our best astronomers, with the application of subtile analytical formulæ to a considerable number of exact observations.

The proper motions of the stars have been known for more than a century, and even Fontenelle used to say in 1738 that the sun has probably a similar motion. The idea of partly attributing the displacement of the stars to a motion of the sun had suggested itself to Bradley and to Mayer. Lambert especially had been very explicit on the subject. Until then, however, there were only conjectures and mere probabilities. Herschel passed these limits. He himself proved that the sun positively moves, and that in this respect that immense and dazzling body must also be classed among the stars; that the apparently inextricable irregularities of numerous sidereal proper motions arise in great measure from the displacement of the solar system; that, in short, the point of space toward which we are annually advancing is situated in the constellation of Hercules. These are magnificent results. The discovery of the proper motion of our system will always be accounted among Herschel's highest claims to glory even after the mention that my duty as historian has obliged me to make of the anterior conjectures of Fontenelle, of Bradley, of Mayer, and of Lambert.

By the side of this great discovery we should place another that seems likely to be expanded in future. The results which it allows us to hope for will be of extreme importance. The discovery here alluded to was announced to the learned world in 1803; it is that of the reciprocal dependence of several stars, connected the one with the other, as the several planets and their satellites of our system are with the sun. Let us to these immortal labors add the ingenious ideas that we owe to Herschel on the nebulæ, on the constitution of the Milky Way, on the universe as a whole—ideas which almost by themselves constitute the actual history of the formation of the worlds—and we cannot have too deep a reverence for that powerful genius that notwithstanding the play of an ardent imagination scarcely ever erred.

Herschel devoted much time to the sun, but only relative to its physical constitution. The observations that he made on this subject and the consequences that he deduced from them equal in interest the most ingenious discoveries for which the sciences are indebted to him. In his important memoir in 1795, the great

astronomer declares himself convinced that the substance by the
intermediation of which the sun shines cannot be either a liquid
or an elastic fluid. It must be analogous to our clouds and float in
the transparent atmosphere of that body. The sun has, according
to him, two atmospheres, endowed with motions quite independent
of each other. An elastic fluid of an unknown nature is being
constantly formed on the dark surface of the sun, and rising up, on
account of its specific lightness, it forms the *pores* in the stratum
of reflecting clouds; then, combining with other gases, it produces
the *striæ* in the region of luminous clouds. When the ascending
currents are powerful they give rise to the *nuclei,* to *penumbræ,*
and the *faculæ.* If this explanation of the formation of solar spots
is well founded we must expect to find that the sun does not
constantly emit equal quantities of light and heat. Recent observations have verified this conclusion. But large nuclei, large penumbræ, striæ, faculæ, do they indicate an abundant, luminous, and
calorific emission, as Herschel supposed? That would be the result
of his hypothesis on the existence of very active ascending currents, but direct experience seems to contradict it.

The following is the way in which a learned physicist, Sir David
Brewster, appreciates this view of Herschel's: "It is not conceivable that luminous clouds, ceding to the lightest impulses and in a
state of constant change, can be the source of the sun's devouring
flame and of the dazzling light which it emits; nor can we admit,
besides, that the feeble barrier formed by planetary clouds would
shelter the objects that it might cover from the destructive effects
of the superior elements."

Sir David Brewster imagines that the non-luminous rays of
caloric, which form a constituent part of the solar light, are emitted by the dark nucleus of the sun, while the visible colored rays
proceed from the luminous matter by which the nucleus is surrounded. "From thence," he says, "proceeds the reason of light
and heat always appearing in a state of combination; the one
emanation cannot be obtained without the other. With this hypothesis we could readily explain why it is hottest when there are most
spots, because the heat of the nucleus would then reach us without
having been weakened by the atmosphere that it usually has to
traverse." But it is far from being an ascertained fact that we experience increased heat during the apparition of solar spots; the
inverse phenomenon is more probably true.

Herschel also studied the physical constitution of the moon. In
1780 he sought to measure the height of the mountains of our
satellite. The conclusion that he drew from his observations was

that few of the lunar mountains exceed 800 meters (2,600 feet). More recent selenographic observations give conclusions different from this. There is reason to remark on this occasion how much the result presented by Herschel differs from any tendency to the extraordinary or the gigantic that has been so unjustly assigned as the characteristic of the illustrious astronomer.

At the close of 1787 Herschel presented a memoir to the Royal Society, the title of which must have made a strong impression on the popular mind. The author therein relates that on the 19th of April, 1787, he had observed in the unilluminated part of the moon—that is, in the then dark portion—three volcanoes in a state of ignition. Two of these volcanoes appeared to be on the decline, the other appeared to be active. Such was his conviction of the reality of the phenomenon that the next morning he made the following record: "The volcano burns with more violence than last night." The real diameter of the volcanic light was 5,000 meters (16,400 English feet). Its intensity appeared very superior to that of the nucleus of a comet then in apparition. He further added: "The objects situated near the crater are feebly illuminated by the light that emanates from it"; and concludes thus: "In short, this eruption very much resembles the one I witnessed on the 4th of May, 1783."

How happens it, after such exact observations, that few astronomers now admit the existence of active volcanoes in the moon? I will explain this singularity in a few words. The various parts of our satellite do not all equally reflect light. Here it may depend on the form, elsewhere on the nature of the materials. Those who have examined the moon with telescopes know how very considerable the difference arising from these two causes may be, how much brighter one point of the moon sometimes is than those around it. Now it is quite evident that the relations of intensity beween the faint parts and the brilliant ones must continue to exist, whatever be the origin of the illuminating light. In the portion of the lunar globe that is illuminated by the sun there are, everyone knows, some points the brightness of which is extraordinary compared to those around them; those same points, when they are seen in that portion of the moon that is only lighted by the earth, or in the ash-colored part, will still predominate over the neighboring regions by their comparative intensity. Thus we may explain the observations of the Slough astronomer without recurring to volcanoes. While the observer was studying in the unilluminated portion of the moon the supposed volcano of the 20th of April, 1787, his nine-foot telescope showed him in truth, by the aid of the secondary rays proceeding from the earth, even the darkest spots. Herschel did not recur to the discussion of the supposedly active lunar volcanoes until 1791. In the volume of the *Philosophical Transactions* for 1792, he relates that in directing a twenty-foot telescope, magnifying three hundred and sixty times to the entirely eclipsed moon, on the 22d of October, 1790, there were visible over the whole face of the satellite about a hundred and fifty very luminous red points. The author declares that he will observe the greatest reserve relative to the nature of all these points, their great brightness, and their remarkable color. Yet is not red the usual color of the moon when eclipsed and when it has not entirely disappeared? Could the solar rays reaching our satellite by the effect of refraction, and after an absorption experienced in the lowest strata of the terrestrial atmosphere, receive any other tint? Are there not in the moon, when freely illuminated, and opposite to the sun, from one to two hundred little points, remarkable by the brightness of their light? Would it be possible for these little points not to be also distinguishable in the moon when it receives only the portion of solar light which is refracted and colored by our atmosphere?

Herschel was more successful in his remarks on the absence of a lunar atmosphere. During the solar eclipse of the 5th of September, 1793, the illustrious astronomer particularly directed his attention to the shape of the acute horn resulting from the intersection of the limbs of the moon and the sun. He deduced from his observation that if toward the point of the horn there had been a deviation of only one second occasioned by the refraction of the solar light in the lunar atmosphere, it would not have escaped him.

He also made the planets the object of numerous researches. Mercury was the one to which he gave least attention; he found its disk perfectly round on observing it during its projection—that is to say, in astronomical language, during its transit over the sun, on the 9th of November, 1802. He sought to determine the time of the rotation of Venus as early as 1777. He published two memoirs relative to Mars, one in 1781, the other in 1784, and we owe to him the discovery of its being flattened at the poles. After the discovery of the small planets Ceres, Pallas, Juno, and Vesta by Piazzi, Olbers, and Harding, Herschel applied himself to measuring their angular diameters. He concluded from his researches that those four new bodies did not deserve the name of planets and he proposed to call them asteroids. This epithet was subsequently adopted, though bitterly criticized by an historian of the Royal Society of London, Dr. Thomson, who went so far as to suggest that the learned astronomer "had wished to deprive the first observers of those bodies of all idea of rating themselves as high as himself in the scale of astronomical discoverers." It should require nothing further to annihilate such an imputation than to put it by the side of the following passage, extracted from a memoir by this celebrated astronomer, published in the *Philosophical Transactions* for the year 1805: "The specific difference existing between planets and asteroids appears now, by the addition of a third individual of the latter species, to be more completely established, and that circumstance, in my opinion, has added more to the *ornament* of our system than the discovery of a new planet could have done."

Although much did not result from Herschel's investigations in regard to the physical constitution of Jupiter, astronomy is indebted to him for several important results relative to the duration of that planet's rotation. He also made numerous observations on the distances and comparative magnitude of its satellites.

The compression of Saturn, the duration of its rotation, the physical constitution of this planet and of its ring were, on the part of Herschel, the object of numerous researches which have contributed much to the progress of planetary astronomy. But on this subject two important discoveries especially added new glory to his name. Of the five known satellites of Saturn at the close of the seventeenth century, Huygens had discovered the fourth, Cassini the others. The field seemed to be exhausted when news from Slough announced that this was a mistake.

On the 28th of August, 1789, the great forty-foot telescope revealed to Herschel a satellite still nearer to the ring than the other five already observed. According to the principles of the nomenclature previously adopted, the small body of the 28th of August ought to have been called the first satellite of Saturn; the numbers indicating the places of the other five would then each have been increased by unity. But the fear of introducing confusion into science by these continual changes of denomination induced a preference for calling the new satellite the sixth. Thanks to the prodigious powers of the forty-foot telescope, a last satellite, the seventh, showed itself on the 17th of September, 1789, between the sixth and the ring. This seventh satellite is extremely faint. Herschel, however, succeeded in seeing it whenever circumstancs were very favorable, even by the aid of the twenty-foot telescope.

The discovery of the planet Uranus and the detection of its satellites will always rank among the greatest discoveries of modern astronomy. On the 13th of March, 1781, between ten and eleven o'clock at night, while Herschel was examining the small stars near

H Geminorum with a seven-foot telescope, bearing a magnifying power of two hundred and twenty-seven times, one of these stars seemed to have an unusual diameter, and it was therefore thought to be a comet. It was under this denomination that it was discussed at the Royal Society of London. But the researches of Herschel and of Laplace showed later that the orbit of the new body was nearly circular, and Uranus was consequently elevated to the rank of a planet.

The immense distance of Uranus, its small angular diameter, and the feebleness of its light scarcely allowed the hope that if that body had satellites they could be perceived from the earth. Herschel was not a man to be deterred by such discouraging conjectures. Therefore, since powerful telescopes of the ordinary construction—that is to say, with two mirrors conjugated—had not enabled him to discover anything, he substituted in the beginning of January 1787 *front-view* telescopes—that is, telescopes throwing much more light on the objects, the small mirror being then suppressed, and with it one of the causes of loss of light eliminated. By this means, with patient labor and observations requiring a rare perseverance, Herschel made (from the 11th of January, 1787, to the 28th of February, 1794) the discovery of the six satellites of his planet and thus completed the system of worlds that belongs entirely to himself.

There are several memoirs by Herschel on comets. In analyzing them we shall see that this acute observer could not touch anything without making further discoveries in regard to it. He applied some of his fine instruments to the study of the physical constitution of a comet discovered by Pigott, on the 28th September, 1807. The nucleus was round and well determined. Some measures taken on the day when the nucleus subtended an angle of only a single second gave as its real diameter $\frac{6}{100}$ of the diameter of the earth. Herschel saw no phase at an epoch when only $\frac{7}{10}$ of the nucleus could be illuminated by the sun. The nucleus then must shine by its own light. This is a legitimate inference in the opinion of everyone who will allow, on the one hand, that the nucleus is a solid body, and on the other, that it would have been possible to observe a phase of $\frac{8}{10}$ on a disk whose apparent total diameter did not exceed one or two seconds of a degree. Very small stars seemed to grow much paler when they were seen through the coma or through the tail of the comet. This faintness may have been only apparent and might have arisen from the circumstance of the stars being then projected on a luminous background. Such is, indeed, the explanation adopted by Herschel. A gaseous medium, capable of reflecting sufficient solar light to efface that of some stars, would appear to him to possess in each stratum a sensible quantity of matter, and to be for that reason a cause of real diminution of the light transmitted, though nothing reveals the existence of such a cause.

This argument, offered by Herschel in favor of the system which transforms comets into self-luminous bodies, has not, as we may perceive, much force. I might venture to say as much of several other remarks by this great observer. He tells us that the comet was distinctly visible in the telescope on the 21st of February, 1808; now on that day its distance from the sun amounted to 2.7 times the mean radius of the terrestrial orbit; its distance from the observer was 2.9: "What probability would there be that rays going to such distances, from the sun to the comet, could, after their reflection, be seen by an eye nearly three times more distant from the comet than from the sun?"

It is only numerical determinations that could give value to such an argument. By satisfying himself with vague reasoning, Herschel did not even perceive that he was committing a great mistake by making the comet's distance from the observer appear to be an element of visibility. If the comet be self-luminous its intrinsic splendor (its brightness for unity of surface) will remain constant at any distance as long as the subtended angle remains sensible. If the body shines by borrowed light its brightness will vary only according to its change of distance from the sun; nor will the distance of the observer occasion any change in the visibility; always, let it be understood, with the restriction that the apparent diameter shall not be diminished below certain limits.

Herschel finished his observations of a comet that was visible in January 1807 with the following remark: "Of the sixteen telescopic comets that I have examined, fourteen had no solid body visible at their center; the other two exhibited a central light, very ill-defined, that might be termed a nucleus, but a light that certainly could not deserve the name of a disk."

The beautiful comet of 1811 became the object of his conscientious labor. With large telescopes he saw, in the midst of the gaseous head, a reddish body of planetary appearance which bore strong magnifying powers and showed no sign of phase. Hence Herschel concluded that it was self-luminous. Yet if we reflect that the planetary body under consideration was not a second in diameter, the absence of a phase does not appear a conclusive argument. The light of the head had a bluish-green tint. Was this a real tint, or did the central reddish body, only through contrast, cause the surrounding vapor to appear colored? Herschel did not examine the question from this point of view. The head of the comet appeared to be enveloped at a certain distance, on the side toward the sun, by a brilliant narrow zone, embracing about a semicircle and of a yellowish color. From the two extremities of the semicircle there arose toward the region away from the sun two long luminous streaks which limited the tail. Between the brilliant circular semi-ring and the head the cometary substance seemed dark, very rare, and very diaphanous.

The luminous semi-ring always presented similar appearances in all the positions of the comet; it was not then possible to attribute to it really the annular form—the shape of Saturn's ring, for example. Herschel sought whether a spherical semi-envelope of luminous matter, and yet diaphanous, would not lead to a natural explanation of the phenomenon. In this hypothesis, the visual rays which on the 6th of October, 1811, crossed the envelope almost tangentially, traversed a thickness of matter of about 399,000 kilometers (248,000 English miles), while the visual rays near the head of the comet did not meet above 80,000 kilometers (50,000 miles) of matter. As the brightness must be proportional to the quantity of matter traversed, there could not fail to be an appearance around the comet of a semi-ring five times more luminous than the central regions. This semi-ring, then, was an effect of projection, and it has revealed a circumstance to us truly remarkable in the physical constitution of comets.

The two luminous streaks that outlined the tail at its two limits may be explained in a similar manner; the tail was not flat, as it appeared to be; it had the form of a conoid, with its sides of a certain thickness. The visual lines which traversed those sides almost tangentially evidently met much more matter than the visual lines passing across. This maximum of matter could not fail of being represented by a maximum of light. The luminous semi-ring appeared one day to be suspended in the diaphanous atmosphere by which the head of the comet was surrounded, at a distance of 518,000 kilometers (322,000 English miles) from the nucleus. This distance was not constant. The matter of the semi-annular envelope seemed even to be precipitated by slow degree through the diaphanous atmosphere. Finally it reached the nucleus; the earlier appearances vanished and the comet was reduced to a globular nebula. During its period of dissolution the ring appeared sometimes to have several branches.

The luminous shreds of the tail seemed to undergo rapid, frequent, and considerable variations of length. Herschel discerned symptoms of a movement of rotation both in the comet and in its tail. This rotatory motion carried unequal shreds from the center toward the border, and reciprocally. On looking from time to time at the same region of the tail—at the border, for example—sensible changes of length must have been perceptible, which, however, had no real existence. Herschel thought, as I have already said, that the beautiful comet of 1811 and that of 1807 were self-luminous. The second comet of 1811 appeared to him to shine only by borrowed light. It must be acknowledged that these conjectures did not rest on anything demonstrative.

In attentively comparing the comet of 1807 with the beautiful comet of 1811, relative to the changes of distance from the sun and the modifications resulting thence, Herschel put it beyond doubt that these modifications have something individual in them, something relative to a special state of the nebulous matter. On one celestial body the changes of distance produce an enormous effect; on another the modifications are insignificant.

I shall say very little as to the discoveries that Herschel made in physics, since everyone is familiar with them. They are to be found in all elementary works, and are given in verbal instruction; they must be considered as the starting point of a multitude of important labors with which the sciences have been enriched during later years. The chief of these is that of the dark radiating heat which is found mixed with light.

In studying the phenomena, not with the eye as Newton did, but with a thermometer, Herschel discovered that the solar spectrum is prolonged on the red side far beyond the visible limits. The thermometer sometimes rose higher in the dark region than in the midst of brilliant zones. The light of the sun then contains, besides the colored rays so well characterized by Newton, invisible rays still less refrangible than the red, and whose warming power is very considerable. A world of discoveries has arisen from this fundamental fact. The dark ray emanating from terrestrial objects more or less heated also became the subject of Herschel's investigations. His work contained the germs of a large number of beautiful experiments more fully developed in our own day.

By successively placing the thermometer in all parts of the solar spectrum, he determined the illuminating powers of the various prismatic rays. The general result of these experiments may be thus enunciated: The illuminating power of the red rays is not very great; that of the orange rays surpasses it, and is in its turn surpassed by the power of the yellow rays. The maximum power of illumination is found between the brightest yellow and the palest green.

The yellow and the green possess this power equally. A like assimilation may be laid down between the blue and the red. Finally, the power of illumination in the indigo rays, and above all in the violet, is very weak.

The memoirs of Herschel on Newton's colored rings, though containing a multitude of exact experiments, have not contributed much to advance the theory of those curious phenomena. I have learned from good authority that he himself held the same opinion. He said that it was the only occasion on which he had reason to regret having, according to his constant custom, published his labors immediately as fast as they were performed.

René Just Haüy *

1743–1822

————◆————

GEORGES LÉOPOLD CHRÉTIEN CUVIER †

IN THE history of science epochs occur when the human mind seems to take a surprising stride. When years have been spent in the patient accumulation of facts and observations and the received theories no longer suffice to harmonize them, ideas respecting natural phenomena become in some measure incoherent and contradictory. System is no longer possible, and the need is universally felt of some new bond of connection. Should a genius appear at such a juncture, capable of rising to a point of view from which some of the required relations may be embraced, fresh courage is diffused among contemporary inquirers, each throws himself with ardor into the new paths which have been opened, and discoveries succeed one another with increasing rapidity. Those who have successfully associated their names with the movement assume in the eyes of their followers of a later generation the proportions of some superior race; and as they pass successively from the stage of life are deplored as heroes whom the world must despair of ever seeing equaled. Such an epoch the close of the eighteenth century unquestionably was, as regards the natural sciences.

The laws of geometry, as concise as comprehensive, extended over the entire heavens; the boundaries of the universe enlarged and its spaces peopled with unknown stars; the course of celestial bodies determined more rigorously than ever, both in time and space; the earth weighed as in a balance; man soaring to the clouds or traversing the seas without the aid of winds; the intricate mysteries of chemistry referred to certain clear and simple facts; the list of natural existences was increased tenfold in every species,

* *A.R.*, 1860, pp. 376–392. Read at the public sitting of the French Academy of Sciences, June 2, 1823.
† See pp. 118–144 for the life of Cuvier.

27

and their relations irrevocably fixed by a survey as well of their internal as external structure; the history of the earth, even in ages the most remote, explored by means of its own monuments, and shown to be not less wonderful in fact than it might have appeared to the wildest fancy: such is the grand and unparalleled spectacle which it has been our privilege to contemplate, but which renders only more bitter the disappearance of those great men to whom we owe it. Few are the years which have seen the tomb close upon a Lavoisier, a Priestley, a Cavendish, a Camper, a De Saussure, a Lagrange; and who but must be startled at the acceleration in our losses, when a few months only have snatched from us Herschel and Delambre, Haüy and Berthollet, leaving us scarce power to render, within the prescribed time, the homage due to them by the societies of which they were the ornament.

We might be the more tempted to believe that Haüy felt this irresistible impulse of his epoch, from his having been determined, almost without being aware of it, to a career for which during the first forty years of his life he had never thought of preparing himself. In the midst of obscure occupations an idea dawns upon him; a single idea, but one equally luminous and prolific. From that moment he never desists from following it; he devotes to it his time, his faculties, his undivided attention, until finally a brilliant success is the crown and recompense of his efforts. No example could better show the grand, I had almost said miraculous, results which spring from the profound and exhaustive study of a subject upon which the mind is concentrated, nor prove more clearly the truth of the maxim that, at least in the exact sciences, it is the patience of a sound intellect, when that patience is indomitable, which truly constitutes what we call genius.

René Just Haüy, an honorary canon of Notre Dame, a member of this academy and of most of those of Europe and America, was born the 28th of February, 1743, at Saint-Just, a small market town in the department of the Oise. A younger brother of his has made himself known by an original method for instructing those born blind, while the father of both was a poor weaver who could probably have given them no other profession than his own, had not the liberality of others come to his aid.

The first change for the better in the fortunes of the two brothers may be ascribed to the pious turn of the elder, manifested in his earliest years and governing his whole life. Even in infancy he evinced a singular pleasure in religious ceremonies, especially in the choirs of the church, a taste for music, the natural concomitant of tender sentiments, having thus early allied itself in him with the feelings of devotion. A Premonstratensian prior of his native town, who had observed the assiduity of his attendance at divine service, engaged him one day in conversation, and being struck with the vivacity of his intelligence procured him the instruction of some of his monks. The child's progress, promptly responding to the care of these masters, interested them more and more and led them to suggest to his mother that by removing him to Paris she might shortly procure through their recommendation such resources as would enable him to complete his studies.

This excellent woman had scarcely sufficient means for a few months subsistence in the capital, but she preferred encountering any extremity to proving false to the future which might await her son. It was long, however, before her tenderness met with any but the most slender encouragement. The place of chorister in a church of the Saint Antoine quarter was the only means of livelihood available to a youth whose name was destined to be one day known to all Europe. This post, he used afterwards pleasantly to say, was at least so far propitious that it prevented him from burying his musical talents; at any rate, by fostering his original taste, it enabled him to become a respectable performer on the violin and harpsichord, two instruments with which he solaced himself during life. Finally, the interest of his patrons of Saint-Just obtained for him a scholarship in the college of Navarre, where it first became possible for him to enter regularly on a course of classic instruction.

Here his conduct and application gained him favor, as they had done at Saint-Just. The heads of the college engaged his services as teacher as soon as he had ceased to be a pupil and even advanced him to the mastership of the fourth class before he had quite reached the age of twenty-one years. Transferred some years later to the College of the Cardinal Lemoine, in a similar but higher capacity, he might seem to have limited his ambition to such modest, however useful, functions. It is true that at Navarre he had imbibed from M. Brisson of that academy some taste for experimental physics, and at moments of leisure had even experimented with electricity; but this was rather by way of recreation than study; while natural history, properly so called, does not appear to have in the least occupied his attention. If at last he found the path which was to conduct him in the end to so high a renown, it was still owing to the gentler dispositions of his nature; so that the fame and fortune of Haüy may be said with literal exactness to have been at every step the recompense of his virtues.

Among the regents of the Collège Lemoine there was at this

time a learned individual who had devoted himself to the instruction of youth from a principle of piety. Capable of enlightening
persons of the maturest age, Lhomond had chosen to restrict himself to compositions for the use of the young, but had contrived
to impart to them so admirable a tone of simplicity and clearness
that their success has been seldom equaled by works of greater
pretension. Between him and Haüy there existed so striking a conformity of character and sentiments that the latter had chosen
him for his friend and confessor, interested himself with the devotion of a son in his affairs, tended him in sickness and was the
companion of his walks. Lhomond cultivated botany, and Haüy,
who had scarcely heard of it, felt a chagrin at not being able to
add the common study of this as a new charm to their intercourse.
In one of his vacations he discovered that a monk of Saint-Just
amused himself with the study of plants. The idea at once struck
him that he might give an agreeable surprise to his friend, and
with this sole view he requested the monk to convey to him some
notions of the science and some acquaintance with different species.
His heart came to the aid of his memory; he comprehended and
retained all that was shown him, and the surprise of Lhomond was
unbounded when at their next herborization Haüy named to him in
the language of Linnæus most of the plants they met with and
showed that he had studied and analyzed their structure.

From that time everything was common between them, even
their amusements; but from that time also Haüy became thoroughly a naturalist and an indefatigable one. It might be said that
his mind had been wakened of a sudden to this new kind of
enjoyment. He prepared a herbarium with unusual care and neat-
ness, and even invented processes by which the color of his flowers
has been preserved to the present day. Here he took his first
lesson in the right use and aims of method, and by frequenting the
Jardin du Roi, which was near his college, he extended his ideas
and exercised himself more and more in the work of classification
and comparison.

Happening one day to join the crowd which at that time attended the lessons on mineralogy given by Daubenton in the Jardin
du Roi, he unexpectedly found himself in the presence of a new
object of study, more congenial to his first taste for physics than
even that of plants. Numerous, however, as was the attendance
on Daubenton's lessons, it was mainly of such auditors as left
botany and mineralogy where they found them. Having come
earlier to the study, they might know more of both than Haüy;

but custom itself, in familiarizing them with the difficulties of those sciences, had caused them to disappear. To Haüy, who came later, these difficulties presented themselves after a different manner. The contrarieties and gaps in the series of ideas strongly arrested the attention of a vigorous thinker who in the height of his powers approached for the first time a new object of study. If the constancy observable in the complicated forms of flowers and fruits and all the parts of organized bodies affected him with admiration and wonder, how is it, he might ask, that the forms of minerals, so much more simple and even geometric, are not subjected to similar laws, for at that time even the partial and imperfect relationship proposed by Romé Delisle in the second edition of his *Crystallography* was unknown. How is it, might Haüy say, that the same stone, the same salt, show themselves in cubes, in prisms, in needles, without the change of an atom in their composition; while the rose has always the same petals, the acorn the same curvature, the cedar the same height and the same development?

While absorbed in these ideas, it chanced that in examining some minerals at the house of a friend, he was so fortunately awkward as to let fall a beautiful group of calcareous spar crystallized in prisms. One of these prisms broke in such a way as to exhibit at the point of fracture planes not less smooth than the original surface, but presenting the appearance of a new crystal wholly different in form from the prism. Haüy observes this fact and attentively examines the planes and angles of the fragment. To his great surprise, he finds that they are the same with those of Iceland spar crystallized in rhomboids. He returns to his own cabinet, selects a specimen crystallized in the form of a six-sided pyramid, such as is usually called *dog tooth spar,* and breaking it, sees the same rhomboid of the Iceland spar emerge; the splinters which fall are themselves smaller rhomboids. He tries a third spar, called from its form *lenticular,* and still it is the rhomboid which discloses itself in the center, and smaller rhomboids detach themselves in the fragments.

He might well exclaim, "All is clear!" The particles of calcareous spar have but one and the same form; it is only in grouping themselves differently that they compose the crystals whose external shape deludes us by its variety. Setting out with this idea, he could readily imagine that those particles, in accumulating and disposing themselves in layers, might form pyramids and polyhedrons of a new configuration, enveloping the primitive crystal as with another whose exterior faces might differ much, both as to number and inclination, from those of the first, according as the successive layers had diminished on one side or another, and in such or such proportions.

If this then was the true principle of the crystallization in question, it could not but prevail in the crystals of other substances, each of which ought in like manner to have its constituent particles the same, a nucleus alike in each species, and superposed or accessory layers producing all the varieties. Haüy, who hesitates not to submit to the hammer his own crystals as well as those he could obtain from his friends, finds everywhere a structure based upon the same laws. In the garnet it is tetrahedral; in fluor spar, octahedral; pyrites presents a cube; while gypsum and heavy spar offer straight four-sided prisms, whose bases, however, have different angles. Invariably the crystals break with faces parallel to those of the nucleus, the exterior form being but the result of the more or less rapid decrease of the superposed laminæ, a decrease which takes place sometimes at the angles and sometimes on the sides. Thus the new surfaces presented are in reality a succession of minute points produced by the retreating laminæ, though they appear smooth to the eye from their extreme tenuity. No crystal which Haüy examines offers any exception to his law, so that he exclaims, and this time with more assurance, "All is clear!"

But that this assurance should be complete, a third condition is to be fulfilled. The nucleus or constituent molecule having in each case a fixed form, geometrically determinable as to its angles and the correspondence of its lines, every law of decrement must cause the secondary surfaces to be in like manner determinable; indeed, the nucleus or molecule being given, it should be possible to calculate beforehand what angles and lines the decrease in each instance would prescribe to all the secondary surfaces. In a word, that the theory should be certain it was necessary here, as in astronomy and every part of physics, that it should not only explain with precision all known facts, but that it should provide with equal precision for those which had not yet come to light.

This Haüy perceived, but fifteen years passed chiefly in teaching Latin had nearly effaced the small portion of geometry taught him at college. Without being deterred by this, he tranquilly set himself to regain it; and as he had so quickly learned botany to please his friend, he could not be long in acquiring enough geometry to complete his discovery. Nor was his recompense delayed beyond the first trial of this new auxiliary. The hexahedral prism which he had broken by accident was found upon calculation to yield a value closely approximate to that of the angles of the

molecule of the spar; other calculations gave him that of the
retreating surfaces, the application of the instrument to the measurement of the angles giving direct confirmation to the previsions
of theory. In other crystals the secondary were found to be as
easily deducible from the primitive planes, while in nearly all
cases the decrements, by which the secondary planes are produced,
were found to exhibit the simple proportions which nature seems
to have established in all the relations of number. Without further hesitation might Haüy now for the third time exclaim, "All
is clear!" And at this stage only of his discoveries did he feel confidence enough to speak of them to Daubenton, the master whose
lessons he had hitherto followed in modest silence. We may judge
in what manner they were received from the fact that Laplace, to
whom they were communicated by Daubenton, and who at once
foresaw their consequences, lost no time in pressing the author to
come forward and present them to the Academy.

This it was not so easy to induce him to do. To the worthy professor of the Collège Lemoine the Academy was a *terra incognita*
at which his diffidence took alarm. Its usages were so little known
to him that he at first presented himself in the long robe which
ancient canons of the church are said to prescribe, but which no
ecclesiastic has for a long time worn in society except on strictly
professional occasions. Certain friends were apprehensive that at
a period of so much levity this robe might occasion a loss of votes;
but to induce so scrupulous a casuist to quit it, nothing less was
necessary than an appeal to the advice of a doctor of the Sorbonne. "The ancient canons of the church" said this wise referee,
"are no doubt highly respectable, but what is of consequence at
this moment is that you should belong to the Academy." We are
at liberty, however, to believe that the precaution was superfluous and that he would have been received no matter in what
vestments he had presented himself. So emulous, indeed, was the
Academy of such an acquisition that, without waiting for the vacancy of a place in physics or mineralogy, one in botany, which
circumstances had rendered disposable, was conferred on him with
nearly entire unanimity and even in preference to learned botanists.

A still more flattering proof of the regard of his new colleagues
was that by several of the most distinguished among them he was
pressed to give a course of lectures and demonstrations in elucidation of his theory. Lagrange, Lavoisier, Laplace, Fourcroy, Berthollet, and Morveau might have been seen repairing to the Collège
Lemoine to attend the lessons of the modest professor, whom we

may well suppose confounded at finding himself become a master where he would have scarcely presumed to call himself a disciple. But in a doctrine so new, yet already nearly complete, the most skillful could be but learners. Never perhaps had a theory of the same extent been presented in the same state of clearness and development from its very origin as that of Haüy, who had invented even the required methods of calculation and had represented in advance by formulas of his own all the possible combinations of crystallography.

From no instance more clearly than from this may we learn to distinguish between the solid labors of genius, on which imperishable structures are reared, and the ideas, more or less happy, which present themselves for a moment to certain minds but for want of being elaborated produce no durable results.

Six or seven years before Haüy, Gahn, a young Swedish chemist, since professor at Abo, had likewise remarked that in breaking a crystal of pyramidal spar its nucleus was a rhomboid similar to Iceland spar, and he had communicated this observation to his master, the celebrated Bergman, who would have been thought capable of following it into all its consequences. But in place of extending it to different crystals, and thus ascertaining by experiment within what limits the fact might be generalized, Bergman launched into hypothesis and lost his way from the outset. From the observed rhomboid of spar he pretended to deduce not only the other crystals of spar, but those of the garnet and hyacinth, which have no conformity of structure. Thus, a savant of the first order, proficient in physics and geometry, bewildered himself in the path to a great discovery and left it to be made by a man who was scarcely beginning to occupy himself with science but who knew how to pursue truth as nature wills it to be pursued: proceeding step by step, observing without remission, and not suffering oneself to be carried away or turned aside by the imagination.

The mineralogists, however, who had been unable to find the right way, now from the same cause proved themselves as little capable of perceiving how far that of Bergman diverged from it, and they charged Haüy with borrowing Bergman's ideas—Haüy, who scarcely knew the name of Bergman and had certainly never seen his memoir. They added, as is always done on similar occasions, that not only was the discovery not Haüy's, but that it was false.

Romé Delisle, a mineralogist not otherwise without merit, but who had long been occupied with crystals without once suspecting the principle of their structure, had the weakness to deny it when discovered by another. He amused himself with calling Haüy a *crystalloclast,* as the breakers of images were called *iconoclasts* under the Lower Empire. But happily we know no heretics in science except those who do not choose to follow the progress of their age; and it is Romé Delisle himself, and others actuated by similar jealousies, who must be referred to the class of the perverse and contumacious.

The only response of Haüy to his detractors consisted in new researches and a still more fruitful application of them. As yet he had but given the solution of a curious problem in physics; his further observations were destined to furnish indications of the highest importance to mineralogy. In his numerous experiments upon the spars he had remarked that the stone called *pearl spar,* which till then had been regarded as a variety of the heavy spar, or sulphate of barytes, has the same nucleus with the calcareous spars; and his analysis proved that, like them, it consists only of carbonated lime. If minerals, he reasoned, well ascertained as to their species and composition, have each a determinate nucleus and constituent molecule, the same must be the case with all the minerals distinguished by nature whose composition is not yet known. For the distinction of substances, then, this nucleus or molecule may supply the place of their composition; and from the first application of this idea he was enabled to carry light into a part of the science which all the labors of his predecessors had failed to make clear.

At this epoch the most expert mineralogists, Linnæus, Wallerius, Romé Delisle, even Saussure himself, confounded under the name of *schorl* a multitude of stones which had nothing in common but a certain fusibility joined to a form more or less prismatic; and under that of *zeolite,* a multitude of others, whose sole distinctive character was to change, with acids, into a sort of jelly. The schorls especially formed a most heterogeneous assortment, every mineral of which there existed no clear idea being referred to it; which led the illustrious Lagrange to say, jestingly, that schorl was the *nectary* of the mineralogists, because the botanists were similarly accustomed to call by the name of *nectary* every part of the flower whose nature they were ignorant of.

On subjecting to mechanical division the stone known as white schorl (*schorl-blanc*), Haüy was surprised at finding the nucleus and molecule of feldspar. A test supplied upon this indication, by the chemist Darcet, manifested the identity of the schorl in all its physical and chemical characters with the feldspars.

Thus encouraged, Haüy proceeded to examine other schorls. He discovered that the black stone with which so many lavas are strewn and which had been called *volcanic schorl* has for its nucleus an oblique prism with rhombic base, and the pretended *violet schorl* of Dauphiné a nucleus whose prism is straight; both therefore were to be separated from the family of schorls. Still later he succeeded in distinguishing the *electric schorl* or *tourmaline* from the *black schorl of primitive formation,* the nucleus of the first being a regular hexahedral prism, that of the last simply tetrahedral. Thus, one after another, under his continued researches the pretended schorls were divorced from the varieties with which they had been improperly associated, and assigned by fixed characters to their proper groups. The same success attended his method in distinguishing the stones confounded under the name of *zeolites.* Chemistry and physics, prompted by these results of crystallography, were everywhere enabled to find in minerals characters or elements which had not before been detected. From this time Haüy might be said to have become the lawgiver of mineralogy. By his researches on the schorls he had inaugurated a new era in the science, and every subsequent year has witnessed some unexpected discovery due to the study of the crystalline structure of minerals.

Among the schorls he finally distinguished fourteen species, six among the zeolites, four among the garnets, five among the jacinths. Not only were the chemists guided by these labors to the detection of unsuspected differences in the composition of stones; there were scarcely less frequent occasions when Haüy could predict that the differences which they had assumed could not exist. Thus, Vauquelin, who had before discovered *glucine* in the *beryl,* was led by the indications of crystallography to find it also in the *emerald.*

It was not always that Haüy recognized at first the indications furnished by his own researches; he might sometimes neglect to compare their results. When Klaproth and Vauquelin for instance, had discovered that the *apatite* and the *chrysolite* of the jewelers were but phosphate of lime, Haüy, on recurring to his papers, found that he had himself long before determined the same structure for both; and this coincidence in the result of operations conducted separately and without concert was in his eyes a decisive triumph for crystallography.

It was imperative on a man who served the sciences after this manner to devote himself exclusively to them. By the counsel of

Lhomond himself, when the twenty years' service requisite for a pension of *emeritus* in the University was fulfilled, Haüy lost no time in demanding it. He had besides a small benefice, the whole not amounting to more than what was strictly needful, but for him, who knew no pleasure but in work, it would have sufficed if that needful at least had been assured to him. Unfortunately, he was to learn within a very short time that the effects of human passions are not so easily calculated as those of the forces of nature.

It will be recollected with what imprudence the Constituent Assembly, under the control of factious spirits allowed itself to combine theological disputes with all the other disputes which then agitated France, thus doubling the asperity of political quarrels by giving them the character of religious persecutions. The new form of government imposed on the Church had divided the clergy, and the men who wished to carry the revolution to extremes took a pleasure in exasperating their dissensions. Such ecclesiastics as resisted innovation were deprived of their places and pensions, and Haüy, whose scrupulous piety consigned him to that class, found himself in a moment as poor as on the day when he aspired to the situation of singing boy. He would have been content, however, had he been allowed to live by his labors; but the persecutors could not be satisfied with a first vexation. One of the earliest acts of the reckless men who mounted to power on the ruins of the throne on August 10, 1792, was to imprison the priests who had not taken the prescribed oath, and the scientific celebrity of Haüy furnished but a reason the more for including him in the common lot.

Little aware in his solitude of what was passing around him, it was with surprise that he one day saw a party of rough men insolently entering his modest retreat. They begin by demanding if he has firearms. "None but this," said Haüy, drawing at the same time a spark from his electric machine. For an instant these brutal personages feel themselves disarmed; but the next they proceeded to seize upon his papers, which contain nothing but algebraic formulas; overturn the collection, his only property; and end with conducting him to the Seminary St. Firmin, contiguous to the Collège Lemoine and recently converted into a prison, where all the priests and professors of that part of Paris were confined.

One cell for another made but little difference to Haüy. Tranquilized, moreover, at finding himself in the midst of many of his friends, he felt but little concern, except to send for his cabinet of drawers and endeavor to restore his crystals to order. Happily, outside the prison there were friends of his, better informed as to the course which things were taking.

Geoffroy de Saint-Hilaire,* Haüy's pupil and subsequently his colleague in this academy, lodged then at the Collège Lemoine. No sooner did he learn what had hapened than he hastened to implore the intervention of all the personages who were likely to be of service. Members of the academy and functionaries of the Jardin du Roi did not hesitate to throw themselves at the feet of the ferocious men who were conducting this frightful tragedy. An order of deliverance is obtained and borne by Saint-Hilaire to the prison, but he arrives a little late in the day. Haüy is so tranquil, so comfortable, that nothing can determine him to leave that evening. The next morning it is almost necessary to withdraw him by force. One shudders to think that the day after was the 2nd of September!

It is a singular fact that from that time he was never molested. Nothing certainly could have induced him to lend his countenance to the extravagances of the period, but no one proposed to him to do so. The simplicity and mildness of his manner and character seem to have stood him in stead of all else. Once only was he summoned to appear at the review of his battalion, but they cashiered him on the spot for his awkward appearance. This was nearly all that he knew or at least saw of the revolution. The convention, at a time when it was proceeding with the most violence, named him a member of the Commission of Weights and Measures and Keeper of the Cabinet of Mines. And when Lavoisier was arrested and Borda and Delambre dismissed, it was Haüy, a recusant priest, discharging every day his ecclesiastical functions, who alone found himself in a position to write in their behalf, and who did so without hesitation and without incurring inconvenience. Considering the time, there is even more cause to wonder at his impunity than his courage.

It was at the Cabinet of Mines and on the invitation and with the aid of the enlightened administration of that department that Haüy prepared his principal work, the treatise on mineralogy. Having at his disposal a vast collection, to which minerals were consigned from all quarters, and at the same time the services of the young and ardent scholars of the polytechnic school (more than one of whom have since become eminent mineralogists), Haüy promptly retrieved the time consumed in other labors and

* See Flourens, "Memoir of Geoffroy Saint-Hilaire," *A.R.*, 1861, pp. 161–174.

in a few years reared that admirable monument of which it may be said that it effected for France what retarded circumstances had accomplished for the author himself, having at once restored that country after long years of neglect to the first rank in this division of natural history. This work unites, indeed, two advantages which seldom meet: the first, that it is founded on an original discovery, entirely due to the genius of the author; the second, that this discovery is followed up and applied with unexampled perseverance, even to the most minute mineral varieties. All is grand in the plan; all is precise and rigorous in the details. It is complete, like the doctrine itself of which it contains the exposition.

Of the departments of natural history, mineralogy, whose objects are the least numerous and least complicated, is that, notwithstanding, which yields itself least readily to a rational classification. The first observers distributed and named the minerals vaguely from their external appearance and use. Only toward the middle of the eighteenth century was the attempt made to submit them to the methods which had rendered such service to zoology and botany, though in thus aiming to establish among them genera and species as among organized beings, it was forgotten that in mineralogy the principle is wanting which has given birth to the idea of species, namely, that of generation; and that even the principle of individuality is scarcely admissible when our conception of it is founded, as in the organic world, on a unity of action among different organs concurring to the support of a single life.

It is not by the material that the identity of species in plants and animals manifests itself, but by the form, as the name *species* itself indicates. No two men, perhaps, nor oaks, nor roses, have the substances which compose their material in the same proportions; and even those substances are in a state of incessant change: they circulate rather than reside within that abstract space and outline which we call the form of the object. In a few years there will remain perhaps not an atom of what composes our body today. It is the form alone which is permanent, and which, transmitted by the mysterious process of generation, will continue to attract to itself through an endless succession of individuals molecules as different in their source as transitory in their condition.

On the contrary, in minerals, where there is no apparent movement, where the molecules remain fixed until separated by some external force; where the material, in a word, is permanent, it would seem at the first glance that this, or in other terms the chemical composition, ought to constitute the essence of the thing. But reflection teaches us that if the things themselves are different, this can scarcely happen except through the form of their molecules; that from the peculiar form of these molecules and their respective mode of grouping there must necessarily result determinate forms in the mass; and that in mineralogy, if there is anything which can represent the individual, it must be those resulting forms when they exhibit a regular whole, that is to say, a crystal; since at the moment at least when this crystal came together, all its constituent molecules must have concurred in a common movement and grouped themselves by the force of some common law. Now nothing proves that in this common movement particles of a different nature which happened to be within the same sphere of action may not have been involved in it, nor that elements or atoms identical in their nature may not, at the moment of contracting their original union, have grouped themselves into different crystallized molecules. But that which the mind conceives as possible, experience has taught us to be real; whence it is evident that in these two cases chemical analysis would give but an incomplete idea of the mineral and one not at all in accordance with those of its properties which are most obvious. Such are the views doubtless which, without being very distinctly taken into account by Haüy himself, guided his genius or, if the expression be preferred, his scientific instinct, and led him to assign crystallization the first rank in his determinations of mineralogical species.

All the discoveries and observations since made, even those which have been looked upon as objections to this fundamental rule, may be said rather to be confirmations of it. Thus, for example, what has been just said of the crystallizing force and its power of engaging other molecules with the essential ones is so true that the former are attracted sometimes in much the greater quantity; and this to such an extent that a single mineralogical species, iron spar (le fer spathique) for instance, which is specifically a calcareous spar or carbonated lime, may contain a fourth or even third of its weight of iron and thus become for the metallurgist a real mine rather than a simple stone; as muriatic spar, which is likewise a calcareous spar, may develop grains of grit (grès) in such measure as to contain little else, without having the angles of its crystals changed by a single second.

It is the same thing in our own laboratories as in that of nature. In causing a mixture of two salts to crystallize, Beudant observed that one of them constrained the other to blend with its crystals in a much larger proportion than that furnished by itself. Which, then, of the two ought to characterize the mineral? The most abundant? By no means; for, with the exception of that abundance, all the characters of the product are given by the other.

Nor is it less certain that the same substance, at the instant of passing into a crystallized form or of individualizing itself, if the expression may be allowed, takes sometimes a very different form from that in which it usually appears. All the efforts of chemists have failed to discover in *aragonite* any essential matter but the carbonated lime, of which calcareous spar is likewise composed; for the small portion of strontian found in the former can only be regarded as accidental; and yet the crystals of aragonite are octahedral, and those of the spar rhomboidal. And here the art of man equally succeeds in imitating nature, or, indeed, effects at will what nature has rarely done. Recent experiments by Mitscherlich seem to prove that certain salts in crystallizing take different elementary forms, according to the circumstances under which they are made to crystallize. But in the small number of cases where nature herself has produced such differences, are we justified in making but one species of these several crystallizations? As well might we make but one of almost all the warm-blooded animals, for they, too, are as identical in the chemical nature of their elements as the two stones named above. An eagle and a dog have the same fibrin in their muscles, the same gelatin in their membranes, the same phosphate of lime in their bony structure. Like the calcareous spar and the aragonite, they differ only in the form which these materials have taken at the moment of constituting the individual.

Let it be remarked that what is here said imports no neglect of the chemical analysis of minerals, as none certainly was ever countenanced by Haüy himself. Such analysis is quite as essential to a knowledge of them as is that of their form; it is much more important as regards their uses. Haüy maintained only that analysis is generally powerless to determine the species of minerals, because it has no certain means of distinguishing their accidental from their essential substances; because it is not competent, as to certain classes of stones, to affirm that it has detected their elements, and every day brings to light results which had escaped its observation.

Werner, long regarded by Europe as the rival and even adversary of Haüy, differed from him in effect only, in not having carried the research of principles to so high a point. Hardness, fracture, tissue, the qualities to which Werner attached himself by preference, are in reality but consequences of the form of the molecules and of their arrangement; and the happy use which this great mineralogist made of them, to recognize and determine so many species of minerals, may enable us to judge with what success he might have resorted to the source when its simple derivatives were made by him so fertilizing. But of that source we are indebted to Haüy, not only for the knowledge, but for the measure also of its force and its abundance. Hence it was practicable for him alone to carry or to reduce to their just value many results which had remained in a manner but half truths in the hands of Werner.

There is at this day scarcely a known crystallizable mineral whose nucleus and molecules, with the measure of their angles and the proportion of their sides, have not been determined by Haüy, and of which he has not referred to those first elements all the secondary forms, by discriminating for each the different decrements which produce it and ascertaining by calculation their angles and faces. In this way he has at length made of mineralogy a science as precise and methodical as astronomy itself. We may say, then, in a word, that Haüy is to Werner and Romé Delisle what Newton was to Kepler and Copernicus.

But what is more peculiarly his own is that Haüy's work is not less remarkable in point of composition and method than for the original ideas on which it is founded. The purity of the style, the elegance of the demonstrations, the care with which all the facts are collected and discussed would have made a classic of the most ordinary system of mineralogy. The trace of his earlier studies reappears in the skillful writer and sound geometrician; and even that of his first scientific recreations may be distinguished in the readiness with which the physicist always comes to the support of the crystallographer, supplying him with ingenious processes and convenient instruments whenever it becomes necessary for him to appreciate the electricity of bodies, their magnetism, and action upon light. There is a rank in science which must be accorded as soon as challenged, and to that rank did Haüy ascend from the day his work was given to the world.

Nevertheless, on the death of Daubenton it was Dolomieu and not Haüy on whom the professorship of mineralogy in the Museum of Natural History was conferred. But at that moment, arrested in violation of all law, Dolomieu languished in the dungeons of Sicily. The only token that he yet lived consisted in a few lines which from the midst of his chains he had found the means of writing with a splinter of wood and the smoke of his lamp, and which the ingenious humanity of an Englishman, seconded by gold, had contrived to extract from the hands of the gaoler. These lines spoke as eloquently in his behalf as his works; and among those who solicited the most warmly for him was Haüy, the rival from whom he had most to apprehend.

It might be thought that such marks of consideration, rendered by such men, would have softened the executioners of Dolomieu; but men in authority, urged by the passions of the hour, as seldom inform themselves of the sentiments of their contemporaries as they foresee the scorn and indignation of posterity. Dolomieu emerged from his dungeon only through an article in the treaty of peace, and a premature death, the fruit of such treatment, but too soon devolved on Haüy the place which he had so generously renounced. He was nominated the 9th of December, 1802.

From that time new life was infused into the establishment; the collections were quadrupled; an order, constantly conforming itself to the most recent discoveries, reigned throughout. The mineralogical public of Europe pressed forward, as well to observe objects so judiciously arranged as to hear a professor so elegant, clear, and withal so complaisant. His natural kindliness showed itself at every instant toward all who desired to learn. He refused himself to no explanations, but received in his privacy and with equal benignity persons of the most opposite conditions in life, for the most learned and august as well as the humblest might have been seen in the retinue of Haüy's disciples.

From its foundation the university had felt itself honored in placing the name of Haüy on the list of one of its faculties and, as no lessons were required from him, an adjunct every way worthy had been assigned him in the person of Brongniart, since a member of the Academy and his successor in the Museum of Natural History. But Haüy had no wish to bear a title without fulfilling its duties. He drew around him the pupils of the normal school and in varied and familiar conversations initiated them into all his secrets. His college life seemed thus to revive for him, as he entered even into the sports of these young people whom he never dismissed without an ample collation.

In this manner his days flowed on, occupied completely by his religious duties, by profound researches continually renewed, and by acts of kindness, especially toward the young. Equally tolerant and pious, he suffered no difference of opinion to influence his conduct toward others; equally pious as faithful to his studies, he would have allowed no contemplation, however sublime, to interfere with the observances prescribed by the ritual, placing, for the rest, on the things of this world only the value which they bear in the eyes of a man penetrated by such sentiments. From the nature of his researches the gems of all Europe were constantly passing under his eyes and even gave rise to a special treatise from his pen; but to him they were only so many crystals; a degree, more or less, in some angle of a schorl or spar would beyond doubt have interested him more than the treasures of the two Indies. Indeed, if he can be reproached with too warm an attachment to anything, it was to his ideas on this subject. It was not without impatience sometimes that he saw them controverted, and here only, where he had concentrated all his interest, could a motive sufficiently powerful be found to disturb his habitual serenity and kindliness. Thus he was prevented from accepting with due acknowledgment, probably, the observations made by means of the new goniometer of Wollaston on the angles of the calcareous and iron spar. But who will not excuse a valetudinarian and recluse who had been attacked from the outset in the most unjust and offensive manner, if he sometimes failed to distinguish from his first ignorant assailants those who, enlightened by his own discoveries, arrived in the sequel at a different estimate of certain facts of detail or even principles which he had too widely generalized? Certain it is that in those moments when such a tribute to human weakness was extorted from him, he felt only for what he supposed to be the interests of science, and if angry, it was simply at what he considered some new obstacle opposed to the triumph of truth.

The government of France, at the time when it was seeking to restore some activity to public instruction, proposed to Haüy the preparation of a treatise on physics for the use of colleges. He had more than one title to this commission, whether from the ingenious manner in which he had applied physics to mineralogy, his many interesting memoirs on the electricity and double refraction of minerals, the elegant exposition which he had given of the theory of Æpinus on electricity and magnetism, or the success which had attended the course of physics delivered at the normal school, established by the Convention in 1795. Notwithstanding these titles, however, Haüy scrupled to abandon even for a time the successful researches to which, as he thought, he had been guided by the hand of Providence, nor did he enter on the task without first consulting the Abbé Emery, a former superior of St. Sulpice. "Do not hesitate," said the latter. "It will be your own fault if, in treating of nature, you neglect to speak of its Author; and fail not to designate yourself on the title page a Canon of the Metropolis." The abbé, whose ability is to be as little questioned as his sincerity, knew that there is no profession which is not exalted by the talents of those who exercise it, and remembered doubtless that the epoch when Christianity made most conquests and its ministers were held in most respect was that when the latter carried the light of letters among the nations they converted, and by the union of these with the truths of religion consituted themselves at once the most eminent and most enlightened order of the state.

If this treatise on physics added little to the scientific reputation of its author, it by no means impaired his literary standing. Marked by the same clearness and purity of style as his mineralogy, it possesses even more interest; it is a book eminently qualified to inspire youth with a taste for the natural sciences and to be received with interest by all. Hence it soon passed to a third edition.

At different times Haüy had been warmly pressed to designate some post for himself, adapted to his pursuits and inclination. As his wishes extended no further than to be enabled to bring his family around him, as a solace in age and infirmity, this object seemed to be accomplished by the appointment of the husband of his niece to a petty place in the public revenues. But, strange to say, this slight recompense disappeared at the next reform, and no other answer to the remonstrances of Haüy's friends could be obtained but that there seemed to be no relation between crystallography and taxation.

Newton, it will be remembered, had in like manner been recompensed for the glory which his genius shed upon his country, by an appointment (far more considerable, it is true) of a financial nature; but he kept it under three kings and ten ministers. How is it that the men who dispose, commonly for so short a time, of the lots of others, forget so often that acts like these will find a more enduring place in history than all the ephemeral details of their administration? Nor was this the only trial that Haüy had to encounter. A short time afterwards the regulations of finance caused him the loss of his pension as being incompatible with a salary for actual services, while his brother, who had been attracted to Russia with a view to the instruction of the blind, returned without the fulfillment of the promises held out to him and with health so shattered as to be thrown entirely on his family for support.

Thus it was that toward the end of his life Haüy saw himself suddenly reduced to the strictly needful, of which he had before had experience. It would have required all his pious resignation to support this reverse, but for the care used by his young relatives to dissemble their own concern for his misfortunes. They redoubled their attentions as his means of acknowledgment diminished, and in recompense might find consolation in the devotion manifested by his pupils and the respect borne him by all Europe. Enlightened men of whatever rank, arriving at Paris, hastened to tender him their homage; even the day before his death the heir of a great kingdom was to be seen sitting by his pillow and evincing his interest by expressions of the most touching sympathy. But to Haüy it was a more solid ground of support that in the midst of his honors and prosperity he had quitted none of the habits of his college or even of his native village. His hours of repast, as well as of rising and lying down, were the same; each day he took nearly the same exercise and in the same places, and while doing so still contrived to manifest his kindliness by conducting strangers who were at a loss, or by giving them tickets of admission to the collections. Many have received these little attentions who never suspected from whom they proceeded. His old-fashioned attire, his simple air, his language (always of an excessive modesty) were not likely to cause his recognition. His former townsmen, when he visited the place of his birth, could little divine from his deportment how considerable a personage he had become at Paris. It may be mentioned as characteristic that on one occasion, having met two old soldiers who were going out for a fight, he inquired into the subject of their quarrel, brought about a reconciliation, and, to make sure that the dispute would not revive, went with them to seal the peace after military fashion—at the alehouse.

The extreme simplicity of his habits would have probably prolonged his life, notwithstanding the frailty of his constitution, had not an accident accelerated the fatal event. A fall which he met with in his chamber fractured the neck of his thigh, and an abscess forming in the articulation rendered the injury incurable. During the long sufferings which preceded his death he ceased not to exhibit the same gentleness, the same pious submission to the decrees of Providence, the same ardor for science, which had characterized his life. His time was divided between prayer, the superintendence of a new edition of his book, and a zealous solicitude for the future welfare of the students who had assisted him in its preparation.

He died the 3d of June, 1822, at seventy-nine years of age, leaving his family but one legacy—a magnificent one, it is true—in that precious collection of crystals of every variety, which the contributions of all Europe during twenty years had enhanced to a degree of which there is no equal.

He was succeeded in each of his places by one of his own pupils; by Brongniart at the Museum of Natural History, Beudant in the Faculty of the Sciences, and Cordier in this Academy. It may be added, indeed, by way of worthily closing this account of his life and labors, that it would be difficult to find in Europe at this day a mineralogist worthy of the name who, if not actually a pupil of Haüy, may not be considered such by the assiduous study of his works and his discoveries.

Alessandro Volta *

1745–1827

———◆———

DOMINIQUE FRANÇOIS ARAGO

ALESSANDRO VOLTA, one of the eight foreign members of the Academy of Science, son of Philip Volta and Madeleine de Conti Inzaghi, was born at Como on the 18th of February, 1745. His early education was carried on at the public school of his native place under his father's watchful care. Great aptitude, steady application, and a well-regulated mind soon placed him at the head of his fellow students. At eighteen he was already in correspondence with Nollet on the most recondite questions of physics. At nineteen he composed a Latin poem, never given to the public, in which he described the phenomena discovered by the most celebrated experimentalists of the time. It has been said that at this period Volta's vocation was undetermined, but I beg to differ from this assertion, for a young man would scarcely hesitate about exchanging the poetic art for a retort, if he had the singular taste to select chemistry as the subject of his literary compositions; and, in fact, with the exception of several of his poems, including that describing Saussure's ascent of Mont Blanc, we shall find the long career of this distinguished physicist devoted solely to the study of nature.

Volta at the age of twenty-four had the temerity to assail in his first essay the delicate question of the Leyden jar. This apparatus had been invented in 1746. The singularity of its effects would have amply sufficed to justify the curiosity it excited throughout Europe; but this curiosity was also due, in a great measure, to Musschenbroek's extravagant exaggeration of the unaccountable terror he experienced on receiving a very feeble discharge, in re-

* A.R., 1875, pp. 115–141. The memoir was read originally to members of the French Academy of Sciences, July 26, 1831. The present version has been considerably condensed.

gard to which, the physicist emphatically exclaimed, he would not again expose himself for the proudest kingdom of the universe. The numerous theories of the jar which were successively offered are scarcely worthy of being enumerated. Franklin has the honor of having solved this important problem, and, it must be acknowledged, Volta has added little to the labors of the illustrious American physicist. The second essay of the physicist of Como appeared in 1771. In this, observation is the only guide of the author in the researches undertaken to determine the nature of the electricity of bodies covered with different coatings; to ascertain the circumstances of temperature, color, and elasticity causing the phenomena to vary; to study the electricity produced by rubbing, percussion, or pressure; or finally, the properties of a new kind of electrical machine in which the movable plate and the insulating supports were of dried wood.

On this side of the Alps the first two essays of Volta were scarcely read at all. In Italy, on the contrary, they produced a lively sensation. Public authority, which is usually unfortunately partial, and which in its blind love of absolute power often even refuses the modest request of reference to competent judges, hastened itself to encourage the youthful experimentalist. He was nominated by it as regent of the Royal School of Como and soon after professor of physics.

The missionaries of Peking in 1755 communicated to the savants of Europe an important fact made known to them by accident, respecting electricity by induction, which in certain bodies is developed or dissipated as these bodies are separated or brought into immediate contact. This fact gave rise to the interesting researches of Æpinus, Wilcke, Cigna, and Beccaria. Volta also made it the subject of special study and found in it the germ of the *perpetual electrophorus,* a wonderful instrument, which, however small, affords an inexhaustible supply of electricity, and which, without the necessity of resorting to friction of any kind, and whatever may be the state of the atmosphere, enables the physicist to command incessant charges of undiminished power.

The essay on the electrophorus was succeeded in 1778 by another very important production. It was known even at this time that a given body, hollow or solid, has the same electrical capacity, provided the surface remains the same. An observation by Lemonnier pointed out, moreover, that besides equality of surface the shape of the body is not without its influence. Volta was the first, however, to establish this principle on a solid basis. His experiments proved that of two cylinders having the same surface, the longer receives the larger charge, so that wherever the situation permits, it is an immense advantage to substitute for the large conductors of ordinary machines a system of very small cylinders, the total capacity of which is, however, not larger than the other. By combining, for example, sixteen rows of slender silver-plated rods, 1,000 feet in length each, a battery would be formed, according to Volta, capable of killing the largest animal.

Not one of the discoveries of the professor of Como was the result of accident. All the instruments with which he enriched science, before being formed by the mechanic, were thoroughly planned in his mind. There was no chance, for instance, in the changes made by Volta in the electrophorus in order to transform it into a *condenser,* a genuine microscope of a new kind which detects the presence of electricity where every other means would fail.

In 1776 and 1777, Volta devoted himself for some months to a subject of pure chemistry, in which, however, electricity, his favorite science, was involved in the most fortunate combinations. At this epoch chemists, having as yet only discovered natural inflammable gas in coal mines and mineral salts, regarded it as belonging exclusively to mineral regions. Volta, whose attention had been directed to this subject by an accidental observation of P. Campi, showed they were mistaken. He proved that the putrefaction of both animal and vegetable matter is always accompanied by the production of inflammable gas; that if stagnant water and the slime of a marsh be stirred up, this gas will escape through the liquid, presenting the appearance of ordinary ebullition. Thus, the inflammable gas of marshes, which for several years so much occupied the attention of chemists is as to its origin a discovery of Volta.

This discovery might lead to the belief that certain natural phenomena, such, for example, as burning marshes and burning springs, arise from a similar cause; but Volta knew too well how nature sports with our feeble understanding to be satisfied with mere analogy. In 1780 he hastened to visit the celebrated marshes of *Pietra Mala* and *Velleja.* He thoroughly examined all he could find in different travels in similar localities and then succeeded in establishing with complete proof and contrary to received opinion the fact that these phenomena did not depend upon the presence of petroleum, naphtha, or bitumen; he demonstrated, moreover, that they were caused alone by the disengagement of inflammable gas. But has Volta proved with the same accuracy that this gas has in all places its origin in the maceration of animal or vegetable matter? I think we may be allowed to question this. The electric spark had been at an early date used to inflame certain liquids, certain vapors, and different gases, such as alcohol, the smoke of a candle just extinguished, and hydrogen gas; but all these experiments were made in the open air. Volta was the first to make them in closed vessels (1777). He is therefore the originator of the apparatus used by Cavendish in 1781 for combining the separated elements of water by synthesis so as to form anew the decomposed body from its two constituent gaseous elements.

Our distinguished associate possessed in the highest degree two qualities rarely found united, a creative genius and great powers of application. He never abandoned a subject without examining it in all its phases, without describing or at least pointing out the various aids which science, ingenuity, and even more curiosity might bring to bear upon it. Thus several experiments on the inflammable nature of the air of marshes gave rise to the electrical gun and pistol, upon which it would be superfluous to dwell here, as they have passed from the hands of physicists into those of the showman, and in public places are daily exhibited to the admiring gaze of gaping idlers. Then came the perpetual hydrogen-gas lamp, so generally known in Germany, which by the most ingenious application of the electrophorus lights itself when needed, and finally the eudiometer, the valuable instrument of analysis, which has been so useful to chemists.

The discovery of the composition of atmospheric air has given rise to this momentous question in natural philosophy: Does the proportion in which the two component parts of air are found united vary with the successive revolutions of ages and according to locality and the changes of seasons? When one reflects that all mankind, all the beasts of the earth and fowls of the air are constantly consuming in the act of breathing one of these two components, oxygen gas; that this same gas is the indispensable food of combustion in our homes, in workshops and vast factories; that a candle or lamp is not lighted without absorbing it; that finally oxygen plays the chief part in the phenomena of vegetation, it may readily be imagined that in the long run the atmosphere varies sensibly in its composition; that at some future time it will become unfit for respiration; that then all the animal creation will be extinguished, not in consequence of one of those physical revolutions of which geologists have discovered so many vestiges, and which, notwithstanding their vast extent, may leave some chance of safety to a few individuals advantageously situated, but from an all-pervading and inevitable cause, in which case the frozen zones of the poles, the burning regions of the equator, the vastness of the ocean, and the snowy summits of the Cordilleras and Himalayas would be equally powerless to save. To study all that can be discovered of this great phenomenon up to the present time, to collect all the exact data with which the centuries to come will be teeming, is the task physicists are hastening to accomplish, especially since the eudiometer with the electric spark has supplied them with the means of so doing. To answer some of the objections to which the first trials of this instrument gave rise, Humboldt and Gay-Lussac submitted it to the most scrupulous examination. When such judges declare that no known eudiometer approaches in accuracy that of Volta, doubt as to its value can no longer exist.

.   .   .

A detailed description of the wonderful effects produced by insignificant causes would perhaps be as interesting in the history of the sciences as in that of nations. If some savant should ever undertake to sketch it, that branch of physics properly called galvanism would occupy one of the first places in it. In fact, it can be proved that the immortal discovery of the pile springs in a very direct manner from a slight cold with which a lady of Bologna was attacked in 1790, who was ordered by her physician a dish of frog soup.

Several of these animals, prepared for the purpose by Madame Galvani's cook, were lying on a table at the time of an accidental discharge of an electrical machine at some distance. The muscles, although not touched by the sparks, evinced at the moment of the discharge the most decided contractions. The experiment, repeated with all kinds of animals, succeeded equally well, whether the electricity were artificial or natural, positive or negative. This phenomenon was very easily explained on the well-known principle of induction, the electricity of the discharge disturbing by repulsion at a distance the natural electricity of the frog. Had it happened to some experienced physicist, familiar with the properties of electricity, it would scarcely have attracted his attention; if remarked at all, the extent of the observation would have been that the extreme sensibility of the frog would render it a very good electroscope. Here was a case, however, though a rare one, where ignorance was great gain. Galvani, though a skillful anatomist, knew very little of electricity. The muscular movements witnessed by him appeared inexplicable; a new world seemed opening before him. He applied himself to the task of varying the experiments in a thousand ways.

It was in doing this that he discovered an entirely new fact, the fact that a frog, even though dead for a long time, manifests very intense contractions, without the intervention of any foreign electricity, when one places a metallic plate, or better still, two plates of dissimilar metals, between a muscle and a nerve. The astonishment of the professor of Bologna was then quite justifiable and that of all Europe with him. An experiment in which the legs, thighs, and trunks of animals dismembered for hours manifested the strongest convulsions, darting about and appearing to return to life, could not long remain uninvestigated. After analyzing it in all its details, Galvani supposed the effect to be produced on the principle of the Leyden jar. According to him, the animals were merely reservoirs of electricity, positive electricity having its seat in the nerves, and negative in the muscles, the metallic plate interposed between these organs being simply the conductor by means of which the discharge is effected.

These views captivated the public; physiologists seized hold upon them, and electricity usurped the place of the nervous fluid then occupying so large a space in the explanation of the phenomena of the principle of life, though by a strange oversight no one had attempted to prove its existence. In a word, all flattered themselves that they had found the physical agent which conveys external impressions to the *sensorium,* which makes, among animals, nearly all of the organs subservient to their intelligence, and the movements of the arms, legs, and head obedient to the will. But, alas! these delusions were not of long duration. The whole beautiful romance was dispelled by Volta's critically severe experiments.

This ingenious physicist first created convulsions, not merely as Galvani did, by interposing two dissimilar metals between a nerve and muscle, but by simply bringing them in contact with a muscle. From this moment the principle of the Leyden jar was acknowledged to have no connection with the phenomenon; there was no longer any possible comparison between them. The negative electricity of the muscles and the positive electricity of the nerves were pure hypotheses, without any solid foundation; the phenomenon seemed to have no connection with anything known, but was obscured by an impenetrable veil.

Volta, nevertheless, was not discouraged. He claimed that in his own experiment electricity was the cause of the convulsions; that the muscle played but a passive part and was to be simply regarded as a conductor by means of which the discharge was effected. Electricity, Volta had the independence to conjecture, was the inevitable result of the contact of the *two metals* between which the muscle was placed. I say the two metals and not the two plates, since, according to Volta, with no difference in *the nature* of the two metals in contact, no electrical development could take place.

The physicists of all Europe, and Volta himself, adopted at the beginning of galvanism the views of the discoverer. They were unanimous in regarding the spasmodic convulsions of the dead animals as one of the greatest discoveries of modern times. But however little one may know of the human heart, it is not difficult to divine that a theory, designed to connect these curious phenomena with the ordinary laws of electricity, would not be admitted by Galvani and his followers without extreme reluctance. In fact, the Bolognese school defended every foot of the immense ground attacked, which had been abandoned without opposition by the supporters of animal electricity. Among the numerous facts presented by this celebrated school to the physicist of Como was one which by its singularity for a moment held all minds in suspense. I allude to the convulsions that Galvani himself created by bringing the muscles of the frog in contact with two plates, not dissimilar as Volta supposed necessary, but both from one and the same slab of metal. This effect, although not continuous, presented apparently an insurmountable objection to the new theory. Volta replied that the plates used by his adversaries might be identical in name and chemical nature, and yet differ in other respects, so as to possess entirely distinct properties. In his hands, in fact, inactive couples, composed of two contiguous parts of the same metallic plate, acquired a certain power from the moment the temperature, the degree of annealing, or the polish of only one of the elements was changed. Thus, this contest did not shake the theory of the celebrated professor. It only proved that the word *dissimilar,* applied to superposed metallic bodies, had been understood in altogether too restricted a sense.

Volta had to endure a last and very formidable assault. This time his very friends thought him vanquished forevermore. Doctor Valli, his antagonist, produced contortions by the simple contact of two portions of the frog, without the intervention of the metallic armatures, which in all similar experiments had been, according to our fellow member, the principal generator of electricity. It was evident from more than one passage in Volta's letters how deeply he was wounded by the tone of assurance with which (I give his own words) the galvanists, *old and young,* boasted of having reduced him to silence. This silence, however, was not of long duration. An attentive examination of Valli's experiments soon proved to Volta that to insure their success this double condition was necessary:

as much heterogeneity as possible between the parts of the animal brought in contact, and the interposition between these same parts of a third substance. The fundamental principle of the Voltaic theory, far from being shaken, only acquired a much greater generality. Metals no longer formed an exclusive class. Analogy led to the fact that two dissimilar substances, whatever their nature, give rise by mere contact to a development of electricity.

There was nothing henceforth serious in the attack of the galvanists. Their experiments were no longer confined to very small animals. They produced strange nervous movements in the nostrils, tongue, and eyes of an ox killed for several days, thus strengthening more or less the hopes of those to whom galvanism had seemed a means of resuscitating the dead; but they threw no new light on the theory. By borrowing arguments, not from nature, but the grandeur of the effects, the adepts of the Bolognese school strongly resembled that savant who, to prove that the atmosphere is not the cause of the rise of the mercury in the barometer, conceived the idea of substituting a large cylinder for the narrow tube of this instrument, and then cited as a formidable difficulty the exact number of quintals of liquid raised.

Volta gave a death-blow to animal electricity. His conceptions were constantly verified by experiments, but these were not well understood, and by means of them it was hoped to undermine him. His conclusions had not, and we may add that they could not have, as yet the entire and unprejudiced approval of physicists. The contact of two metals, of two dissimilar substances, gave rise to a certain agent which, like electricity, produced spasmodic movements. About this fact there was no doubt; but was the agent in question really electrical? Were the proofs given sufficiently satisfactory?

When two dissimilar metals are placed on the tongue in a certain order, at the moment of contact an acid taste is produced. If the order of these metals be reversed the taste becomes alkaline. Now, by simply applying the tongue to the conductor of an ordinary electrical machine, the taste is acid or alkaline, as the conductor is charged plus or minus. In this case the phenomenon is undoubtedly due to electricity. "Is it not natural," said Volta, "to infer an identity of causes from a resemblance of the effects; to assimilate the first experiment with the second; to find but one difference between them, namely, the mode of producing the principle which excites the organ of taste?" No one questioned the importance of this comparison. Volta's penetrating genius saw in it the basis of a thorough conviction. Most physicists required more explicit proofs. These proofs, these incontestable demonstrations, before which all opposition must vanish, Volta found in a capital experiment which can be explained in a few words.

Two polished disks of copper and zinc, with insulated handles, are brought exactly in contact, with nothing intervening; by means of these same handles, the disks are then suddenly separated; and finally, each in turn is presented to the ordinary condenser, armed with an electrometer, when *the straws instantly diverge.* It was proved too, by the same means, that the two metals are in opposite states of electricity; that the zinc is positive and the copper negative. By repeating several times the contact of the two disks, their separation from and contact with the condenser in turn, Volta succeeded as with an ordinary machine in producing bright sparks. After these experiments the theory of galvanic phenomena was fully established.

The production of electricity by the mere contact of dissimilar metals was ranged among the most important and best-established facts of the physical sciences. If, after this there was anything left to be desired, it was an easy means of increasing this kind of electricity. Such means are now known to all experimentalists, and it is to Volta's genius that they are indebted for them.

At the beginning of the year 1800 (the date of so wonderful a discovery could not be passed over in silence), in consequence of some theoretical views, the illustrious professor contrived a high column, consisting of pairs of copper and zinc, each pair being separated from the adjoining ones by pieces of moist cloth, scrupulous care being taken not to invert this order. But *à priori,* what was to be expected from such a combination? Well, I do not hesitate to say that this apparently inert mass, this singular assemblage, this pile of so many pairs of dissimilar metals separated by a small quantity of liquid is, with respect to the singularity of its effects, the most marvelous instrument ever invented by man, without even excepting the telescope and steam engine. I am quite sure I shall escape all reproach of exaggeration if, in the enumeration I am about to make of the properties of Volta's apparatus, I shall be allowed to cite both those properties discovered by this scientist and those whose discoveries are due to his successors.

Every one will remark in the short description I have given of the composition of the pile, that its two extremities are necessarily dissimilar; that if zinc be at the base copper must be at the top, and conversely. These two extremities are called the *poles.* Let us now suppose two wires attached to the opposite poles, copper and zinc, of a voltaic pile, the apparatus, so arranged, being ready for the different experiments I wish to describe. If one of the wires alone be grasped, no sensation is felt; but the moment both are touched a violent shock is experienced. This, as is evident, is nothing more than the phenomenon of the famous Leyden jar which in 1746 excited in so high a degree the wonder of all Europe. But the jar could only be used once, after each shock it being necessary to recharge it to repeat the experiment. The pile, on the contrary, supplied a thousand successive shocks. It may be compared consequently with regard to the nature of its effects to the Leyden jar, with this additional proviso, that after each discharge it immediately returns to its original condition. If the wire from the zinc pole is placed on the end of the tongue and that from the copper on some other part of the body, a very decided acid taste is the result. To vary the nature of this taste or to make it alkaline it is only necessary to reverse the order of the wires.

The sense of sight does not escape the action of this protean instrument. Here the phenomenon will appear the more interesting from the fact that the luminous sensation is excited without the necessity of touching the eye. If the end of one of the wires be applied to the forehead, cheeks, nose, chin, or even the throat, the very moment the observer seizes the other wire with his hand he perceives, with his eyes closed, a flash of light whose intensity and form vary according to the part of the face in contact with the conductor. Similar combinations create in the ear sounds or, rather, peculiar noises. It is not alone on healthy organs that the pile acts. It excites or appears to revive those in which life seemed altogether extinct. In one instance, by the combination of the two wires, the muscles of a head, severed from the body, evinced contortions so frightful that the spectators fled terrified. In another the body of the victim half arose, its hands shaking and striking the nearest objects, and raising weights of several pounds. The pectoral muscles imitated the respiratory movements; and, in a word, every lifelike motion was so accurately reproduced that the question was involuntarily asked whether the experimentalist was not guilty of a culpable act, whether he was not adding cruel sufferings to those just inflicted on the criminal by the hand of the executioner.

Insects also, subjected to these experiments, gave interesting results. The wires of the pole, for example, greatly increased the brilliancy of the glowworm, restored motion to a dead grasshopper, and made it sing.

. . .

If, laying aside the physiological properties of the pile, we consider it merely as an electrical machine, we shall find ourselves in that department of science which has been brought to a high degree of perfection by Nicholson and Carlisle, Hisinger and Berzelius, Oersted and Ampère, and Davy.

At first each wire, taken separately, will indicate the ordinary temperature, that of the surrounding air; but the moment these wires are brought into contact they will acquire an intense heat. When sufficiently attenuated they become incandescent; still more attenuated, they melt together, to the consistency of a liquid, even if they be of platinum, the least fusible of all known metals. We may add that with a powerful battery two slender wires of gold or platinum exhibit at the moment of contact a disintegration so complete that they vanish in the form of a light vapor.

Charcoal, applied to the two extremities of these same wires, takes fire as soon as the wires are brought into contact. The light diffused by them is so pure, so dazzling, so remarkable for its whiteness, that it is not transcending the limits of truth to compare it to that of the sun. Who knows even whether this analogy may not be carried still further, whether this experiment may not solve one of the greatest problems of natural philosophy and give the clew to that peculiar kind of combustion displayed by the sun for so many ages with no sensible loss of matter or brilliancy? The carbon attached to the two wires of the pile in fact becomes incandescent, even in the most perfect vacuum. Nothing then is taken from or added to their substance. After an experiment of this kind, whatever may have been its duration, the carbons are found, as to their inner nature and weight, in their original condition.*

Everyone knows that platinum, gold, copper, etc., do not act sensibly on a magnetic needle. Wires of these different metals attached to the two poles of the pile follow the same law if taken separately. But on the contrary, from the moment they come in contact a very intense magnetic action is developed. Besides, during the whole period of contact these wires are themselves genuine magnets; they attract iron filings and communicate a permanent magnetism to steel bars placed transversely to them. When the pile is very powerful and the wires, instead of touching, are at some distance, a bright light unites their extremities. In fact, this light is magnetic; a magnet can attract or repel it. If today, without being prepared for it, I mean with only the knowledge of their day, Franklin and Coulomb should hear me speak of a flame being

* This is not correct; there is a transfer of the particles of carbon from one pole to the other. [Joseph Henry's note.]

attracted by a magnet, the most flattering sentiment I could expect would undoubtedly be one of decided incredulity.

Let us suppose the same wires slightly separated and immersed in a liquid—pure water, for example. The water will be instantly decomposed; the two gaseous elements forming it will be disunited; the oxygen will be liberated from the surface of the end of the wire from the zinc pole; and the hydrogen quite distant from that at the point of the wire from the copper pole. The bubbles rise separately through the liquid, and the two constituent gases may therefore be collected in two separate vessels. If we substitute for the pure water a liquid holding in solution saline matter, the pile will then analyze this matter. The acids will pass to the zinc pole and the alkalies to the copper. This is the most powerful method of analysis known. It has recently enriched science with a multitude of important results. It is, for instance, to the pile we are indebted for the first decomposition of a great number of alkalies and earths which were before considered as simple substances; it is by it that all those bodies are known to be oxides; that chemistry now possesses metals such as potassium, which can be kneaded by the fingers like wax and will float on the surface of the water, because lighter than it, and is spontaneously kindled, diffusing the brightest light.

This would be the place to introduce all that is mysterious, I should say almost incomprehensible, in the decompositions effected by the voltaic pile; to dwell upon the separate disengagements, completely distinct, of the two disunited gaseous elements of a liquid, on the precipitation of the constituent solid principles of the same saline molecule, which is effected by the particles of the fluid dissolving at great distances from each other; on the strange, wild commotions that these different phenomena seemed to involve. But time fails me. However, before finishing this picture, I will remark that the pile is not merely a means of analysis. If, by considerably changing the electrical affinities of the elements of bodies, it often leads to their complete separation, its power, delicately managed, has become on the contrary in the hands of one of our fellow members the regenerative principle of a large number of combinations almost endless in nature and which art, up to this time, knew not how to imitate.

I will add a few more words still, to point out the different modifications undergone by the pile since passing from the hands of its illustrious inventor. The characteristic feature of the pile consists of a large number of pairs, or binary combinations, of dissimilar metals. These metals are usually copper and zinc, and these elements, the copper and zinc of each pair, can be soldered together.

The pairs follow in the same order. Thus, when zinc is below in the first, it is indispensably necessary it should be below in all the others. Finally, the pairs must be separated by a liquid conductor of electricity. Now, who cannot see how easy it is to fulfill these conditions without superposing the elements, without forming them into a pile? This first arrangement, which, by the way, was the origin of the name of the apparatus, has been changed. The pairs are not now vertical, but succeed each other so as to form as a whole a horizontal parallelopiped. Each of them is immersed in a trough containing a liquid, which is a decided improvement over the merely moist pieces of pasteboard or cloth used in the beginning.

Apparatus has been constructed by several physicists under the denomination of *dry piles,* which only comparatively may be so called, as strictly speaking they do not deserve the name. The best known, those of Professor Zamboni, are composed of several thousands of disks of paper, tinned on one side and covered on the other by a thin layer of pulverized oxide of manganese, which is rendered adhesive by means of a paste of flour and milk. The disks, of course, being piled up in the same order, their dissimilar surfaces, or I should say the tin and manganese surfaces of two contiguous pairs are in contact. Here, then, we have the two metallic elements of different kinds which constitute what were called *pairs* in the description of Volta's first pile. With regard to the intermediary conducting liquid, those who object to apply the name of *dry piles* to those of Zamboni will discover the cause of the humidity in the hygrometrical property always preserved by the paper placed between each plate of tin and layer of powdered manganese.

The wonderful results obtained by physicists by means of voltaic piles are owing undoubtedly in a measure to the remarkable improvements introduced by them in their construction, but the chief cause is the enormous dimensions they have succeeded in giving them. The metallic pairs in Volta's first piles were scarcely larger than a five-franc piece. In Children's pile each element had a surface of thirty-two English square feet. Volta, as well as can be discovered from the analysis I have just given of his views, accounted for the development of electricity by the mere contact of the two metals of different natures constituting each pair. The liquid between them simply performed the office of conductor. This theory, called the theory of contact, was attacked at an early date by Fabbroni, one of Volta's countrymen. He supposed that the oxidation of the metallic surfaces of the pairs, induced by the liquid touching them, was the principal cause of the phenomenon of the pile. Wollaston, some time after, developed this same idea with his usual sagacity; Davy supported it in his turn by ingenious experiments; and finally today this chemical theory of the pile prevails almost unanimously among physicists.

I hazarded the opinion, just now, with some timidity, that the pile was the most marvelous instrument ever invented by the human mind. If, in the enumeration you have just heard of its different properties, my voice has not been altogether without power, I might now repeat my first assertion and consider it thoroughly established.

According to some biographers, Volta's brain, exhausted by long-continued work and especially by the production of the pile, refused to furnish anything more. Others saw in an obstinate silence of nearly thirty years only the effects of a puerile fear, which the illustrious physicist had not the courage to overcome. He feared, it is said, that on comparing his more recent researches with those on electricity by contact, the public would immediately conclude that his mind was weakened. These two explanations are doubtless very ingenious, but they labor under the signal defect of being entirely superfluous. For the pile was invented in 1800, and two ingenious essays, one on the "Phenomenon of Hail" (Le Phénomène de la grêle) and the other on the "Periodicity of Storms and the Cold Accompanying Them," (La Périodicité des orages et le froid qui les accompagne") were not published until six and seventeen years after.

.   .   .

The painful duties which devolved upon Volta, almost from earliest youth, detained him in his native city till 1777. This year, for the first time, he left the picturesque banks of Lake Como and traveled through Switzerland. His absence lasted several weeks but was not marked by any important event. At Berne Volta visited the celebrated Haller, who was fast bringing his life to a close by an immoderate use of opium. Thence he went to Ferney, where every description of talent was secure of a kind welcome. . . . At Geneva Volta formed a close friendship with the celebrated historian of the Alps, a man most capable of appreciating his discoveries. That was a great century in which a traveler in a day's journey, without losing sight of the Jura, could render homage to a Saussure, a Haller, Jean-Jacques [Rousseau], and Voltaire.

Volta returned to Italy by way of Aigne-Belle, taking with him to his countrymen that precious root, the potato, which by proper cultivation would render a complete famine impossible. In Lombardy, where frightful storms destroy in a few moments cereals distributed over a vast region of country, an article of food which develops, grows, and matures under the ground, sheltered from the ravages of hail, was an inestimable gift to the whole population.

.   .   .

Human institutions are so strange that the fortunes, the well-being, the whole future of one of the greatest geniuses of whom Italy can boast, were at the mercy of the administrator-general of Lombardy. I suppose that the ruling powers, in selecting this functionary, were led by their fastidiousness to require that a certain knowledge of finance should be superadded to the quarterings of nobility imperiously prescribed by etiquette; notwithstanding, here was the man called on to decide, decide too without appeal from his judgment, whether Volta deserved to be transferred to a wider theater, or indeed left a martyr at the small school of Como, where he should be deprived during his whole life of costly accessories that certainly cannot supply the place of genius, but invest it with great power. Let us be quick to acknowledge that so far as Volta was concerned chance remedied the folly incident to such a state of dependence. Comte de Firmian, the administrator, was a friend to literature. The school of Pavia became the object of his assiduous care. He founded there a professorship of physics, and in 1779 Volta was elected to fill it. For many years crowds of young men from all countries thronged the lectures of the illustrious professor; there they learned, I will not say the details of science, for nearly all works on the subject give these, but the philosophical history of the principal discoveries; the subtile correlations which escape ordinary intelligence; and a matter which very few individuals have the privilege of divulging, the progress of discovery.

Volta's style was lucid, unaffected, and sometimes monotonous, but always characterized by modesty and refinement—qualities which, when united to talents of the first order, are always attractive to youth. In Italy, where the imagination is so easily excited, they produced a genuine enthusiasm. The desire to boast before the world of the honor of being a disciple of Volta contributed vastly for more than the third of a century to the wonderful success of the University of the Tessin.

.   .   .

Volta only left the banks of his native Lario for the purpose of scientific researches. I do not think his travels in Italy extended as far as Naples and Rome. If in 1780 he crossed the Apennines to go from Bologna to Florence, it was with the hope of finding an opportunity in the fires of *Pietra Mala, en route,* of submitting his views on the origin of natural inflammable gas to a decisive proof. If in 1782, accompanied by the celebrated Scarpa, he visited the capitals of Germany, Holland, England, and France, it was to make the acquaintance of Lichtenberg, Van Marum, Priestley, Laplace, and Lavoisier, and to enrich the laboratory of Pavia with certain instruments for investigation and demonstration, of which descriptions and drawings, even those best executed, could give but an imperfect idea.

Accepting an invitation from General Bonaparte, the conqueror of Italy, Volta returned to Paris in 1801. He there repeated his experiments on electricity by contact, before a large committee of the Institute. The First Consul wished to be present at the meeting where the committee were to give a detailed account of these wonderful phenomena. Their conclusions were scarcely reached when he proposed to confer upon Volta a gold medal to commemorate the gratitude of the French scientists. Custom or, we may add, academic regulations, scarcely sanctioned such a request, but rules are made for ordinary occasions, and the professor of Pavia had just placed himself outside of this line. The medal was therefore voted by acclamation, and as Bonaparte did nothing by halves, the learned traveler received the same day from the public fund the sum of 2,000 crowns to defray his traveling expenses. The creation of a prize of 60,000 francs to be awarded to him who would give to the sciences of electricity and magnetism an impulse comparable to that received by the first of these sciences from Franklin and Volta is not a less characteristic evidence of the enthusiasm of the great captain. This impression was lasting. The professor of Pavia became Napoleon's type of genius. Thus, step by step, we see him decorated with the crosses of the Legion of Honor and the Iron Crown, elected member of the Italian consulate, and elevated to the dignity of Count and Senator of the Kingdom of Lombardy. When the Italian Institute appeared at the palace, if Volta accidentally was not in the front ranks, the abrupt questions: "Where is Volta? Can he be sick? Why did he not come?" proved, only too evidently perhaps that in the eyes of the sovereign, notwithstanding all their learning, the other members were but mere satellites of the inventor of the pile. "I cannot consent," said Napoleon in 1804, "to Volta's withdrawal. If his duties as professor are too fatiguing, they must be lessened. Let him deliver but one lecture during the year, if desired; but the University of Pavia would receive its death-blow the moment I allowed so illustrious a name to disappear from the list of its members. Besides," added he, "a good general should die on the field of honor." The good general found the argument unanswerable, and the youth of Italy, whose idol he was, were thus enabled to enjoy a few more years of his delightful lectures.

Newton, during his parliamentary career, it is said, never spoke but once, and that was to ask the doorkeeper of the House of Commons to close a window to prevent a current of air giving cold to an orator when speaking. If the doorkeepers of Lyons during the Italian consulate, and those of the senate at Milan had been less careful, Volta perhaps from mere goodness of heart, if but for a moment, might have overcome his extreme reserve; but the opportunity not offering, the distinguished physicist will be inevitably classed with those personages who, whether from timidity or indifference during long revolutions are members of the most animated popular assemblies without giving an opinion or uttering a single word.

It has been said that happiness, like matter, is composed of imperceptible elements. If this idea of Franklin be correct, Volta was happy. Entirely devoted, in spite of high political dignities, to his studies, nothing disturbed his tranquillity. According to Solon's law he would have been exiled, for not one of the parties for nearly a quarter of a century agitating Lombardy could boast of numbering him in its ranks. The illustrious professor's name only reappeared after the storm as an ornament to the existing authorities. Even in his most private intimacies Volta had the greatest aversion to any conversation relating to public matters. He did not hesitate, as soon as there was an opening, to cut it short by one of those witticisms or puns, called in Italy *freddure* and in France *calembour*. But it must be confessed, practice here did not make perfect, as several of the *freddure* of the great physicist, not considered unworthy of being quoted, are far from being as irreproachable as his experiments.

Volta was married in 1794, at the age of forty-nine, to Mademoiselle Thérèse Peregrini. He had three sons, two surviving him and the other dying at the age of eighteen, just when he had given promise of the most brilliant talents. This was the only sorrow, I believe, our philosopher ever experienced during the whole of his long career. His discoveries were too brilliant, without any doubt, not to have aroused envy, but it never dared attack them, even under its most usual disguise, as it never questioned their novelty.

Contentions with regard to priority have been the torments of inventors in all ages. . . . Volta was never exposed to such contentions. The Bolognese school for a long time undoubtedly upheld the doctrine of animal electricity. Honorable sentiments of nationality induced them to desire that Galvani's discovery should remain entire, that it should not form a part of the grand phenomena of voltaic electricity as a peculiar clause; and yet they never alluded to the voltaic phenomena but with admiration. Never did an Italian mouth pronounce the name of the inventor of the pile without coupling it with the most unequivocal terms of esteem and profound respect, and without prefixing a word most expressive in its simplicity and especially sweet to the ears of a fellow-citizen; from Rovérédo to Messina, educated people always spoke of the physicist of Pavia as *nostro* Volta.

I have mentioned the honors conferred upon him by Napoleon. All the great universities of Europe had invited him to join them. Of the eight foreign members of the Institute he belonged to the first rank. So many honors never once excited in Volta's soul a sensation of pride. The small village of Como was always his favorite place of residence. The tempting and often repeated offers from Russia could not induce him to exchange the beautiful skies of Lombardy for the fogs of the Neva. The predominant traits of the illustrious professor were strength and quickness of mind, comprehensiveness and justness of views, and truth and warmth of nature. No act of his life was ever prompted by ambition, love of money, or a spirit of rivalry. The love of study, his ruling and only passion, remained through life pure and unspotted by the world.

Volta was tall, with features as noble and regular as those of an antique statue; his broad brow was deeply furrowed by profound meditation and his countenance expressed both tranquillity of soul and penetration of mind. His manner always retained traces of the rusticity contracted in his youth. Many persons remember having seen him in Paris every day enter the baker's, and afterward, while walking the streets, eat the large rolls which he had just bought, without seeming to suspect that any one would remark it. . . .

When in 1819 Volta finally resigned the trust with which he had been invested at the University of the Tessin, he retired to Como. From this time all his relations with the scientific world ceased. He rarely received any of the numerous travelers who, attracted by his great reputation, came to pay him homage.

In 1823 a slight attack of apoplexy developed very serious symptoms, but prompt remedies soon succeeded in relieving him. Four years after, in 1827, in the beginning of March, the venerable old man was attacked by a fever, which in the course of a few days deprived him of his remaining strength. On the 5th of the same month he expired without suffering, at the age of eighty-two years and fifteen days. Como celebrated Volta's obsequies with great pomp. The professors and students of the college, and all the friends of science, and the educated inhabitants of the village and its environs, hastened to accompany to their last resting place the mortal remains of the illustrious scientist, the charitable citizen, and the man exemplary in all his domestic relations. The beautiful monument erected to his memory, near the picturesque village of Camnago, the native place of Volta's family, is a striking testimony of the sincerity of their regrets, and finally all Italy participated in the mourning of the Milanese.

Pierre Simon de Laplace *

1749–1827

———◆———

DOMINIQUE FRANÇOIS ARAGO

THE MARQUIS DE LAPLACE, peer of France, one of the forty of the French Academy, member of the Academy of Sciences and of the Bureau des Longitudes, an associate of all the great academies or scientific societies of Europe, was born at Beaumonten-Ange, of parents belonging to the class of small farmers, on the 28th day of March, 1749. He died on the 5th of March, 1827.

The first and second volumes of the *Mécanique Céleste* were published in 1799; the third volume appeared in 1802; the fourth volume in 1805. As regards the fifth volume, books XI and XII were published in 1823; books XIII, XIV, and XV in 1824, and book XVI in 1825. The *Théorie des Probabilités* was published in 1812. . . .

Astronomy is the science of which the human mind may most justly boast. It owes this indisputable pre-eminence to the elevated nature of its object, to the grandeur of its means of investigation, to the certainty, the utility, and the unparalleled magnificence of its results. From the earliest period of the social existence of mankind, the study of the movements of the heavenly bodies has attracted the attention of governments and peoples. To several great captains, illustrious statesmen, philosophers, and eminent orators of Greece and Rome it formed a subject of delight. Yet, let us be permitted to state, astronomy truly worthy of the name is quite a modern science. It dates only from the sixteenth century. Three great, three brilliant phases have marked its progress. In 1543 Copernicus overthrew with a firm and bold hand the greater part of the antique and venerable scaffolding with which the illusions of the senses

* *A.R.,* 1874, pp. 129–168. From the Eulogy read before the French Academy, translated by Baden-Powell (1796–1860), Professor of Geometry, Oxford. The present version has been considerably condensed.

67

and the pride of successive generations had filled the universe. The earth ceased to be the center, the pivot of the celestial movements. It henceforward modestly ranged itself among the planets; its material importance, amid the totality of the bodies of which our solar system is composed, found itself reduced almost to that of a grain of sand.

Twenty-eight years had elapsed from the day when the Canon of Torun expired while holding in his faltering hands the first copy of the work which was to diffuse so bright and pure a flood of glory upon Poland, when Würtemberg witnessed the birth of a man who was destined to achieve a revolution in science not less fertile in consequences, and still more difficult of execution. This man was Kepler. Endowed with two qualities which seemed incompatible with each other, a volcanic imagination and a pertinacity of intellect which the most tedious numerical calculations could not daunt, Kepler conjectured that the movements of the celestial bodies must be connected together by simple laws or, to use his own expression, by harmonic laws. These laws he undertook to discover. A thousand fruitless attempts, errors of calculation inseparable from a colossal undertaking, did not prevent him a single instant from advancing resolutely toward the goal of which he imagined he had obtained a glimpse. Twenty-two years were employed by him in this investigation, and still he was not weary of it! What, in reality, are twenty-two years of labor to him who is about to become the legislator of worlds; who shall inscribe his name in ineffaceable characters upon the frontispiece of an immortal code; who shall be able to exclaim in dithyrambic language, and without incurring the reproach of anyone, "The die is cast; I have written my book; it will be read either in the present age or by posterity, it matters not which; it may well await a reader since God has waited six thousand years for an interpreter of his works!" To investigate a physical cause capable of making the planets revolve in closed curves; to place the principle of the stability of the universe in mechanical forces and not in solid supports such as the spheres of crystal which our ancestors had dreamed of; to extend to the revolutions of the heavenly bodies the general principles of the mechanics of terrestrial bodies, such were the questions which remained to be solved after Kepler had announced his discoveries to the world.

Very distinct traces of these great problems are perceived here and there among the ancients as well as the moderns, from Lucretius and Plutarch down to Kepler, Bouillaud, and Borelli. It is to Newton, however, that we must award the merit of their solution. This great man, like several of his predecessors, conceived the celestial bodies to have a tendency to approach toward each other by virtue of an attractive force, deduced the mathematical characteristics of this force from the laws of Kepler, extended it to all the material molecules of the solar system, and developed his brilliant discovery in a work which even in the present day is regarded as the most eminent production of the human intellect.

.   .   .

Five geometers, Clairaut, Euler, d'Alembert, Lagrange, and Laplace, shared between them the world of which Newton had disclosed the existence. They explored it in all directions, penetrated into regions which had been supposed inaccessible, pointed out there a multitude of phenomena which observation had not yet detected. Finally—and it is this which constitutes their imperishable glory—they reduced under the domain of a single principle, a single law, everything that was most refined and mysterious in the celestial movements. Geometry had thus the boldness to dispose of the future. The evolutions of ages are scrupulously ratifying the decisions of science.

.   .   .

If Newton gave a complete solution of the question of the celestial movements in the case wherein two bodies attract each other, he did not even attempt an analytical investigation of the infinitely more difficult problem of three bodies. The problem of three bodies (this is the name by which it has become celebrated), the problem for determining the movement of a body subjected to the attractive influence of two other bodies, was solved for the first time by our countryman Clairaut.* From this solution we may date the important improvements of the lunar tables effected in the last century.

.   .   .

After having enumerated the various forces which must result from the mutual action of the planets and satellites of our system, even the great Newton did not venture to investigate the general nature of the effects produced by them. In the midst of the laby-

* The problem of three bodies was solved independently about the same time by Euler, d'Alembert, and Clairaut. The two last-mentioned geometers communicated their solutions to the Academy of Sciences on the same day— November 15, 1747. Euler had already, in 1746, published tables of the moon, founded on his solution of the same problem, the details of which he subsequently published in 1753. [TRANSLATOR'S NOTE.]

rinth formed by increases and diminutions of velocity, variations in the forms of the orbits, changes of distances and inclinations which these forces must evidently produce, the most learned geometer would fail to discover a trustworthy guide. This extreme complication gave birth to a discouraging reflection. Forces so numerous so variable in position, so different in intensity, seemed to be incapable of maintaining a condition of equilibrium except by a sort of miracle. Newton even went so far as to suppose that the planetary system did not contain within itself the elements of indefinite stability; he was of opinion that a powerful hand must intervene from time to time to repair the derangements occasioned by the mutual action of the various bodies. Euler, although farther advanced than Newton in a knowledge of the planetary perturbations, refused also to admit that the solar system was constituted so as to endure forever. Never did a greater philosophical question offer itself to the inquiries of mankind. Laplace attacked it with boldness, perseverance, and success. The profound and long-continued researches of the illustrious geometer established with complete evidence that the planetary ellipses are perpetually variable; that the extremities of their major axes make the tour of the heavens; that, independently of an oscillatory motion, the planes of their orbits experience a displacement by virtue of which their intersections with the plane of the terrestrial orbit are each year directed toward different stars. In the midst of this apparent chaos there is one element which remains constant or is merely subject to small periodic changes, namely, the major axis of each orbit and consequently the time of revolution of each planet. This is the element which ought to have chiefly varied according to the learned speculations of Newton and Euler.

The principle of universal gravitation suffices for preserving the stability of the solar system. It maintains the forms and inclinations of the orbits in a mean condition which is subject to slight oscillations; variety does not entail disorder; the universe offers the example of harmonious relations, of a state of perfection which Newton himself doubted. This depends on circumstances which calculation disclosed to Laplace, and which, upon a superficial view of the subject, would not seem to be capable of exercising so great an influence. Instead of planets revolving all in the same direction, in slightly eccentric orbits, and in planes inclined at small angles toward each other, substitute different conditions, and the stability of the universe will again be put in jeopardy, and, according to all probability, there will result a frightful chaos.

·   ·   ·

The memoir in which Laplace communicated his results on the invariability of the mean motions or mean distances is dated 1773. It was in 1784 only that he established the stability of the other elements of the system from the smallness of the planetary masses, the inconsiderable eccentricity of the orbits, and the revolution of the planets in one common direction around the sun. The discovery . . . excluded, at least from the solar system, the idea of the Newtonian attraction's being a cause of disorder; but might not other forces, by combining with attraction, produce gradually increasing perturbations, as Newton and Euler dreaded? Facts of a positive nature seemed to justify these fears. A comparison of ancient with modern observations revealed the existence of a continued acceleration of the mean motions of the moon and the planet Jupiter and an equally striking diminution of the mean motion of Saturn. These variations led to conclusions of the most singular nature. In accordance with the presumed cause of these perturbations, to say that the velocity of a body increased from century to century was equivalent to asserting that the body continually approached the center of motion. On the other hand, when the velocity diminished, the body must be receding from the center.

Thus, by a strange arrangement of nature, our planetary system seemed destined to lose Saturn, its most mysterious ornament, to see the planet, accompanied by its ring and seven satellites, plunge gradually into unknown regions, whither the eye, armed with the most powerful telescope, has never penetrated. Jupiter, on the other hand, the planet compared with which the earth is so insignificant, appeared to be moving in the opposite direction, so as to be ultimately absorbed in the incandescent matter of the sun. Finally, the moon seemed as if it would one day precipitate itself upon the earth. There was nothing doubtful or speculative in these sinister forebodings. The precise dates of the approaching catastrophes were alone uncertain. It was known, however, that they were very distant. Accordingly, neither the learned dissertations of men of science nor the animated descriptions of certain poets produced any impression upon the public mind.

It was not so with our scientific societies, the members of which regarded with regret the approaching destruction of our planetary system. The Academy of Sciences called the attention of geometers of all countries to these menacing perturbations. Euler and Lagrange descended into the arena. Never did their mathematical genius shine with a brighter luster. Still the question remained undecided. The inutility of such efforts seemed to suggest only a feeling of resignation on the subject, when from two disdained corners of the theories of analysis the author of the *Mécanique Céleste* caused the laws of these great phenomena clearly to emerge. The variations of velocity of Jupiter, Saturn, and the moon flowed, then, from evident physical causes and entered into the category of ordinary periodic perturbations, depending upon the principle of attraction. The variations in the dimensions of the orbits, which were so much dreaded, resolved themselves into simple oscillations, included within narrow limits. Finally, by the powerful instrumentality of mathematical analysis, the physical universe was again established on a firm foundation.

I cannot quit this subject without at least alluding to the circumstances in the solar system upon which depend the long-unexplained variations of velocity of the moon, Jupiter, and Saturn. The motion of the earth around the sun is mainly effected in an ellipse, the form of which is liable to vary from the effects of planetary perturbation. These alterations of form are periodic; sometimes the curve, without ceasing to be elliptic, approaches the form of a circle, while at other times it deviates more and more from that form. From the epoch of the earliest recorded observations the eccentricity of the terrestrial orbit has been diminishing will begin to deviate from the form of a circle, and the eccentricity from year to year; at some future epoch the orbit, on the contrary, will increase to the same extent as it previously diminished, and according to the same laws.

Now Laplace has shown that the mean motion of the moon around the earth is connected with the form of the ellipse which the earth describes around the sun; that a diminution of the eccentricity of the ellipse inevitably induces an increase in the velocity of our satellite, and *vice versa;* finally, that this cause suffices to explain the numerical value of the acceleration which the mean motion of the moon has experienced from the earliest ages down to the present time. The origin of the inequalities in the mean motions of Jupiter and Saturn will be, I hope, as easy to conceive.

Mathematical analysis has not served to represent in finite terms the values of the derangements which each planet experiences in its movement from the action of all the other planets. In the present state of science this value is exhibited in the form of an indefinite series of terms diminishing rapidly in magnitude. In calculation it is usual to neglect such of those terms as correspond in the order of magnitude to quantities beneath the errors of observation. But there are cases in which the order of the term in the series does not decide whether it be small or great. Certain numerical relations between the primitive elements of the disturbing and disturbed planets may impart sensible values to terms which usually admit of being neglected. This case occurs in the perturbations of Saturn produced by Jupiter, and in those of Jupiter produced by Saturn. There exists between the mean motions of these two great planets a simple relation of commensurability, five times the mean motion of Saturn being, in fact, very nearly equal to twice the mean motion of Jupiter. It happens in consequence that certain terms, which would otherwise be very small, acquire from this circumstance considerable values. Hence arise, in the movements of these two planets, inequalities of long duration, which require more than 900 years for their complete development, and which represent with marvelous accuracy all the irregularities disclosed by observation. Is it not astonishing to find in the commensurability of the mean motions of two planets a cause of perturbation of so influential a nature; to discover that the definitive solution of an immense difficulty, which baffled the genius of Euler, and which even led persons to doubt whether the theory of gravitation was capable of accounting for all the phenomena of the heavens, should depend upon the fortuitous circumstance of five times the mean motion of Saturn being equal to twice the mean motion of Jupiter? The beauty of the conception and the ultimate result are here equally worthy of admiration.

We have just explained how Laplace demonstrated that the solar system can experience only small periodic oscillations around a certain mean state. Let us now see in what way he succeeded in determining the absolute dimensions of the orbits. What is the distance of the sun from the earth? No scientific question has occupied in a greater degree the attention of mankind; mathematically speaking, nothing is more simple. It suffices, as in common operations of surveying, to draw visual lines from the two extremities of a known base to an inaccessible object. The remainder is a process of elementary calculation. Unfortunately, in the case of the sun the distance is great, and the bases which can be measured upon the earth are comparatively very small. In such a case the slightest errors in the direction of the visual lines exercise an enormous influence upon the results.

In the beginning of the last century Halley remarked that certain interpositions of Venus between the earth and the sun, or to use an expression applied to such conjunctions, the transits of the planet across the sun's disk, would furnish at each observatory an indirect means of fixing the position of the visual ray very superior in accuracy to the most perfect direct methods. Such was the object of the scientific expeditions undertaken in 1761 and 1769 on which occasions France—not to speak of stations in Europe—was represented at the isle of Rodrigo by Pingré; at the isle of San Domingo by Fleurin; at California by the Abbé Chappe; at Pondicherry by Legentil. At the same epochs England sent Maskelyne to St. Helena; Wales to Hudson's Bay; Mason to the Cape of Good Hope; Captain Cooke to Otaheite, etc. The observations of the Southern Hemisphere, compared with those of Europe, and especially with the observations made by an Austrian astronomer, Father Hell, at Wardhus in Lapland, gave for the distance of the sun the result which has since figured in all treatises on astronomy and navigation.

No government hesitated in furnishing academies with the means, however expensive they might be, of conveniently establishing their observers in the most distant regions. We have already remarked that the determination of the contemplated distance appeared to demand imperiously an extensive base; for small bases would have been totally inadequate to the purpose. Well, Laplace has solved the problem numerically, without a base of any kind whatever. He has deduced the distance of the sun from observations of the moon made in one and the same place! The sun is, with respect to our satellite, the cause of perturbations which evidently depend on the distance of the immense luminous globe from the earth. Who does not see that these perturbations would diminish if the distance increased; that they would increase, on the contrary, if the distance diminished; that the distance finally determines the magnitude of the perturbations? Observation assigns the numerical value of these perturbations; theory, on the other hand, unfolds the general mathematical relation that connects them with the solar parallax and with other known elements. The determination of the mean radius of the terrestrial orbit then becomes one of the most simple operations of algebra. Such is the happy combination by the aid of which Laplace has solved the great, the celebrated problem of parallax. It is thus that the illustrious geometer found for the mean distance of the sun from the earth, expressed in radii of the terrestrial orbit, a value differing only in a slight degree from that which was the fruit of so many troublesome and expensive voyages. According to the opinion of very competent judges, the result of the indirect method might not impossibly merit the preference.

The movements of the moon proved a fertile mine of research to our great geometer. His penetrating intellect discovered in them unknown treasures. He disentangled them from everything which concealed them from vulgar eyes with an ability and a perseverance equally worthy of admiration. The reader will excuse me for citing another of such examples.

The earth governs the movements of the moon. The earth is flattened; in other words its figure is spheroidal. A spheroidal body does not attract like a sphere. There ought, then, to exist in the movement, I had almost said in the countenance, of the moon a sort of impression of the spheroidal figure of the earth. Such was the idea as it originally occurred to Laplace. It still remained to ascertain (and here consisted the chief difficulty) whether the effects attributable to the spheroidal figure of the earth were sufficiently sensible not to be confounded with the errors of observation. It was accordingly necessary to find the general formula of perturbations of this nature, in order to be able, as in the case of the solar parallax to eliminate the unknown quantity.

The ardor of Laplace, combined with his power of analytical research, surmounted all obstacles. By means of an investigation which demanded the most minute attention, the great geometer discovered in the theory of the moon's movements two well-defined perturbations depending on the spheroidal figure of the earth. The first affected the resolved element of the motion of our satellite, which is chiefly measured with the instrument known in observatories by the name of the transit instrument; the second, which operated in the direction north and south, could only be effected by observations with a second instrument, termed the mural circle. These two inequalities, of very different magnitudes, connected with the cause which produces them, by analytical combinations of totally different kinds, have, however, both conducted to the same value of the ellipticity. It must be borne in mind, however, that the ellipticity thus deduced from the movements of the moon is not the ellipticity corresponding to such or such a country, the ellipticity observed in France, in England, in Italy, in Lapland, in North America, in India, or in the region of the Cape of Good Hope, for the earth's materials having undergone considerable upheavings at different times and in different places, the primitive regularity of its curvature has been sensibly disturbed by this cause. The moon—and it is this circumstance which renders the result of such inestimable value—ought to assign, and has in reality assigned, the general ellipticity of the earth; in other words, it has indicated a sort of mean value of the various determinations obtained at enormous expense and with infinite labor as the result of long voyages undertaken by astronomers of all the countries of Europe.

.   .   .

What are the elements which it has been found necessary to confront with each other in order to arrive at results expressed even to the precision of the smallest decimals? On the one hand, mathematical formulæ deduced from the principle of universal attraction; on the other hand, certain irregularities observed in the returns of the moon to the meridian.

An observing geometer who from his infancy had never quitted his chamber of study, and who had never viewed the heavens except through a narrow aperture directed north and south, in the vertical plane of which the principal astronomical instruments are made to move—to whom nothing had ever been revealed respecting the bodies revolving above his head except that they attract each other according to the Newtonian law of gravitation—would, however, be enabled to ascertain that his narrow abode was situated upon the surface of a spheroidal body, the equatorial axis of which surpassed the polar axis by a three-hundred-and-sixth part; he would have also found in his isolated immovable position his true distance from the sun.

It is to d'Alembert we owe the satisfactory mathematical explanation of the phenomenon of the precession of the equinoxes. But our illustrious countryman, as well as Euler, whose solution appeared subsequently to that of d'Alembert, omitted all consideration of certain physical circumstances, which, however, did not seem to be of a nature to be neglected without examination. Laplace has supplied this deficiency. He has shown that the sea, notwithstanding its fluidity, and that the atmosphere, notwithstanding its currents, exercise the same influence on the movements of the terrestrial axis as if they formed solid masses adhering to the terrestrial spheroid.

Do the extremities of the axis around which the earth performs an entire revolution once in every twenty-four hours correspond always to the same material points of the terrestrial spheroid? In other words, do the poles of rotation, which from year to year correspond to different stars, undergo also a displacement at the surface of the earth? In the case of the affirmative, the equator is movable as well as the poles; the terrestrial latitudes are variable; no country during the lapse of ages will enjoy, even on an average, a constant climate; regions the most different will in their turn become circumpolar. Adopt the contrary supposition, and everything assumes the character of an admirable permanence.

The question which I have just suggested, one of the most important in astronomy, cannot be solved by the aid of mere observation, on account of the uncertainty of the early determinations of terrestrial latitude. Laplace has supplied this defect by analysis. The great geometer has demonstrated that no circumstance depending on universal gravitation can sensibly displace the poles of the earth's axis relatively to the surface of the terrestrial spheroid. The sea, far from being an obstacle to the invariable rotation of the earth upon its axis, would on the contrary reduce the axis to a permanent condition in consequence of the mobility of the waters and the resistance which their oscillations experience. The remarks which I have just made with respect to the position of the terrestrial axis are equally applicable to the time of the earth's rotation, which is the unit, the true standard of time. The importance of this element induced Laplace to examine whether its numerical value might not be liable to vary from internal causes, such as earthquakes and volcanoes. It is hardly necessary for me to state that the result obtained was negative. The admirable memoir of Lagrange upon the libration of the moon seemed to have exhausted the subject. This, however, was not the case.

The motion of revolution of our satellite around the earth is subject to perturbations, technically termed secular, which were either unknown to Lagrange or which he neglected. These inequalities eventually place the body, not to speak of entire circumferences, at angular distances of a semicircle, a circle and a half, etc., from the position which it would otherwise occupy. If the movement of rotation did not participate in such perturbations, the moon in the lapse of ages would present in succession all the parts of its surface to the earth. This event will not occur. The hemisphere of the moon which is actually invisible will remain invisible forever. Laplace, in fact, has shown that the attraction of the earth introduces into the rotary motion of the lunar spheroid the secular inequalities which exist in the movement of revolution. Researches of this nature exhibit in full relief the power of mathematical analysis. It would have been very difficult to have discovered by synthesis truths so profoundly enveloped in the complex action of a multitude of forces.

We should be inexcusable if we omitted to notice the high importance of the labors of Laplace on the improvement of the lunar tables. The immediate object of this improvement was, in effect, the promotion of maritime intercourse between distant countries and, what was indeed far superior to all considerations of mercantile interest, the preservation of the lives of mariners.

Thanks to a sagacity without parallel, to a perseverance which knew no limits, to an ardor always youthful, and which communicated itself to able coadjutors, Laplace solved the celebrated problem of the longitude more completely than could have been hoped for in a scientific point of view, with greater precision than the art of navigation in its utmost refinement demanded. The ship, the sport of the winds and tempests, has no occasion in the present day to be afraid of losing itself in the immensity of the ocean. An intelligent glance at the starry vault indicates to the pilot in every place and at every time his distance from the meridian of Paris. The extreme perfection of the existing tables of the moon entitles Laplace to be ranked among the benefactors of humanity.

In the beginning of the year 1611 Galileo supposed that he found in the eclipses of Jupiter's satellites a simple and rigorous solution of the famous problem of the longitude, and active negotiations were immediately commenced with the view of introducing the new method on board the numerous vessels of Spain and Holland. These negotiations failed. From the discussion it plainly appeared that the accurate observation of the eclipses of the satellites would require powerful telescopes, but such telescopes could not be employed on board a ship tossed about by the waves. The method of Galileo seemed, at any rate, to retain all its advantages when applied on land and to promise immense improvements to geography. These expectations were found to be premature. The movements of the satellites of Jupiter are not by any means so simple as the immortal inventor of the method of longitude supposed them to be. It was necessary that three generations of astronomers and mathematicians should labor with preserverance in unfolding their most considerable perturbations. It was necessary, in fine, that the tables of those bodies should acquire all desirable and necessary precision, that Laplace should introduce into the midst of them the torch of mathematical analysis.

In the present day the nautical ephemerides contain several years in advance the indication of the times of the eclipses and reappearances of Jupiter's satellites. Calculation does not yield in precision to direct observation. In this group of satellites, considered as an independent system of bodies, Laplace found a series of perturbations analogous to those which the planets experience. The rapidity of the revolutions unfolds, in a sufficiently short space of time, changes in this system which require centuries for their complete development in the solar system. Although the satellites exhibit hardly an appreciable diameter even when viewed in the best telescopes, our illustrious countryman was enabled to determine their masses. Finally, he discovered certain simple relations of an extremely remarkable character between the movements of those bodies, which have been called the *laws of Laplace*. Posterity will not obliterate this designation; it will acknowledge the propriety of inscribing in the heavens the name of so great an astronomer beside that of Kepler.

Let us cite two or three of the laws of Laplace:

If we add to the mean longitude of the first satellite twice that of the third and subtract from the sum three times the mean longitude of the second, the result will be exactly equal to 180°. Would it not be very extraordinary if the three satellites had been placed originally at the distances from Jupiter and in the positions, with respect to each other, adapted for constantly and rigorously maintaining the foregoing relation? Laplace has replied to this question by showing that it is not necessary that this relation should have been rigorously true at the origin. The mutual action of the satellites would necessarily have reduced it to its present mathematical condition if once the distances and the positions satisfied the law approximately. This first law is equally true when we employ the synodical elements. It hence plainly results that the three first satellites of Jupiter can never all be eclipsed at the same time. Bearing this in mind, we shall have no difficulty in apprehending the import of a celebrated observation of recent times, during which certain astronomers perceived the planet for a short time without any of its four satellites. This would not by any means authorize us in supposing the satellites to be eclipsed. A satellite disappears when it is projected upon the central part of the luminous disk of Jupiter and also when it passes behind the opaque body of the planet.

The following is another very simple law to which the mean motions of the same satellites of Jupiter are subject: If we add to the mean motion of the first satellite twice the mean motion of the third, the sum is exactly equal to three times the mean motion of the second. This numerical coincidence, which is perfectly accurate, would be one of the most mysterious phenomena in the system of the universe if Laplace had not proved that the law need only have been approximate at the origin and that the mutual action of the satellites has sufficed to render it rigorous.

The illustrious geometer, who always pursued his researches to their most remote ramifications, arrived at the following result: The action of Jupiter regulates the movements and rotation of the satellites, so that, without taking into account the secular perturbations, the time of rotation of the first satellite, plus twice the time of rotation of the third, forms a sum which is constantly equal to three times the time of rotation of the second. Influenced by a deference, a modesty, a timidity, without any plausible motive, our artists in the last century surrendered to the English the exclusive privilege of constructing instruments of astronomy. Thus, let us frankly acknowledge the fact: at the time when Herschel was prosecuting his beautiful observations on the other side of the Channel, there existed in France no instruments adapted for developing them; we had not even the means of verifying them. Fortunately for the scientific honor of our country, mathematical analysis is also a powerful instrument. Laplace gave ample proof of this on a memorable occasion when, from the retirement of his chamber, he predicted, he minutely announced, what the excellent astronomer of Windsor would see with the largest telescopes which were ever constructed by the hand of man.

When Galileo, in the beginning of the year 1610, directed toward Saturn a telescope of very low power, which he had just executed with his own hands, he perceived that the planet was not an ordinary globe, without, however, being able to ascertain its real form. The expression, *tri-corporate,* by which the illustrious Florentine designated the appearance of the planet, implied even a totally erroneous idea of its structure. Our countryman Roberval entertained much sounder views on the subject, but from not having instituted a detailed comparison between his hypothesis and the results of observation, he abandoned to Huyghens the honor of being regarded as the author of the true theory of the phenomena presented by the wonderful planet. Every person knows in the present day that Saturn consists of a globe about 900 times greater than the earth, and a ring. This ring does not touch the ball of the planet, being everywhere removed from it at a distance of 20,000 (English) miles. Observation indicates the breadth of the ring to be 54,000 miles. The thickness certainly does not exceed 250 miles. With the exception of a black streak, which divides the ring throughout its whole contour into two parts of unequal breadth and of different brightness, this strange, colossal bridge without piles had never offered to the most experienced or skillful observer either spot or protuberance adapted for deciding whether it was immovable or endued with a movement of rotation.

Laplace considered it to be very improbable, if the ring was immovable, that its constituent parts should be capable of resisting by their mere cohesion the continual attraction of the planet. A movement of rotation occurred to his mind as constituting the principle of stability, and he hence deduced the necessary velocity. The velocity thus found was exactly equal to that which Herschel subsequently deduced from a course of extremely delicate observations.

The two parts of the ring being placed at different distances from the planet could not fail to experience, from the action of the sun, different movements of rotation. It would hence seem that the planes of both rings ought to be generally inclined toward each other, whereas they appear from observation always to coincide. It was necessary, then, that some physical cause should exist which would be capable of neutralizing the action of the sun. In a memoir published in February 1789 Laplace found that this cause must reside in the ellipticity of Saturn produced by a rapid movement of rotation of the planet, a movement the existence of which Herschel announced in November 1789. The reader cannot fail to remark how, on certain occasions, the eyes of the mind can supply the want of the most powerful telescopes and lead to astronomical discoveries of the highest importance. Let us descend from the heavens upon the earth. The discoveries of Laplace will appear not less important, not less worthy of his genius.

The phenomena of the tides, which an ancient philosopher designated in despair *the tomb of human curiosity,* were connected by Laplace with an analytical theory in which the physical conditions of the question figure for the first time. Accordingly, calculators, to the immense advantage of the navigation of our maritime coasts, venture in the present day to predict several years in advance the details of the time and height of the full tides without more anxiety respecting the result than if the question related to the phases of an eclipse.

There exists between the different phenomena of the ebb and flow of the tides and the attractive forces which the sun and moon exercise upon the fluid sheet which covers three-fourths of the globe an intimate and necessary connection, from which Laplace, by the aid of a series of twenty years of observations executed at Brest, deduced the value of the mass of our satellite. Science knows in the present day that seventy-five moons would be necessary to form a weight equivalent to that of the terrestrial globe, and it is indebted for this result to an attentive and minute study of the oscilations of the ocean. We know only one means of enhancing the admiration which every thoughtful mind will entertain for theories capable of leading to such conclusions. An historical statement will supply it. In the year 1631 the illustrious Galileo, as appears from his *Dialogues,* was so far from perceiving the mathematical relations from which Laplace deduced results so beautiful, so unequivical, and so useful, that he taxed with frivolousness the vague idea which Kepler entertained of attributing to the moon's attraction a certain share in the production of the diurnal and periodical movements of the waters of the ocean.

Laplace did not confine himself to extending so considerably and improving so essentially the mathematical theory of the tides; he considered the phenomenon from an entirely new point of view. It was he who first treated of the stability of the ocean. Systems of bodies, whether solid or fluid, are subject to two kinds of equilibrium, which we must carefully distinguish from each other. In the case of stable equilibrium, the system, when slightly disturbed, tends always to return to its original condition. On the other hand, when the system is in unstable equilibrium, a very insignificant derangement might occasion an enormous dislocation in the relative positions of its constituent parts. If the equilibrium of waves is of the latter kind, the waves engendered by the action of winds, by earthquakes, and by sudden movements from the bottom of the ocean, have perhaps risen in past times, and may rise in the future, to the height of the highest mountains. The geologist will have the satisfaction of deducing from these prodigious oscillations a rational explanation of a great multitude of phenomena, but the public will thereby be exposed to new and terrible catastrophes.

Mankind may rest assured; Laplace has proved that the equilibrium of the ocean is stable, but upon the express condition (which, however, has been amply verified by established facts) that the mean density of the fluid mass is less than the mean density of the earth. Everything else remaining the same, let us substitute an ocean of mercury for the actual ocean and the stability will disappear, and the fluid will frequently surpass its boundaries, to ravage continents even to the height of the snowy regions which lose themselves in the clouds.

.   .   .

It was impossible that the great geometer, who had succeeded so well in the study of the tides of the ocean, should not have occupied his attention with the tides of the atmosphere; that he should not have submitted to the delicate and definitive tests of a rigorous calculus the generally diffused opinions respecting the influence of the moon upon the height of the barometer and other meteorological phenomena. Laplace, in fact, has devoted a chapter of his splendid work to an examination of the oscillations which the attractive force of the moon is capable of producing in our atmosphere. It results from these researches that at Paris the lunar tide produces no sensible effect upon the barometer. The height of the tide, obtained by the discussion of a long series of observations, has not exceeded two-hundredths of a millimeter, a quantity which in the present state of meteorological science is less than the probable error of observation.

.   .   .

No person was more sagacious than Laplace in discovering intimate relations between phenomena apparently very dissimilar; no person showed himself more skillful in deducing important conclusions from those unexpected affinities. Toward the close of his days, for example, he overthrew with a stroke of the pen, by the aid of certain observations of the moon, the cosmogonic theories of Buffon and Bailly which were so long in favor. According to these theories, the earth was inevitably advancing to a state of congelation which was close at hand. Laplace, who never contented himself with a vague statement, sought to determine in numbers the rapid cooling of our globe which Buffon had so eloquently but so gratuitously announced. Nothing could be more simple, better connected, or more demonstrative than the chain of deductions of the celebrated geometer.

A body diminishes in volume when it cools. According to the most elementary principles of mechanics, a rotating body which contracts in dimensions ought inevitably to turn upon its axis with greater and greater rapidity. The length of the day has been determined in all ages by the time of the earth's rotation; if the earth is cooling, the length of the day must be continually shortening. Now, there exists a means of ascertaining whether the length of the day has undergone any variation. This consists in examining for each century the arc of the celestial sphere described by the moon during the interval of time which the astronomers of the existing epoch called a day; in other words, the time required by the earth to effect a complete rotation on its axis, the velocity of the moon being, in fact, independent of the time of the earth's rotation.

Let us now, after the example of Laplace, take from the standard tables the least considerable values, if you choose, of the expansions or contractions which solid bodies experience from changes of temperature; search then the annals of Grecian, Arabian, and modern astronomy for the purpose of finding in them the angular velocity of the moon, and the great geometer will prove by incontrovertible evidence founded upon these data that during a period of 2,000 years the mean temperature of the earth has not varied to the extent of the hundredth part of a degree of the centigrade thermometer. No eloquent declamation is capable of resisting such a process of reasoning or withstanding the force of such numbers.

The mathematics have been in all ages the implacable adversaries of scientific romances.

The fall of bodies, if it was not a phenomenon of perpetual occurrence, would justly excite in the highest degree the astonishment of mankind. What, in effect, is more extraordinary than to see an inert mass—that is to say, a mass deprived of will, a mass which ought not to have any propensity to advance in one direction more than in another, precipitate itself toward the earth as soon as it ceases to be supported? Nature engenders the gravity of bodies by a process so recondite, so completely beyond the reach of our senses and the ordinary resources of human intelligence, that the philosophers of antiquity, who supposed that they could explain everything mechanically according to the simple evolutions of atoms, excepted gravity from their speculations.

Descartes attempted what Leucippus, Democritus, Epicurus, and their followers thought to be impossible. He made the fall of terrestrial bodies depend upon the action of a vortex of very subtle matter circulating around the earth. The real improvements which the illustrious Huyghens applied to the ingenious conception of our countryman were far, however, from imparting to it clearness and precision, those characteristic attributes of truth.

Those persons form a very imperfect estimate of the meaning of one of the greatest questions which have occupied the attention of modern inquirers who regard Newton as having issued victorious from a struggle in which his two immortal predecessors had failed. Newton did not discover the cause of gravity any more than Galileo did. Two bodies placed in juxtaposition approach each other. Newton does not inquire into the nature of the force which produces this effect. The force exists. He designates it by the term attraction; but at the same time he warns the reader that the term, as thus used by him, does not imply any definite idea of the physical process by which gravity is brought into existence and operates. The force of attraction being once admitted as a fact, Newton studies it in all terrestrial phenomena, in the revolutions of the moon, the planets, satellites, and comets; and, as we have already stated, he deduced from this incomparable study the simple, universal, mathematical characteristics of the forces which preside over the movements of all the bodies of which our solar system is composed.

The applause of the scientific world did not prevent the immortal author of the *Principia* from hearing some persons refer the principle of gravitation to the class of occult qualities. This circumstance induced Newton and his most devoted followers to abandon the reserve which they had hitherto considered it their duty to maintain. Those persons were then charged with ignorance who regarded attraction as an essential property of matter, as the mysterious indication of a sort of charm, who supposed that two bodies may act upon each other without the intervention of a third body. This force was then either the result of the tendency of an ethereal fluid to move from the free regions of space, where its density is a maximum, toward the planetary bodies, around which there exists a greater degree of rarefaction, or the consequence of the impulsive force of some fluid medium.

Newton never expressed a definitive opinion respecting the origin of the impulse which occasioned the attractive force of matter—at least in our solar system. But we have strong reasons for supposing, in the present day, that in using the word *impulse* the great geometer was thinking of the systematic ideas of Varignon and Fatio de Duillier, subsequently re-invented and perfected by Le Sage. These ideas, in fact, had been communicated to him before they were published to the world. According to Le Sage, there are in the regions of space bodies moving in every possible direction and with excessive rapidity. The author applied to these the name of *ultramundane corpuscules*. Their totality constituted the gravitative fluid, if indeed the designation of a fluid be applicable to an assemblage of particles having no mutual connection. A single body placed in the midst of such an ocean of movable particles would remain at rest although it were impelled equally in every direction. On the other hand, two bodies ought to advance toward each other, since they would serve the purpose of mutual screens, since the surfaces facing each other would no longer be hit in the direction of their line of junction by the ultramundane particles, since there would then exist currents, the effect of which would no longer be neutralized by opposite currents. It will be easily seen, besides, that two bodies plunged into the gravitative fluid would tend to approach each other with an intensity which would vary in the inverse proportion of the square of the distance.

If attraction is the result of the impulse of a fluid, its action ought to employ a finite time in traversing the immense spaces which separate the celestial bodies. If the sun, then, were suddenly extinguished, the earth after the catastrophe would, mathematically speaking, still continue for some time to experience its attractive influence. The contrary would happen on the occasion of the sudden birth of a planet: a certain time would elapse before the attractive force of the new body would make itself felt on the earth.

Several geometers of the last century were of opinion that the force of attraction is not transmitted instantaneously from one body to another; they even assigned to it a comparatively inconsiderable velocity of propagation. Daniel Bernoulli, for example, in attempting to explain how the spring tide arrives upon our coasts a day and a half after the syzygies, that is to say, a day and a half after the epochs when the sun and moon are most favorably situated for the production of this magnificent phenomenon, assumed that the disturbing force required all this time (a day and a half) for its propagation from the moon to the ocean. So feeble a velocity was inconsistent with the mechanical explanation of attraction, of which we have just spoken. The explanation, in effect, necessarily supposes that the proper motions of the celestial bodies are insensible, compared with the motion of the gravitative fluid. After having discovered that the diminution of the eccentricity of the terrestrial orbit is the real cause of the observed acceleration of the motion of the moon, Laplace on his part endeavored to ascertain whether this mysterious acceleration did not depend on the gradual propagation of attraction.

The result of calculation was at first favorable to the plausibility of the hypothesis. It showed that the gradual propagation of the attractive force would introduce into the movement of our satellite a perturbation proportional to the square of the time which elapsed from the commencement of any epoch; that in order to represent numerically the results of astronomical observations, it would not be necessary to assign a feeble velocity to attraction; that a propagation eight millions of times more rapid than that of light would satisfy all the phenomena.

Although the true cause of the acceleration of the moon is now well known, the ingenious calculation of which I have just spoken does not the less on that account maintain its place in science. In a mathematical point of view, the perturbation depending on the gradual propagation of the attractive force which this calculation indicates has a certain existence. The connection between the velocity of perturbation and the resulting inequality is such that one of the two quantities leads to a knowledge of the numerical value of the other. Now, upon assigning to the inequality the greatest value which is consistent with the observations after they have been corrected for the effect due to the variation of the eccentricity of the terrestrial orbit, we find the velocity of the attractive force to be fifty millions of times the velocity of light. If it be borne in mind that this number is an inferior limit, and that the velocity of the rays of light amounts to 77,000 leagues (192,000 English miles) per second, the philosophers who profess to explain the force of attraction by the impulsive energy of a fluid will see what prodigious velocities they must satisfy.

. . .

The author of the *Mécanique Céleste* supposed, like Newton, that light consists of material molecules of excessive tenuity and endued in empty space with a velocity of 77,000 leagues in a second. However, it is right to warn those who would be inclined to avail themselves of this imposing authority that the principal argument of Laplace in favor of the system of emission consisted in the advantage which it afforded of submitting every question to a process of simple and rigorous calculation; whereas, on the other hand, the theory of undulations has always offered immense difficulties to analysts. It was natural that a geometer who had so elegantly connected the laws of simple refraction which light undergoes in its passage through the atmosphere, and the laws of double refraction which it is subject to in the course of its passage through certain crystals, with the action of attractive and repulsive forces, should not have abandoned this route before he recognized the impossibility of arriving by the same path at plausible explanations of the phenomena of diffraction and polarization. In other respects the care which Laplace always employed in pursuing his researches as far as possible to their numerical results will enable those who are disposed to institute a complete comparison between the two rival theories of light to derive from the *Mécanique Céleste* the materials of several interesting relations.

Is light an emanation from the sun? Does this body launch out incessantly in every direction a part of its own substance? Is it gradually diminishing in volume and mass? The attraction exercised by the sun upon the earth will in that case gradually become less and less considerable. The radius of the terrestrial orbit, on the other hand, cannot fail to increase, and a corresponding effect will be produced on the length of the year. This is the conclusion which suggests itself to every person upon a first glance at the subject. By applying analysis to the question and then proceeding to numerical computations founded upon the most trustworthy results of observation relative to the length of the year in different ages, Laplace has proved that an incessant emission of light, going on for a period of two thousand years, has not diminished the mass of the sun by the two-millionth part of its original value.

Our illustrious countryman never proposed to himself anything vague or indefinite. His constant object was the explanation of the great phenomena of nature according to the inflexible principles of mathematical analysis. No philosopher, no mathematician, could have maintained himself more cautiously on his guard against a propensity to hasty speculation. No person dreaded more the scientific errors which the imagination gives birth to, when it ceases to remain within the limits of facts, of calculation, and of analogy. Once, and once only, did Laplace launch forward, like Kepler, like Descartes, like Leibnitz, like Buffon, into the region of conjectures. His conception was not then less than a cosmogony.

All the planets revolve around the sun, from west to east, and in planes which include angles of inconsiderable magnitude. The satellites revolve around their respective primaries in the same direction as that in which the planets revolve around the sun, that is to say, from west to east. The planets and satellites which have been found to have a rotatory motion turn also upon their axes from west to east. Finally, the rotation of the sun is also directed from west to east. We have here, then, an assemblage of forty-three movements, all operating in the same direction. By the calculus of probabilities the odds are four thousand millions to one that this coincidence in the direction of so many movements is not the effect of accident.

It was Buffon, I think, who first attempted to explain this singular feature of our solar system. Having wished in the explanation of phenomena to avoid all recourse to causes which were not warranted by nature, the celebrated academician investigated a physical origin of the system in what was common to the movements of so many bodies differing in magnitude, in form, and in distance from the principal center of attraction. He imagined that he discovered such an origin by making this triple supposition: A comet fell obliquely upon the sun; it pushed before it a torrent of fluid matter; this substance transported to a greater or less distance from the sun, according to its mass, formed by concentration all the known planets. The bold hypothesis of Buffon is liable to unsurmountable difficulties. I proceed to indicate, in a few words, the cosmogonic system which Laplace substituted for that of the illustrious author of the *Histoire Naturelle*.

According to Laplace, the sun was at a remote epoch the central nucleus of an immense nebula which possessed a very high temperature and extended far beyond the region in which Uranus revolves in the present day. No planet was then in existence. The solar nebula was endued with a general movement of revolution directed from west to east. As it cooled it could not fail to experience a gradual condensation and in consequence to rotate with greater and greater rapidity. If the nebulous matter extended originally in the plane of the equator as far as the limit at which the centrifugal force exactly counterbalanced the attraction of the nucleus, the molecules situated at this limit ought, during the process of condensation, to separate from the rest of the atmospheric matter and form an equatorial zone, a ring revolving separately and with its primitive velocity.

We may conceive that analogous separations were effected in the higher strata of the nebula at different epochs, that is to say, at different distances from the nucleus, and that they give rise to a succession of distinct rings included almost in the same plane and endued with different velocities. This being once admitted, it is easy to see that the indefinite stability of the rings would have required a regularity of structure throughout their whole contour, which is very improbable. Each of them accordingly broke in its turn into several masses which were plainly endued with a movement of rotation, coinciding in direction with the common movement of revolution, and which in consequence of their fluidity assumed spheroidal forms. In order, then, that one of those spheroids might absorb all the others belonging to the same ring, it will be sufficient to assign to it a mass greater than that of any other spheroid. Each of the planets while in the vaporous condition to which we have just alluded would manifestly have a central nucleus gradually increasing in magnitude and mass and an atmosphere offering, at its successive limits, phenomena entirely similar to those which the solar atmosphere, properly so called, had exhibited. We here witness the birth of satellites and that of the ring of Saturn.

The system of which I have just given an imperfect sketch has for its object to show how a nebula endued with a general movement of rotation must eventually transform itself into a very luminous central nucleus (a sun) and into a series of distinct spheroidal planets, situated at considerable distances from each other, revolving all around the central sun in the direction of the original movement of the nebula; how these planets ought also to have movements of rotation operating in similar directions; how, finally, the satellites, when any of such are formed, cannot fail to revolve upon their axes and around their respective primaries, in the direction of rotation of the planets and of their movement of revolution around the sun. We have just found, conformably to the principles of mechanics, the forces with which the particles of the nebula were originally endued, in the movements of rotation and revolution of the compact and distinct masses which these particles have brought into existence by their condensation. But we have thereby achieved only a single step. The primitive movement of rotation of the nebula is not connected with the simple attraction of the particles. This movement seems to imply the action of a primordial impulsive force.

Laplace is far from adopting in this respect the almost universal opinion of philosophers and mathematicians. He does not suppose that the mutual attractions of originally immovable bodies must ultimately reduce all the bodies to a state of rest around their common center of gravity. He maintains, on the contrary, that three bodies in a state of rest, two of which have a much greater mass than the third, would concentrate into a single mass only in certain exceptional cases. In general, the two most considerable bodies would unite together, while the third would revolve around their common center of gravity. Attraction would thus become the cause of a sort of movement which would seem to be explicable solely by an impulsive force.

.   .   .

According to the cosmogonic ideas of Laplace, comets did not originally form part of the solar system. They are not formed at the expense of the matter of the immense solar nebula. We must consider them as small wandering nebulæ, which the attractive force of the sun has caused to deviate from their original route. Such of those comets as penetrated into the great nebula at the epoch of condensation and of the formation of planets fell into the sun, describing spiral curves, and must by their action have caused the planetary orbits to deviate more or less from the plane of the solar equator, with which they would otherwise have exactly coincided.

With respect to the zodiacal light, that rock against which so many reveries have been wrecked, it consists of the most volatile parts of the primitive nebula. These molecules, not having united with the equatorial zones, successively abandoned in the plane of the solar equator, continue to revolve at their original distances and with their original velocities. The circumstance of this extremely rare substance being included wholly within the earth's orbit, and even within that of Venus, seemed irreconcilable with the principles of mechanics; but this difficulty occurred only when the zodiacal substance being conceived to be in a state of direct and intimate dependence on the solar photosphere, properly so called, an angular movement of rotation was impressed on it equal to that of the photosphere, a movement in virtue of which it effected an entire revolution in twenty-five days and a half. Laplace presented his conjectures on the formation of the solar system with the diffidence inspired by a result which was not founded upon calculation and observation.

Perhaps it is to be regretted that they did not receive a more complete development, especially in so far as it concerns the division of the matter into distinct rings; perhaps it would have been desirable if the illustrious author had expressed himself more fully respecting the primitive physical condition, the molecular condition of the nebula at the expense of which the sun, planets, and satellites of our system were formed. It is perhaps especially to be regretted that Laplace should have only briefly alluded to what he considered the obvious possibility of movements of revolution having their origin in the action of simple attractive forces and to other questions of a similar nature.

Notwithstanding these defects, the ideas of the author of the *Mécanique Céleste* are still the only speculations of the kind which, by their magnitude, their coherence, and their mathematical character may be justly considered as forming a physical cosmogony; those alone which in the present day derive a powerful support from the results of the recent researches of astronomers on the nebulæ of every form and magnitude which are scattered throughout the celestial vault.

In this analysis we have deemed it right to concentrate all our attention upon the *Mécanique Céleste*. The *Système du Monde* and the *Théorie Analytique des Probabilités* would also require detailed notices. The *Exposition du Système du Monde* is the *Mécanique Céleste* divested of the great apparatus of analytical formula which ought to be attentively perused by every astronomer who, to use an expression of Plato, is desirous of knowing the numbers which govern the physical universe. It is in the *Exposition du Système du Monde* that persons unacquainted with mathematical studies will obtain an exact and competent knowledge of the methods to which physical astronomy is indebted for its astonishing progress. This work, written with a noble simplicity of style, an exquisite propriety of expression, and a scrupulous accuracy, is terminated by a sketch of the history of astronomy, universally ranked in the present day among the finest monuments of the French language.

. . . .

The calculus of probabilities, when confined within just limits, ought to interest, in an equal degree, the mathematician, the experimentalist, and the statesman. From the time when Pascal and Fermat established its first principles, it has rendered, and continues daily to render, services of the most eminent kind. It is the calculus of probabilities which, after having suggested the best arrangements of the tables of population and mortality, teaches us to deduce from those numbers, in general so erroneously interpreted, conclusions of a precise and useful character; it is the calculus of probabilities which alone can regulate justly the premiums to be paid for assurances; the reserve funds for the disbursement of pensions, annuities, discounts, etc. It is under its influence that lotteries and other shameful snares cunningly laid for avarice and ignorance have definitively disappeared. Laplace has treated these questions and others of a much more complicated nature with his accustomed superiority. In short, the *Théorie Analytique des Probabilités* is worthy of the author of the *Mécanique Céleste.*

A philosopher, whose name is associated with immortal discoveries said to his audience, who had allowed themselves to be influenced by ancient and consecrated authorities, "Bear in mind, gentlemen, that in questions of science the authority of a thousand is not worth the humble reasoning of a single individual." Two centuries have passed over these words of Galileo without depreciating their value or obliterating their truthful character.*

* An Appendix (pp. 165–168) here omitted gives a brief notice of other research carried on by Laplace.

.   .   .

Adrien Marie Legendre *

1752-1833

———◆———

JEAN BAPTISTE ÉLIE DE BEAUMONT †

IT HAS BEEN said that the distinctive stamp of our age is the aspiration after material well-being. Science is accused of having fostered this instinct by the numerous useful applications with which it has endowed humanity; and it is true that in our day chemistry, steam, electricity, have remodelled the face of the world. It is quite certain also that scientific education better understood and more generally distributed has multiplied the number of those who, without having received from nature faculties of the first order, have yet proved capable of deriving from science great advantages as well for others as themselves. We may well suppose that even minds still more developed, seduced by the allurements of fortune or yielding to stern necessity, have sometimes deviated from the arduous paths of pure science into the more inviting paths of applied science. But we have seen also, and see daily, men of a more robust temperament who, listening only to the inspirations of genius, devote their whole existence to strenuous labors which for the moment will contribute merely to the increase of science; of which future generations alone can make useful applications; which will not be appreciated even in a manner somewhat general until long after the death of their authors; and from which those authors will themselves have derived no other enjoyment than the majestic and exciting spectacle of great truths covered as yet with an impenetrable veil to all eyes but their own, together with the consciousness of a duty fulfilled toward Providence, who has intrusted to them the instruments of the future progress of the human race.

* A.R., 1867, pp. 137–157. The present version has been condensed.
† French geologist (1798–1874), perpetual secretary of the French Academy of Sciences.

Among those who seem to have been born to vindicate our age from an unjust reproach and to exalt humanity in its own esteem, a high rank must be accorded to a geometer who occupied a place in this Academy for nearly 50 years, who has enriched our publications with some of their most valuable contents, and bequeathed to future ages works of paramount importance; whose merit is every day more generally recognized, and whose memory awaits by just title an official testimonial of the sympathetic admiration which has survived him in the affectionate remembrance of all his colleagues.

Adrien Marie Legendre was born September 18, 1752, in a condition of life which left to him the credit of being indebted to his own merit for all that he might eventually become. He finished in good season, at the Collège Mazarin, those solid classical studies from which he derived a lasting taste for the literature of the ancients, the happy fruits of which are to be recognized in the elegance, the purity, and the lucid conciseness of his writings. There also he commenced the study of mathematics under a highly distinguished master, the Abbé Marie, who failed not to remark his ardor and was struck with the perspicuity of his exercises. But a little time had elapsed after his retirement from college when the judicious professor, publishing in 1774 a treatise on mechanics, thought proper to embody in it several remarkable fragments derived from his disciple. The modesty of the scholar inclined him to shrink from designation, but the Abbé felt it to be a duty to indicate to men of science the passages which had proceeded from the pen of the young Legendre, aged at that time 22 years. Among these passages is the definition of accelerative forces, distinguished by a precision and clearness of expression which seem sometimes to be among the happy privileges of youth. This definition is so natural and now so familiar to scientific minds that, when recalled, it is with difficulty conceived how it could ever have presented anything of originality and novelty. It is but just to say that it forms no exceptional feature in the work of the Abbé Marie, who in many respects was in advance of his age, and whose merit was not limited to that of having divined the talents of Legendre.

D'Alembert had said, with just foresight, that the fate of the new calculus (differential and integral) would depend on the reception it met with from the younger geometers; these therefore he sought to allure to the method in question, which was as yet imperfectly comprehended, by the degree of esteem and consideration which he accorded to such among them as evinced a capacity for following it. He was not likely long to overlook the penetrating and precocious talent which disclosed itself in the young Legendre; and scarcely had the first glimpses of genius given presage of what might be expected from the disciple of the Abbé Marie, when he was named professor of mathematics at the military school of Paris. Here from 1775 to 1780 he continued to give lessons on the scientific grounds of the military art to that ardent and intelligent body of youths from which have sprung not a few of our warlike celebrities, and whose number would have been more considerable had not circumstances forced a part of them into emigration. It may be inferred that the instruction given by the young professor embraced the first elements of *ballistics,* the art, namely, of throwing projectiles, and that he studied the learned treatises which Bezout, Borda, and other eminent men had published on these difficult problems; for when the Royal Academy of Sciences and Belles-lettres of Prussia proposed for the prize of 1782 the question of *determining the curve described by balls and shells, regard being had to the resistance of the air, and giving the rules for ascertaining the range which corresponds to different initial velocities and to different angles of projection,* M. Legendre was quite in readiness to enter into the competition. His memoir, prepared on this occasion, was crowned with success in the public meeting of June 6, 1782, and was published at Berlin under the title of *Recherches sur la trajectoire des projectiles dans les milieux résistants.*

Newton, it is stated in this memoir, was the first who made researches respecting trajectories in resisting media. He particularly considers that which takes place on the hypothesis of a resistance proportional to the simple velocity; but he gives merely approximations, and those but rough ones, for the trajectory which results when the resistance is proportional to the square of the velocity. The honor of the discovery is due to Jean Bernoulli, who published a general solution of the problem, supposing the resistance to be as any power whatever of the velocity. Long after, Euler discussed the same question in the *Memoirs of the Academy of Berlin* for the year 1753. His object was to apply the theory to ballistics, and for that he proposed very ingenious means. In the *Memoirs* of the same Academy for the year of 1765 and elsewhere we find very extended researches by Lambert with the same object. Borda in the *Memoirs* of the Academy of Sciences of Paris for the year 1769 has treated this question with his usual elegance and ingenuity. Conformably with the idea of Newton, he substitutes for the true trajectory that which would be described in virtue of a density but slightly variable, and he obtains by this means an approximation much superior to that of Newton. Lastly, Bezout, in his *Course of Artillery,* published in 1772, made a more particular application of methods of his own to the trajectory of shells and bullets.

Legendre propounds the equation of the movement of the projectile on the supposition that the resistance of the air is proportional to the square of the velocity. He integrates this equation wih elegance, and the reduction into series forms more especially the remarkable part of the memoir. Although the hypotheses which he advances on the variation of the density of the air have been modified, his calculations have remained the type of those that have been made more in detail on the supposition of a resistance proportional to the square of the velocity.

Français, professor at the schools of artillery, and General Didion have only supplied improvements to his method. But this solution of the ballistic question is simply a monument, so to speak, in the history of the science, since the necessity has been recognized of introducing, in the expression of the resistance of the air, a term proportional to the cube of the velocity. It is not the less certain, however, that by his memoir Legendre, young as he yet was, has earned for himself a distinguished place in the series of mathematicians to whom is due the superiority of the European artillery; a series which commences with Newton, in which Poisson occupies an eminent rank, and which is continued with so much éclat by the learned officers to whom we owe the actual precision of our artillery and the employment of rifled cannon.

But however seductive this first success might appear, Legendre did not continue to occupy himself with the application of science to military art, and we read at this early stage on the title page of the *Dissertation on Ballistics,* printed in 1782, the announcement that it is "by A. M. Legendre, *late* professor of mathematics in the military school at Paris." The youthful veteran, to whom perhaps the military discipline had never been particularly congenial, had decided to reserve his whole time for the study of departments of mathematics which, while not more difficult, pertain to an order of ideas generally considered as more elevated.

He had been occupied for some time with researches on the mutual attractions and forms of the planetary spheroids, and read at the Academy of Sciences of Paris, January 22, 1783, a memoir on the attraction of spheroids, for the examination of which d'Alembert and Laplace were named commissioners.

.   .   .

Legendre read to the Academy, July 4, 1784, "Researches on the Figure of Planets," in which he again discussed in a felicitous manner a subject treated by Laplace. It had been ascertained by illustrious geometers that when a planet, supposed to be fluid and homogeneous, revolves upon itself, it arrives definitively at an ellipsoidal figure, slightly flattened at the two poles of rotation, and that among the figures which may be attributed to the meridian curve, the ellipsis is one of those which satisfy the condition of equilibrium; but no one had yet discovered that the ellipsis is the only curve which can satisfy the condition. Laplace in his memoir of 1772 had said positively that he would not venture to assert that this figure was the only one which could do so; that it would be first necessary to know in finite terms the complete integral of the differential equation of the problem, and that he had not yet been able to obtain it. This Legendre accomplished by availing himself of the ingenious analysis of his memoir on the attraction of the spheroids, and he concludes that if a planet in equilibrium be supposed to have the figure of a solid of revolution little different from a sphere, and divided into two equal parts by its equator, the meridian of that planet will necessarily be elliptical.

.   .   .

In the course of his memoir Legendre finds that the terrestrial spheroid, which is in equilibrium when the axes are in the ratio of 230 to 231, may still be so if the axes be supposed in the ratio of 1 to 681, which affords quite a strange figure, but one which recalls the ring of Saturn. He adds that d'Alembert was the first to remark that there might be several elliptical spheroids which would comport with equilibrium. We see by these different examples what emulation existed among those fine intellects d'Alembert, Lagrange, Laplace, Legendre; with what rapidity their labors succeeded while they mutually completed one another. It may further be remarked that Legendre supposes only in an implicit manner that the spheroid is one of revolution. The equation found by him is that of the meridian curve, and his analysis is in no respect contradicted by the discovery, as curious as it was unexpected, made in our time almost simultaneously by Liouville and Jacobi, that the planetary ellipsoid may have its three axes unequal, and that the equator may itself be an ellipse.

Legendre subsequently resumed the questions treated in these first and memorable memoirs, particularly in 1790, in the sequel of his researches on the figure of the planets; in 1789 in a memoir on double integrals, in which he completes the analysis of his memoir on the attraction of spheroids; and still later in a memoir read to the Academy in 1812. After having pointed out in this last the improvements contributed to his preceding labors on this subject by Biot, who had conceived the happy idea of applying thereto an integral given by Lagrange for another object, Legendre avails himself of the substitution discovered by Ivory to present the entire theory of the attraction of homogeneous ellipsoids with all the simplicity of which it is susceptible. But these important labors were far from entirely absorbing Legendre's attention, and the varied nature of the memoirs which he presented in great frequency to the Academy, to a mere enumeration of which I must here confine myself, evinced the extent of his knowledge and the surprising fecundity of his genius.

In 1785 he read to the Academy a masterly memoir entitled "Researches on Indeterminate Analysis," which includes numerous propositions on the theory of numbers, and especially the celebrated *theorem of reciprocity* known under the name of the *law of Legendre;* in 1786 a memoir on the manner of distinguishing *maxima* from *minima* in the calculation of variations; also, two memoirs on integrations of arcs of the ellipsis, and on the comparison of these arcs, memoirs which contain the first rudiments of his *theory of elliptical functions;* in 1787 a memoir on the integration of certain equations with partial differences. By a simple change of variables he arrives rigorously at the integral of an equation which Monge had only integrated by a process depending on certain metaphysical principles about which there still existed some doubts. By proving that the integral was exact Legendre contributed to corroborate the reputation of the illustrious author of the application of analysis to geometry, whose name also is one of the characteristic glories of the French mathematical school. In this same memoir he gives by his method the integrals of several classes of equations with partial differences of superior orders; then, very happily extending an idea of Lagrange for the integration of non-linear equations of the first order, he distinguishes therein six cases of integrability which they may present. Again, in 1790 he read a memoir on the *particular integrals* of differential equations, of which he modestly says that the principle and demonstration are only consequences very easily to be deduced from the theory which Lagrange had given in the *Memoirs* of the Academy of Berlin for 1774. He establishes that particular integrals are always comprised in a finite expression in which the number of arbitrary constants is less than in the complete integral, thus preparing the way for the definitive labors which Poisson has since made public on this subject.

But at this epoch Legendre was already engaged in another series of researches which occupied him at intervals for a great number of years, and in which his labors were fertile in important results.

In 1787, some doubts having been raised upon the respective position of the observatories of Paris and Greenwich, it was decided to connect the meridians by a chain of triangles which should extend from one point to the other. The Academy of Sciences confided to three of its members, Cassini, Mechain, and Legendre, the execution of this operation, in concert with Major General Roy and several other English savants. These important labors were accordingly performed with all the exactness which the state of science then permitted—by the help of an excellent quadrant prepared by the celebrated English artist Ramsden, and the repeating circle constructed by Lenoir upon the principles of Borda. Legendre calculated all the triangles situated in France and afterwards those also which extended in England as far as Greenwich. On this occasion he went to London, where he was received with the distinction due to him and was named member of the Royal Society of London. He published at this time in the *Memoirs* of the Academy for the year 1787 (printed in 1789) an important paper entitled, "Memoir on the Trigonometrical Operations of which the Results Depend on the Figure of the Earth. "Of this he has himself explained the object in terms which I take the liberty of abridging:

The only question here is that which regards operations exacting extreme precision, such as the measurement of the degrees of the meridian or of a parallel, and the geographical determination of the principal points of a large area from the triangles which connect them. Operations of this kind may be carried henceforward to a great degree of precision by means of the repeating circle. In effect, the use which we have made of this instrument, in 1787, has convinced us that it can give each angle of a triangle to about two seconds, or even more exactly, if all circumstances are favorable. It is further necessary that the calculations established on such data should not be inferior to the latter in exactness; especially is it requisite to take account of the reduction to the horizon, which amounts quite often to several seconds; and thence arise triangles of infinitely small curvature, the calculation of which demands special rules; for, by considering them as rectilinear, we should neglect the small excess of the sum of the three angles over 180°, and by considering them as spherical, the sides would be changed into very small arcs, the calculation of which by the common tables would be neither exact nor commodious.

I have assembled in this memoir [continues Legendre] the necessary formulas, as well for the reduction and calculation of these sorts of triangles, as for what relates to the position of the different points of a chain of triangles on the surface of the spheroid. In these calculations [he adds] there are some elements susceptible of a slight uncertainty. . . . In order that the calculation need be made but once, and to judge at a glance of the influence of errors, I have supposed the value of each principal element to be augmented by an indeterminate quantity which denotes the correction of it. These literal quantities, which are to be regarded as very small, do not prevent the calculation from being proceeded with by logarithms in the usual manner.

This was an important addition to the methods of calculation employed till then, and still later he further added the *method of least squares.* He gives in this memoir formulas for the reduction of an angle to the horizon, as also for other determinations, and especially the important theorem known under the name of the *theorem of Legendre,* through which the calculation of a spherical triangle of small extent is reduced to that of a rectilinear triangle, by subtracting from each of the three angles the third of the spherical excess of their sum, that is to say the inconsiderable quantity by which this exceeds 180°. Legendre subsequently demonstrated that this fundamental theorem is applicable also to spheroidal triangles, whether traced on an ellipsoid of revolution or even on a spheroid slightly irregular.

He also occupies himself in the same memoir with the value of the degrees of the meridian in the elliptical spheroid and with with the determination of the respective position of different places deduced from the nature of the shortest line which can be traced on the surface of this spheroid from one extremity to the other of the chain of triangles and from the intersections of that line with the different sides of the triangles or with their prolongations. This line, which Legendre at different times and always with success made the object of his researches, bears the name of the *geodesic line;* on the regular ellipsoid it is of double curvature, unless it coincides with a meridian. Finally, he occupies himself with the operations which have for their object the measurement of the degrees of the meridian and concludes with some theoretical and practical reflections on the use of the repeating circle of Borda in the delicate operations which relate to that object.

These reflections were judicious; but at the moment of recording them Legendre, struck with the progress which the construction of instruments had recently made, did not foresee those improvements which it was even then on the point of receiving. They were such that at the end of 30 years the operations of 1787 were found to be inferior in the measurement of angles and bases, the observation of night-signals, etc., to those generally executed in this way. Hence it resulted that the geodesic connection of Dunkirk and Greenwich had to be redetermined in 1817. This new undertaking was confided to Arago and Mathieu, associated with Captain Kater and other English savants. What remained and will always remain of the operations of 1787 are the formulas and theorems which it furnished Legendre the occasion of establishing, and which in the sequel he still further developed and improved.

His memoir was written in the anticipation of new and more extended applications; for the project already existed of resuming the measurement of the meridian which traverses France from north to south, and which had been once measured, in 1739 and 1740, in the great and admirable geodesic operation which had supplied the basis of the chart of Cassini. The National Assembly, in fact, having adopted the plan of establishing a new system of weights and measures for all France, a report was made to the Academy of Sciences, March 19, 1791, by Borda, Lagrange, Laplace, Monge, and Condorcet, on the choice of a unit of measure. The report, after a profound discussion of the subject, proposed to take as the unit of measure the *metre,* representing the ten-millionth part of a quarter of the meridian, calculated from the measured length of the arc comprised between Dunkirk and Barcelona. It proposed at the same time the execution of different preliminary operations, one of the most important of which was the verification, by new observations, of the series of triangles employed for the measurement of the meridian of Cassini and its prolongation to Barcelona.

It was afterwards agreed that Cassini, Mechain, and Legendre, the same who had connected the meridian of Paris with that of Greenwich, should be charged with this new operation. Yet Legendre is not comprised in the number of the 12 commissioners nominated (April 17, 1795) to conduct all the labors necessary for fixing the bases of the metrical system. These commissioners designated from their own number Mechain and Delambre * to execute the measurement of the angles, the astronomical observations, and the measurement of the dependent bases of the meridian, and it was they in effect who in very difficult times had the merit of

* See Joseph Fourier, "Memoir of Delambre," *A.R.,* 1864, pp. 125–134.

executing this vast operation with means often greatly restricted; yet a few years afterwards we find Legendre among the members of the mixed commission, formed of a union of French and foreign savants, to which the duty of examining and verifying the whole work was entrusted. All the triangles were separately calculated by four persons, Trallés, Van Swinden, Legendre and Delambre, each employing the method he preferred, and the results were only admitted when there was a satisfactory agreement between the four calculations. Legendre signed with the other commissioners the report made to the National Institute, June 17, 1799, on the basis of the metrical system, and he continued to take part in all the ulterior calculations and the different verifications rendered necessary by certain discordances which had been remarked and by some doubts which had arisen on the exactness of several parts of the operation. The method he followed was that of which he had established the basis in his memoir of 1787. In applying it on so extensive a scale he improved and developed it and gave a large number of new theorems leading to more rapid reductions, to more convenient formulas. He read to the first class of the Institute, March 3, 1806, a new memoir entitled, "Analysis of Triangles Traced on the Surface of a Spheroid," in which he considers the triangles as no longer described on the sphere, but on a spheroid. He inquires and demonstrates the properties of the shortest lines traced on its surface; extends and thus generalizes the numerous applications of the theorem which bears his name and, reviewing the principal operations offered by geodesy, gives the most complete analysis of them. He concludes that there can remain no doubt of the exactness of the calculation of the triangles from which the distance of the parallels between Dunkirk and Montjouy, near Barcelona, has been computed, as well as the length of the metre; but he considers it beyond question that the results deduced from different chains of triangles do not always exactly accord among themselves, on account of certain anomalies in the latitudes and azimuths which may be due to local attractions.

At this epoch, in 1805, Legendre had just published, in the sequel of his new methods for the determination of the orbits of comets, an appendix on the *method of least squares*. Here he proposed that method which has generally been adopted for deriving from the measures yielded by observation the most exact results which they are susceptible of furnishing. Laplace has since demonstrated that it is the most advantageous of which we can make use in practice. Legendre, after having developed it, made an immediate application of it to the measurement of the degrees of the meridian of France, and he concluded, as in the geodesic memoir, that the anomalies in the latitudes ought not to be attributed to the observations, and that they pertain probably to local attractions which act irregularly on the plumb line. Gauss in 1809 seems to have thought for the moment that he had rights of priority to the invention of the *method of least squares;* but if it cannot be contested that so eminent a savant may have had the same idea with Legendre, and may even have applied it in his labors, it is certain that Legendre had on his part discovered the method and was the first who published it.

Legendre continued henceforth to make part of the commission of weights and measures; but though his labors of 1787 had rendered his co-operation indispensable in the great enterprise which that commission was charged with conducting to a successful issue, there was a period during which, as we have said, he ceased to be officially attached to it: this was under the reign of terror. Like most of the savants of his epoch, he was favorable to the ideas which have become the basis of modern society; but he remained a stranger to the excesses which imbrued the Revolution in blood. Perhaps, indeed, his caustic turn had not wholly spared its authors; certain it is that during the violence of the storm he was forced to hide himself. It was one of the most happy incidents of his life; for, in the retreat which he found in Paris itself, he formed the acquaintance of a young and engaging female, Marguerite-Claudine Couhin, whom he espoused shortly afterwards, and who constituted his happiness during 40 years. Much younger than her husband, she bore no inefficient part in his great labors by the tranquillity, the assiduous attentions, the watchful solicitude, with which she environed him, proving herself, in all circumstances, a model of discretion, grace, and amiability.

The revolutionary turbulence, however, did not interrupt the labors of Legendre. In the year II of the republic, toward the end of 1793, he published a new memoir on *elliptical transcendents,* forming a quarto volume of more than 100 pages; but in the quietude of his happy retreat he turned his thoughts to other subjects. The former professor of mathematics in the military school began anew to occupy himself with the *Elements of Geometry.* The first edition of his work under this title, a work written with elegant simplicity, and in which all the propositions are disposed in a natural and methodical order, appeared in 1794. The author, modelling himself upon Euclid, remands the science to the severity of the Greek school. In this, without perhaps designing it, he accommodated himself to the spirit of his epoch. Architecture, abandoning the distorted forms of the reign of Louis XV, was returning, more and more, to the elegant simplicity of the Greek style. A few years previous our great painter, David, had inaugurated, by his picture of the *Horatii,* a complete revolution in painting, which, after his example, reverted likewise to the imitation of the ancients.

The work attained at once the first rank among classical books. In less than 30 years fourteen editions were published, of which the last has undergone a large number of impressions: more than 100,000 copies of it have been sold in France alone. Legendre's *Elements of Geometry* has been reproduced in the principal languages of Europe, and has even been translated into Arabic for the schools established in Egypt by the viceroy, Mehémet-Ali. The author, prepossessed with the method of Euclid, has perhaps somewhat unduly availed himself of the *reductio ad absurdum,* which might often be replaced by more facile demonstrations; but his work has served to excite a sort of vigorous intellectual gymnastics by which mathematical studies have been invigorated, and its influence has been undoubtedly salutary. Among other things, Legendre here demonstrates in a novel manner the equality of volume of two symmetrical polyhedrons formed of equal plane faces, adjusted under the same angles, but with an inverse arrangement which does not admit of their being superposed. The first editions did not contain the excellent treatise on trigonometry which the author has added to subsequent ones. He has also enriched these with notes, in which he treats analytically certain parts of geometry on a new system, as where he demonstrates that the ratios of the circumference to the diameter and to its square are irrational numbers.

The ratio of the circumference to the diameter, being an irrational number, is not susceptible of being exactly expressed by any fraction, however great the whole numbers which form the numerator and denominator. Hence results the *impossibility* of ever finding the quadrature of the circle, and it was in consequence of a proposition of Legendre, based on this demonstrated impossibility that the Academy renounced all further attention to a problem the importance of which is in some sort axiomatic among persons little versed in mathematics. But whatever might be the success of his *Elements,* Legendre did not question the feasibility of using other methods with success, and himself contributed in 1802 to the publication of a new edition of Clairaut's *Elements of Geometry,* to which he added notes derived probably from his memoranda of the military school. Geometry is further indebted to him for a method, directly demonstrated by himself, of inscribing in the circle a regular polygon of 17 sides. Algebra, properly so called, owes to him, among other things, two different methods for the solution of numerical equations, methods which make known with much rapidity all the roots, whether real or imaginary, of those equations.

So highly was Legendre appreciated as a skillful calculator, that rarely was any great series of numerical operations undertaken in France without recourse being had to his services. In 1787 he had been called to take part in the commission charged with connecting trigonometrically Dunkirk and Greenwich. For the same reason M. de Prony, placed in the year II (1794) at the head of the *cadastre* (registry of the survey of lands), did not deem it expedient to dispense with his services. The decimal division of the circle, then regarded as a necessary complement of the metrical system, required new trigonometrical tables. M. de Prony caused them to be constructed with incredible celerity by means of the division of labor and by processes wholly new, which admitted of the employment of arithmeticians of even the most indifferent qualifications. The work was prepared by a section of analysts over which presided Legendre, who contributed greatly to facilitate the operation by devising new and ingenious formulas for determining the successive differences of the sinus. For the other sections it only remained to make the additions. The labors of this board of calculation produced two copies of tables entirely independent one of the other, and affording by their identity a mutual verification. This monument of labor and skill, the most vast of its kind which has ever been executed or even conceived, has no other defect, said Delambre, but its *very immensity,* which has so long delayed its publication.

When the revolutionary tempest had begun to subside, one of the first cares of government was to reorganize public instruction; but Legendre, whether he was not in favor with the men in power or for whatever other reason, was not invited to co-operate. His name does not figure either at the close of 1794 among those of the first professors of the   polytechnic school, or in January 1795 in the list of the professors of the normal schools; nor yet was he comprised among the 48 savants whom the government selected to form the nucleus of the Institute; but at the earliest opportunity his colleagues hastened to redress this injustice by summoning him to their ranks. It will not be amiss to recall here the succession of events as facts not destitute of historical interest.

The Academy of Sciences having been suppressed by a decree of the convention of the 8th of August, 1793, the National Institute, of which the first class represented that Academy, was established by a law of the 5 fructidor, year III (August 22, 1795), and was organized by a second law of the 3 brumaire, year IV (October 25, 1795). By the ninth article of this law it was enacted that "for the formation of the National Institute, the Executive Directory shall nominate 48 members, who shall elect 96 others." To form the nucleus of the first class of the Institute, 20 members were accordingly nominated by the directory, December 6, 1795, being two for each section; those for the section of mathematics were Lagrange and Laplace. Two other members, Borda and Bossut, were elected in the meeting of the 9th of December, and the section, which was to be composed of six members, was completed on the 13th of the same month by the election of Legendre and Delambre. In this list Bossut appeared by just title for his labors in hydraulics; Borda and Delambre were included with not less right for their important services in relation to geodesy, to measures of precision and astronomical calculations; Lagrange, Laplace, and Legendre were essentially the representatives of the higher analysis and occupied during life the foremost place among the geometers of the Institute. All three continued till death to justify this proud position by labors worthy of themselves and of the illustrious body to which it was their pleasure as well as duty to communicate them.

In 1805 Legendre published new methods for the determination of the orbits of comets, to which he added, in 1806 and 1820, two supplements; in the latter stages of life he had collected the most recent observations on comets of short periods, in the design of still further applying and improving his processes of calculation. Previous to the publication of his first two memoirs in 1805 and 1806, the question had in his opinion been always treated in an imperfect manner and merely by approximations. He considered himself as having first indicated two certain modes of arriving at a solution, at once the most simple and exact, namely, *the method of indeterminate corrections,* proposed by him as early as 1787, but the applications of which had been few in number, and the *method of least squares,* which then appeared for the first time. Nevertheless, this analytic perfection, to which the author sought to add as often as he retouched his formulas, has seemed to astronomers to be more than counterbalanced by the length of the calculations and by other inconveniences. They prefer employing the methods of Olbers and Gauss, which, while giving perhaps a less certain approximation, furnish it in all cases more rapidly. In 1806 Legendre further published, in the *Memoirs* of the Institute, a new formula for reducing to true distances the apparent distances from the moon to the sun or to a star. Its object was to simplify and accelerate the labors of practical astronomers. These last publications were in some sort excursions made by the indefatigable author beyond the habitual sphere of his researches, and, seeing with what promptness and facility Legendre thus passed from one subject to another, it might be thought that he was completely at liberty in the employment of his time. He found means, however, in the midst of his purely scientific labors to reconcile with the duties of the academician those of several important functions.

Some time after the creation of the Polytechnic School, the former laureate of the ballistic competition was appointed examiner in mathematics for the graduating students destined for the artillery, and he continued to fulfill these honorable and delicate functions till 1815, when he voluntarily withdrew and was replaced by M. de Prony. From the creation of the university in 1808 Legendre was of its council. At the death of Lagrange in 1812 he was chosen to succeed him at the Bureau of Longitudes, in position of geometer. He thus took his place by the side of Laplace, whom he had replaced in 1783 as adjunct member of the Academy of Sciences, when the illustrious author of the *Mécanique Céleste* became an associate member. Thus, at an interval of 2 years and under circumstances assuredly very different, no one was found in France who by his scientific merit could more naturally be called than Legendre to replace Laplace or Lagrange. That he owed to his merit alone a choice so honorable for himself and those who made it may be gathered from a slight anecdote which is related of him. Having, from the creation of the Legion of Honor, been inscribed in the number of its chevaliers, though he failed not to record this testimony to his merit in the title-page of his works, his natural modesty, we are told, long prevented him from attaching the red riband to his buttonhole. Legendre continued, moreover, as has been already said, to form part of the commission of weights and measures as long as it existed, and more than once was a member of other commissions charged with objects of importance.

Yet independently of these numerous occupations and varied labors, all impressed with a peculiar character of vigor and precision, by which he bore a large part in the scientific movement of his epoch, Legendre had besides certain *household gods,* to which he sacrificed with ever renewed pleasure in the silence of his closet. I mean the *theory of numbers* and the *elliptical functions.* To these he consecrated during the latter 50 years of his life all the leisure left him by his daily occupations and more conspicuous labors. He has thus reared two monuments which by their extent represent, no doubt, the better part of his time, and which, though having had few readers and capable of having but very few judges, will prove perhaps in the eye of posterity two of his principal titles to renown.

The *Theory of Numbers* appeared in 1830 in two quarto volumes, after being preceded at divers intervals by preliminary publications. Legendre says, in the advertisement:

The work having received all the improvements which the author has been able to bestow upon it, as well through his own labors as those of other geometers of which he could avail himself, it has been thought proper to give it definitively the title of *Theory of Numbers,* in place of that of an *Essay* on the subject which it has heretofore borne.

The *Essay on the Theory of Numbers* had passed through two editions, one in 1798, the other in 1808; this last had been followed by two supplements. The *Essay* had itself been preceded by a considerable work published in the *Memoirs* of the Academy for 1785, and entitled *Recherches d'analyse indéterminée,* which relates principally to the study of the properties of numbers. In fine, we learn from the manuscript proceedings of the Academy before cited that among the memoirs which Laplace in the session of March 15, 1783, indicated as having been presented by Legendre, occur two memoirs on the resolution of indeterminate equations of the second degree and on the properties of continual fractions, and a memoir on the summation of these fractions. Now, from the objects of which they treat, and indeed from the titles alone, these memoirs bear a very natural relation to certain paragraphs of the great memoir of 1785. They were probably the first rudiments of it. Hence we see that Legendre had been occupied with the theory of numbers from his youth. He had labored upon it for more than 50 years. Yet he concludes the advertisement of the *Theory of Numbers,* dated April 1, 1830, with the following words, which are certainly modest enough:

We shall not pretend that certain matters treated of in this work do not need to be improved or even rectified by new researches. Nevertheless, the author has thought that it would be better to leave them in this state of imperfection than to suppress them altogether; they will offer a subject of investigation to those who may be disposed in the future to occupy themselves with the advancement of the science.

This part of the science has received in fact, since the publication of the *Theory of Numbers,* important accessions; but if we compare the contents of this learned work with what had been discovered during the 2,000 years which preceded 1785, we shall see that no savant has marked his passage in this branch of mathematics by traces in any degree comparable to these efforts of Legendre. It cannot surprise us that a science which had advanced with but slow and progressive steps under the hands of men as eminent as Euclid and Diophantus among the ancients, as Viète, Bachet, Fermat, Euler, and Lagrange among the moderns, should not all at once have been carried to a point which comported with no further progress. It behooves us, on the contrary, candidly to avow that Legendre, in speaking of new developments which still awaited it, gave proof of perspicuity almost as much as of modesty.

The science of numbers is difficult, and it is above all difficult to convey an idea of it to persons whose attention has never been occupied with it. Everyone knows that numbers are distinguished into two great classes: even and odd numbers, which alternately succeed one another. The even numbers are divisible by 2, while the odd numbers are not, though they have often other divisors. Whole numbers differ much from one another in the possibility of being divided by other and smaller integers. It has been long ago remarked that the number 10, the basis of our decimal system, has but two divisors, 2 and 5, the last of which is not subdivisible, while the number 8 has two divisors, 2 and 4, of which the last is further subdivisible by 2, and the number 12 has three divisors, 2, 3, and 4, the last of which is again subdivisible by 2; whence it follows that the number 8 and especially the number 12 have, as the basis of a system of measures susceptible of being successively subdivided, an incontestable superiority over the number 10. This inferiority of the latter number is one of the obstacles to the general adoption of the decimal system of weights and measures, which presents in other respects such great advantages.

But the number 10 is more favored in this regard than the number 9, divisible only by 3, of which it is the square. It is still more so than the numbers 3, 5, 7, 11, 13, 17, which have no divisors, or, to speak the language of science, have no other divisors but themselves and unity. Number 7, which enumerates the seven days of the week, the seven wonders of the world, the seven sages of Greece, passes for possessing a certain degree of excellence; but number 13, as well as 17, is looked upon as inauspicious, by reason, it may be, of this absence of divisors which renders both numbers refractory. All those numbers which have no other divisors but themselves and unity are called *prime numbers*. There are prime numbers of all magnitudes, but when the numbers are somewhat great it is not easy to discover immediately whether they are prime or not. The prime numbers are distributed among the odd numbers with an apparent irregularity which is yet subject to certain laws. The search for them, the determination of the quantities of them which exist in a given interval of the numeric scale, form one of the objects of the theory of numbers.

Numbers may be ranged by series in each of which may be remarked the constant existence of certain properties. Such are the triangular numbers 1, 3, 6, 10, 15, etc., each expressing a number of units which may be arranged triangularly; the quadratic numbers 1, 4, 9, 16, 25, which in the same way correspond to the square; polygonal numbers, pyramidal, etc.; and these series give rise to combinations more or less curious. Certain numbers are the squares of other smaller ones, as 4 the square of 2, 9 of 3, etc.; others, as 8, 13, 18, are the sum of two squares; others again, like 17 for example, are the sum of three squares. Lagrange and Euler have proved that *there is no number which is not the sum of four or of a less number of squares*.

These properties and many others are at once remarked in examples taken among numbers of little amount, and it becomes a matter of curiosity to follow them among the larger numbers in order to learn whether they are general or not. Hence proceed researches which are often very difficult and provoke a lively interest. The final conclusion evades detection so much the longer from the circumstance that frequently there exists as yet in science no rule for seeking it. It is a prey which for a long time eludes the pursuit of the hunter. Again, there are certain properties of numbers which come to light unexpectedly in their combinations, and which, presenting something enigmatical and surprising, have been often held to pertain to the mysterious. Hence the virtues which necromancers have pretended that they detected in cabalistic numbers, virtues which are to the theory of numbers not unlike what astrology is to astronomy.

·   ·   ·

The first researches of Legendre on numbers, contained in his distinguished memoir of 1785, constituted a direct sequel to those of Euler and Lagrange which they extended and developed in several important particulars; but Legendre embodied also in this work many discoveries entirely new, and particularly the *theorem of reciprocity,* known likewise under the name of the *law of Legendre,* one of the most fertile laws of the theory of numbers. This theorem, more readily expressed in algebraic than ordinary language, consists in this: two prime numbers m and n being given, if m be raised to the power n minus 1 divided by 2 and the result be divided by n, then n to the power m minus 1 divided by 2, and the result be divided by m, the remainders of the two divisions, which are always capable of being expressed by plus 1 or minus 1, will both be of the same sign, or else of the contrary sign, in certain determinate cases—a result which has found and continues to find numerous applications in researches relating to the properties of numbers.

Legendre, in reproducing in successive editions of the *Theory of Numbers* the demonstration of this theorem as he had given it in 1785, discovered that in a determinate case it presents a lacuna, without the theorem itself having been ever found in default. Gauss, who by his *Disquisitiones Arithmeticæ,* published in 1801, had placed himself in the first rank of the savants who have dealt with the theory of numbers, gave a demonstration of the theorem of reciprocity which left nothing further to be desired. Legendre reproduced this demonstration in his *Theory of Numbers* in 1830, observing that it is the more remarkable as resting on the most elementary principles, and at the same time gave another yet more simple, proposed by Jacobi. Still later, Liouville and other eminent geometers have given other demonstrations of the same law. The exactness of the *law of Legendre* is therefore more than sufficiently demonstrated; but here the inventor has left to those who have followed him the privilege of *completing* his discovery.

But if Legendre took delight, like Euler, in the combinations, so arduous in appearance, of the theory of numbers, like Euler he excelled also in the research of the integrals of differential quantities, a research which is itself not directed by any certain rule, and in which the inquirer is conducted to the result only by a certain intuitive prevision of the combinations and reductions which will be available in the formulas and figures. The finest integrals appear often to have been found by chance; but these chances, as Legendre said in speaking of Euler, *never occur to any but those who know how to create them.* This remark, insufficient doubtless to make us comprehend how a differential expression is integrated, will enable us perhaps to conceive how the mind may be stimulated to this pursuit, as to that of the properties of numbers, and how these two kinds of research, which seem to call into play analogous faculties, were the two dominant passions of Euler and Legendre.

A differential quantity given by a problem of geometry, mechanics, or physics does not always correspond to an analytic expression existing in the science, and in order not to leave certain problems without solution it becomes an object to enrich analysis with new functions. After having exhausted expressions purely algebraic, we succeed in integrating a great number of differentials by means of arcs of the circle and of logarithms which are the most simple of transcendent quantities; but in order to extend still further the applications of the integral calculus, it was necessary to have recourse to transcendents of a more composite order. Euler thought that instead of being limited to the circle, other curves of the second degree, especially the ellipsis and hyperbola, might be considered, and that tables analogous to the tables of logarithms and to those of circular functions might be drawn up in reference to them. By one of those happy combinations, which seem almost fortuitous, he found under a purely algebraic form the complete integral of a differential equation composed of two separate but similar terms, each of which is only integrable by arcs of conic sections. This important discovery led the illustrious geometer to compare, in a manner more general than had been done before, not only the arcs of the same ellipsis or the same hyperbola, but in general all the transcendents of which the differential approximates to those of these two curves, in presenting, like them, a rational algebraic function of the variable divided by the square root of an algebraic polynome of the fourth degree. One of the results of this comparison was that the integration by arcs of the hyperbola may always be reduced to integration by arcs of the ellipsis. From this time Euler foresaw that by means of a suitable notation the calculation of arcs of the ellipsis and other analogous transcendents might become of almost as general use as that of arcs of the circle and of logarithms; but with the exception of the English geometer Landen, who demonstrated in a memoir of 1775 that *every arc of the hyberbola is immediately rectified by means of two arcs of the ellipsis,* no one but Legendre recognized the importance of realizing the prevision of Euler; and it may be said that our learned colleague alone occupied himself with this subject from the year 1786, when he published his first researches on integrations by arcs of the ellipsis, until the year 1825, when his *Treatise of Elliptic Functions* appeared.

Arcs of the ellipsis, being after arcs of the circle and logarithms one of the most simple transcendents, might become in some sort a new instrument of calculation, if we were once familiarized with their properties and possessed ready means of calculating them with precision. Legendre applied himself to this important subject in two memoirs inserted in the volume of the Academy of Sciences for 1786. In both of them the author demonstrates by means peculiar to himself that the rectification of the hyperbola depends on that of the ellipsis and presents no special transcendent, and in the second he shows that in an infinite series of ellipses formed after the same law we can reduce the rectification of one of these ellipses to that of two others taken at choice in the same series. This, he says with characteristic modesty, is one step more in a difficult path.

In the first memoir Legendre gives convergent series adapted for the easy calculation of the length of an arc of an ellipsis, whether in the case in which the ellipsis but slightly eccentric approximates to a circle, or in that when, greatly elongated, it recedes but little from its greater axis; and in the second he adds:

If the zeal of calculators could furnish us with tables of arcs of the ellipsis for different degrees of amplitude and eccentricity, and each arc were accompanied by the coefficient of its partial difference, we should have the means of integrating by these tables a very large number of differentials, and especially all those which d'Alembert and Euler have referred to the arcs of conic sections.

Legendre had then attained the age of 34 years; he knew not that it would be permitted him to labor till that of 80 years and that unassisted he would himself accomplish the task of which he here traces the program. In the course of these two memoirs, and particularly toward the end of the second, he indulges himself in a just tribute of praise to the learned geometers (Euler, Landen, and Fagnani) who before himself had demonstrated in a different manner a part of the theorems with which they are filled to profusion. But in the publications of 1786, remarkable as they were, these rich materials hardly yet formed a completed edifice, and Legendre was not long in perceiving that this subject and in general the theory of transcendents whose differential enters into the form above indicated, required to be treated in a manner more methodical and thorough. This he undertook to do in a *Mémoire sur les transcendentes elliptiques,* read by him to the Academy of Sciences in April 1792, and published toward the end of 1793, in which he proposed to compare among themselves all the transcendents in question, to class them according to their different kinds, to reduce each of them to the most simple form of which it is susceptible, to estimate their value by approximations the most prompt and facile; and, in fine, to form from the collective theory a sort of algorism which should serve to extend the domain of analysis.

Taking in its most general algebraic form the differential already indicated as a point of departure for this kind of researches, he analyzes it with extraordinary address, lays aside all the parts which are integrable, whether by arcs of the circle or logarithms, and thus reduces it to its quintessence; that is to say, to the parts whose integrals are transcendents of a superior order. Then, transforming this remainder by means of circular functions, he reduces it to a form of wonderful simplicity, containing but five quantities: an arc of the circle designated by the name of *amplitude,* null at the point where the integral commences, and developing itself in proportion as that is extended; a *modulus* always real and smaller than the unit, which, in the case when an ellipsis is in question, represents its eccentricity; a *parameter* of any magnitude, positive or negative, capable of being reduced to zero but to which it would be useless to attribute imaginary values; lastly, two coefficients whose values, independent of all the rest, may be anything, provided they be not null simultaneously. The amplitude is the variable in relation to which the integration is made; it is null only at the point of departure from the integral. The modulus cannot be null without the expression being completely altered in its nature, but the three other quantities may be null independently of one another, or fulfill in their relations of magnitude certain conditions according to which elliptic transcendents are divided into three classes.

The second class is the only one which represents arcs of the ellipsis. The first class is a transcendent more simple than arcs of the ellipsis; it may itself be expressed by means of such arcs, but an arc of the ellipsis cannot be expressed by transcendents of this first class. The third class, on the contrary, the only one in which the parameter is not null, is more composite than arcs of the ellipsis. The gradation which exists in the complexity of these three classes of transcendents is manifested especially by this circumstance, that transcendents of the first species may be joined with one another, by addition and subtraction, so as to form a sum constantly null. Transcendents of the second species may unite in like manner, so as to form a sum whose value is expressed in terms purely algebraic, like the celebrated integral of Euler before referred to. Lastly, transcendents of the third species may also be united to form a sum of which the value, without being null or even algebraic, is notwithstanding of a more simple nature than each of the former in itself; for it may be expressed by arcs of the circle and logarithms, which are the most simple of transcendents. These differences and several others which exist between the three species of *elliptical transcendents* suffice to vindicate the division established by Legendre; but at the same time they do not prevent our perceiving a profound analogy between all these transcendents which justifies their union under the same denomination. The first and second species may be expressed by arcs of the ellipsis; the third is the most compounded, but it has so much analogy with the two others that all three may be regarded as forming but one and the same order of transcendents, the first after arcs of the circle and logarithms. As Legendre elsewhere says, "the denomination of *elliptic function* is improper in some respects; but we nevertheless adopt it on account of the great analogy which exists between the properties of this function and those of arcs of the ellipsis."

Legendre resumed these questions with several others in a great work in three quarto volumes which he published in 1811, 1816, and 1817, under the title of *Exercises de calcul intégral sur divers orders de transcendantes et sur les quadratures.* In this work, part of which was devoted to two classes of definite integrals to which the author has given the name of *intégrales eulériennes,* he occupied himself also with a great number of questions about the integral calculus, into the details of which it would be difficult here to enter; but the most extensive and in his eyes the most important part was that which treats of elliptic functions, of their application to different problems of geometry and mechanics, and the tables necessary for the use of those functions. Finally, in 1825 and 1826 he combined anew all his results, with the developments and improvements which incessant labor had enabled him to supply, in a work entitled *Théorie des fonctions elliptiques.* This first appeared in two volumes, followed at a later period by three supplements, which constitute the third and last volume.

Among the improvements which Legendre bestowed on his previous labors when he published them anew in 1825, one of the principal was the discovery of a second scale of *modules,* different from that which alone was known at the time of the publication of the exercises on the integral calculus. "This second scale," as he remarks in the 31st chapter of the first volume, "completed in many respects the labors of the author upon this theory; it afforded an easy method of arriving at many striking results of analysis which till then it had been impracticable to demonstrate except by very laborious integrations. By the combination of the two scales the transformations of functions of the first species could be prodigiously multiplied; this the author has made evident by constructing a sort of tessellated table (*damier*) infinite in its two dimensions, all the divisions of which might be filled by the different transformations of which one and the same function is susceptible."

The development of the properties and uses of elliptical functions, considered with this generality, composed the whole first volume of the publication of 1825. The second was devoted in part to tables intended to facilitate the conversion of the integrals obtained into numerals. Calculated by the author himself with the greatest precision, these tables constituted in themselves an immense labor. "By means of them," said Legendre, "the theory of *elliptical* functions, enlarged and nearly completed by many successive labors, might be applied with almost as much facility as those of circular and logarithmic functions, answerably to the wishes and hopes of Euler." After the developments which the theory of elliptical functions had received by the discovery of the second scale of modules, further progress seemed scarcely probable; but the fecundity of the methods created by Legendre was such that results which he had hardly ventured to anticipate were very soon realized.* . . .

I might still further speak of important labors published by Legendre on the *integrals,* styled by him *eulerian,* from the name of Euler, who had first occupied himself with them, labors which occupy a large space in his exercises on the integral calculus, and which he partially introduced, while he improved on them in the second volume of his theory of elliptical functions. I might also show how, parallel with the employment of *elliptic transcendents,* he opened the way to the numerical realization of a vast class of integrals by the tables which he has given for calculating the new transcendent, designated by him under the name of the function *grand gamma;* but although Binet has shown that the labors accessory to those which Legendre has given to the public on these subjects alone would constitute no inconsiderable title for a distinguished geometer, I should fear to weary the attention of my auditors by dwelling at greater length on topics of this nature.

* Several paragraphs omitted from this memoir contain Legendre's generous tributes to two geometers, Jacobi and Abel, who worked on the theory of elliptic functions.

Like Euler, his model, and like many other great geometers who preceded him, Legendre prosecuted his labors to the last without having to regret any enfeeblement of his faculties; the volume of our memoirs, which immediately preceded his death, contains one of his studies upon a difficult question of the theory of numbers. He was then 80 years of age. So vigorous an organization could scarcely be broken up without great suffering. The malady which terminated the life of our colleague was long and painful, but he endured it with firmness, without indulging any illusion as to its fatal issue, and with a resignation which, as was said by Poisson at his grave, must have been rendered difficult by the happiness of his home, the tenderness and fond solicitude which there surrounded him. . . .

. . .

Lagrange was the reformer of analysis. By rendering more evident some of the bases of that science, he has conferred upon it greater force, at the same time that by his immortal discoveries he has extended its domain. One of our greatest geometers has dwelt with admiration on the perfection of his analytical style. Clear and smooth as the verses of Racine, the formulas of Lagrange have augmented the number of the adepts of science, while they have facilitated their labors. *Laplace,* in applying to the laws of the universe the faculties of a geometer of the first order, advances a claim to be considered as the lawgiver of the celestial movements. By his vast acquisitions in the empire of nature, he has earned a right to be styled the Newton of France. *Legendre,* more profound than popular, was our Euler; like Euler and after his example, he has bequeathed to the future a multitude of those analytical results which genius alone knows how to obtain, and which enrich in perpetuity the domain of the human intellect.

. . .

Georges Léopold Chrétien Cuvier *

1769–1832

———◆———

PIERRE JEAN MARIE FLOURENS †

THE HISTORY of Cuvier, if we recall all that the natural sciences owe to him, is scarcely less in fact than the history of those sciences in the earlier part of the nineteenth century. The eighteenth had already contributed considerably to their rapid progress. Two individuals, Linnæus and Buffon, had especially co-operated in producing this movement, and although endowed otherwise with very different qualities it is to be remarked, nevertheless, that it was from the same cause that both had failed in their aim. Those phenomena, indeed, those beings, those facts, which the comprehensive genius of Linnæus sought to distinguish and to classify, those facts which the soaring genius of Buffon sought to combine and to explain, were not yet sufficiently known in their intimate nature to supply either their true classification or their real explanation.

The primary merit of Cuvier, and it was by this merit that he communicated from the first a new life to the natural sciences, was the distinct perception that the classification as well as explanation of facts could be founded only on their inmost nature thoroughly understood. In a word, and taking into view only the natural history of animals, that branch of natural history in general which Cuvier has most directly elucidated by his labors, it is evident that what had been wanting to Linnæus and to Buffon, whether for the classification of animals or for the proper explanation of their phenomena, was the adequate knowledge of their internal structure or organization; and it is not less evident that the

---

* *A.R.*, 1868, pp. 121–140. Read before the French Academy of Sciences, December 29, 1834.

† French physiologist (1794–1867), perpetual secretary of the French Academy. See his "History of the Works of Cuvier," *A.R.* 1868, pp. 141–165.

118

laws of all classification, as of the whole natural philosophy of these beings, could spring only from the laws of that organization itself.

It will presently be seen that it was by the assiduous study of these fruitful laws that Cuvier renovated in succession zoology and comparative anatomy; that he renovated one by means of the other; and that he founded on both the science of fossil animals—a science altogether new, wholly due to his genius, and which has thrown light in its turn on the science of the earth itself. But before we come to these last and astonishing results, the fruits of so many grand conceptions and so many unexpected discoveries, let us first see what he has done in particular for each of the sciences just mentioned, in order that we may afterward be better able to comprehend and embrace in a general view what he has done for all. I commence with zoology.

Linnæus, who of all the naturalists of the eighteenth century had exerted the most general influence on the human mind, particularly in point of method, divided the animal kingdom into six classes: quadrupeds, birds, reptiles, fishes, insects, and worms. In this Linnæus committed a first general error, for in placing in the same line these six primitive divisions, he assumed that an equal interval separated them one from another, than which nothing could be less exact. On the other hand, almost all these classes, especially the last, at one time separate animals the most nearly related, at another unite those which are most incongruous. In a word, classification, which has no other end but to mark the true relations of beings, in this instance almost everywhere severed those relations. . . .

This whole classification of Linnæus was, therefore, to be recast, and nearly the entire framework of the science to be reconstructed. Now, to attain this end, it was first necessary to found the classification on organization, for it is organization alone which gives the true relations; in other terms, it was necessary to found zoology on anatomy; it was next necessary to introduce into the method [system] itself views more just and elevated than had been previously applied. It was, in fact, these elevated views, as regards method, these profound studies on organization, which shone forth in the first labors of Cuvier; it was these potent resources by means of which he succeeded in effecting successively the reform of all the branches of zoology, one after the other, and in finally renovating in its whole extent that vast and grand science.

I have said that it was chiefly in the class *Vermes* of Linnæus that disorder and confusion prevailed. He had thrown into it all animals with white blood—that is to say, more than half the animal kingdom. It was in the first of his memoirs, published in 1795, that Cuvier pointed out the great difference of the beings till then confounded under this vague name of white-blooded animals, and that he separated them with precision from one another, first into three great classes: *mollusks,* which, like the octopus, the cuttle-fish, the oyster, have a heart, a complete vascular system, and breathe by means of branchiæ or gills; *insects,* which have, in place of a heart, only a simple dorsal vessel, and breathe by tracheæ; and lastly, *zoophytes*—animals whose structure is so simple as to have gained them this name, signifying animal-plants, and which have neither heart, nor vessels, nor distinct organ of respiration. By subsequently forming three other classes—*Vermes, Crustacea, Echinodermata*—all the animals with white blood are found to be distributed into six classes: *mollusks, crustaceans, insects, worms, echinoderms,* and *zoophytes.*

Everything was new in this distribution; but everything was at the same time so evident that it was generally adopted, and thenceforward the animal kingdom assumed a new face. Moreover, the precision of the characters on which each of these classes was founded, the perfect conformity of the beings which were assembled under each of them, could not but prove convincing to naturalists; and what doubtless appeared to them not less worthy of admiration than these direct and immediate results was the sudden light which thereby broke on the highest points of the science—the grand ideas on the subordination of the organs and on the role of this subordination in their employment as characters—those great laws of the animal organization thus and so early apprehended: that all animals with white blood which have a heart have also branchiæ or a circumscribed respiratory organ; that all those which have no heart have only a trachea; that wherever the heart and the branchiæ exist, the liver exists; that wherever they are wanting the liver is wanting. Assuredly, no one had as yet thrown a glance so comprehensive, so penetrating on the general laws of the organization of animals, and it was easy to foresee that if he should pursue the investigation of those laws with anything like the same continuity, Cuvier, whose first views had imparted to science so brilliant an impulse, would not be long in extending its boundaries in every direction. He has often recalled since, and even in his last works, this first memoir, from which in truth date the germs both of the grand renovation which he effected in zoology and of the greater part of his most fundamental ideas in comparative anatomy.

Never, indeed, had the domain of a science been so rapidly augmented. With the exception of Aristotle, whose philosophic genius had neglected no part of the animal kingdom, scarcely had any one studied, at any epoch, more than the vertebrate animals alone, at least in a general and thorough manner, The *animals with white blood,* or, as Lamarck has since called them, *the animals without vertebræ,* formed in some sort a new animal kingdom, almost unknown to naturalists, and of which Cuvier had at once revealed to them as well the different plans of structure as the particular laws to which each of these plans is subjected. All these animals—so numerous, so varied in their forms, and the knowledge of which has since so greatly extended the basis of general physiology and natural philosophy—were then of scarcely any account to the physiologist and the philosopher; and even long after these great labors of Cuvier of which I speak, how many systems have we not seen which, pretending to embrace under one sole point of view the entire animal kingdom, have embraced in reality only the *Vertebrata?* So vast was the new route which he had traced for naturalists, and so difficult was it found to follow him therein, on account of its very vastness.

In his first memoir, then, Cuvier succeeded in finally establishing the true division of animals with white blood. In a second, taking up specially one of their classes, that of the mollusks, he laid the foundations of his great work on those animals—a labor which occupied him for so many years, and which has produced an assemblage of results the most surprising perhaps and at least the most essentially new of all modern zoology, as of all modern comparative anatomy. Till then there had been no example of an anatomy so exact and bearing on so great a number of fine and delicate parts. Daubenton, that model of precision and exactness, had scarcely described with equal detail more than the skeleton and the viscera of quadrupeds. Here there was the same attention and a still more eminent degree of sagacity of observation transferred to all the parts of the animal—to its muscles, its vessels, its nerves, its organs of sense. Swammerdam and Pallas, who had embraced all the parts of the animal in their anatomizations, had confined these to certain species; in another genus Lyonnet had confined himself to a single one; in the case of Cuvier there was an entire class of animals, and of all animals the class least known, of which almost all the species were described and all the details, even the most delicate and obscure, of their structure were brought to light and developed.

The mollusks all have a heart, as already said; some, however, have but a single one, like the oyster and snail; others have two; others again, like the octopus and cuttlefish, have as many as three distinct hearts. And yet it was with these animals whose organization is so rich, which have a brain, nerves, organs of sense and of secretion, that it had been the custom to confound others which, like the zoophytes and polyps, for example, have for their whole organization only an almost homogeneous pulp.

The experiments of Trembley have rendered famous the polypus of fresh water, that animal which puts forth buds like a plant, and each part of which, separated from the others, forms a new and complete individual. The whole structure of this singular zoophyte is reduced to a sac—that is to say, to a mouth and stomach. Cuvier made known another zoophyte [the blue rhizostone] whose structure presents something still more surprising, for it has not even a mouth; it is nourished by means of ramified suckers, like a plant, and its internal cavity serves by turns as a stomach and sort of heart, for vessels enter it which conduct to it the nutritive juices, and other vessels issue from it which convey these juices to the members.

One of the most curious problems of the physiology of whiteblooded animals which Cuvier resolved is that of the nutrition of insects. Insects, as has been already said, have in place of a heart only a simple dorsal vessel; and moreover this dorsal vessel has no branch, no ramification, no particular vessel which either enters or issues from it. This was already known through the celebrated researches of Malpighi, Swammerdam, and Lyonnet. But Cuvier goes much further; he examines, one after the other, all the parts of the bodies of insects, and by this detailed examination he shows that no sanguineous vessel, or, what amounts to the same thing, no circulation, exists in these animals. How, then, is their nutrition effected?

Cuvier begins by remarking that the final object of the circulation is to conduct the blood to the air. Hence, all animals which have a heart have a circumscribed respiratory organ, whether lungs or branchiæ, and the blood returned from the members to the heart is invariably constrained to traverse this organ, in order to be there subjected to the action of the air before returning to the members. But in insects the apparatus of respiration is wholly different. It is no longer a circumscribed organ which receives the air; it is an immense number of elastic vessels, called *tracheæ,* which convey it into all parts of the body, and which thus conduct it even to the nutritive fluid itself, which continually bathes those parts. In a word, while in other animals it is the nutritive fluid which by means of the circulation goes in search of the air, the phenomenon is reversed in insects, and it is the air, on the contrary, which goes to seek the nutritive fluid and thereby renders all circulation useless.

Another discovery of Cuvier, not less important, is that of the circulatory apparatus of certain *worms,* such as the earthworm and leech, which had until then been confounded with those *zoophytes* of a structure incomparably more simple, which live only in the interior of other animals. By a remarkable singularity the blood of these worms with a circulatory apparatus is red: a new circumstance to show how inexact and vague was the denomination of animals with white blood, given till then in a general manner to animals without vertebræ.

By means of these admirable investigations Cuvier, it will be seen, had fixed the limits of the class of *mollusks;* he had determined that of the *worms with red blood,* he had completely separated both from that of the *zoophytes;* finally, he had marked the true place of the zoophytes themselves, thenceforth consigned to the extreme limit of the animal kingdom. But a principle which he had employed in all these researches must needs lead him still further. This principle is that of the subordination of organs or of characters.

Classification should not be limited to representing indistinctly the relations of structure; it ought to mark, besides, the particular order of these relations and the relative importance of each; and it is precisely to this end that the principle of the subordination of organs serves. Bernard and Laurent de Jussieu had already applied this principle, as fruitful as it is infallible, to botany, but the zoologists had not yet ventured to make the application of it to their own science, determined, no doubt, by the great number and complication of the organs which constitute the animal body, and which for the most part are wanting in vegetables. The principle of subordination of organs could be introduced into zoology only when preceded by anatomy. The first step to be taken was to know the organs; the determination of their relative importance could be only the second. These two steps accomplished, there remained only to found the characters on the organs, and to subordinate these characters one to the other, as the organs are subordinated among themselves. Such was properly the object of *The Animal Kingdom Distributed According to Its Organization, (Règne Animal),* that great work in which the new zoological doctrine of the illustrious author is displayed in all its entirety and co-ordinated in all its parts.

Dating from this work the art of classification has assumed a new face. Linnæus, as is well known, had seen in this art only a means of distinguishing species. Cuvier was the first who undertook to make it the very instrument of the generalization of facts. "*Méthode*," viewed in itself, is for him only the subordination of propositions, of truths, of facts, one to another, according to the order of their generality. Applied to the animal world, it is the subordination of groups among themselves, according to the relative importance of the organs which constitute the distinctive characters of those groups. Now, the most important organs are also those which involve the most general resemblances. Whence it follows that in founding the inferior groups on the subordinate organs, and the superior groups on the dominating organs, the superior groups will always necessarily comprise the inferior, or, in other terms, it will always be practicable to pass from one to the other by progressive propositions, becoming more and more general in proportion as we ascend from the inferior groups toward the superior. Classification, therefore, properly considered, is but the generalized expression of science; it is science itself, but science reduced to its most simple expressions. It is still more: this linking together of facts according to their analogies, this linking together of analogies according to their degree of comprehensiveness, is not limited to the representation of known relations. It brings to light a multitude of new relations, contained one in another; it disengages them from one another; it thus gives new force to the understanding for perceiving and discovering; it creates for the mind new processes of logic.

Hitherto, Cuvier had seen in each of these grand classes of invertebrate animals (*mollusks, insects* and *zoophytes*) only a group like each of the four classes of vertebrate animals (*quadrupeds, birds, reptiles* and *fishes*). It was because he had as yet considered only the organs of circulation. In considering the nervous system, which is a much more important organ, he saw that each of the three great classes of animals without vertebræ corresponded or was equivalent not to such or such a class of *vertebrate* animals taken separately, but to all these vertebrate animals taken together. A first form of the nervous system unites all these vertebrate animals in a single group; a second form unites all the mollusks; a third unites the insects to the worms with red blood, and both to the crustacea, constituting the group of articulata; a fourth form, finally, unites all the zoophytes. There are thus four plans, four types in the animal kingdom, four *embranchements,* as Cuvier calls them; or, in plainer terms, and divested of everything vague, there are four general forms of the nervous system in animals.

In the sciences of observation and experiment the supreme art of genius is to transform simple questions of reasoning into questions of fact. For more than a century the question had been debated whether, in animals, there was but one plan of organization or whether there were several. This question, couched till then in terms so vague, is transformed by Cuvier into this other question, positive and to the point, namely: How many distinct forms are there of the nervous system in animals? Now, as I have just said, there are four—one for the *vertebrata,* one for the *mollusca,* one for the *articulata,* one for the *zoophyta,* these four plans or types comprising the whole animal kingdom. Such is the light thrown upon the animal kingdom by the great work under consideration that, guided by this, the mind is enabled precisely to apprehend the different orders of relation which connect animals with one another: the relations of conformity *(d'ensemble)* which constitute the unity, the character of the kingdom; the relations more or less general which constitute the unity of the *embranchements* of the classes; the more particular relations which constitute the unity of the orders, of the genera.

Nevertheless, this work of so vast a scope, of such immense detail, was not yet what Cuvier would have wished. It is the property of genius always to see something beyond and better than all that it has done. And indeed, though all the species had been reviewed in this great work, the greater part of them had been scarcely more than indicated; it was therefore only an abridged, not a complete classification of animals. Now, the idea of a complete classification, in which all the species should be not only indicated, distinguished, classified, but represented and described in their whole structure, was one project with which Cuvier was most constantly occupied. Hence, scarcely was this great treatise on the animal kingdom terminated, when another was already commenced, and on a plan not less vast. I mean the *Natural History of Fishes (Histoire naturelle des poissons),* the first volume of which appeared in 1828.

After having effected in the earlier of these two works the complete reform of the classification of animals, what he wished in the second was to show by a detailed and thorough exposition of all the known species of a class what could be done for all other species and all other classes. With this view he chose the class of *fishes* as being, among all those of the vertebrata, the most numerous, the least known, and that most enriched by the recent discoveries of travellers. The latest authors of note in ichthyology, Bloch and Lacépède, were scarcely acquainted with so many as 1,400 species of fish; in the work of Cuvier the number of species would amount to more than 5,000; the entire work would include not less than 20 volumes. All the materials were placed in order, and the nine volumes which made their appearance in less than six years fully attest the wonderful rapidity with which it was intended that this vast undertaking should proceed.

.   .   .

Such is the assemblage of great labors by which Cuvier has renovated zoology; but a reform still more important, and of which that is in reality but the consequence, is what he had already effected, or was at the same time effecting in *comparative anatomy*. It is impossible to speak of the progress which this science owed to the researches of Cuvier without profound respect and even grateful acknowledgment; he himself regarded this branch of investigation and with justice as the regulator of all those which relate to organized beings. Death surprised him still meditating that great work to which he had consecrated himself and in which, collecting anew all its forces, his vast genius would have undoubtedly appeared in all its grandeur. But though this work remained unaccomplished, its principal elements subsist, as they are scattered in various memoirs, especially in his *Leçons d'anatomie comparée* and his *Recherches sur les ossements fossiles,* immortal labors which have communicated to comparative anatomy such an impulsion that, after having been so long the most neglected of the branches of natural history, it has suddenly outstripped and taken the lead of all of them.

The history of comparative anatomy counts three epochs clearly marked—the epoch of Aristotle, that of Claude Perrault, and that of Cuvier. Every one knows with how much genius the foundations of the science were laid by Aristotle among the ancients. But what is not as well known, though not less worthy of being so, is the force of intellect with which Claude Perrault, at the middle of the seventeenth century, undertook the reconstruction of the entire science from its very base—that is to say, from the consideration of particular facts. His descriptions are the first assured step taken by comparative anatomy in modern times. Daubenton advanced it still another, for he rendered those descriptions comparable. Vicq-d'Azyr went yet further. Rich through the labors of Daubenton, of Haller, of Hunter, of Monro, of Camper, of Pallas,

Vicq-d'Azyr embraced comparative anatomy in its completeness; he brought to it that penetrating genius which sees in science the end to be attained, and that spirit of tenacity which attains it; and by no one more than by him was that great reform promoted which Cuvier finally achieved for the science in question. It was certainly fortunate for this science to have passed immediately from the hands of one of these two eminent men into the hands of the other. Vicq-d'Azyr had thrown on it the glance of the physiologist; M. Cuvier threw on it more particularly that of the zoologist, and we may concede that it had an equal need of being considered under both these points of view. It may well be thought that its reform would not have been so complete and its influence so general except that, having been by turns studied and adapted with a view both to zoology and physiology, it has become alike for both the guide and the beacon. However this may be, comparative anatomy was still but a collection of particular facts touching the structure of animals when Cuvier transformed it into the science of the general laws of animal organization. After having transformed, as we have seen, the zoological system from being a simple nomenclature into an instrument of generalization, he now proceeded to dispose the facts in comparative anatomy in such an order that from their simple collocation have proceeded so many admirable and progressively ascending laws; as, for example, that each kind of organ has its fixed and determined modifications; that a constant relation connects all modifications of the organism with one another; that certain organs exert on the collective animal economy a more marked and decisive influence, whence the law of their *subordination;* that certain facts of organization necessarily involve the presence of each other, while there are such, on the contrary, as are incompatible and exclusive one of the other, whence the law of their *correlation* or *coexistence;* besides so many other laws, so many other general relations which have in the end created and developed the philosophic part of the science.

Among so many discoveries, so many particular facts with which he has enriched that science, I must necessarily confine myself to a citation of the most prominent, and still the catalogue of even these will be far from complete. The researches of Hunter and of Tenon had already afforded valuable contributions to the theory of the development of the teeth; it was Cuvier who carried this theory to a perfection beyond which there can be little to desire. Those little bones which we call teeth appear at first glance to be very simple and scarcely to merit the attention of the observer. These little bodies, however, are very complex; they possess secretory organs, as their *germ,* their *proper membrane;* secreted substances, such as their *enamel,* their *ivory;* and each of these substances appears in its turn, each at a fixed epoch. They spring up, are developed, push forth their roots, die, fall, and are replaced by others with admirable order and regularity. Nor is it less admirable, though under another point of view, that all the circumstances of their organization and development are today rigorously demonstrated. It was chiefly through a study of the teeth of the elephant, where everything is seen on a large scale, that Cuvier succeeded in establishing the precise epoch at which each part of the tooth is formed and by what mechanism it is formed; how each of these parts, having performed its function of productive organ, disappears; how the entire tooth disappears in its turn to give place to another, which will also have its development, both in the whole and in detail, its point of complete organization, and its decay and its fall.

Perrault, Hérissant, Vicq-d'Azyr had, before Cuvier, distinguished some points in the structure of the vocal organs of birds. He made that structure known in a general manner and by detailed comparisons. It was he also who first placed in a clear light the singular arrangement of the organ of hearing and the still more singular arrangement of the nasal *fossæ* in the cetaceous tribes.

Everyone knows the marvellous metamorphosis experienced by the frog in passing from the state of fœtus or tadpole to the adult state. It is known that after having breathed in the first case by gills, like the fishes, it breathes in the second by lungs, like the terrestrial animals. Cuvier has taught us the structure of the organs of respiration and circulation in a species of reptiles, which presents something still more curious. The frog is by turn a fish in its first stage and a reptile in its second. These new reptiles, still more singular, such as the *proteus,* the *axolotl,* the *siren,* are all their lives reptiles and fish, have all the time both *branchiæ* or gills and lungs, and can hence breathe alternately in the air and in water.

Cuvier again was the first to give a connected comparison of the brain in the four classes of vertebrate animals; the first to point out the relations of the development of that organ with the development of intelligence, a branch of comparative anatomy which has since become so fruitful and extensive; the first, in fine, to deduce in a rigorous manner from the respective quantity of respiration of these animals, not only the degree of their natural heat, but that of all their other faculties, their force of movement, their subtility of perception, their rapidity of digestion. But the most novel and brilliant application which he has made of comparative anatomy is that which relates to *fossil bones*. Everyone now knows that the globe which we inhabit presents almost everywhere irrefutable traces of stupendous revolution. The productions of the actual creation, of living nature, everywhere cover the remains of an earlier creation, of a ruined nature. On the one hand, immense masses of shells and of other marine bodies are found at great distances from any sea, at heights to which no sea could now attain, and from thence have been derived the first facts in support of all those traditions of deluges preserved among so many tribes of mankind. On the other hand, the large bones discovered from time to time in the bowels of the earth, in the caverns of the mountains, have given rise to those other popular traditions, not less diffused and not less ancient, of races of giants who peopled the world in its first ages.

The traces of the revolutions of our globe have therefore at all times impressed the minds of men, but they long impressed them in vain, and only with a fruitless astonishment. For a long time, indeed, ignorance was carried to such a point that an opinion very nearly universal, and I speak not here of popular opinion, but of the opinion of savants and philosophers, regarded the stones charged with the impressions of animals or plants and the shells found in the earth as *sports of nature*. "It was necessary," says Fontenelle, "that a common potter, who knew neither Latin nor Greek, should dare, about the end of the sixteenth century, to say in Paris, and in the face of all the doctors, that the fossil shells were real shells, deposited heretofore by the sea in the places where they were then found; that animals had impressed on the figure-bearing stones all their different figures, and that he should boldly defy the whole school of Aristotle to contest his proofs."

This potter was Bernard Palissy, renowned for having made barely a first step in a route traversed since then by so many great men, and which has conducted them to such astonishing discoveries. In truth, the ideas of Palissy could scarcely be expected to attract notice at the epoch when they appeared, and it was not till about a century later—that is to say, toward the close of the seventeenth century—that they began to revive and, again to recall an expression of Fontenelle's, "to thrive in the world as they deserved to do." But from that time such was the activity put forth, both in collecting the remains of organized bodies buried beneath the surface of the earth and in studying the strata which contain them, and under this twofold relation so rapidly were significant facts multiplied, that some bold and perspicacious minds were not afraid even then to combine them in generalizations and attempt to ascend to their causes. It was, in fact, at the close of the seventeenth century and during the first half of the eighteenth that the celebrated systems of Burnet, Leibnitz, Woodward, Whiston, and Buffon made their appearance—all of them premature and more or less erroneous, no doubt, but productive of this advantage, that they accustomed the human intellect to contemplate these astounding phenomena in a philosophic spirit and not to shrink from measuring itself against them. Another advantage of even greater moment was that all these systems, by exciting a strong interest, presently drew together from all parts observations at once more numerous, precise, and complete, the first effect of which was to overturn all that was imaginary and absurd in those systems, and the second, to found on their ruins the true theory, the positive history of the earth.

The eighteenth century, which advanced so rapidly in so many directions, perhaps witnessed nothing more rapid than the progress of the science of which we are speaking. The same century which in its first half had seen all the systems just spoken of, structures both brilliant and frail, either rise or fall, saw in its second half the first foundations of the enduring monument which was to succeed them, cast by the hands of a Pallas, a Deluc, a De Saussure, a Werner, a Blumenbach, a Camper, and others who so ably seconded them.

Among these advances it is proper that I should here especially recall those which relate to the fossil remains of organized bodies. It was these remains, in fact, witnesses as they are of so many revolutions, so many violent subversions sustained by the globe, which had given rise to the first hypothesis of the *fantastic* geology; and it was again these remains which, in the hands of Cuvier, furnished the results the most evident and the laws best ascertained of the *positive* geology. The researches of Cuvier were principally directed to the fossil bones of quadrupeds—a part of the animal kingdom till then little studied under this new point of view, but the study of which was calculated to lead to consequences much more precise and decisive than that of any other class.

I have already mentioned the large fossil bones discovered at different epochs and the absurd ideas of giants, which were renewed at each discovery which was made of them. Daubenton was the first to overthrow all these ideas; it was he who first applied comparative anatomy to the determination of the remains in question; but, as he himself avows, this science was as yet far from being sufficiently advanced to furnish in all cases and with sufficient certainty the species or genus of animal to which an unknown and isolated bone might appertain; and yet such was the problem to be solved. The memoir in which Daubenton attempted for the first time the solution of this important problem appeared in 1762.

In 1769 Pallas published his first memoir on the fossil bones of Siberia. It was not without surprise that the demonstration was here seen of the fact that the elephant, the rhinoceros, the hippopotamus—animals which at present live only under the torrid zone—had heretofore inhabited the most northern portions of our continents. The second memoir of Pallas could not but excite still more wonder, for he there reports the fact, which could scarcely seem credible at that time, that a rhinoceros had been found entire in the frozen earth with its skin and flesh—a fact corroborated, as is known to all, by the elephant discovered in 1806 on the shores of the glacial sea, and so well preserved that dogs and bears devoured its flesh and disputed its remains with one another.

The impulse once communicated by Pallas, the relics of animals of the south were soon found, not only in the countries of the north, but in all the regions of the old as well as new world. Buffon from these facts hastened to deduce his hypothesis of the gradual refrigeration of the polar regions and of the successive migration of animals from the north to the south. But the last fact observed by Pallas, and which has just been cited, had already overthrown this assumption. That fact effectually demonstrated in the most formal manner that the refrigeration of the globe, far from having been gradual, had on the contrary necessarily been sudden, instantaneous, without any gradation; it demonstrated that the same instant which destroyed the animals in question had rendered the country of their habitat glacial; for had they not been frozen as soon as killed it is evident that they could not have descended to us with their flesh and skin and every part in perfect preservation. The hypothesis of gradual refrigeration being thus untenable, Pallas substituted that of an irruption of water coming from the southeast—an irruption which, he maintained, would have transported into the north the animals of India; but this second hypothesis was not more happy than the first, for the fossil animals are very different from those of India, and indeed from all animals now living—a final fact more extraordinary still than all which preceded it, and which it was reserved for Cuvier to place in the clearest light.

The fact of an ancient creation of animals entirely distinct from the existing creation and long since entirely lost is the fundamental fact on which rest the most evident proofs of the revolutions of the globe. It cannot therefore be without interest to observe how the idea of this fact, assuredly the most extraordinary which scientific research has been enabled to discover and to prove, had its first rise, its subsequent development, and final confirmation. We have seen how, toward the end of the sixteenth century, Bernard Palissy had ventured, first among the moderns, to maintain that the bones, the impressions, the fossil shells, so long regarded as casual freaks of nature, were the remains of real creatures, the veritable spoils of organized bodies. In 1670 Augustine Scilla reaffirmed the opinion of Palissy and sustained it with vigor. Shortly after, in 1683, Leibnitz lent to it the authority of his name and genius. Finally, in the eighteenth century, Buffon enunciated it even more brilliantly and popularized it. But are these organized beings, of which innumerable relics are scattered everywhere, the analogues of those which are now living, whether in the places where these relics are found or in others? or have, indeed, their species, their genera, perished? It is here that the difficulty lies, and we may well believe that this difficulty would never have been resolved, at least with complete certainty, as long as the inquiry had been restricted, for example, to the study of fossil shells or of fishes. It would have availed little, in fact, to find new shells, new fishes; we should have been always at liberty to suppose that their species were still living, whether in distant seas or at inaccessible depths. Not so, however, as regards quadrupeds. The number of these is greatly more limited, especially for the larger species. We may count on attaining a knowledge of all of them—how vastly more easy then to satisfy ourselves whether certain unknown bones belong to one of these species still living, or whether they proceed from such as are lost.

This it is which gives to the study of fossil quadrupeds a peculiar importance and to the deductions which may be drawn from it a force which deductions derived from a study of most of the other classes could not possess. Buffon seems to have felt this. It was chiefly on the great fossil bones of Siberia and Canada that he sought to sustain the conjecture (for, in view of the state of comparative anatomy at the time when he wrote, it could be only a conjecture) of certain lost species. Besides, even this conjecture was so imperfectly established in his own mind, at least in relation to quadrupeds, that after having regarded, in his *Théorie de la terre,* all the animals to which these extraordinary bones had belonged as lost, he afterwards declared, in his *Époques de la nature,* that he no longer recognized more than a single lost species—that which has been called the *mastodon*—and that all the other bones in question are merely those of the elephant and the hippopotamus. Camper went much further, as might have been expected, for comparative anatomy had not failed to advance by long strides since the days of Buffon. In 1787 in a memoir addressed to Pallas, Camper boldly enunciates the opinion that certain species have been destroyed by the catastrophes of the globe and, moreover, sustains it by the first really positive facts, though still very incomplete, which had yet been advanced in its support. Thus, the determination of fossil bones, studied in the light of comparative anatomy, strengthened the theory of lost animals. It was, in fact, this light of comparative anatomy which had been wanting in so many laborious researches of so many naturalists. But it is easy to see that toward the epoch of which I speak, toward the close, namely, of the eighteenth century, everything was prepared for the long-sought solution; the moment was at hand for some revelation, some complete and definitive result respecting these strange and marvellous phenomena.

The 1st pluviôse, an IV (February 1796) being the day of the first public session held by the National Institute, Cuvier read before the assembled body his memoir on the fossil species of the elephant compared with the living species. It was in this memoir that he announced, for the first time, his views on extinct animals. Thus, on the same day when the Institute opened the first of its public sessions was revealed also one of the greatest discoveries which natural history has made in our age: a singular coincidence, which the history of the sciences should not fail to mark and commemorate.

Cuvier had now initiated that brilliant series of researches and labors which occupied him so many years and which, during the whole time, called forth renewed surprise and admiration on the part of his contemporaries. In this first memoir he does not confine himself to demonstrating that the fossil elephant is a distinct species from the existing species—that it is a species extinct and lost; he expressly declares that the greatest step which could be made toward the perfection of the theory of the earth would be to prove that none of those animals whose remains are found dispersed over nearly all points of the globe, any longer exist. He adds that what he then established in regard to the *elephant* he would soon establish in a not less incontestable manner in regard to the fossil *rhinoceros, bear,* and *deer,* all of them species equally distinct from living species, all of them equally lost. Finally he concludes with the following remarkable words, in which he seemed to announce all that he has since discovered: "If it be asked why we find so many remains of unknown animals, while we find none of which it can be said that they belong to species that we know, it will be seen how probable it is that they have all pertained to the creatures of a world anterior to our own; to creatures destroyed by some catastrophe of the globe; to creatures whose place has been filled by those which exist today."

Thus the idea of an entire creation of animals anterior to the actual creation, the idea of an entire creation destroyed and lost had at last been fully conceived, and had found an utterance which proved to be a final solution of the doubts which for a century had so strongly occupied the human mind. But in order to transform into a positive result views thus vast and elevated, it was necessary to assemble from all quarters the remains of the lost animals, to pass them in review, to study them under this new aspect; it was necessary to compare them all, one after the other, with the remains of living animals; and first of all it was necessary to create and determine the art itself by which this comparison was to be made.

Now, for a right conception of all the difficulties of this new system, this new art, it is sufficient to remark that the *débris* of the animals in question, the *fossil bones,* are almost always isolated and dispersed; that often the bones of several species, and those the most diverse, are mingled in confusion; that almost always these bones are mutilated, broken, reduced to fragments. It was requisite, therefore, to refer each bone to the species to which it pertains; to reconstruct, if possible, the complete skeleton of each species, without omitting any of the pieces which were its own, without intercalating any which were foreign to it. Let us now represent to ourselves this confused intermingling of mutilated and imperfect relics assembled together by Cuvier. Let us conceive each bone, each portion of a bone, taking its place under his skillful hand, each uniting itself to the bone or portion of bone to which it had pertained. Let us observe all these species of animals, destroyed for so many ages, thus rising before us in their various forms, with each character, each attribute restored, and we shall scarcely realize that we are witnessing a simple anatomical operation, but rather a sort of resurrection, nor will it abate anything of the marvel that it is a resurrection effected at the voice of science and of genius. I say *at the voice of science.* The method employed by Cuvier for this wonderful reconstruction, is, indeed, but the application of the general rules of comparative anatomy to the identification of fossil bones. And these rules themselves are a not less grand, less admirable discovery than the surprising results to which they have led.

It has been seen above how a rational principle, that of the *subordination of organs*, everywhere applied . . . had changed the face of the classification of the animal kingdom. The principle which presided at the reconstruction of lost species is that of the *correlation of forms*, a principle by means of which each part of an animal may be given by each other part, and the whole animal by a single part. In a mechanism as complex, and yet as essentially a unit as that which constitutes the animal frame, it is evident that all the parts must necessarily be constructed one with reference to the others, so as to correspond, to adapt themselves to one another, to form, in a word, by their assemblage, one being, one unique system. A single one of these parts, therefore, cannot change its form without necessitating a change in form of all the others. Hence from the form of one part may be deduced the form of all the other parts.

Consider a carnivorous animal: it will necessarily have the organs of sense and of movement; the claws, teeth, stomach, intestines, adapted for scenting, seizing, tearing, digesting its animal prey, and all these conditions will be rigorously likened with one another; for, if one be wanting, the others would be without effect, without result; the creature could not subsist. Consider, on the other hand, an herbivorous animal: all this assemblage of conditions will have changed. The teeth, the feet, the stomach, the intestines, the organs of movement and of sense will all have assumed new forms, and these new forms will always be proportioned and related one to the others. From the form of a single one of these parts, therefore, from that of the teeth alone, for example, we may infer, and infer with certainty, the form of the feet, of the jaws, of the stomach, of the intestines.

All the parts, all the organs, are deducible, then, one from the other; and such is the rigor, such the infallibility of this deduction that Cuvier has been often known to recognize an animal by a single bone, nay by the facet of a bone; that he has been known to determine unknown genera and species from a few broken bones, and this from such or such a bone taken at random, reconstructing in this way the entire animal from a single one of its parts, and causing it to reappear, as at will, from each of them: results which cannot be recalled without recalling in effect all that admiration, mingled with surprise, which they at first inspired, and which is not yet exhausted.

That precise and rigorous method of distinguishing bones confounded together—of referring each bone to its species, of reconstructing the entire animal from some of its parts—that method once conceived, it was no longer by isolated species but by groups and masses that these extinct populations, antique monuments of the revolutions of the globe, reappeared. An idea might then be formed not only of their extraordinary appearance, but of the prodigious multitude of their species. It was seen that they comprised creatures of all classes, quadrupeds, birds, reptiles, fishes, down to crustacea, mollusks, and zoophytes. Nor, though I speak here only of animals, does the study of fossil vegetables furnish consequences less curious than those drawn from the animal kingdom. All these organized beings, all these first occupants of the globe, are distinguished by their proper characters, often by the most singular and grotesque.

Among the quadrupeds, for example, we first observe the *palæotherium,* the *anoplotherium,* those strange specimens of *pachydermata,* discovered by Cuvier in the environs of Paris, and of which none bearing this peculiar character has descended to our times. Afterwards comes the *mammoth,* that elephant of Siberia covered with long hairs and a thick wool; the *mastodon,* an animal almost as large as the mammoth, and whose teeth, armed with points, long caused it to be regarded as a carnivorous elephant; and those enormous sloths, the *megatherium,* the *megalonyx,* animals of which the existing species do not exceed the size of a dog, while some of those which are lost equalled the largest rhinoceros. Still more extraordinary were the reptiles of those first ages of the world, whether from their gigantic proportions, for there were lizards as large as whales, or from the singularity of their structure, for some had the aspect of the *cetacea* or marine mammals, and others the neck and beak of birds, and even a kind of wing.

And what is still more surprising is that all these animals did not live at one and the same epoch; that there were several generations, several populations, so to speak, successively created and destroyed. Of these Cuvier has counted as many as three distinctly marked. The first comprised the mollusks, the fishes, the reptiles, all those monstrous reptiles just spoken of; among them were already found some marine mammals, but no terrestrial ones, or scarcely any, then existed. The second epoch was chiefly characterized by these strange species of *pachydermata* of the environs of Paris, above mentioned, and it was now only that the terrestrial mammals began to predominate. The third was the epoch of the mammoth, the mastodon, the rhinoceros, the hippopotamus, the gigantic sloths. A remarkable fact is that among all these animals there is scarcely one of the *quadrumana,* scarcely one of the ape tribe. And still more remarkable, there was no man. The human race therefore was contemporaneous neither with any of these lost species nor with the catastrophes which destroyed them.

Thus, then, after the age of reptiles, after that of the first terrestrial mammals, after that of the mammoths and mastodons, arrived a fourth epoch, a fourth succession of created beings, that which constitutes the actual population, that which may be called the *age of man,* for from this age only dates the human species. The creation of the animal kingdom, therefore, has undergone several interruptions, several successive destructions; and what is not less wonderful, though altogether certain, is that there was an epoch, the first of all, when no organized being, no animal, no vegetable, existed on the globe. All these extraordinary facts are demonstrated by the relations of the remains of organized beings to the strata which form the crust of the globe. Thus there was a first epoch when these beings did not exist, for the primitive or primordial formations contain none of their remains; the reptiles prevailed in the following epoch, for their remains abound in the formations which succeed the primitive; the surface of the earth has been several times covered by the seas, and again left dry, for the remains of marine animals cover turn by turn the remains of terrestrial animals and are alternately covered by them.

Thus has science, guided by genius, been enabled to ascend to the most remote epochs of the history of the earth; to compute and determine those epochs; to mark both the first moment when organized beings appeared on the globe, and all the variations, modifications, and revolutions they have experienced. It were unjust, doubtless, to convey the impression that all the proofs of this great history have been collected by Cuvier; but even where others after him have made discoveries in the same field, some portion of glory must redound to him by whose footsteps they have been guided. It may be said, indeed, that the more valuable those discoveries, the more important all those which shall be made in the future, the more will his renown be enhanced, even as the name of Columbus has been exalted in proportion as the navigators who have come after him have rendered better known the whole extent of his conquest. This unknown world opened to naturalists is undoubtedly the most brilliant discovery of Cuvier.

.   .   .

[The] generalization of facts was the potent instrument by which he created the science of fossil remains, by which he renewed, in every part, geology and comparative anatomy, by which he was enabled in every order of facts to pursue them to . . . their ultimate principle, carrying zoological classification to its rational principle, the *subordination of organs;* founding the reconstruction of extinct animals on the principle of the *correlation of forms;* demonstrating the necessity of certain intervals, certain interruptions in the scale of beings, by the very impossibility of certain coexistencies, of certain combinations of organs.

. . . .

In Cuvier two things equally strike us: first, the extreme precocity of his views (for it was by his first memoir on the class *vermes* of Linnænus that he reformed not only that class, but through it the whole of zoology). It was by his first course of comparative anatomy that he recast the entire science and re-established it on a new basis. It was by his first memoir on fossil elephants that he laid the foundation of a science wholly new, the science of extinct animals. Secondly, it was that devoted spirit of perseverance, of undiverted constancy, by which he developed and fertilized his views, consecrating an entire life to establish, to demonstrate them, to mature them by experiment, to transform them finally from simple views, fruits of a bold conception, of a sudden inspiration, into truths of fact and observation.

If we follow this celebrated man in the different paths he has traced, we find throughout those dominant qualities of his genius: order, comprehensiveness, elevation of thought, clearness, precision, force of expression. We find all these qualities united to a style even more lively, varied, and forcible in those *Éloges historiques* which long formed so large a part of the charm and *éclat* of the public meetings of the Academy. On these memoirs praise has been already lavishly bestowed, nor would it be easy too highly to extol the spirit and animation which diffuse through them so much movement and life; the art of so piquantly recounting an anecdote or painting a characteristic; the vigor of conception which binds all the parts of the discourse into a whole so compactly put together that it might seem to have been created at a single stroke; the singular aptitude, in fine, to rise to the most varied and comprehensive considerations and to depict so many different personages in a manner equally just and striking. If examined with somewhat closer attention we remark, and with perhaps even greater pleasure, the same sagacity of observation, the same analogical subtlety, the same art of comparing and subordinating, of ascending to the ultimate generalization of facts, here transferred to another field, and in addition to all this, those luminous and penetrating touches which suddenly arrest the attenion of the reader and transport him to great intellectual heights.

Cuvier seems indeed to have been destined to give a new character to whatever passed through his hands. Into his instructions upon natural history he introduced those philosophic and general views which had scarcely before penetrated to the schools. In his eloquent lectures the history of the sciences became the history of the human mind itself, for in going back to the causes of their progress and their errors he was always careful to point out that those causes were to be found in the right or the wrong processes which the human mind had pursued. It was here that, to use one of his own happy expressions, he *submitted the human mind to experiment,* showing by the whole testimony of the history of the sciences that the most ingenious hypotheses, the most brilliant systems, do but pass and disappear, and that facts alone remain— opposing everywhere to the methods of speculation, which have never produced any durable result, the methods of observation and experiment, to which we owe all the discoveries and all the real knowledge which constitute the actual heritage of mankind.

. . .

The delivery of Cuvier was in general grave, and even somewhat slow, especially toward the opening of his lectures, but soon his utterance became animated by the movement of his thoughts, and . . . the penetrating voice, the inspiration of his genius reflected in his eyes and on his features, all conspired to produce upon his audience the most vivid and profound impression. . . . Into the career of the professor he carried the same character of invention as into the career of research and discovery. After having remodelled the school of comparative anatomy at the Jardin des Plantes, he converted a simple chair of natural history at the College of France into a true chair of the philosophy of the sciences: two creations which well portray his genius and which in the eyes of posterity must reflect honor on the age.

Cuvier has left memoirs of his life designed, as he himself writes, for him who should have to pronounce his eulogy before this Academy. The care which he has thus taken in favor of my auditory makes it imperative on me to add some details taken from those memoirs. . . . Georges Cuvier was born August 23, 1769, at Montbéliard, a city then belonging to the Duchy of Würtemberg, but which has since been reunited to France. His family was originally from a village of the Jura which still bears the name of Cuvier. At the era of the Reformation it had established itself in the little Principality of Montbéliard, where some of its members have filled distinguished places. The grandfather of Cuvier was of one of the poorer branches; he was town clerk. Of two sons whom he had, the second entered a Swiss regiment in the service of France, and having become through good conduct and bravery an officer and chevalier of the Order of Merit, married, at the age of fifty years, a woman still quite young, and whose memory should be dear to posterity, for she was the mother of Cuvier, and, moreover, his first preceptor. A woman of superior mind, a mother full of tenderness, the instruction of her son soon became her whole occupation. Although she did not know Latin, she made him repeat his lessons, execute his drawings under her eyes, read to her many books of history and literature, and it was thus that she developed, that she nourished in her young pupil that passion for reading, and that curiosity about all things, which, as Cuvier himself says in the memoirs intrusted to me, had formed the mainspring of his life.

At an early age there was seen in this child that prodigious aptitude for all mental labor, which still later formed one of the distinctive traits of his genius. Everything aroused, everything excited his activity. A copy of Buffon, which he finds by chance in the library of one of his relations, suddenly kindles his taste for natural history. He immediately sets about copying the figures and coloring them from the descriptions—a labor which at so early an age certainly denotes observation of a high order.

The residence of the young Cuvier at the academy of Stuttgart is too well known to be long dwelt upon. The sovereign of a small state, Charles, Duke of Würtemberg, seemed to have proposed to show to the greatest nations what they might do for the instruction of youth. There were here collected in a magnificent establishment more than 400 pupils, who received the lessons of more than 80 masters. Here were trained at the same time painters, sculptors, musicians, diplomatists, jurists, physicians, soldiers, professors in all the sciences. Of the higher faculties there were five: law, medicine, administration, military art, and commerce. The course of philosophy finished, the pupils passed into one of these faculties. Cuvier chose that of administration, and the motive he assigns for it should be reported: "It was," he says, "because in this faculty there was much to do with natural history, and, consequently, frequent opportunities of herborizing and of visiting the cabinets."

Everything in the life of a great man interests us, but doubly so whatever serves to throw light on the process of his labors. We would gladly follow him through the whole course which he has traversed in changing the face of the sciences, and even from his earliest steps would divine something of the direction and character of his thoughts. It has just been seen that our naturalist, yet a child, at sight of the first figures of natural history which fall into his hands, at once conceives the idea of coloring them after the descriptions. While still at Stuttgart one of the professors, whose lectures he had translated into French, makes him a present of a volume of Linnæus. It was the tenth edition of the *Système de la nature,* and this book formed for ten years his whole library of natural history. But in default of books he had the objects, and this direct, exclusive study of the objects engraved them much better in his mind than if, to use his own expression, he had had at his disposal any number of prints and descriptions. Besides, having neither figures nor descriptions he made them for himself.

Still, all these excursions into natural history had not interfered with the prescribed studies: he had borne off almost all the prizes, had obtained the order of *chevalier,* which was accorded to only five or six of all those young persons, and, according to appearances, he might have promptly obtained an appointment. But fortunately for him and for natural history—and these two destinies were thenceforth inseparable—the situation of his parents did not permit him to wait. It was necessary for him to decide, and the place of preceptor having been offered to him by a family of Normandy at the moment when he was quitting Stuttgart, he hastened to accept it, and at once set out for Caen, where he arrived in July 1788, being then something less than 19 years of age.

From this moment his passion for natural history acquired new force. The family of Herici, to which he was attached, went to reside at a country seat of Caux, a short distance from Fécamp. It was here that our young naturalist lived from 1791 to 1794, surrounded, as he says, with the most diversified specimens from the sea and land, yet almost without books, having no one to whom he could communicate. It was at this period, in fact, that his mind began to turn to new paths; it was then that at the sight of some *terebratulæ,* disinterred near Fécamp, he conceived the idea of comparing fossil with living species; that the dissection of some mollusks suggested to him that other idea of a reform to be introduced in the methodical distribution of animals; so that the germs of his two most important labors, the comparison of fossil with living species, and the reform of the classification of the animal kingdom, belong to this epoch.

From this epoch also date his first relations with Tessier, whom the storms of the Revolution then retained at Fécamp, and who had there occupied for some time the place of physician-in-chief of the military hospital. Tessier could not have seen the young Cuvier without being struck with the extent of his knowledge. He first engaged him to deliver a course of botany to the physicians of his hospital; he afterwards wrote to all his friends in Paris to impart to them the happy discovery which he had made, and especially to those of the Jardin des Plantes, who at once conceived the idea of calling the young naturalist thither as assistant to Mertrud, then in charge of the department of comparative anatomy. "Often," says Cuvier, in reference to this circumstance, "has a phrase of M. Tessier, in his letter to M. de Jussieu, recurred to me: *You remember,* he said, *that it was I who gave Delambre to the Academy; in another field this also will be a Delambre.*" It was to Tessier therefore that the Academy of Sciences owed both Delambre and Cuvier. A man who should have rendered but these two services to the sciences might count on the respect and gratitude of all who cultivate them. But how much more vividly do such incidents touch us when they embellish a life wholly consecrated to science, its progress and application, and spent in a long succession of useful labors and virtuous actions!

It was said by Fontenelle to be a piece of good fortune on the part of savants, whom their reputation might afterwards call to the capital, to have had leisure to lay up a good stock of funds in the care of a province. Cuvier's stock was so good that some months after his arrival in Paris, in 1795, his reputation already equalled that of the most celebrated naturalists, and the same year, which was also that of the creation of the National Institute, he was named adjunct of Daubenton and Lacépède, who formed the nucleus of the section of zoology. The year following he commenced the courses which became so rapidly celebrated at the central school of the Pantheon. In 1799 the death of Daubenton led to his appointment to the much more important chair of natural history at the College of France; and in 1802, Mertrud being dead, he became titular professor at the Jardin des Plantes.

It will be recollected that the functions of secretary of the Institute were at first temporary. Cuvier was called among the first to fulfill these functions in his class, and soon afterwards, in 1803, a new organization of the learned body having re-established the perpetuity of these offices, he was chosen perpetual secretary for the physical or natural sciences, with nearly entire unanimity.

It was in this new capacity of perpetual secretary that he composed his memorable *Report on the Progress of Natural Sciences since 1789.* Delambre had been charged with the report on the mathematical sciences, and thus each class of the Institute was called upon to present one on the sciences or arts which fell within its province. It is well known with what state the Emperor received these reports. The peculiar satisfaction which that of Cuvier gave him was expressed by a happy turn of words. "He has praised me," said the imperial personage, "as I like to be praised." "And yet," remarks Cuvier, "I had done no more than invite him to imitate Alexander, and to make his power instrumental to the progress of natural history." But this sort of praise is precisely that which must most flatter a man who had comprehended all kinds of glory and would willingly remain a stranger to none. We are at liberty to think, moreover, that the praise which has no other object but to induce a sovereign to do worthy things is not unworthy of a philosopher.

To all these occupations as historian of the sciences, perpetual secretary, professor at the Museum and at the College of France, Cuvier added several others. He was named member of the council of the University in 1808 and master of requests in 1813. Nor was the Restoration insensible to his merit. He preserved his position and was even invested with new functions. Appointed successively counsellor of state, president of the commission of the interior, chancellor of public instruction, and finally in 1831 peer of France; his genius embraced all orders of ideas and lent itself to all kinds of labor.

It may well be supposed that he was a member of all the learned academies of the world; for what academy could have afforded to omit the inscription of his name on its list? And that which is an honor, of which there were few examples before him, he belonged to three academies of the Institute: the *Académie française,* the Academy of Sciences, and that of Inscriptions and Belles-lettres. His great renown brought to him from all parts whatever occured in the way of observation and discovery. It was, moreover, in great part his genius, his lectures, his works, which animated all observers and everywhere created them; and never could it have been said of any man with more truth than of him, that nature heard herself everywhere interrogated in his name. Hence there is nothing comparable to the rich collections which he created at the museum and which were all placed in order by him. And when we think of that direct study of objects which was the principal occupation of his life, and through which he has contributed so much . . . it cannot surprise us that he was often heard to say that he believed himself to have been not less useful to science by his collections alone than by all his other works. In the course of a career so full of success and of honors, Cuvier sustained not a few severe blows. He lost his first two children, either a few days or a few years after birth; the third, a son, died at the age of seven, and all these sorrows were renewed, and with far more bitterness, when he lost his daughter, a young lady of rare qualities, who offered not only in mind but in features no faint resemblance to her father. In all the misfortunes of life his consolation was ordinarily sought in redoubled labor; but a consolation still more efficacious consisted in the affectionate attentions with which his family and, above all Madame Cuvier, were sedulous to surround him.

If we consider the numerous public appointments of Cuvier, his unintermitting researches, his voluminous and important works, it seems astonishing that a single life could have sufficed for so much. But besides the superior faculties of his understanding, he possessed an ardent curiosity which impelled him to the pursuit of all knowledge, a memory which partook of the wonderful, and a facility even still more wonderful of passing from one labor to another immediately, without effort—a singular faculty which perhaps contributed more than any other to add to his time and his energy. Moreover, no one ever made so thorough, and, if I may thus express myself, so methodical a study of the art of not losing a single moment. Each hour had its stated labor; each labor had a cabinet which was destined for it, and in which all was found that related to that labor—books, drawings, objects. Everything was prepared, everything foreseen, so that no external cause might intervene to distract or retard the mind in the course of its meditations and researches. The address of Cuvier was grave, and his was not a politeness which diffused itself in words, but he possessed a goodness of heart and a kindness which were prone to proceed always directly to action. . . .

I need not, in concluding, recall to my auditors that death, so much deplored and so sudden, which surprised him in the midst of so many labors and great designs. That event is too recent, the remembrance too painful, and the regrets of his colleagues in this Academy, still vivid and profound, are the homage most worthy of his memory. [Cuvier died Sunday, May 13, 1832.] . . . His glory must increase with the progress of the sciences which he created. . . .

Leopold von Buch *

1774–1853

———◆———

PIERRE JEAN MARIE FLOURENS

"DATING FROM the first years of the age of Louis XIV," says Voltaire, "a general revolution has been effected in our arts, our genius, our manners, which must forever serve to mark the true glory of our country. This revolution," he adds, "did not stop in France; it extended to England, carried taste into Germany, science into Russia, and reanimated the languishing spirit of Italy." The period of which Voltaire speaks was in truth distinguished by the rise of an honorable and strenuous rivalry among all the nations of Europe, and by an alliance of intellects which, deriving new force from mutual support, no longer feared to submit to investigation those great and fundamental questions whose solution might have seemed forever hidden from us.

In Germany one of those who most contributed to inspire science with courage for arduous enterprises was Leibnitz. While this rare genius was meditating the project of endowing his country with a great literary and scientific association, a colony of French savants, driven into exile by the revocation of the Edict of Nantes, came to seek shelter in his neighborhood. Profiting by this valuable aid, the Academy of Berlin was established. But the course of its prosperity was short. The reign of William I, the rigorous tactician who thought of nothing but war, who measured the merit of his subjects by their stature, and defined savants as *frivolous inutilities,* supervened. The learned assembly found itself from that moment discountenanced and was only restored to its position under the influence of the great Frederick. This last monarch practiced no disguise as to his admiration for France, of which he loved alike the literature, the philosophy, the language, and above all the men of letters, whom he would fain have lured away to

* A.R., 1862, pp. 358–372.

Berlin. In default of Voltaire or d'Alembert, he took from us Maupertuis and made him president of his Academy.

Frederick impressed on all the mental activities of his country the ardor which governed himself. Enlightened by his example, the oldest and most noble families perceived that to dedicate their sons to the higher objects of intellectual toil was at once to reflect honor on themselves and to acquire for the nation inexhaustible resources of utility and fame. At Stolpe, in the Uckermark, in the tranquillity of a residence inherited from many generations, one of these families, which could already point to names illustrious in diplomacy and letters, numbered among an attractive group of brothers and sisters a young enthusiast, active and intelligent, but wayward and contemplative, who, neglecting the usual sports and pleasures of his age, devoted his childish admiration to the objects presented by the beautiful scenery in which he was nurtured.

After a preliminary course of instruction the young Leopold von Buch, born April 26, 1774, quitted the banks of the Oder in order to enter, at scarcely sixteen years of age, upon new and more severe studies. The school of mines, a first step to geology, was that in which his aptitude and energy received their earliest development.

Few sciences are at once so recent and so old as geology. In every age men have sought to know how the globe they inhabit was formed, and the problem has always proved highly embarrassing. Hence certain ancient philosophers were led to solve the difficulty by the very convenient supposition that the world is eternal. Fortunately, a writer much older than these philosophers, and, without himself suspecting it, much more learned, has transmitted to us a singularly faithful indication of the manner in which things had their beginning and of the stages by which they have arrived at the state in which we now see them. The record of Moses had become, at the end of the XVIIth century, the theme which exercised all intellects. Steno, Burnet, Woodward, Whiston applied themselves to the study of the deluge described in Genesis and thought that all the changes of the globe might be explained by the effects of that deluge alone. Leibnitz was the first to comprehend that previous to the action of the waters a still more energetic action, that of fire, must have been exerted; for all has been melted, all has been liquefied. "And what other agent," he cries, "what other agent but fire could have been capable of dissolving those mighty bones of the globe, those naked rocks and imperishable boulders: *magna telluris ossa, nudæque illæ rupes atque immortales silices!*"

To Leibnitz succeeded Buffon. In his *Theory of the Earth,* Buffon as yet saw nothing but the action of water; in his system on the *Formation of the Planets,* he sees nothing but the action of fire; in his *Epochs of Nature,* his best-considered and most perfect work, he skillfully subordinates the action of water to that of fire, assigns to each of these agents its part, to every event its place, to every fact its age; but this admirable book came too late. From the appearance of the two earlier productions of Buffon his contemporaries had been divided; some had taken sides for his *theory,* some for his system. The first imagined everything to have been formed by water, the last by fire; these were called *Vulcanians,* those *Neptunians.* In England the Vulcanians acknowledged as their chiefs Hutton and Playfair, in France Desmarets and Dolomieu. The school of Freiberg, where Germany flocked around Werner, became the center of *Neptunism.* It was here that the young von Buch arrived in 1791.

Confided to the care of Werner, he was his favorite disciple and an inmate of his house. In long and paternal colloquies the master, who united with the genius of method the charm of eloquence and the seductiveness of good nature, found himself happy in an opportunity of communicating to a quick and penetrating intellect the treasures of knowledge which had been accumulated by long years of meditation and observation, and which a disinclination for writing, only to be accounted for by his happy facility of speech, left him no other means of imparting.

About the same period with von Buch there arrived at the school of Freiburg several young men with whom he naturally entered into relations of friendship. These attachments, so easily contracted in youth, so often dissolved amid the conflicts of life, were with him as enduring as life itself. No similarity of aims ever disturbed the uniformity of his regard for Charles Friesleben, and throughout his whole career his love and admiration for Alexander von Humboldt, who to a less candid nature might have seemed a dangerous rival, were as unrestricted as they were disinterested.

At eighteen years of age he made a first trial of his strength by publishing a *descriptive mineralogy,* from the motto of which we learn the boldness of his aspirations: "What is new," he says, "extends, what is great exalts, the circle of our observation." Soliciting, two years after, employment in the service of mines, he addressed to the Minister Heinitz a second essay, equally evincing the early penetration of his intellect: "What I have sought to prove," he says, "is the possibility of finding constant laws according to which the formation of crystals takes place." A royal

scholarship, with a commission for directing the working of the
mines, was speedily conferred on him and imposed engagements
whose restraints he submitted to for three years. But independent
in spirit and in fortune, with a rich future before him, knowing as
yet no explanation of the great phenomena of the globe but those
which the school of Freiburg admitted, and too clear-sighted to
content himself with these, he threw aside the shackles of the
artificial world with the badge of the engineer and resumed his
liberty. This fortunate breach of discipline, the first awakening of
genius, was silently connived at by government, to the subsequent
advantage of both parties.

Of the disciples of Werner it has been said that "they dispersed
themselves through all countries, from pole to pole, in order to
interrogate nature in the name of their master." Von Buch was
pre-eminently one of those indefatigable interrogators of nature.
He set out in 1797, directing his course toward the Alps, wandered for some time in the mountainous districts of Styria, passed
a winter at Salzburg, and then turned his steps toward Italy. He
wished to visit the places where violent commotions have ruptured the crust of the earth and opened it, according to his own
expression, to the eyes of observers. It was here, however, that
his confidence in the infallibility of his school was destined speedily
to be shaken.

From Perugino the young Neptunian already writes: "Here
the different species of rocks seem to have been overwhelmed by
chaos itself. I find the beds of porphyry above the secondary
limestone, and the micaceous schists above the porphyry. Does
not all this threaten with ruin the fine systems which determine
the epoch of formations?" In a series of letters to his friend De
Moll we see that Italy appeared to his youthful and enthusiastic
imagination a promised land; and that, though science is always
in his thoughts, nothing escapes notice and all sorts of observations gratify him. If the Albanian hills constrain him to modify
the ideas which he had brought with him respecting the insignificance of volcanic effects, yet in the midst of constantly recurring alarms for the system of his master he pleases himself
with the description of the beauties unfolded before his eyes:
"Nature," he exclaims, "seems here inexhaustible in the creation
of delights which spring up at every step. Whoever has not seen
the sun set in the sea while his rays gild the cupolas of the eternal
city, whoever has not watched on Lake Nemi the alternating play
of the light, can form no conception of the charm of those regions." A tone such as this reveals the man for whom, during a

long career, study and the seductions of travel are to be inseparably linked, and who in research is intent only on that which
is exalted and aggrandized by its union with the emotions of the
soul.

Arriving at Rome, he there observes the doubtful traces of
extinct volcanoes, and his disquietude increases. "I am lost," he
says, "in the contradictions which seem to have been here accumulated. One knows not what to believe, nor even if it is
permitted to trust one's own eyes."

To him Vesuvius had always held out the promise of a revelation. At length, after several delays, he saw it, on the 19th of
February, 1799. "I arrived," he tells us, "by way of the fair
plains of the Campagna; a fog which covered the horizon suddenly vanished, and before me rose sublime the double peak of
Vesuvius crowned with eternal flame. There it is! was the involuntary cry which an expectation so keen and so often disappointed drew from me; while the cloud in lifting itself seemed
to aspire to unite the vast mountain with the heavens."

On approaching Naples the young German, brought into contact with a vivacious and impassioned population, felt a natural
surprise at the singular contrast which the brisk petulance of the
inhabitants of these climates forms with the phlegmatic earnestness of his native Germany. "Here," he says, "where language
seems scarcely the competent organ of expression, where gesture
seems the true language, how does everything recall the idea of
that mysterious fire which we know only by its effects, and which
strikes us in so unexpected a manner!"

Vesuvius, whose mysteries he so earnestly longed to penetrate,
baffled him on this occasion with delusive hopes. He brought
away little but a presentiment of the vast labors which lay before
him: "I have seen the crater and descended it," he writes, "but I
have realized nothing but a religious horror which certainly gives
me no insight into the connection of causes and effects." Following the currents of lava, he retraces that which filled Naples with
dismay in 1767, as well as the fiery torrent which some years
later swept away the town of Torre del Greco and spread far
into the sea; and animated by recitals still impressed with terror,
he paints the effects of this fearful unloosening of subterranean
forces with a poetic energy which recalls the celebrated letter of
the younger Pliny. From this first expedition our young savant was
taught to comprehend that the study of strata tranquilly deposited
by the waters is not, as was thought at Freiberg, the whole of
geology, that nature reveals herself in crises, and it is only at such

epochs that we can hope to detect secrets which were otherwise impenetrable. Von Buch left Italy, where fire in activity spreads its ravages, only to pass into France, where Auvergne offered him the most suitable of theatres for the study of extinct volcanoes.

Buffon had seen in volcanoes nothing but a congeries of sulphurs and pyrites situated quite near the summit of mountains. The sagacious and patient De Saussure had too long meditated and suffered among the snows of Mont Blanc to concede much influence to mountains of fire. Werner, averse to what might disturb the regular order of nature, which he had elaborated, and interrupt the tranquil flow of his instructions, accepted volcanoes but as local and limited accidents. It was thus that matters stood and would perhaps have long stood, had not two travellers, who happened to be detained on the road to Moulins, been struck at observing the great difficulty experienced by a mason at work near them in breaking the stones with which he was constructing a fountain; their hardness, color, and porous structure recalled to one of the observers the lavas of Vesuvius. "Whence do you bring these stones?" he asked. "From Volvic, near Riom." "*Volvic!* *Vulcani, vicus;* there must have been a volcano there," said our celebrated naturalist, Guettard, to his friend Malesherbes; "let us take the road to Auvergne." This they did; it was in 1751. Guettard discovered a whole chain of extinct volcanoes and revealed to his fellow citizens that they trod a soil once on fire; the lavas, the cinders, the scoriæ, the mountains with their craters, all lent confirmation to the fact. The unexpected announcement was received, we are told, with astonishment and even with alarm.

Twelve years later the practical and sagacious Desmarets in the course of one of those excursions in which he traversed the whole of France on foot, made a visit to the Puy de Dome and clearly distinguished the pillars of black stone, whose figure and position struck him with their resemblance to what he had read respecting basalts and giant causeways. In their regularity these columns bore the indications of a melted product; and further investigation left no doubt in the mind of Desmarets that they had been cast by the action of fire.

The igneous origin of basalts, the action of fire, then, was established, but where did this formidable agent reside? It was another French geologist who ventured for the first time to answer, *at great depths beneath the solid crust of the globe*—a revelation which we owe to the genius of Dolomieu, so severely tried with misfortune, but endowed sometimes with an utterance which might seem little less than inspired. These extinct craters and melted basalts, these fires at profound depths strangely interfered with the system of the excellent Werner, who would admit of nothing beneath the granite and could see nothing above it but deposits of aqueous formation. It was a step therefore toward independence when Leopold von Buch ventured, first among the German Neptunians, into the very heart of Vulcanism, to assure himself whether Auvergne, as it was described, really pertained to the existing world. The surprise he had felt at Perugino was here of course redoubled. Here, not nature alone offered him her guidance, but the men of genius also who had preceded him. What might not this young and vigorous intelligence hope, if successful in recovering the clue of those grand ideas with which these localities and phenomena had inspired his predecessors!

His exploration of Auvergne was persistent and profound. He applied to it all the resources of his mind, and may be said by this forcing process to have here conceived the germs of all the lofty views to the development of which his after life was consecrated. The account of this visit is filled with the traces of hesitation and of effort. At the sight of the basalts, he exclaims, "How is it possible to believe in their igneous origin when we recall the rocks which accompany them in Germany; and yet *here* how is it possible to doubt of it?" In view of the subverted and displaced strata, he says: "I see the whole edifice fall to pieces which, by a sweeping arrangement of the series of rocks, gave us the structure of the world at the same time with its history." Contemplating that long chain of heights *(Puys)* which stretch in succession from the Mont-Dore, he is struck by the possibility of the upheaval of the entire mass of these volcanoes: "What, indeed, prevents us," he asks, "from conceiving the whole mass of the Mont-Dore to have been thus lifted up?"

Voltaire tells us that a Frenchman who in his time had passed from Paris to London would find things not a little changed. He had left the universe a *plenum;* he would find it a *vacuum.* He had left behind a philosophy which explained everything by impulsion; he would find one which explained everything by attraction. When our young savant passed from Germany into France something of the same sort had occurred to him.

Werner had declared that all rocks without exception, porphyry, granite, even basalt, were the product of water; *here* the granite, the porphyry, the basalt bore irrefutable testimony to the action of fire. Werner had taught that the superposition of strata had observed always the same order; the granite below the gneiss and porphyry below the limestone, etc. In Italy and Auvergne the whole order was reversed; in one place the granite, elsewhere the porphyry, occurred above the limestone. Werner had said that the seat of volcanoes did not descend below the limit of the coals, the source, as he taught, of the materials which maintain them. Here the focus of the volcanoes showed itself beneath the deepest rocks, the porphyry, the granite, the terrestrial envelope. Werner, in fine, had seen in volcanoes only accidental and local phenomena of comparatively small potency. In Auvergne everything demonstrated the extent and power of those hidden and profound forces which had sufficed to elevate immense rocks and even entire mountains, such as the Cantal and the Mont-Dore.

The exploration of Auvergne, in opening to von Buch a whole series of sublime views, impressed him with the necessity of calling new resources to his aid. It was said of him by an Englishman, that "he went everywhere to take the measure of those who cultivated his favorite science," and what he had learned respecting the sagacity of the French savants seems now to have inspired him with the desire of *taking their measure.* He went to Paris, formed connections there, and among others with Haüy, the kindness of whose reception he acknowledges in terms which show how highly he prized the words of encouragement extended to him by this great master. The museums, the collections, the libraries, were no less objects of eager interest than the conversation of accomplished men. Levying contributions from every source, he referred all to his one great task of active labor and incessant meditation. Among the common elements of character, vanity was one in which he seemed wholly deficient. Impelled to constant observation as if by a necessity of his nature, he may be said, on leaving Auvergne, to have made but one tour, but it was a tour which lasted his whole life. "What mode of conveyance do you prefer?" he was asked by somebody who thought himself an observer. "What!" replied von Buch, leaning on his inseparable umbrella, "you do not know how a geologist ought to travel?" As regards himself, he might have been seen traversing afoot at one time the entire chain of the Apennines; at another, that of the Alps; passing in the same way from the craters of Vesuvius to the mountains of Scotland; from Etna to the snows of the polar circle; again at his favorite station of the Mont-Dore, on his route to Paris, where the society of kindred minds might delay but could not detain him. He gave no notice of his arrival and still less of his departure. A savant, surprised at receiving a visit from him and going to return it, would not improbably find that he had again disappeared, and learn by a letter from Naples perhaps, or Stockholm, where it would be necessary to inquire for von Buch. At Paris one day a geologist of note going to see him met him on the threshold of his hotel, umbrella in hand. It was a bad sign. "You are going out; allow me to accompany you." "Willingly." "But where are you going?" "To Berlin."

Setting out as was his wont every spring, he took with him no companion but the faithful one just mentioned, no guide but his impulse, no baggage but his book of notes, his barometer, two or three favorite volumes, and above all, that indefatigable pick to whose blows so many rocks have resounded—all contained in the vast pockets of a double vestment, which, always the same and proof against every change of temperature, generally bore the marks of this manifold service. If night overtook him he directed his steps to the nearest town and presented himself at the best hotel, where his odd equipment could not but lead occasionally to singular mistakes. But as the fragrance of his probity and kindness survived all other impressions, these strange apparitions of his came at last to be regarded by the villagers among whom he passed somewhat in the light of those of the benevolent genii of the old German legends. Each season saw him return at a stated time to the paternal manor, where a brother, who was blind, awaited him, and whom he would allow no one but himself to conduct to the waters of Carlsbad.

In 1804, Vesuvius having shown some signs of disturbance, he repaired thither anew; this time in company with Humboldt and Gay-Lussac. The combined observations of these eminent men resulted in a scientific exposition of all the effects associated with volcanic eruptions. Vibrations of the earth were recognized as their inseparable concomitants; the nature of the gases exhaled, the composition of the lavas, the force, development, and duration of these terrible phenomena were all, for the first time, submitted to a discriminative examination.

Nominated in 1806 a member of the Academy of Sciences of Berlin, von Buch read on the occasion a discourse on the progression of forms in nature. The philosophic view of the succession of beings had been advanced by Buffon, and the recent labors of Cuvier had furnished a wonderful commentary. Germany was struck with admiration at these sublime views, derived from France. In this discourse the author paints the successive gradations of the creation: inorganic bodies serving for elements in a world which is preparing for animated beings; animated beings taking their place one after the other, from the most simple up to the most complicated; up to man, the last term of the progress, whose appearance suggests these striking words: "To the existence of this being, the freest and most exalted of all, a vast concourse of physical causes was necessary. He alone encompasses the globe from one pole to the other; detaches himself, by an internal force, from matter; elevates himself above it, and, this achieved, who shall presume to trace for him a limit?"

Some thirty years before the date of these expressions the famous book of Pontoppidan had in some sort revealed to Europe countries which belong to it but which were then as little known as certain tracts of India or America. The soil of the Scandinavian peninsula—at that time a virgin one as regards researches—held out to von Buch a promise of new impressions. No sooner, in fact, does he arrive at Christiana than he finds mountains of porphyry resting on limestone and enormous masses of granite supported by fossil-bearing strata. Thus was the last blow given to his early faith, and from this time he thought no more of defending Neptunism. He devoted two years to a study of the formations of Sweden and Norway. Proceeding with his accustomed energy, sometimes by land, sometimes by sea, he explored the singularly indented coasts of the Scandinavian peninsula, ascending as far as the barren rocks of the North Cape. He was occupied with the solution of an imposing problem.

For more than a half century the inhabitants of the coast thought they had observed a gradual depression of the level of the sea. At the suggestion of the celebrated astronomer Celsius there had been marks cut in the rocks at Gefle and Calmar. Linnæus had himself traced a level on a block, which he describes with botanical precision. Here a maritime city having become an inland one, there an arm of the sea having been transformed into a highway, and all tradition concurring, the people of the country could no longer doubt of a diminution of the waters. "How singular a phenomenon!" exclaims von Buch; "and to how many questions does it give rise?" After due consideration he adds: "It is certain that the level of the sea cannot subsíde; the equilibrium of the waters forbids it. Yet the phenomenon of their retreat is no less unquestionable, and there remains but one admissible idea—that of a general upheaval of the land from Fredericshall to Abo, and perhaps to St. Petersburg."

When this striking idea was announced, the full importance of its bearing could not be at once foreseen. The demonstration of an upheaval of part of our continent is the discovery which has most strongly contributed to fortify the new theory of volcanoes and that of the origin of mountains, while it has given the most general insight into the continual effort, the incessant reaction of the interior of the globe against its envelope. At the extremity of the peninsula other phenomena awaited the observer. The eternal snows, which hover in an atmosphere still capable of developing organized beings, and which, in the torrid zone, maintain themselves at the level of the summit of Mont Blanc, occupy, on the coasts of Finmark, hills scarcely more than five or six times the height of our tallest buildings. Here our ingenious Regnard had once essayed to brave the rigors of a region then deemed inaccessible, and, in view of the interminable wastes of ice, had described himself in verses which, he says, "were destined to be read only by the bears," as having reached the end of the world:

Hic tandem stetimus nobis ubi defuit orbis.

Much further than this *end of the world,* and beyond the polar circle, after the long and dismal winter, von Buch was witness of that *boreal summer,* so curious and so little known, which he calls the *season of day*—a day which lasts for two months. Writing on the 4th of July, he says:

The continual presence of the sun and constant serenity of the air give to the days of these countries a peculiar charm. At the approach of midnight, when that orb prolongs its course towards the north, the whole region enjoys a perfect calm; the clearness is at every moment the same. It is only by the sinking of the mercury that the advance of the evening can be ascertained. After no long interval all nature begins once more to be reanimated; the mists rise from the surface of the earth; small waves on the waters show that the air which comes from the north presses with more force towards the south. The sun ascends from the horizon, its rays operate, and the murmur of rivulets, swelled by the melting snow, sensibly increases, until, through the effect of another night, one feels nothing but a soothing warmth.

Nor is Scandinavia less characterized by its inhabitants than its physical phenomena. Its icy waters and its lichens suffice to sustain the agility and vigor of the reindeer, that noble and docile companion of the nomadic life of the Laplander, a specimen of our race who bears in his stunted form and rustic manners the impress of the zone into which he has ventured to introduce our common humanity. By his side, but with marked differences, appear the Norwegian of the coasts, disdainful of his shrunken neighbor, and the agricultural Finn, who in his softened manners has carried civilization to the limits of the habitable world and even aspires to borrow from us our most refined enjoyments. "I have seen," says von Buch, "in a town near the North Cape, a public library, in which, by the side of the Danish poets, appeared the masterpieces of Corneille, Molière, and Racine."

As a scientific authority von Buch now stood so high that he might well feel conscious of being a master in the field of higher generalizations, a field so vast and so rarely attained. His return was greeted with respect by his country, his academy, by learned Europe in general. Recurring to the theater of his earlier labors, he traversed, for several following years, the mountain chains of Central Europe, with an attention always fixed on the grand ideas which he had propounded, namely, that the disorder of the primitive strata of the globe pertains to a profound subterranean cause which is connected with volcanic action; that not only the basalts but all crystalline rocks have issued from the earth in the state of lava, and that to the reactions of the earth are to be referred the elevation of mountains and that of entire countries such as Sweden. In the winter of 1814, while absorbed in these thoughts, he found himself at London, as he might at times be found everywhere, and there encountered an accomplished Norwegian, the botanist Smith. "Our conversation" says von Buch, "happened to turn on the facility with which one may transport himself from that capital to almost every known region, and the desire of profiting by it became so strong that we presently resolved to set out for the Canary Islands"—a fortunate resolution which has endowed geology with a work that will remain the mark of one of its most important advances.

The Canary Islands had been already visited by skillful observers among whom we may distinguish one of our former and most valued colleagues, Cordier, the successor of Dolomieu; but hitherto they had only been studied for themselves. Von Buch studied them in subordination and with reference to his general conceptions. His book is composed of two parts. The first embraces all the details of description: the study of rocks, elevation of mountains, variations of climate, etc. In the second and more important, the author sets forth in a few pages, equally admirable for precision of language and fullness of information, his whole theory of volcanoes, the result of long and critical observation of what is most general and constant in those grand but hitherto mysterious phenomena.

After succinctly defining a volcano to be "a permanent communication between the atmosphere and the interior of the globe," he distinguishes the effort which *elevates* from the effort which *ruptures;* the first gives him what he calls the *crater of elevation,* the second the *crater of eruption.* He shows that in each volcano there is a central point around which the eruptions take place and that this central point is always the highest summit—the *peak*—of the volcano. He discerns further a common action between all the volcanoes of the Canary Islands, connecting with the peak of Teneriffe the eruptions of the Isle of Palma, and these last with those of Lancerotte; for these eruptions are all associated *(solidaires),* and one never commences until the other has ceased. As in hands so skillful the thread of analogy once seized is never broken, from the volcanoes of the Canaries he passes to those of the entire globe and ranges them all under two classes, central volcanoes and volcanic chains. The first form the center of a number of eruptions which take place around them; the second are all disposed in line, each following the other in the same direction, like a great rent or fissure of the globe, being, as von Buch adds, probably nothing else but such a rent. From these isolated points of rock, elevated by fire, transporting his view over the innumerable isles everywhere scattered in the ocean, he combines them all under the generic name of *isles of elevation,* thus dispelling the opinion which long regarded the former as the relics of a submerged continent.

Scarcely had he returned from the Canaries (about 1819) when some inquiry led him to the Hebrides, whose basalts formed the object of his visit, and thus the Giant's Causeway became the route which reconducted him to Germany. There a new problem hurries him to Paris, and though it is the midst of winter, and a bruised arm, the result of his precipitation, threatens to detain him, he takes with him a young relative, and this time travels post, for his impatience is extreme. "If," said he, "Humboldt should have quitted Paris, the great city would seem a desert to me." He arrives, however, in season, and the two friends meet; but how is time to be found for long conversations? All the salons are eager for Humboldt's presence. The interviews, however, take place regularly, only they commence at midnight and do not terminate until morning.

This strain of scientific excitement, added to the cold, renders von Buch really ill. M. d'Arnim, his young relative, hazards some expressions of blame. "True, it is my own fault," replies the culprit, "the fire of the chimney near which we were talking had gone out and I felt chilled; but by making a movement to rekindle it I should have perhaps hastened Humboldt's departure. I preferred suffering to being deprived of his conversation, and am well content, for I have gained much by it."

Hitherto von Buch had presented his leading idea of the upheaval of mountains with the reserve distinctive of the conscientious though bold inquirer. In 1822, after a new exploration of the south Tyrol, he shows himself more decided, and in a letter to Humboldt on that country has given us his ultimate determination in regard to those great and hazardous questions. Here he pronounces, with an authority which no one as yet had acquired on this subject, that all the projecting masses on our globe owe their present position to an actual upheaval. In this he finds an explanation of the fact, till then inexplicable, that marine shells occur on the summits of the highest mountains, not that the seas have risen to those summits. It is the mountains which have been raised from the bottom of the seas. Never had a graver difficulty, nor one which longer resisted the efforts of ingenious minds, been solved in a simpler manner. By reversing the fact and presenting it as it really occurred, the explanation at once presents itself and changes the face of the science.

With von Buch it was inevitable that one discovery should lead to others. Thus, a first view reveals to him the upheaval of mountains and that of continents; a second, the mechanism of the formation of volcanoes; a third, the relation which connects the displacement of seas with the elevation of mountains. One of his most prolific views, that of the *discordance* of rocks, disclosed to our distinguished colleague. Élie de Beaumont (a geologist who, by his own labors, has united the researches of Cuvier with those of von Buch), the first germ of his learned theory of the *relative age* of mountains. We owe still another highly ingenious and novel conception to von Buch. His explanation of the formation of dolomite, or, more generally, of the alteration produced on deposited and sedimentary rocks by the incandescent rocks of elevation which have traversed them, though still subject to some difficulties, must always be looked upon as a suggestion of a high order and as having marked out for modern geology one of its most important objects, the study of the secondary action of fire on the envelope of the globe.

After so many brilliant labors, the smiling banks of the Spree, with the return of every autumn, continued to recall this eminent and indefatigable man to the quiet retreat which he had chosen. There a simplicity, the more charming as it was wholly voluntary, presided over the economy of his daily life. The necessity of peaceful labor and therefore of silence had induced him to limit his personal retinue to one, and when age had relaxed the activity of this one faithful domestic, von Buch, like Leibnitz, had his food brought to him from without. Often his door was opened by himself. If the stranger was one whose presence seemed likely to be importunate, to the question, "Is M. von Buch at home?" he would quietly reply, "No," and closing the door, return to his occupations. The young princes of the royal family were sometimes among those who hazarded the experiment, and their admission was due not so much to their rank as to the affectionate relations which existed between von Buch and his sovereign, who, among other marks of his favor, had made him one of his chamberlains—a chamberlain, it must be confessed, of very slender assiduity in his office. If the interruption was occasioned by the arrival of a savant, on the very threshold, and without waiting to bid good day, he would encounter the visitor with some such question as this: "Is the *semi-bi-lobate divided ammonite* found also in Thuringia?"

An unappeasable curiosity had directed our geologist's inquiries to that part also of the terrestrial envelope which is traceable to the action of water and which paleontology had recently occupied in its search for the remains of extinct races. Since life appeared on the globe it has undergone many vicissitudes and clothed itself with many forms. Different species have succeeded one another, and as each has surrendered its spoils to the contemporary strata, these relics determine the relative age of the deposits, and the history of life serves to illustrate and complete the history of the globe. Von Buch, after Buffon, aptly compares fossil shells to medals, and adds in terms of his own that these medals also have their *language.* In a series of memoirs on the *ammonites,* the *terebratula,* the *productus,* etc., he has taught us the means of interpreting that language—the new and difficult art of distinguishing with certainty the species which identify the several strata, by characters on which he had bestowed the most earnest and profound study. Nor were his efforts to restore the ancient annals of the world limited to shells. To fossil botany he brought the same aid, a precise determination of characters, which he had conferred on fossil geology, so that the expressive epithet which he gave to certain fossil shells and leaves, calling them *guiding* ones (*conductrices*), might well be transferred to himself. He has truly proved, in these delicate investigations, a guide to other geologists.

But to be an intellectual *guide* did not alone suffice for this good and eminent man. Wherever he could discover young persons whose success seemed trammelled only by the rigors of fortune he was sure to interpose; and, as if to compensate for the modesty of his own wants, he acted on those occasions with a regal munificence. Such instances were numerous and were seldom made public. Toward a vessel ready to sail a young savant was one day directing his steps. His baggage was light, though he had divested himself of his patrimony to procure the means of pursuing his explorations in America. By the wayside a stranger is waiting for him, and says: "A friend, impelled by a desire to promote the progress of science, begs you to employ this in its service"; he places a purse in the hands of the traveller and disappears. Being once at Bonn, von Buch received a visit from a youthful professor of that university who desired letters of recommendation, as he was about to join a scientific expedition. Return tomorrow, replied the distinguished savant. The interval is employed in seeking information. At the hour prescribed the young man presents himself, the letters are ready, they converse. Von Buch becomes animated, affectionate, gives advice, and finally says to the visitor at taking leave, "I have a service to ask of you." "Compliance will give me pleasure," is the prompt response. "Yes, yes," cries von Buch, "they all say the same thing, and afterwards complain that I have charged them with commissions which annoy them." The young man protests, cannot conceive how he should be suspected of insincerity and ingratitude. "Very well," replies the adroit interlocuter, "give me your word of honor that you will not even answer me after receiving my commission." The other pledged himself. "Now that I have your word," resumes von Buch, "here are 2,000 dollars which you are to make use of in your travels." As the injunction did not extend to silence, the recipient felt constrained afterwards to share the secret with others besides his benefactor. A young painter, tormented alike by the fever of art and the anguish of destitution, was languishing at Rome. There was nothing which singled him out but his talent and his misery. Von Buch charges one of the embassies with the remission of a considerable sum, and that the artist may be restrained by delicacy from attempting to penetrate the mystery, he is to be told that it is a family restitution of an ancient date.

As it was one of the chief pleasures of von Buch's life to restore hope to the unfortunate, so it peculiarly suited his character to act as a peacemaker between the learned when divided in opinion. Before all things, however, it was indispensable that science, his sublime mistress, should be treated with the most exact respect.

Just and generous in his appreciation of men, he was always zealous in setting forth the merit of the labors of his contemporaries. A sure and constant friend, though blunt, eccentric, and at times impatient, he was ever ready if umbrage were taken to make the advances necessary for conciliation. Among intimates he was fond of recounting the ludicrous mistakes which had been occasioned during his travels by the grotesque appearance under which he presented himself.

He loved society but not what is called the great world. Those who had seen him at court, whither his office as well as the proprieties of his station in life sometimes led him, might have thought him drawn thither by his tastes, but his resort even there was to the circles in which intelligence supplied the attraction. In these the graces of language springing from an active and full mind, reenforced by a surprising memory, gave to his conversation when he was in the vein a peculiar charm. Polished in the company of females, he knew how to appreciate those who in the courteous collisions of which our salons are the lists, and which we call conversation, furnish by their sprightly sallies often the best, but certainly the most graceful contingent. This admiration, however, never trenched upon the liberty which he had consecrated to science. Von Buch never married, but in return the family affections exercised over him the blandest and most potent influence, and his love for the young, toward whom he could find indulgence for everything but self-sufficiency, prompted many of the actions of his life.

When far advanced in age, he still quitted his domestic roof with the first breath of spring. "I shall travel," was his simple announcement, and a walk would conduct him from Berlin to Dresden, to the surprise of his more sedentary associates in the latter place. Thence his course would be prolonged as far as Bohemia or Switzerland. It was when an old man that he scaled the mountain ranges of Greece, seeking among the extinct populations only those which ally themselves with the real world, and finding more attraction and instruction in the chronology of a shell than in all the brilliant fictions which animated Parnassus and Hymettus.

In 1850, a German university having summoned naturalists to a congress intended to celebrate the memory of Werner, von Buch was present and of course became the center of all regards, a tribute which with an affectionate simplicity he studiously referred to his early master. "As for myself," he pleasantly said, in allusion to the only official title which he had ever adopted, "I am nothing more than the oldest of the royal pupils of the kingdom of

Prussia." His return from this reunion conducted him through the country of his birth, and the view of those fair scenes which recalled to him the memories of his youth, plunged him into reverie. It was observed that he passed a long night in deep meditation, in which he seemed to address to the places he was regretfully leaving a touching and silent adieu. He came once more, however, to visit France, whose genius he loved, and to sit in that Academy to which he prided himself in belonging. He left Paris only in the last days of 1852 and peacefully breathed his last in the spring of 1853.

Von Buch, who had qualified himself for the direct contemplation of nature by always and everywhere pursuing her indications, has left us an example of one of the noblest of scientific careers. He had the happiness to consecrate a long life and a penetrating genius to the profound and unwearied study of one of the highest questions of natural philosophy. Descartes had suspected the igneous origin of the globe; Leibnitz had inferred its incandescence from the traces everywhere apparent of a vast pristine fusion; Buffon had demonstrated the existence of the primitive fire, still subsisting, and more and more concentrated in the interior of the earth; Dolomieu finally had pronounced before this Academy the words adopted by Lagrange: "This globe, at first incandescent and fluid throughout its whole mass, is still so in its interior, and has nothing solid but its crust." But no one more contributed than von Buch to prepare the vast and sublime generalization which dares to place in this profound and central fire, of which, however, he himself has nowhere pronounced the name or fully admitted the idea, the first and sole, the potent and terrible cause of all the revolutions of our globe.

Hans Christian Oersted *

1777–1851

―――◆―――

JEAN BAPTISTE ÉLIE DE BEAUMONT

HANS CHRISTIAN OERSTED was born August 14, 1777, at Rudkjöbing, in the island of Langeland, one of the smallest of the archipelago of Denmark. His father exercised the profession of apothecary, and although the town of Rudkjöbing then counted less than 1,000 inhabitants, he had full occupation. For fear that the young Christian should not be properly looked after in the paternal dwelling, he was sent every day to the house of a wig-maker, whose wife enjoyed the confidence of his parents. A brother, one year younger, who became in after life the celebrated jurisconsult André Sandöe Oersted, accompanied him thither the following year. The wig-maker and his wife formed a warm attachment for the two brothers. The wife taught them to read; the husband instructed them in German, which was his mother tongue. The pupils made rapid progress, owing perhaps in reality more to a happy natural aptitude than to any talent in the teachers, but which sufficed to induce many other families to send their own children likewise to this improvised school where knowledge was imparted so quickly and so well. The wig-maker transformed into schoolmaster daily read to his pupils some pages of a German Bible, which was thus perused from beginning to end and afterwards in great part read over anew. It was the daily task of the young Christian to translate word by word into Danish what had been read in German, and this exercise so far profited him that at the age of seven years he often embarrassed by his citations those who sought to put his sagacity to the test; whence the gossips of the vicinity used to say of him, "This child will not live; he is too smart!"

* A.R., 1868, pp. 166–184. Read originally at the annual public sitting of the French Academy of Sciences, Dec. 29, 1862.

The wig-maker further taught him addition and subtraction. It was all he himself knew of arithmetic, but with some slight help from others and a book found at his father's the child was not slow in learning the rest as far as the rule of three—unequivocal proof of unusual precocity. An extraordinary memory was early remarked in him and was retained till death, equally with all the other happy endowments which he had received from nature.

When Christian had reached the age of 12, he and his brother, who was then 11, entered as apprentices the pharmacy of their father, whereby their secret wishes were at first contravened, for both had conceived the project of devoting themselves to the study of theology. The elder of the two, however, soon began to acquire a taste for pharmaceutical operations and labored zealously in the paternal laboratory, reading at the same time all the books of chemistry and natural history which fell into his hands. Thus early was developed the inclination which led him to the study of nature. A student in theology daily devoted some hours to the instruction of the brothers in Greek and Latin. The elder applied himself moreover to the acquisition of the French, the younger to that of the English language. From this period the former evinced a decided taste for poetry, a taste which remained with him all his life. He translated about this time several odes of Horace and a part of the *Henriade* into Danish.

These rather precarious means of instruction still bore happy fruits. In the spring of the year 1794 the brothers, aged respectively 17 and 16, were qualified to proceed to Copenhagen where, after but a few months' preparation by a skillful master who perfected them in the study of the ancient languages, they sustained with much honor an examination at their exit from the academy. Some two years afterwards Christian, who had in the meantime earned testimonials of distinction on all hands, bore off an academic prize for his reply to a question "on the shades to be observed in the choice of expressions, according as one writes in prose or in verse." Finally, during the autumn of 1799 he obtained the degree of doctor of philosophy upon the presentation of a thesis in metaphysics, *"De forma metaphysices elementaris naturæ externæ."*

In that year last named and others immediately following, he published divers short dissertations and critical analyses, which were generally inserted in the periodical collections. He thus evinced in turn the tendency of his mind to literature, to poetry, and to philosophy. These formed indeed only an accessory occupation; but apart from his natural predisposition, favorable circumstances rendered these momentary efforts of singular advantage in the development of his faculties. His brother, with whom he always lived in the most cordial intimacy, had chiefly devoted himself to the study of philosophy, and the habit, which was maintained during life, of a daily interchange of ideas led our physicist to a profitable participation in the same pursuit. Having become familiar with the writings of Kant, Fichte, and Schelling, he caught sight of a great general law of unity in the physical world, which continued always to be one of the habitual subjects of his meditation. Struck at the same time with the beauty of natural laws, he became sensible of something profoundly poetic in nature, on which his innate taste for poetry seized with avidity.

His first essays, which had fixed the attention of the citizens of Copenhagen, placed him on terms of friendly intimacy with most of his young contemporaries who were rising into distinction, particularly with Oehlenschläger, who as a poet achieved some years afterwards so brilliant and well-merited a reputation. This attractive intercourse impelled him to the study of belles-lettres. To no important production of Danish or German literature or of the older French literature was he a stranger. His admirable memory was garnished with the choicest passages which even at an advanced age he was wont to cite with singular appositeness. Nor did he fail sometimes to exercise his own poetic powers, and, in the eyes of persons competent to judge of Danish verse, an *Ode to the French,* which he composed about this time, seemed to indicate genuine talent. A happy concurrence of circumstances brought Oersted also into intercourse with Steffens, and the two brothers Mynster, with whom he long continued to maintain philosophical and even theological discussions which, whatever their vivacity, were never permitted to interfere with the claims of a reciprocal friendship. The rectitude of his judgment always prevented these accessory exercises of thought from impairing the progress of his scientific studies; but they did not a little contribute to draw general attention to him—a kindly attention which greatly facilitated the development of his subsequent career.

Of that career positive science was always the basis, and his success was rapid. At his examination in pharmacy, May 20, 1797, he astonished his judges by the extent of his knowledge, and one of them on going away, having met with Professor Manthey, proprietor of the pharmacy in which Oersted had labored, addressed him in these words: "What a candidate is this you have sent us; he knows more than all of us together!" The following year Oersted obtained a new prize from the Academy, this time on a question of medicine. In 1800 Professor Manthey, being about to travel abroad, entrusted to him the direction of his pharmacy and nominated him as a substitute lecturer at the Academy of Surgery. The same year Oersted became an adjunct of the faculty of medicine.

At this epoch he occupied himself very actively with chemistry. The researches of Winterl on the simple galvanic chain had already led to the conception of an electro-chemical theory, and Ritter had inferred, from the ordinary chemical and electrical facts, the identity of the forces which produce them. The labors of Berthollet on the laws of affinities had also introduced new general views on chemical forces. Herein lay the subjects of Oersted's investigations during the years 1799 and 1800. Earlier studies had prepared him for these general views, and efforts to surmount certain lines of demarcation established in science by distinctions too decisive had even directly revealed to him some of them. An analysis of the chemical philosophy of Fourcroy, read by Oersted in 1799 to the Scandinavian Society and printed the following year in its bulletin, is unfortunately the sole trace which remains of these first essays. We find there the alkalis and earths already ranged in a single series which, commencing with the most energetic alkalis, terminates with a body rather acid than alkaline, silicium preceded by aluminum.

But in 1800 the discovery of the electric pile by Volta* threw all the chemists into commotion. Throughout Europe there was a desire to witness its effects. Everywhere were constructed similar piles or columns formed of pairs composed each of a disk of copper and a disk of zinc, pairs superposed on one another and separated by a piece of moistened cloth. Soon, everyone in the modish as in the learned world knew by experience the strange shocks and sensations felt in the wrists, in the elbows, when in each hand is held a metallic wire terminating at one of the two opposite poles of the pile and one is thus placed in the course of the electric current to which the pile gives rise. Oersted was not among the last to make experiments with this wonderful instrument. Having applied it especially to the decomposition of divers saline solutions, he gave expression to this first law, that the quantities of alkalis and acids set at liberty in a solution by the action of the pile are in proportion to their respective capacities of saturation. Here then was a step in the career in which he was destined one day to immortalize himself.

Oersted was now 23 years of age: The time had come for him

* See pp. 56–61 of this volume.

to travel, as in their youth the German and Scandinavian savants almost always do. He set out in 1801, and his absence extended to two and a half years. Everywhere he found with the learned a reception which surpassed the hopes of his friends. His natural animation, joined to a candid and unaffected self-reliance, stood him in better stead than the strongest letters of recommendation. His countenance seemed to bespeak a certain timidity, but no sooner did any subject awaken in him a special interest, such as a point of science to discuss or error to combat, than he was seen to put forth a boldness, a force of intellect, an eloquence which would scarcely have been suspected from his modest exterior and reserved demeanor.

He first traversed a great part of Germany, passed six months at Berlin, and sojourned for some time at Freiburg, Jena, and Munich. A new life then animated that country. Poets and philosophers of eminence had there given to the human mind an unexpected impulse. This movement bore especially on the natural sciences, and that assemblage of somewhat vague ideas which was called the philosophy of nature was in process of development. Oersted, with his philosophic and poetic views on the unity and the beauty of nature, was sufficiently disposed to lend attention to the new German doctrines, and he himself avows their influence by saying in the preface of one of his works published in 1813: "The philosophy of nature, which has been cultivated within 20 years in Germany, might also assert its claim to some of the views which we are about to offer." Yet he never allowed himself to be turned aside from the severe and positive study of facts and of experiment.

He enjoyed constant conversations with Klaproth, Hermstadt, Paul Erman, Trommsdorff, with Kielmeyer, the master and friend of Cuvier, with the celebrated Werner at Freiburg, and with the profound mineralogist and crystallographer Weiss. He met also Fichte, Schelling, Franz Baader, Schleiermacher, Tieck, and the two Schlegels. But he associated himself more particularly with the ingenious physicist Ritter, already celebrated for his experiments in galvanism, in which he had established among other things that a constant development of electricity accompanies the phenomena of life. They executed in common a series of remarkable experiments, and Oersted conceived from that time a high opinion of the scientific capacity of his collaborator which frequently appears in his writings, and particularly in the following passage of the preface of his *Researches on the Identity of Chemical and Electrical Forces,* published in 1813: "Ritter may, in this respect, be regarded as a creator. His grand conceptions, and his labors, met with a zeal which obstacles and sacrifices could not subdue, have shed light on almost all parts of the science." Oersted often expressed the opinion that with more perseverance in his labors Ritter would have discovered the electric pile before Volta. Unfortunately, Ritter joined with a very ingenious mind great eccentricity, which crippled his pursuits and abridged his days.

After sojourning some time at Munich with Ritter, Oersted published at Ratisbon in 1803 a small work entitled *Materials for a Chemistry of the XIXth Century,* in which occur highly interesting views respecting the new horizons opened to chemistry by the discovery of the voltaic pile. Before parting with Ritter, who remained at Munich, Oersted had rendered him services which could only have been inspired by a warm and sympathetic friendship. He proceeded afterwards to Paris and passed there 15 months in habitual intercourse with Cuvier, Haüy, Vauquelin, Charles, Berthollet, Biot, Guyton de Morveau, Thénard; assiduously following the courses of the distinguished professors and sometimes making communications on his own experiments to the Philomathic Society.

During his stay at Paris he translated into French a German memoir of Ritter on the *pile à charger,* or secondary pile (*Ladung's Säule*). This translation, accompanied by notes on the experiments made by himself, was presented to the first class of the Institute and printed in the *Journal de Physique* for *brumaire, an* XII (1803). Ritter, who had cooperated in the translation by an uninterrupted correspondence with Oersted, was fully satisfied with it and even avowed that he understood himself in the French version better than in his own original German text. He died soon afterwards, and Oersted, independently of his own original ideas, remained the representative and in some sort the heir of those of Ritter, of whom he had been the last collaborator and interpreter.

Some prepossessions, whatever their origin, perhaps the fear of being received with a certain superciliousness, had led Oersted to pass almost the whole time of his sojourn in Paris without going to present to the celebrated Fourcroy, professor of chemistry at the Polytechnic School, a letter of Professor Manthey of Copenhagen. He decided at last to do so at the instance of the chargé d'affaires of Denmark. The elegance, the clearness, the authority with which Fourcroy discharged the functions of professor gave him great ascendency over his pupils, but out of the chair he did not always sufficiently divest himself of magisterial dignity. He congratulated the young and modest Oersted on having come to

Paris and having acquired a knowledge of so many remarkable men, superior beyond doubt to all the chemists of the north. "I must acknowledge," replied Oersted, "that you possess at Paris more dexterity than exists elsewhere in chemical manipulations; but there is scarcely to be found in the north a single chemist who cannot read in the original the *Système des connaissances chimiques* of M. de Fourcroy, which few French chemists could do for works written in the Scandinavian languages." To the question if he had seen the Polytechnic School Oersted replied of course affirmatively, and Fourcroy having made him duly sensible that this school gave to Paris a great superiority over Denmark, Oersted rejoined, with perhaps too ingenuous a confidence: "I admit that my country wants much which is needed for the fruitful development of chemistry, but I do not despair of contributing hereafter to establish there something not unlike the Polytechnic School." Upon which, Fourcroy begged him, somewhat ironically, to be sure to preserve when he returned home a kind recollection of the French chemists. This Oersted did not fail to do, and I shall show further on how he proved it.

In returning to Denmark, Oersted traversed Holland and at Harlem made a great number of electrical experiments with the learned physicist Van Marum. At Bremen he contracted a friendship with the astronomer Olbers and with Treviranus, celebrated for his labors in physiology and comparative anatomy. He finally re-entered his country in the month of January 1804. On his return the duty, at first temporary and limited to three years, of delivering lectures on physics at the University of Copenhagen was confided to him. In 1806 he was named professor extraordinary of physics in the same university. He had here the first opportunity of combining his scientific views in a systematic shape, the outline of which he preserved during his entire life, only modifying certain parts according to the progress of science. His lectures commanded a large attendance. They bore a form which was peculiar to himself. The skillful professor usually commenced in a subdued tone, with particular considerations and explanations, frequently, indeed, with the definition of certain expressions turning on the translation of technical words into the Danish language. Assured thenceforth of being fully understood, he followed the logical course of ideas and, warming by degrees, collected the facts into groups and these groups into a whole still more comprehensive. The liveliness of the lecture, in giving more freedom to his delivery, called forth his favorite thoughts on the unity, the beauty of nature, and figures and images presented themselves which keenly interested his auditors, especially the younger portion of them, for those who had already followed other lectures were more surprised at still finding something unusual in his.

It was sometimes objected to Oersted that he saw or imagined in nature combinations much more rational than those which can be expected to occur in an assemblage of material objects; but he replied that nothing is too rational to be attributed to the supreme reason which has created everything. On such a theme it would be easy to argue a long time without coming to a conclusion. It would be to plunge into the depths of those German discussions in which so many a subtle genius has exhausted itself without exhausting the subject. But the obscurity of these depths is sometimes quite *à la mode* on the shores, always a little foggy, of the Baltic Sea. It seems certain, however, that the lectures of Oersted were well received by the youth and the public of Copenhagen, for they were always much frequented, and they secured for the professor an eminent position among his fellow citizens. He was not long in establishing agreeable relations with persons of the highest position in the capital of Denmark and even with the princes of the royal family. But a part of his success might also be attributed to his lively and intellectual conversation, to the frequent articles which he put forth on various subjects, and to the works which he published at this epoch, such as his *Considerations on the History of Chemistry,* his *Experiments Respecting the Figures Produced by Nodal Lines on Vibrating Surfaces,* a subject to which Chladni had already devoted an important work, and a *Discourse on the Pleasure Produced by Sound,* a discourse in which he developed, under a point of view peculiar to himself, the laws of the beautiful.

He thus continued to publish, as he had done from his youth, a multitude of memoirs and articles of more or less extent on different subjects relating to the natural sciences and to philosophy, all of which met with appreciative readers. Nevertheless, Copenhagen was not a center to which everything converged as is Paris or London. In a city of secondary importance one may keep himself informed of what is written, but the inconvenience is soon felt of not knowing what is talked about in the learned world. Oersted, who had need of direct communication with entire Europe, felt himself impelled to undertake new expeditions. He set out for Berlin May 7, 1812, where he passed three months and gave to the press in the German language one of his most important works, entitled *Views of the Chemical Laws of Nature* (*Ansichten der chemischen Naturgesetze*). In passing through

Germany he visited Oken, Schweiger, and Hegel, and established friendly relations with the ingenious physicist Seebeck, who some years afterwards made the discovery of thermo-electricity. He then revisted Paris, where he made quite a long stay, and about the middle of the year 1813 returned to Copenhagen, there to receive anew from his countrymen tokens of the cordial consideration which he had long before inspired.

In 1814 Oersted published in the program of the university an essay on a chemical nomenclature common to all the Germanic Scandinavian languages. The names proposed were so happily appropriate to the genius of those tongues that they were generally adopted and are still in use in all the countries of the north. In 1815, the Royal Society of Sciences of Copenhagen having lost its excellent secretary, Bugge, Oersted was chosen to replace him, and the same year the King named him a chevalier of the order of Danenbrog. Two years afterwards the university conferred on him the title of Professor in Ordinary *(professor ordinarius)*, a title superior to that of Professor Extraordinary which he had borne for more than 10 years. About this time Oersted undertook a remarkable series of experiments on the compressibility of water and found almost exactly, though by new means of his own invention, the numbers which the celebrated English physicist Canton had obtained half a century before.

In 1818 and 1819 he undertook with Esmarch and Forschhammer explorations in the island of Bornholm for the purpose of examining its geological constitution with reference to the working of the coal and iron ores which are found there, and he made these investigations the subject of several publications. This was the commencement of a geological study of Denmark, established on new scientific bases. Oersted, however, was unable to prosecute this operation, which, continued by Forschhammer, has given to Denmark the excellent geological chart well known to this Academy. The journeys to Bornholm did not interrupt the habitual course of Oersted's publications on science and philosophy. Among his memoirs on physics should be particularly cited one on the trough-battery, executed in conjunction with his friend, Professor Esmarch. Another work, entitled *Principles of the New Chemistry,* which appeared at Copenhagen in 1820, had been composed for the auditors of his course with a view to placing within their reach the doctrines taught in his numerous writings on chemistry and electricity, and particularly in his *Views of the Chemical Laws of Nature.* First printed at Berlin, as I have said, this exposition of his favorite ideas had been translated into French by Marcel de Serres and published at Paris in 1813, with the con-currence of its author and that of our distinguished colleague, Chevreul, under the title of *Researches on the Identity of Chemical and Electric Forces,* a title which clearly defined its object.

This learned and ingenious work, dedicated to the author of the *Statique Chimique,* our illustrious Berthollet, was in truth the prin-cipal fruit of the labors and meditations of Oersted from his earli-est youth. A citation of some passages of this admirable book will suffice to give an idea of the profound and original views which had presided over its composition:

The chemical part of the natural sciences is far from having attained the perfection which their mechanical part has reached, and cannot, like the latter, deduce from a small number of principles, already con-nected with one another, all the other principles; but it has been obliged to seek each particular proposition, each particular law, by means of experiments undertaken solely with that particular view. Now the greater part of these laws have hitherto so little enabled us to see the bonds which unite them, that it was necessary to be convinced, by gen-eral considerations, of the unity which exists in all the works of nature, in order not to be deceived as regards that unity.

The actual state, in 1813, of the chemical part of the natural sciences might be compared to that of their mechanical part before Galileo, Descartes, Huyghens, and Newton had taught us to reduce the more compound movements to their most simple principles. Before these il-lustrious physicists, it is true, a great number of important facts were known, even some remarkable series of facts, but that great principle of unity to which science owes its present high degree of perfection had not yet been arrived at.

Oersted saw this great principle of unity in the uniformity of the general laws of mechanics, and he found an example of the duality, which also he everywhere sought, in the two forces which concur in producing circular or curvilinear motion:

To find examples of the confusion which had preceded the discovery of these forces, it is sufficient to read what was written on the classifica-tion of motions by the celebrated Bacon, who, although a contemporary of Galileo, still speaks of a violent and natural motion, and of so many other kinds of motions, which he knew no better how to reduce to a single principle than do the chemists at the present time know how to reduce the affinities of the alkalis, acids, earths, oxides, combustible bodies, and oxygen to one identical primitive action. . . .

By referring all motions to their fundamental laws, the mechanical part of the natural sciences [adds Oersted] has been raised to that pres-ent degree of perfection which embraces all the movements of the universe as one great mechanical problem, whose solution enables us to calculate in advance an infinitude of particular phenomena. In order to prepare the chemical part of the natural sciences for a like perfection, we must endeavor to reduce all chemical actions to the primitive forces which produce them; we shall then also be in a position to calculate all the chemical properties of the primitive forces and their laws. Thus, chemistry being only occupied with these properties, this whole science will be converted into a theory of forces, to which mathematics may be applied, and it will thereby acquire perhaps new capacities, like those which have been derived from the application of mathematics to movement.

In this work, as in his earlier essays of 1799, Oersted placed aluminum after the alkaline earths as less alkaline than all these latter, and indeed almost an acid. After aluminum came silicium, more acid than alkaline; while glass, he said, might be considered as a salt. It will be admitted that from thence to the theory of the silicates there was but a step. This new advance was achieved some time afterwards by Smithson Tennant, but as everyone knows, it was Berzelius beyond all others who developed the theory of the silicates. . . .

In another passage, seeking to find among authors already become antique—such as Winterl, Ritter, etc.—the first rudiments of the ideas which occupied him, and which it was the object of his book to develop, Oested added: "The advantage which we may attain over these predecessors of ours will be, for the greatest part, due to the profound researches of the celebrated Berthollet, and to the grand discoveries of Davy and Berzelius, three illustrious savants on the possession of whom our era can never cease to pride itself."

There was the more merit on the part of Oersted in thus ranking Berzelius among the great lights of chemistry, inasmuch as Berzelius, rather younger than himself, was his rival in the branch of the science to which he attached the most interest; and it should never be forgotten that if the honor of having completely unfolded the electro-chemical system reverts to Berzelius, Oersted had arrived before him at a closely analogous result, although one less developed. For the rest, what at the present day is of most import to the memory of Oersted in relation to this work is perhaps the palpable proof found therein of his ceaseless preoccupation with the subject of electrical phenomena. He had made great improvements on the pile; he was one among the most practiced experimenters in employing it; he had formally indicated magnetism as one of the phenomena of which it would some day furnish the explanation, and no one was better prepared than himself to ad-vance to the practical realization of this new conquest. Yet all the attempts thus far made had remained unfruitful. The expedient had been tried of placing the two poles of a battery as highly charged as possible in a parallel line with the poles of a strongly magnetized needle; no effect, however, had been produced. Nevertheless, the conviction still prevailed, especially with Oersted, that a relation must exist between galvanism and electricity. The route to the discovery was unknown, though chance might open it unexpectedly.

Fortune, it might be said, ceased to be blind at the moment when to Oersted was allotted the privilege of first divining that it was not electricity in repose that accumulated at the two poles of a charged battery, but electricity in movement along the conductor, by which one of the poles is discharged into the other, which would exert an action on the magnetized needle. While thinking of this—it was during the delivery of a lecture before the as-sembled pupils—Oersted announces to them what he is about to try; he takes a magnetic needle, places it near the electric battery, waits till the needle has arrived at a state of rest; then seizing the conjunctive wire traversed by the current of the battery, he places it above the magnetic needle, carefully avoiding any manner of collision. The needle—every one plainly sees it—the needle is at once in motion. The question is resolved! Oersted has crowned by a great discovery the labors of his whole previous life.

It was on the 21st of July, 1820, that Oersted communicated to learned Europe the important fact with which his genius had just enriched science. He consigned it to a small tract written in Latin of only four pages in quarto which, notwithstanding its concise-ness, presented with perfect clearness the results of more than fifty experiments and left scarcely anything to be added on the subject. This composition, entitled *Experimenta circa effectum, etc. (Experiments on the Effect of the Electrical Conflict * upon the Magnetic Needle)* was addressed the same day by post to all the societies in Europe concerned with the natural sciences. A French translation of it appeared in the number of the *Annales de chimie et de physique* for August 1820, from which I transcribe a few expressions employed by Oersted on this occasion:

The first experiments on the subject I undertake to explain were made in the lectures which I gave last winter on electricity and magnetism. They evinced in general, that the magnetic needle changed its direction

* In the French translation *"Conflit electrique."* See below.

through the influence of the voltaic apparatus, and that this effect took place when the circuit was formed, and not when it was interrupted; a process which had been attempted in vain by celebrated physicists, some years before. But, as my experiments had been made with an apparatus of small energy, the effect of which was not so striking as was called for by the importance of the fact to be established, I invited my friend Esmarch, judicial councillor to his Majesty, to unite with me in repeating them with a more powerful apparatus. We had also for associates and witnesses the Chevalier de Vlengel, MM. Hauch and Reinart, professors of natural history; Jacobson, a very skillful physician and chemist, and Zeise, professor of philosophy. I made other experiments when alone, and if these taught me anything new, I took the precaution of repeating them in the presence of these eminent men of science. . . . In order to make the experiment, we put in communication the opposite poles of the voltaic apparatus by a metallic wire, which we will call, for brevity, the *conducting* or *conjunctive wire;* and we will designate the effect which is manifested in this conductor and around it during the voltaic action by the term *electric conflict [l'épithète de "conflit électrique"].*

Let us suppose now that the rectilinear part of this wire is horizontal, and placed above and parallel to a magnetic needle freely suspended. . . . The latter will move in such a manner that, under the part of the conjunctive wire which is nearest to the negative pole of the apparatus, it will deviate towards the west. . . . If the conjunctive wire is arranged horizontally *under* the needle, the effects are of the same nature with those which take place when the wire is above the needle; but they act in an inverse direction—that is to say, the pole of the needle, under which is the part of the conjunctive wire that receives the negative electricity of the apparatus, inclines towards the east. . . . It appears, from the facts stated, that the "electric conflict" is not inclosed in the conducting wire, but that it has around it quite an extensive sphere of activity. We may conclude from the observations that this "conflict" acts by a vortical or whirling movement.

Such was the theory of Oersted: we shall presently see that he was less happy in his theory than in his experiment. In publishing the memoir of Oersted in the *Annales de chimie et de physique,* Arago added a note in which he said that the results there recorded, "however singular they might appear, are accompanied by too many details to leave room for any suspicion of error." He cited, moreover, the experiments of verification made in his presence at Geneva by de la Rive. The explanation proposed by Oersted for the capital fact which he had just discovered recalled in some respects the vortices of Descartes. This did not much savor of the spirit of the present epoch; it met consequently with but little acceptance. At the end of barely a few weeks Ampère had replaced it by another, based on a law of attraction. I borrow the recital of this scientific event from the spirited and learned *Éloge* of Ampère,* read by Arago to this Academy, the 21st of August, 1839:

The discovery of Oersted reached Paris by way of Switzerland. In our weekly session of Monday, 11th September, 1820, an academician who had come from Geneva [it was Arago himself] repeated before the Academy the experiments of the learned Dane. Seven days after, Ampère laid before us a fact much more general than that of the physicist of Copenhagen. In so short an interval of time he had divined that two conjunctive wires, that two wires traversed by electric currents, would act one on the other; he had devised extremely ingenious arrangements for rendering these wires movable, without the necessity of detaching the extremity of each of them from the respective poles of their batteries; he had realized, transformed these conceptions into instruments susceptible of operating; he had finally submitted his capital idea to a decisive experiment. I know not if the vast field of physics ever presented so admirable a discovery, conceived, made and completed with equal rapidity.

Of this brilliant discovery of Ampère the following statement may suffice: two parallel conjunctive wires attract each other when electricity traverses them in the same direction; they repel one another if the electric currents move in opposite directions.

The sequel of Ampère's labors showed that the reciprocal action of the elements of two currents is exerted in conformity with the line which unites their centers; that it depends on the mutual inclination of those elements, and that it varies in intensity in the inverse ratio of the square of the distances. Ampère finally succeeded in establishing that a conjunctive wire wound into a helix with very close spirals is sensitive to the magnetic action of the earth. For many weeks there was to be seen in his cabinet "a conjunctive wire of platina whose position was determined by the action of the terrestrial globe." Ampère, by constructing a galvanic compass, had shown that the forces which act in the magnetic needle are electric currents, and by his learned calculations on the reciprocal action of those currents he accounted for all the actions which the conjunctive wire of the pile exerts, in the experiments of Oersted, on the magnetic needle.

Electro-magnetism had thus become the common glory of Oersted and Ampère, and renown, by uniting the names of these two illustrious savants, not unnaturally calls attention to the resemblances or the contrasts which existed between them. They

* See *A.R.*, 1872, pp. 111–171.

were throughout nearly contemporary, Ampère having been born the 22nd of January, 1775, and Oersted the 14th of August, 1777. Both had begun life in a very modest condition; both had had slender means of instruction and had at first taught themselves with little help from masters and even little from books. Oersted had composed poetry not without merit; Ampère, in his youth, wrote French verses full of delicacy and grace, some of which have appeared to Arago no unworthy ornaments for his eulogy. Oersted always saw in the harmonies of nature a poetry superior to all other poetry; Ampère, in the evening of his life, composed in Latin verse a general table of the classification of the sciences, in which elegance vies with precision. Oersted, a declared disciple of Kant, applied his ideas to the material world as a consummate physicist; Ampère, an enthusiastic sympathizer with Maine de Biran, Royer Collard, and Cousin, exercised his acute and powerful faculties and manifested a lively interest in disentangling the most subtle problems of metaphysics. Both were skilled in communicating to their learned instructions a peculiar attraction, though each in a different kind. Each of them has left among friends, colleagues, and pupils remembrances full of that affectionate admiration which can never be effaced.

Oersted made his first scientific essays in the pharmacy of his father; before all else he was a chemist. Ampère at the age of thirteen borrowed from the public library of Lyons the mathematical works of Bernoulli: he was born a geometer, but the *Encyclopedia* having been his first book, he had from his infancy embraced all the branches of human knowledge and had even become profound in many of them. Arago has felt authorized to say of him, in speaking of his labors in chemical classification, that "during one of the last revolutions of science, Ampère, the geometer Ampère, proved always in the right, even when his opinions were opposed to those of almost all the chemists of the world." Without Oersted electro-magnetism might not have existed; without Ampère it might have been confined to an exceedingly curious but limited experiment. The cooperation of Oersted and Ampère made it in a very little time a complete science, a science destined to change the face of the world by the surprising applications of it which have been already realized.

. . .

I have often heard it asked who was the true inventor of the electric telegraph. Reference has been made to ingenious physicists who in the course of the last century transmitted instantaneous signals to a distance by means of the electric spark. As well might the learned, when the brothers Chappe had in 1792 invented the aerial telegraph, recall the fact that the Gauls had transmitted distant signals by means of wooden beams set in motion. Neither the Gauls nor the older physicists had created any regular means of communication.

Among those whom I have the honor of addressing, several may be able like myself to recall the memorable lectures which Ampère delivered at the College of France at the commencement of 1832, in which he had the boldness to express his ideas on the relations of the structure of different classes of animals in contradiction to Cuvier, who lectured in the adjacent amphitheater—ingenious ideas which Cuvier overwhelmed at each lecture with peremptory facts, and which Ampère, accommodating himself to those facts, reproduced still more ingeniously in his subsequent lecture. In this course, naturally much frequented, and which was in substance a course of experimental physics, Ampère spoke one day of electrical currents, and, after exhibiting on the table four small magnetic needles with metallic wires suitably encompassing them, he explained how an electric current transmitted at will in such or such a manner, by means of these wires, would cause a declination of such or such of these needles in definite directions, so as to produce divers combinations, to each of which might be attributed the value of one of the letters of the alphabet; how, in fine, by varying at will and with the rapidity of writing the mode of propagation of the electric current, words, phrases, discourses might be formed by the succession of these conventional letters.

Ampère particularly cherished this idea and often recurred to it in conversing with his friends, but his fertile imagination did not stop with a single process, and sometimes instead of needles he proposed the employment of vases filled with water in which should be produced alternately disengagements of oxygen and hydrogen by the decomposition of the liquid. On the whole, it is impossible to deny that from that time the fundamental idea of a future electric telegraph existed among the auditors and friends of Ampère. There remained nothing more than to execute it practically. Such execution was rendered much more easy by the result of the experiments of Arago on the momentary magnetization of soft iron by the electric current, and by the knowledge of the laws of the remarkable phenomenon of induction established by Faraday.

Everyone knows how, from station to station, long metallic threads placed on insulating supports have been stretched in order to transmit the electric current from point to point. In the first arrangements of apparatus for this purpose, in that especially which Wheatstone established between Paris and Versailles and which was in operation in 1845, the electric current was produced by magnets, for which was afterwards substituted an electric battery as being susceptible of more energetic action. The conducting wires were reduced for each apparatus to a single one, the mass of the earth sufficing for the return of the current. The needles were also reduced to a single one, which stopped in any desired position before a dial-plate bearing on its circumference all the letters of the alphabet, the 10 numerals, points, etc. To bring the needle to a certain radius of the dial and to a definite letter, the dentated wheel on which it depended was made to traverse a suitable number of notches, by as often interrupting and re-establishing the electric current. This idea of suspending and restoring the current by interruptions variously diversified was the most essential addition which had been made to the fundamental idea of Ampère. The interruptions and re-establishments of the current occasion, so to speak, a succession of electric waves, comparable in a certain measure to the sonorous waves by means of which our voice is propagated, but infinitely more rapid.

Since these first essays the mechanism employed has been singularly varied. The dials and needles have been suppressed and replaced by other combinations. A multitude of ingenious instruments—cut-offs, pole-changers, manipulators, electro-magnets, magnets variously armed—have been devised by a throng of men of talent. This pursuit, still so new, is one of those in which the inventive spirit of our age has most favorably displayed itself; but whatever the process, it always substantially consists in operating, at a distance and even beyond the seas, with the electro-magnetic currents of Oersted and Ampère.*

In a very interesting account of Oersted, from which I have borrowed many of the details here cited, Professor Hauch of

---

* This statement can scarcely be considered as correct, even in view of the rhetorical license of the eulogist. The currents used in telegraphing are, strictly speaking, neither the discoveries of Oersted nor of Ampère, but of Volta and of Faraday. There are three different forms of the telegraph: first, that of pure electricity which transmits messages by a galvanic current, and makes signals by sparks or by marks on chemical paper. Second, that of the needle moved by a galvanic current, first suggested by Ampère. Third, that of an electro-magnet which produces sounds, and also marks on paper at a distance. The first of these depends essentially on the discovery of Volta, and the other two on the primary fact of Oersted, extended, applied, and modified by others. [Joseph Henry's note.]

Copenhagen compares with justifiable enthusiasm his master Oersted discovering, after long meditation, the action of the pile on the magnetic needle and thus opening for science horizons altogether new, to Christopher Columbus discovering America, after having dreamed all his life of the existence of a great continent beyond the ocean. He might have added that Oersted, more fortunate than Columbus, encountered no Amerigo Vespucci to dispute with him the glory of his discovery. Ampère, the most modest of men, had need of no glory but his own, if, indeed, he ever occupied himself with that; and moreover in electro-magnetic science the work of Oersted and of Ampère has remained perfectly distinct. If the fundamental experiment is the incontestable property of Oersted, the developments immediately added by Ampère were the fruit of a spirit of invention that yields not in merit to the most original experiment, and of an analytical science which could only be met with in a geometer like Ampère, and, it may be added, in those colleagues of ours who bore a part in his calculations—Savary, Liouville, and our president, Duhamel.

The members of this Academy, the colleagues of Ampère, were the first in proclaiming all the merit of Oersted. . . . We read accordingly, in the statement regarding the prizes awarded on the 8th of April, 1822:

The Academy announced in its public session of the 27th of March, 1820, that in that of March 1822 it would award the prize of mathematics, consisting of a gold medal of the value of 3,000 francs, to the best work or memoir on pure or applied mathematics, which shall have appeared or been communicated to the Academy during the space of two years which are accorded to competitors.

Many physico-mathematical researches, worthy of high praise, have appeared in that interval. . . . But the importance of the discovery of the action of the voltaic pile on the magnetic needle, a discovery which furnishes a new principle to applied mathematics, and which has already given rise to interesting applications of analysis, has determined the commission to award to it the prize of mathematics. The commission charged with the examination of articles for the prizes of mathematics is in the habit of adjudging those prizes without the co-operation of the Academy. But as the discovery in question is not explicitly comprised in the program, it has been thought that the authorization of the society should be invoked for awarding the prize to this admirable discovery. This proposal, having been submitted to the deliberations of the Academy, was unhesitatingly adopted.

A place having soon afterwards become vacant among the correspondents of the Academy for the section of physics, the nomination of Oersted to fill it was made June 9th, 1823. (Subsequently the highest scientific distinction at the disposal of the Academy was conferred on him on April 11th, 1842, by his election as one of its eight foreign associates to replace the distinguished botanist de Candolle.) The just éclat which had attended the discovery of Oersted by no means diminished his desire of communicating personally with the savants of other countries. In 1822 he again went to Germany, where, independently of those who more peculiarly ranked as savants, Goethe, the illustrious poet, to whom nothing in the domain of intellect was alien, received him with distinction, as is testified by the manner in which Oersted's discovery is spoken of in several passages of his writings.

Oersted was now for some time engaged in thermo-electric experimenths with Seebeck and afterwards came to Paris, in 1823. The Academy shared the pleasure which he experienced on taking his place in its ranks and, during his sojourn, was entertained by several series of experiments which he performed in its presence, not the least curious of which were those executed in common by himself and Fourier.* In these, bars of bismuth and of antimony soldered together alternately and forming a closed circuit were employed. By heating or cooling the solderings, electrical currents were produced which appeared more abundant but less intense than the currents developed by weak hydroelectric action, and gave occasion to many interesting observations.

Toward the middle of summer Oersted passed into England and Scotland and was received, as he had been in France, with a cordiality and attention which testified to the high estimation in which the author of the discovery of electro-magetism was equally held in those countries. On his return to Copenhagen, he resumed his life of labor with more ardor than ever. The north of Europe then exhibited the spectacle of a brilliant scientific arena. At Stockholm, Berzelius, one of the princes of chemistry, at Copenhagen, Oersted, one of the princes of physics, formed, as it were, two centers of labor and discovery around which gravitated, like so many brilliant satellites, men destined themselves to a just and well-earned celebrity—Arfvedson, Nordenskiold, Bonsdorff, Mitscherlich, Gustave and Henry Rose.

The noble relationship established between the laboratories of the two capitals can be readily imagined. Oersted reapplied himself to chemistry. Resuming at the end of a quarter of a century his investigations of 1799 on alumina, he accomplished in 1824 a work which placed him in the rank of the most eminent practical chemists, and obtained after prolonged efforts chloride of alu-

* See Arago, "Joseph Fourier," *A.R.*, 1871, pp. 137–176.

minum. No one before him had effected the decomposition of alumina. Yet he did not succeed in isolating aluminum. This last important step was reserved for Wöhler, the distinguished chemist of Göttingen. Still later, our young and learned colleague, Henri Sainte-Claire Deville, formed of aluminum a new and valuable element of metallurgic industry.

One of the last labors of Oersted relates to the celebrated diamagnetic discoveries of our illustrious colleague Faraday, whose experiments had already added so many curious facts to electromagnetism, as well as to the researches made on the same subject by some German savants, especially by Reich of Freiburg. Oersted presented his first results to the Royal Society of Sciences of Copenhagen, June 30th, 1848, and gave a review of them in the *Compte Rendu* of the transactions of the society. He soon afterwards drew up a more complete memoir, published in French, in which he recognized a decreasing magnetic progression which includes the magnetic bodies properly so-called, the attractable diamagnetic bodies, the repellable diamagnetic bodies. The magnetism of these last may, according to him, be considered as negative, if we regard the magnetism of iron and of the attractable diamagnetic bodies as positive. Oersted showed that . . . he always kept himself abreast of the progress of physics and particularly of electromagnetism.

Indeed the weight of years never relaxed his activity. Were I to undertake a bare enumeration of the researches and writings of every kind which he executed at Copenhagen during the last twenty-five years of his life, I should much exceed the time at my disposal. But while omitting this long catalogue, in which are numbered nevertheless important memoirs on electricity and magnetism, on the compressibility of liquids and of gases, on the heat developed by the compression of water, on capillary phenomena, on works of literature and philosophy, etc., I feel bound to point out . . . that the favors of fortune never weakened his devotion to the duties of the savant, and that after having made a discovery whose brilliancy rendered it difficult further to augment his reputation, he believed that he still owed to science and his country the constant tribute of assiduous labor.

It was one of the happy events of Oersted's life that he witnessed, in 1829, under the reign of Frederic VI, the founding at Copenhagen of a Polytechnic School. Of this he was named director, an honorable title which he retained till his death. . . . In the Danish institution, Oersted continued to profess physics till his last year with unremitting zeal, animation, and success. As director he treated the pupils with a mixture of kindness, sagacity, and firmness, which secured their unreserved devotion and willing obedience.

During his third journey Oersted found himself crossing the channel from France to England, on his forty-sixth birthday, August 14th, 1823. It is an anniversary which the people of the north style "the day of one's fête." Accustomed in Denmark to pass it in the bosom of his family and friends, he was now left to his solitary thoughts, and these, naturally reverting to his country, inspired him with the design of founding something on his return which should be at once a profitable and pleasant memorial of the vows which on this occasion he addressed to his distant home. The plan of a society for the promotion of the study of nature formed in his mind and was so thoroughly wrought out during the short trip that nothing was required on landing at Dover but to reduce it to writing. The plan met with cordial acceptance in Denmark, and by aid of the new association courses of natural history were established not only at Copenhagen but in other cities of the country. Nor has this institution since ceased to bear the useful fruits which Oersted had anticipated.

He was also member of a literary society. In connection with this a monthly publication was edited, in which he often inserted articles on the most varied subjects, not excepting religious and philosophical ones. He belonged, moreover, to an association established for the right use of the liberty of the press. In fact, his co-operation seems to have been claimed almost universally at Copenhagen, nor was a sense of its value without frequent manifestations in other cities of Denmark and even in those of the neighboring countries. To the last, he was accustomed to make numerous excursions . . . into the north of Germany and into the Scandinavian peninsula, to attend the meetings of naturalists which were held at different places. It was a cherished idea of his that through these gatherings not only might the exchange of scientific views be facilitated and a more intimate union among the representatives of science be cemented, but that their benefits might be extended to a wider circle by expositions placed within the reach of all and introducing even among the popular masses the habit of comprehending and mutually exchanging their idioms and forms of literature. Especially was it his hope that the three Scandinavian nations might thus become, as it were, three branches drawing in common their intellectual nourishment from the same racial stock.

It was never the misfortune of Oersted to witness any diminution of reputation. In 1846, in the sixty-ninth year of his age, he again traveled into Germany, France, and England. In an interesting notice on Oersted read November 7th, 1851, before the Royal Society of Sciences of Copenhagen, Forschhammer, who had accompanied him, tells us that this journey resembled an ovation. In England especially Oersted was received by the most eminent politicians and men of science with a distinction which has rarely been the portion of a stranger and above all of a simple savant. His purpose was to take part in the meeting at Southampton of the British Association for the Advancement of Science. In one of the sessions of that body Sir John Herschel made an address to him remarkable for the signal recognition rendered to his scientific labors.

Honored in his public, Oersted was happy in his private life. His younger brother, whom he had taught to read under the roof of the wig-maker of Rudkjöbing, ever continued to be his faithful and intimate companion. The latter had himself acquired great celebrity by his labors in philosophy and jurisprudence and had filled the position of president of the Royal Society of Copenhagen. Only with the death of the elder brother terminated the auspicious habit, contracted in childhood, of daily exchanging their impressions and ideas. In 1814 Oersted had espoused Brigitte Ballum, daughter of a Lutheran minister of Kjedby, in the isle of Möen, and found in her an accomplished companion whose character, admirably adapted to his own, formed their mutual happiness. Of five daughters and three sons born of this union, only three of the former and two of the latter survived Oersted, to be the consolation of their mother. One of his daughters married Sharling, professor of chemistry in the University of Copenhagen, long known for important researches on respiration.

Around Oersted, however, there existed a still more extensive family. It was composed, we might say, of the whole city of Copenhagen, where he was as much loved as esteemed, as much esteemed as admired. Of this his fellow citizens gave him a touching proof in the latter days of his life. The day (November 7th, 1850) which marked the fiftieth anniversary of his entrance upon public duties, and was what is called in the north his "jubilee," was celebrated by a general festival in Denmark, with the somewhat quaint forms of Teutonic good-fellowship, but accompanied by a substantial testimonial of gratitude to the man who was regarded as the honor of the whole nation. It had been determined by the friends, the pupils, and indeed the simple admirers of the philosopher, to make this the occasion of securing to him for the remainder of his life the possession of *Fasanenhof* (Pheasant Court), a delightful summer residence in the garden of Fredericksburg. The choice of the dwelling was so much the more delicate and so much the more pleasing to Oersted from its having been previously the habitation of Oehlenschläger, the friend of his youth. Oersted was conducted thither on the day of his jubilee. At the same time the King raised him to the rank of councillor of private conferences, a title never before conferred on a professor of the university, and much higher than that of councillor of ordinary conferences, which Oersted had borne for ten years. His bust, executed by a celebrated statuary, was set up at Fasanenberg in presence of an immense crowd, in which were intermingled the most illustrious personages of the kingdom. The rector of the university formally presented him with the gold ring of a doctor, on which was engraved a head of Minerva encircled with diamonds. The Seigniory of the association of students notified him that he had been elected an honorary member of that society, and a deputation of the Guild of arts and trades tendered him thanks for what he had done in behalf of the industry of the country. To all the discourses addressed to him Oersted replied with a force, a composure, and a choice of expression which surprised his audience. The choir of the students commenced and terminated the fête with a chant, the words of which had been composed by one of the best poets of Denmark. In the evening a procession with torches and a new chant by the students greeted the object of this enthusiastic commemoration.

The day on which classes so numerous and so diversified had vied with each other in testifying their affection and admiration for him must have been to Oersted one of the sweetest of his life. He had received from his sovereign and his fellow citizens the most exalted testimonials of esteem with which any Danish savant had been ever honored, and in spite of his modesty his conscience could not have failed to insinuate to him that he was not unworthy of them. The hope of passing his last years, surrounded by his family and dedicated to a tranquil scientific activity in the smiling retreat which his countrymen had thought proper to offer him was calculated to blend the satisfaction of the heart with the consecration of his renown. Yet this pleasing hope was but a deceptive gleam, and although his mind still vigorous and his frame replete with life seemed yet to promise length of days, it was not granted to Oersted so much as to take possession of his new domicile, for before the return of spring he had ceased to live.

He died at Copenhagen, March 9th, 1851, at the age of seventy-three years and seven months. . . .

.   .   .

Oersted was not only eminent as a physicist, profound as a thinker, he was a man of rare excellence of character. Author of one of the capital discoveries of the century, promoter of one of the schools which confer most honor on his country, founder of many important scientific and literary institutions, dear to the youth and to the public of Copenhagen, whom he had charmed during 50 years by a system of poetic and philosophic ideas in harmony with their natural instincts, he had never failed to avail himself of the credit which his high position in science had given him with an enlightened government, and even of the friendship of a well-informed King, to render innumerable services to studious youth, and to savants less fortunate than himself, to a multitude of persons whom he recognized as worthy of his regard. . . .

Joseph Louis Gay-Lussac *

1778–1850

———◆———

DOMINIQUE FRANÇOIS ARAGO

JOSEPH LOUIS GAY-LUSSAC, one of the most illustrious scientists of which France can boast, was born September 6, 1778, at Saint Leonard, a small town of the ancient province of Limousin, situated near the frontier of Auvergne. His grandfather was a physician and his father king's procurateur (prosecutor) and judge at Pont de Noblac. Those who have had an opportunity of observing the frigid reserve which characterized Gay-Lussac in mature age will be undoubtedly surprised to hear me say that in his childhood he was boisterous, turbulent, and very venturesome. . . . Gay-Lussac began the study of the Latin language under the direction of a priest who resided in Saint Leonard, for whom he always testified the sincerest attachment. That his taste for the noisy pastimes of youth might not interfere with his desire to perform his duties, he devoted a portion of the night to study, after playing all day with his comrades.

The revolution of 1789, so legitimate in its objects, and which began with so much grandeur and majesty, had ended by rushing into the most deplorable digressions. The law against suspicious persons reached Gay-Lussac's father. The removal of this excellent man to Paris would probably have been followed by his death. Our friend, filled with alarm, repaired diligently to the club, which met in his native town, to ascertain the slightest indication which could threaten his father. The sight of a strong and valiant youth inspired the leaders of the epoch with a desire to enroll him in the army, then fighting the Vendeans. Gay-Lussac might gladly have donned the military capote and shouldered his musket, but his filial affection prevailed; he proved that,

* A.R., 1876, pp. 138–172. The present version has been considerably condensed.

according to the letter of the law (he was but fifteen years of age)
he was exempt from joining the defenders of the Republic, and he
was left undisturbed. After the ninth Thermidor, Gay-Lussac's
father, who had fortunately remained in the prisons of Saint
Leonard, regained his liberty. The first use he made of it was
to devote himself to the future of the highly gifted son, who, during his imprisonment, had given him the most intelligent proofs
of love. He placed him at M. Savouret's school in Paris. This was
in 1795. The scarcity and impossibility of procuring food for his
pupils induced M. Savouret to close his establishment. Gay-
Lussac was soon after received into the boarding school of M.
Sensier, which, established first at Nanterre and afterward at
Passy outside the walls of Paris, enjoyed some advantages of
which the schools of the capital were deprived at that time.

I have recently met in our assemblies old college-mates of Gay-
Lussac, and all have preserved the most pleasant recollections of
him. One of them, M. Darblay, a representative of the people,
said to me, with feeling: "He was the model of his schoolfellows;
we never saw him, notwithstanding his uncommon spirit, give
way toward anyone to an impulse of anger or impatience; as to
his diligence, that was never relaxed." A pupil, taken to the
theater by his friend, when asked at what hour he returned,
would reply: "I do not know, but it must have been very late, as
there was no light in Gay-Lussac's chamber."

The difficulties under which M. Savouret had succumbed very
soon reached M. Sensier himself. Of all his pupils, he only retained Gay-Lussac, whose parents secretly were in the habit of
sending him small quantities of flour. Reduced to the most cruel
extremities, Madame Sensier every night carried to Paris, for
sale, the milk of two cows, fed in her garden, but the road being
unsafe, Gay-Lussac begged and obtained the favor of daily escort-
ing his benefactress, armed with a large sword suspended to his
belt. It was during the return, which was made by daylight, that
our friend, stretched on the straw of the cart of the impromptu
milk-woman, studied geometry and algebra, thus preparing himself for the examinations for the Polytechnic School, which he
was soon to undergo.

The sixth Nivôse, year VI, after brilliant examinations, Gay-
Lussac received the much-coveted title of pupil of the Polytechnic
School. We see him in this establishment always conversant with
the required duties and giving during the hours of recreation pri-
vate lessons to young men who were intended for public service.
It was in this way he added small sums to the thirty francs that

each pupil of the original Polytechnic School received as his monthly allowance and that he succeeded in maintaining himself in Paris without imposing fresh sacrifices on his family. Gay-Lussac was one of the most distinguished of the scholars of the Polytechnic School as at a later period he was one of the most illustrious and popular of the professors.

Berthollet, who had returned from Egypt with General Bonaparte, requested in 1800 a pupil from the Polytechnic School whom he wished to make his aid in the work of the laboratory. Gay-Lussac was this privileged pupil. Berthollet suggested to him an investigation whose results were diametrically opposite to those expected by the illustrious chemist. I could not venture to affirm that Berthollet was not somewhat disturbed at finding himself mistaken in his predictions, but it is certain that, unlike many other scientists whom I could name, after the first impulse of vexation, the frankness of the young experimentalist only served to increase the esteem that the author of *Static Chemistry* had already conceived for him. "Young man," said he to him, "your destiny is to make discoveries; henceforth you shall be my collaborator. I desire, and it is a title of which one day I am sure I shall be able to boast, I desire to be your father in matters of science." Some time afterward, without giving up his position with Berthollet, Gay-Lussac was chosen assistant professor of the Fourcroy course and often supplied Berthollet's place, which soon gained him the reputation that was constantly growing of one of the most distinguished among the very able professors at that time collected at the capital.

Man, by reason of his weight and limited muscular force, seemed condemned to move forever on the surface of the earth, and only to be able to study the physical properties of the elevated regions of our atmosphere by painfully climbing to the summit of mountains; but what are the difficulties over which genius allied to perseverance cannot triumph?

A scientist who was a member of this Academy, Montgolfier, calculated that by rarefying, by means of heat, the air contained in a paper balloon of limited size, he would obtain an ascensional force sufficient to raise men, animals, and instruments of all kinds. This idea was partially realized June 1783 in the town of Annonay. The astonished Parisian population saw, November 21 of that same year, the intrepid voyagers, Pilatre de Roziers and d'Arlandes, sail through the air, suspended from a *montgolfière*. Charles, another physicist whom the Academy has also numbered among its members, showed the possibility of making balloons of

a varnished material almost impermeable to hydrogen, the lightest
of known gases, which could take the place of heated air with
advantage. From his voyage made December 1, 1783, in company with Robert the artist, in a balloon thus inflated, date ascensions infinitely less adventurous and which in our day have
become a pastime for idlers. It is to the original Academy of
Sciences we must likewise go back, if we wish to find one of the
first scientifically useful ascensions made with hydrogen-gas
balloons.

Experiments made during an ascension by Robertson and
Lhoest at Hamburg, July 18, 1803, and renewed at St. Petersburg, under the auspices of the Imperial Academy of that city,
by the same Robertson and the Russian physicist, Saccharoff,
June 30, 1804, seemed to show that the magnetic force which
directs the needle at the surface of the earth grew considerably
weaker in proportion as they rose in the atmosphere. This fact,
which confirmed the diminution of this same force that De
Saussure supposed he had discovered in his celebrated journey to
the Col du Géant, seemed to the principal members of the Institute with good reason to justify an especial experiment. This was
confided to the physicists Biot and Gay-Lussac, both young, en-
terprising, and courageous.

·   ·   ·

Our two physicists ascended from the garden of the Conser-
vatoire des Arts et Métiers August 24, 1804, furnished with all
the instruments necessary for investigation, but the small dimensions of their balloon did not allow them to exceed a height of
4,000 meters. At this elevation they endeavored with the aid of
the oscillations of a horizontal magnetic needle to solve the problem which had been the chief object of their ascension, but the
rotary motion of the balloon presented unforeseen and serious
obstacles. They succeeded, however, in partly surmounting them,
and they determined in these aerial regions the duration of five
oscillations of the magnetic needle. It is known that this duration
must increase when the magnetic force which brings back the
needle to its natural position has decreased, and that this duration
must be shorter as the same directing force has increased. It is
therefore a case entirely analogous to that of the oscillating pendulum, although the motion of the needle is performed in a horizontal direction. The consequences deduced from their experiments
seem to me subject to difficulties which I shall point out after

giving an account of the ascension made a few days later by Gay-Lussac alone.

This ascension took place September 16, 1804, at forty minutes after nine in the morning. This time Gay-Lussac ascended to a height of 23,000 feet, 7,016 meters above the sea, the greatest well-authenticated height that man had then succeeded in attaining, and which since that epoch has been but once slightly exceeded by Messrs. Barrel and Bixio. This second ascension has enriched physics with several important results, which I will endeavor to explain in a few words.

We find, for instance, that at the moment when Gay-Lussac's thermometer at a height of 7,016 meters indicated 9.5° below the freezing point, that of the Observatory of Paris in the shade and with a northern exposure stood at + 27.75°. Therefore 37° was the range of the thermometrical scale to which Gay-Lussac found himself exposed during the interval from 10 o'clock in the morning till 3 in the afternoon. It was therefore no longer possible to attribute the perpetual snows existing on the summits of high mountains to any special action exerted by those rocky summits on the surrounding strata of air, as no considerable terrestrial elevation existed in the regions above which Gay-Lussac's balloon had successively passed. Are these enormous variations of temperature connected in any way by a simple mathematical law with the changes of height?

By taking as exact the thermometrical observations about which Gay-Lussac himself raises some doubts, on account of the rapidity of the ascensional motion of the balloon and the time required by a thermometer to indicate exactly the temperature of the mediums into which it is immersed, we would arrive at this curious result that the temperature would vary less for a given change of height near the earth than in the regions of the atmosphere of a mean elevation.

But I must remark that the ordinary manner of discussing aerostatic observations leads us into a vicious circle. The analytical formula, by means of which the successive heights of the balloon are calculated, absolutely supposes, in fact, an equal abatement of temperature in every region of the atmosphere for the same change of height. The observations of 1804 and those subsequently made will only give results free from all objection when discussed according to the profound method for which we are indebted to our ingenious and illustrious associate Biot. The difficulties might have been avoided if observers furnished with theodolites and distributed at proper distances had determined trigonometrically by their combined observations the successive heights of the balloon. Scientists and academies desiring to enter anew upon the scientific study of the physical constitution of our atmosphere will certainly not fail to take my suggestions into serious consideration.

The hygrometer of De Saussure gave indications during the ascent of Gay-Lussac of an irregular movement, but taking into account at the same time the degrees indicated by this instrument and the temperature of the strata in which it was observed, our associate found that the amount of humidity contained in the air continued to diminish with extreme rapidity. It was already known at the time of this memorable ascension that air in all latitudes and at a height very slightly above the level of the sea contained about the same proportions of oxygen and azote. This resulted with proof from the experiments of Cavendish, Macarty, Berthollet and Davy. It had also been ascertained by the analyses of Theodore De Saussure, of air brought from the Col du Géant, that at the height of that mountain the air contains the same proportions of oxygen as that of the plain below.

The eudiometrical analyses of Gay-Lussac, made with the greatest care, of air collected at a height of 6,636 meters, established the fact that the air of those high regions was not only composed of oxygen and nitrogen, like that at the surface of the earth, but moreover that it did not contain an atom of hydrogen. It is not necessary to insist here upon the importance of these results; they showed the vagueness of the explanations given them by meteorologists of shooting stars and other atmospheric phenomena.

.   .   .

Let us now pass on to the experiment which was the chief object of the two aerostatic voyages undertaken under the auspices of the first class of the Institute. The question was, as I have previously said, to assure themselves whether, as announced, the magnetic attraction exerted by the earth on a magnetic needle decreases very rapidly with the height. Gay-Lussac succeeded, in this second ascension, in counting in a given time twice as many oscillations as in the first. The results must therefore furnish much greater exactness. He found that a needle which at the surface of the earth required 42.2″ to make ten oscillations, at a height of 4,808 meters above Paris made the same number of oscillations in only 42.8″. The time was 42.5″ at 5,631 meters, and 41.7″ at

6,884 meters. These numbers do not give much regularity; it would have been necessary, as Gay-Lussac himself remarks, in order to deduce rigorous conclusions, to combine them with the corresponding measurements of the inclination, which could not be effected. Our friend, as Biot did, from the discussion of the numbers collected in the first ascension, drew from his observations the conclusion that magnetic attraction is constant at all accessible heights. This consequence was logical at a period when it was not generally known that in a given place and under given circumstances the duration of the oscillations of a magnetic needle is influenced by its temperature, and that a decrement of the thermometer of 37° must produce the most remarkable changes. We see that owing to the imperfect state of the instruments and of science in 1804 it was impossible to arrive at an exact solution of the problem in question. Moreover, it would be astonishing at the present time to hear that the problem had been solved. No considerations of any nature would authorize throwing a veil over the gaps of science. This reflection especially concerns the works of men whose authority is incontestable and uncontested.

Gay-Lussac, after having finished all his investigations with the calmness and composure of a physicist seated in his laboratory, landed at forty-five minutes after three o'clock, between Rouen and Dieppe, forty leagues from Paris, near the hamlet of St. Gourgon, whose inhabitants executed with great readiness all the maneuvers directed by the aerial voyager in order that the car should avoid the shocks that would have placed the instruments in danger.

The dignity of this assembly and of the narrative should not, I think, prevent my relating a singular anecdote, for which I am indebted to my friend. Having reached a height of 7,000 meters Gay-Lussac was desirous to rise still higher, and for this purpose rid himself of every article not absolutely needed. Among these was a white wooden chair, which fell by chance into a bush near a young girl guarding some sheep. What was the astonishment of the shepherdess, as Florian might have said. The sky was clear, the balloon invisible. How explain the chair, if it came not from paradise? The only argument against this conjecture was the coarseness of the work; the workmen, said the skeptics, must be very unskillful above. The dispute was at this point when the journals, publishing the particulars of Gay-Lussac's voyage, put an end to it, and classed among natural effects what until then had seemed to them a miracle. The ascensions of Biot and Gay-

Lussac will live in the memory of men as the first which have been made with marked success for the solution of scientific questions.

The very remarkable meteorological phenomenon of a lowering of the temperature to 40° below freezing at a height of 7,049 meters, verified by Bixio and Barrel during an ascension undertaken at their own expense July 27, 1850, clearly proves that glorious discoveries are awaiting those who will follow in their footsteps, provided they have the necessary information and are furnished, as were these two physicists, with a collection of exact instruments.

. . .

However slightly conversant with the literary history of the first half of this century, all have heard of the warm and profound friendship of Humboldt for Gay-Lussac and of the influence it exerted over the scientific career of the able chemist. But it is not so well known how it originated and was developed, and this deserves to be related.

Before starting on the memorable journey which has made America known to us under so many different aspects, Humboldt prepared himself for it by diligent study. The object of one of his researches was the eudiometrical means in use to determine the constituent principles of air; this work, done in haste by an imperfect process, was somewhat inaccurate. Gay-Lussac perceived this and criticized the error with an alacrity that I would venture to condemn, if it were not rendered excusable by the author's youth.

. . .

One day Humboldt noticed among the company assembled in the salon of the countryseat of Arcueil, a tall young man of modest but dignified bearing. "This is," said someone to him, "Gay-Lussac, the physicist, who recently fearlessly ascended into the atmosphere to the greatest height yet reached by man, to solve important scientific questions." "This is," added Humboldt aside, "the author of the sharp criticisms on my eudiometrical work." But soon mastering resentment naturally inspired by such a reflection on a high-spirited nature, he approached Gay-Lussac, and, after some complimentary remarks on his ascension, extended his hand and affectionately offered his friendship. . . . Such was the origin of an attachment that was never interrupted and that soon bore the happiest fruits. We see in fact immediately afterward the two new friends executing conjointly an important eudiometrical work.

This work, read at the Academy of Sciences, the 1st Pluviôse, year XIII, had for its principal object an estimate of the exactness that could be obtainable in an analysis of air with Volta's eudiometer, but the authors at the same time touched upon a multitude of questions relating to the chemistry and physics of the earth, throwing great light upon them and making very ingenious conjectures. It is in this memoir that the remark is found (which has since received, at the hands of Gay-Lussac, developments so important) that oxygen and hydrogen, considered in volumes, unite to form water, in the definite proportion of 100 of oxygen and 200 of hydrogen.

Our scientific annals present a large number of memoirs published under the names of combined authors. This kind of association, much less common abroad, is not without its drawbacks. If we except the very rare case, of which however I could cite instances, where the part of each collaborator was clearly defined in the joint editorship, the public is obstinate in refusing an equal share to both associates. It frequently dismisses, as caprice dictates, the formulas "We thought, we imagined," on the very plausible pretext that the same idea cannot present itself at the same time to the minds of both associates. It refuses to one of them all intellectual initiative and reduces his share to the mechanical execution of the experiments.

These inconveniences of publishing in common, almost inherent in human nature, disappear when, as an exception, one of the associates resolves not to indulge the public in its prejudiced and often malicious surmises, by unhesitatingly disclaiming any part belonging to the other. It was the good fortune of Gay-Lussac to meet with such a collaborator. Here is, in fact, what I read in a note by Humboldt:

Let us insist upon the remark contained in this memoir, that 100 parts in volume of oxygen require 200 parts in volume of hydrogen gas for saturation. Berzelius has already reminded us that this phenomenon is the germ of what was discovered later about definite proportions, but the fact of complete saturation is due to the sagacity of Gay-Lussac alone. I co-operated in this part of the experiments, but he alone foresaw the importance of the result to the theory.

A declaration so frank and loyal from this illustrious and venerable academician will astonish no one. . . .

Gay-Lussac, assistant professor of the Fourcroy course, ob-

tained through the friendly intervention of Berthollet leave for a
year to accompany Humboldt in his travels through Italy and
Germany. The two friends before leaving Paris provided themselves with meteorological instruments and especially apparatus
suitable for determining the inclination of the magnetic needle
and the intensity of the variable force which directs the magnetic
needle in different latitudes. They left Paris March 12, 1805, and
experimented with their instruments at Lyons, Chambéry, St. Jean
de Maurienne, St. Michel, Lanslebourg, and Mont Cenis, etc. . . .
Gay-Lussac had imbibed in his youth the meteorological theories
of Deluc, some of which had almost captivated him, but in his
passage over the Alps his ideas were entirely modified. He felt the
need, for example, of having recourse to the action of ascending
atmospheric currents to explain a large number of curious phenomena.

·   ·   ·

Gay-Lussac and his illustrious fellow traveler, after visiting
Genoa went to Rome, where they arrived July 5, 1805, and
alighted at the palace Tommati alla Trinita di Monte, the residence
of William von Humboldt, chargé d'affaires of Prussia. . . . Gay-
Lussac's sojourn in Rome was not without fruit to the science of
chemistry. Thanks to the courtesy of Morrichini in placing a
chemical laboratory at the disposal of the young traveler, he was
able to announce on July 7 that fluoric acid existed with phos-
phoric acid in the bones of fishes. On July 9 he finished the
analysis of the alum rock of the Tolfa.

On July 15, 1805, Humboldt and Gay-Lussac left Rome and
started for Naples, accompanied by Leopold von Buch*, who,
though still young, had already distinguished himself by very
valuable geological researches. Vesuvius, in a state of rest at that
period, suddenly exhibited the most magnificent and terrible evolutions (as if to celebrate the arrival of the three illustrious observers), eruptions of dust, torrents of lava, electrical phenomena—nothing was wanting. Finally, Gay-Lussac had the *good
fortune* (the expression is not mine; I borrow it from one of the
fellow travelers of the learned chemist)—he had the good fortune of witnessing one of the most frightful earthquakes ever
experienced at Naples.

Gay-Lussac eagerly seized this opportunity of coping with the
problem which since Empedocles had defied the sagacity of observers. We will soon give an account of the results collected by

* See pp. 145–162 of the present volume.

our friend in the six ascensions of Vesuvius which followed each other in quick succession. The time not devoted by Gay-Lussac to the study of the burning volcano was employed in examining the collections of natural history, and especially of former volcanic eruptions which are found in great numbers in Naples. . . . In his expeditions around Naples by land and water Gay-Lussac corrected some erroneous ideas, then generally entertained. He found, for example, that the air confined in sea water contained instead of 21 parts of oxygen, as ordinary air does, above 30 parts of oxygen for 100. He visited Monte Nuovo and Epomeo with von Buch. On seeing Monte Nuovo Gay-Lussac fully adopted the opinion that von Buch was then beginning to disseminate in the scientific world, according to which mountains may suddenly spring out of the earth by means of upheavals. Epomeo seemed to them to have the characteristics of an abortive volcano, without fire, or smoke, or crater of any kind.

After having finished their labors in Naples, our travelers returned to Rome, where they remained but a short time. On the 17th of September, 1805, Humboldt, von Buch, and Gay-Lussac quitted Rome for Florence. They took the mountain road in order to visit the celebrated baths of Nocera . . . There an important problem was presented. Morrichini had found by chemical analysis that air obtained from these waters contained 40 per cent of oxygen—that is to say, about double the proportion of the same gas in atmospheric air, which seemed incredible. Gay-Lussac discovered in reality that the air procured from the water of the baths contained 30 per cent of oxygen, as spring water usually does. The salutary effects of the waters must therefore be sought elsewhere, as they were found so remarkably pure, no reagent disturbed them. Is it this purity that renders them so efficacious?

. . .

These scientists reached Florence September 22. . . . On the way from Florence to Bologna, where our three travelers arrived safely September 28, they stopped at Piétra-Mala to study the perpetual flames previously examined by Volta.

. . .

Humboldt, von Buch, and Gay-Lussac reached Milan October 1. Volta was then in that city but they had great difficulty in finding him.

. . .

Our three young travelers learned in Milan that the scientific world was alive with the rumor of an alleged discovery by Configliachi. According to the Italian chemist, water was composed of muriatic acid and soda, elements that the battery decomposed without difficulty. Volta, consulted by our three travelers as to the merit of the observation, replied, "I have seen the experiment, but I do not believe in it."

.   .   .

On the 14th and 15th of October our travelers crossed Saint Gothard. Gay-Lussac was denied the enjoyment of a spectacle from which he had anticipated much pleasure and instruction, a thick fog concealing from view even the nearest objects for a whole day. He compensated himself for this disappointment by a minute study of General Pfiffer's fine relief map of Switzerland. At Göttingen, November 4, the great naturalist Blumenbach, at that time full of life and activity, cordially extended the honors of the university to our young countryman. On the 16th of the same month Gay-Lussac arrived at Berlin, where he remained all winter under the roof of Humboldt, kindly welcomed and appreciated by all the distinguished men of the city. He passed much of his time in the society of Klaproth, the chemist, and Erman, the physicist. Gay-Lussac quitted Berlin in the spring of 1806. He very suddenly determined to leave on learning that the death of Brisson left a vacancy in the Institute and that he might be chosen to fill the place of the aged physicist.

In examining now the works of Gay-Lussac's contemporaries who in 1806 were in a position to contend with him for the vacancy in the Academy of Sciences it seems astonishing that his presence should have been indispensable to his success; but we forget that at the end of the eighteenth century and beginning of the nineteenth no one was a real physicist unless possessed of a valuable collection of instruments well polished, well varnished, and arranged in glass cases. It was not without trouble that Gay-Lussac, who owned only a few instruments of research, succeeded in overcoming such prejudices. . . .

A short time before Gay-Lussac, now a member of the Institute, had begun to apply his experimental talent to the study of the changes of the elastic force of gases with the temperature and the formation and diffusion of vapors, the same field of research had been explored in England by an equally clever man, Dalton, who was numbered by the Academy among its eight foreign members. Dalton, although his genius was not unknown to his countrymen, occupied in the small town of Kendal the very humble and somewhat unprofitable position of private tutor of mathematics and had only at his command for his experiments imperfect instruments. There would then have been no impropriety in subjecting his results to careful verification. Gay-Lussac was not acquainted with the works of the illustrious English physicist, as there was no mention of them in the full and instructive account of the experiments made by the physicists who had preceded him. Dalton had found that air expands 0.392 in the interval between 0° and 100° of the centigrade thermometer. Already previously, as I had ascertained from a printed document, Volta had given for this expansion 0.38. Finally, in 1807 Gay-Lussac found it to be 0.375. This number was generally adopted up to a recent period and employed by all the physicists of Europe.

According to the late determinations of Rudberg and Magnus* and Regnault, there was an error of about 1/36 in the value of the expansion of air given by Gay-Lussac; our colleague never objected to the number 0.3665 substituted by our fellow laborer, Regnault, for the number 0.375 which he had given. But what could be the real cause of this difference? Gay-Lussac has never given any public explanation of this disagreement. . . . It would not be uninteresting, however, to investigate how so careful a physicist could allow himself to be drawn into such an error. . . .

What could be the causes of error in the experiments of Volta, Dalton, and Gay-Lussac that these illustrious physicists had not perceived? I have heard it said that the drop of mercury designed to intercept communication between the vessel in which the air was expanded and the external atmosphere, leaving a slight space and giving passage to a portion of the dilated air, was not displaced as much as it would have been without that; but this cause would evidently have given too small a coefficient, and it was in the opposite direction, according to the recent observations, that the number upon which Gay-Lussac had decided was in fault. It was much more probable that the interior of the sides of the vessel in which the celebrated academician operated were not sufficiently dry; that the hygrometric vapor, adhering to the glass at low temperatures, evaporated when the apparatus was submitted to high temperatures; that it increased, therefore, without any means of detecting it, the volume of the elastic fluid upon

* See "Life and Labors of Henry Gustavus Magnus," *A.R.*, 1870, pp. 223–230.

which they desired to operate. I point out this cause with the more
confidence that it is now established that the glasses, according to
their composition and even according to their degree of annealing,
are diversely hygrometrical; so that the degree of heat which
would cause complete desiccation in one of these glasses would
be insufficient when operating in another apparatus. Gay-Lussac
had perfectly understood the effect that hygrometric vapor should
produce, and he attributed to this cause the errors of his predecessors. Therefore, it was in following with a little more precaution in the paths traced by our friend that this error of 1/36
imputed to him was discovered, an error which could do no real
injury to the just and legitimate reputation for exactness which
this learned physicist had acquired and which subsequent works
so fully justified.

When Gay-Lussac was occupied with the numerical determination of the expansion of elastic fluids by heat, our most skillful
physicists thought that different gases have different coefficients.
Witness, for example, what Monge says, which I quote from his
memoir on the composition of water: "Elastic fluids are not all
equally dilatable by heat." Gay-Lussac found within the limits to
which his experiments were confined that this was an error. Since
then there has been a return to the first opinion. Indeed, it is
almost a consequence of the fact verified by Davy, and especially
by our colleague, Faraday, that gaseous bodies can be liquefied,
and under pressures different for each one of them.

In 1807 Berthollet formed a private scientific society, composed of a small number of individuals and called the Society of
Arcueil after the commune in the neighborhood of Paris in which
the countryseat of this illustrious chemist was situated. Gay-Lussac,
as may be readily imagined, was one of the first members of the
new society. . . . His publications in the three volumes of the
Memoirs of the Society of Arcueil deserve in every respect, from
their variety, their novelty, and also their exactness, to occupy
the most distinguished place in an impartial history of the sciences.

The first volume of the collection published by the Society of
Arcueil begins by a memoir in which Gay-Lussac has combined
the results of all the magnetic observations made in conjunction
with Humboldt during the journey through France, Italy, and
Germany, of which we have already spoken at length. This
branch of the science has for some years been making very considerable progress, and yet we can confidently recommend to
physicists those pages on which Gay-Lussac has examined all the

causes of error which may affect the measurements of inclination and intensity and the precautions to be taken to avoid them. We know now that the horizontal force which directs the magnetic needle is subject to a diurnal variation which depends in part, but only in part, upon a corresponding variation in the inclination. We have likewise learned that in a given place and at a given time the duration of the oscillations of a needle depends upon its temperature. It would therefore be necessary, if a magnetic voyage were undertaken, to take into account all of these disturbing causes; but, and we can say it without flattery, at the period when it was published the work of Humboldt and Gay-Lussac was a model.

If we cast our eyes over the second volume of the Memoirs of Arcueil, we will find there, among other clever works of interest, a "Mémoire sur la combinaison des substances gazeuses entre elles" ("Memoir on the Combination of Gaseous Bodies with Each Other"). This memoir contains results so remarkable, so important, that they are habitually called the laws of Gay-Lussac. It would now be very difficult for me to give a detailed and perfectly accurate account of the atomic theory. This sketch should, I think, go back as far as Higgins, an Irish chemist, whose work, published in 1789, is only known to me through very short quotations by Humphry Davy. Then come the researches of Dalton in 1802. It is a matter of certainty that the law of volumes was demonstrated experimentally by our associate in 1808, without any knowledge on his part of the first more or less systematic investigations of his predecessors. The laws to which we have alluded may be announced in these terms:

Gases, in acting upon each other, combine in volume in the simplest ratios, such as 1 to 1, 1 to 2, or 2 to 3. Not only do they unite only in these proportions, but again, the apparent contraction of volume which sometimes occurs by the combination bears also a simple ratio to the volume of one of the combined gases. Gay-Lussac later had the boldness to deduce from his laws the density of the vapors of several solid bodies, such as carbon, mercury, and iodine, integral parts of certain gaseous combinations. This boldness, as proved by subsequent experiments, was crowned with perfect success.

Recently it was thought possible to deduce from the unequal expansion of different gases by heat the proof that the law of volumes is not mathematically exact. Let us suppose, the learned critics say implicitly, that two gases combine in equal volume and at a fixed temperature—for example, that of 20° centigrade—

and that the combination is made molecule by molecule. Let us raise to 40° the temperature of the two gases. If at 20° equal volumes contain the same number of elementary particles, such would not be the case at 40°. There will then be unequal volumes which will enter into combination, supposing that the union must always be effected molecule by molecule. It will be seen that the criticism implies the absolute truth of the atomic theory of combination, which, by the way, may seem not so firmly established as the law of Gay-Lussac. Besides, would not that have been a very singular coincidence which should have led our colleague to operate precisely at the temperatures at which this law should be rigidly exact?

Let us remark, in point of fact, that in the study of nature it has rarely happened that experiment has led, through some light deviations, to simple laws, unless these laws have become the definite regulators of the phenomena. The system of the earth offers a striking example of this truth. The laws of the elliptical movement of the planets are only exact by disregarding the irregularities known under the name of perturbations, and which place each planet sometimes in advance, sometimes behind the position assigned to it by the immortal laws of Kepler. If it is ever established by direct experiment that the principles laid down by Gay-Lussac are not confirmed when the temperatures come to vary, it will be time to investigate whether there be not a natural cause to which these perturbations may be attributed.

In the limited compass assigned me I could only present simple doubts on the nice question I have ventured to broach; at all events, the assimilation which they have suggested to me seems of a nature to satisfy the most enthusiastic partisans of the scientific glory of Gay-Lussac. When Laplace, looking at capillary phenomena in a new light, desired to compare the results of his skillful calculations with those of observation, and when he wished the subject to have the final seal of experiment, he applied to Gay-Lussac. The latter fully responded to the confidence of the immortal geometer. I should add that the instrument which he invented is of small dimensions—the same, under the name of cathetometer, now so generally in use among physicists. I leave to those who consider they have the right, the responsibility of laying claim to priority in the use of the word cathetometer now generally adopted; but the instrument in principle and even in form will not the less remain one of the valuable inventions with which our colleague has endowed science.

We have now reached the period when, treading in the path so successfully opened by Nicholson and Carlisle and followed by Berzelius and Hisinger, Sir Humphry Davy succeeded by means of the battery in transforming potash and soda into metals which could be kneaded with the fingers like wax, which float on the surface of water, because lighter than it, and which ignite spontaneously in this liquid, diffusing the brightest light. The announcement of this brilliant discovery at the close of 1807 created a profound sensation in the scientific world. The Emperor Napoleon took part in it and placed at the disposal of the Polytechnic School the funds necessary for the erection of a colossal battery. While this powerful instrument was being constructed, Gay-Lussac and Thénard*, to whom it was to be confided, conceiving that ordinary affinity well directed would suffice for the production of potassium and sodium, attempted various very dangerous experiments and succeeded beyond their expectations. Their discovery was published March 7, 1808. From this time the two new metals, which were obtained only in very small quantities by the battery, could be produced in great abundance and thus became the usual instrument of chemical analysis.

As may be easily imagined, our two celebrated countrymen did not allow the means of investigation they had just so skillfully prepared to remain idle in their hands. They placed the potassium and sodium in contact with nearly all known chemical substances and noticed during the experiment the reactions most fertile in theoretical consequences. We will content ourselves by citing here the decomposition of the acid formerly known as boracic, and the discovery of its radical, called by its discoverers *boron.* We must likewise rank very high in their investigations the very difficult and varied experiments by which they determined the actions exerted by the two new metals on ammonia; the results of their work on fluoric acid, now called *fluohydric,* and the discovery of the new gas which they named *fluoboric.* Following the chain of their researches, the two illustrious chemists were led to attempt the analysis of the substance then denominated *oxygenated muriatic acid.* They made known the results of their numerous experiments February 27, 1809. Their communication finished with this paragraph which I transcribe literally:

According to the facts reported in this memoir, it might be supposed that this gas (oxygenated muriatic acid gas) is a simple body. The

* See Flourens, "Memoir of Louis Jacques Thénard," *A.R.,* 1862, pp. 372–383.

phenomena which it presents are sufficiently well explained in this hypothesis; we do not seek, however, to vindicate it, because it seems to us that they are explained still better by regarding oxygenated muriatic acid gas as a compound body.

They made by this declaration a large concession in favor of the prevailing opinions of the Society of Arcueil, to those supported with great warmth by Laplace and Berthollet. Sir Humphry Davy, who was in no wise constrained by personal considerations, maintained that the first interpretation alone was admissible; he regarded oxygenated muriatic acid as a simple body that Ampère proposed to call *chlorine;* common muriatic acid became then the combination of this radical with hydrogen under the name of hydrochloric or chlorohydric acid. This manner of interpreting facts is now generally adopted. It is seen by this example that there are cases where the counsels of genius, when they assume the imperious character that counsels should never have, may sometimes lead the soundest minds astray from truth.

When the colossal battery constructed with the funds granted the Polytechnic School by Napoleon was finished, Gay-Lussac and Thénard were eager to study its effects, but less energy was shown than was expected. So after various trials without striking results, the two illustrious chemists confined themselves to laying down general principles on the mode of action of these apparatuses when they exceed the usual dimensions. We find in their work a chapter in which they examined the different causes which create a variation in the energy of the galvanic battery, in which they give the means of measuring its effects, and in which they study the influence exerted by the liquid contained in the troughs, according to its nature and the variations of intensity, which may depend upon the number and surface of the plates employed.

The analysis of animal and vegetable substances for some years has achieved immense development and led to the most important results. This progress of the science is chiefly due to a method invented by Gay-Lussac to effect organic analyses and which has been adopted by all chemists. Our colleague burned the substance to be analyzed with the oxide of copper. This process was a great improvement upon the one he used with his associate and friend M. Thénard, in which combustion was effected by means of oxymuriate of potash, now known as chlorate of potash.

Courtois, a manufacturer of saltpeter in Paris, discovered about the middle of 1811 in the ashes of seaweed a solid substance which corroded his boilers and which since, at the suggestion of Gay-Lussac, has been called *iodine,* from the extremely remarkable violet color of its vapor. Courtois sent samples of this substance soon after its discovery to Desormes and Clément, who made it the subject of experiment. Clément did not make public Courtois's discovery and the results he had obtained conjointly with Desormes until the meeting of the first class of the Institute, December 6, 1813. Sir Humphry Davy, who on account of his scientific genius had obtained from the Emperor especial permission to pass through France, was then in Paris. He received from Clément a short time after his arrival numerous samples of the mysterious substance. Gay-Lussac learned this and saw at a glance what mortifying crticisms affecting the honor of our experimentalists and academies might arise from resigning the priority, through chance and thoughtlessness, to the investigations of a foreign chemist. He went immediately to Rue du Regardà, to the poor workman, obtained a small amount of the matter discovered by him, set himself to the task, and produced in a few days a work equally remarkable for the variety, the importance, and the novelty of the results. The iodine, under the searching eye of our colleague, became a simple body, furnishing a peculiar acid by combining with hydrogen and a second acid by uniting with oxygen. The first of these acids proved by a new example that oxygen was not the only acidifying principle, as was believed for a long time. This work of Gay-Lussac upon iodine was subsequently completed; and there are found in a very long and beautiful memoir, read August 1, 1814, and published among those of the Academy, the varied results of the investigations of our colleague.

Every chemist who has read this work admires in it the fertility of the author in varying experiments and the soundness of judgment which always guides him when necessary to interpret them and draw from them general consequences. In several chapters of this very remarkable work the author dwells especially upon the analogy which he establishes between chlorine, iodine, and sulphur, which throws great light upon several branches of the science then involved in obscurity.

Prussian blue, a substance known to manufacturers and painters, had been the subject of the researches of a large number of scientists, among whom we will chiefly cite the academician Macquer, Guyton de Morveau, Bergman, Scheele, Berthollet,

Proust, and Porrett. Gay-Lussac, in his turn, entered the lists. His results are recorded in a memoir which was read before the first class of the Institute September 18, 1815. From this moment everything doubtful became a certainty; light succeeded obscurity. This memoir, one of the most beautiful of which science can boast, revealed a multitude of new facts of immense interest to chemical theories. Those who will read it with care will see at the cost of what fatigue, with what precautions, what sobriety in the deductions, what soundness of judgment, an observer succeeds in avoiding false steps, and bequeathing to his successors a definitive work—I mean a work which subsequent investigations will not essentially modify.

In that admirable memoir the author first gives an exact analysis of the acid which enters into the composition of Prussian blue, and which was called by Guyton de Morveau prussic acid, but which was never obtained until the work of our friend, in a state of purity, but mixed only with water. He then showed how he succeeded in separating the radical, which has since been denominated cyanogen, from prussic acid. He established the fact that cyanogen is a compound of azote and carbon; that prussic acid is definitively formed from hydrogen and this radical; and that it should take the name of hydrocyanic acid, for which chemists now often substitute that of cyanhydric acid. He points out with the greatest care its reactions on a great number of substances, simple or compound, solid or gaseous. He makes known the combination of cyanogen with chlorine, which should naturally bear the name of chlorocyanic acid. In brief, in this work Gay-Lussac filled a gap in chemistry by showing that there exists a combination of azote and carbon. He proved that cyanogen, although a compound, plays the part of a simple body in its combinations with hydrogen and metals; which at the period when our colleague wrote was the sole example in the science. I have said that to establish results so grand Gay-Lussac displayed indefatigable perserverance. If proof of it is wanted, I will mention, for instance, that, wishing to know what modifications electricity could produce in a mixture of two gases, he passed into it at least fifty thousand sparks. We read with great regret, in the memoir of our colleague, the following paragraph:

I had indulged the hope, in devoting myself to these researches, of being able to throw some light on all the combinations of hydrocyanic acid; but the duties I have to perform have forced me to interrupt them before they had reached the degree of perfection to which I expected to bring them.

What were these duties which, in 1815, hindered Gay-Lussac from completing this work of genius? It was—and I mention it with regret—the necessity of providing for his family, by giving public lectures almost daily, which consumed the time our friend had wished to devote more usefully to the advancement of science. Cyanogen, one of the constituent principles of Prussian blue, furnishes, by combining with hydrogen, a poison so subtle that a celebrated physiologist, the first to use it in experiments on living animals, exclaimed, on seeing its effects, "Henceforth one may believe all that antiquity has said of Locusta." The same learned academician has proved by his experiments that in the poisoned animals no lesion in the organs essential to life is seen. This action of the liquid obtained for the first time by Gay-Lussac will appear the more mysterious from the fact that it is produced by a substance composed of azote, one of the constituent principles of atmospheric air, of hydrogen, one of the constituent principles of water, and carbon, whose innocuousness is proverbial.

.   .   .

Gay-Lussac published in 1816 the description of a portable siphon barometer, now so widely used, especially since the improvements made in it by the artist Bunten. This is not the only service rendered to meteorology by our friend. In a note inserted in 1822 in the twenty-first volume of the *Annales de chimie et de physique,* he has explained his views on the manner in which clouds are suspended. On looking at the upward motion that ascending atmospheric currents give to soap bubbles, evidently heavier than the air, he though he might attribute the suspension of vesicular molecules to this same current at much more considerable elevations.

Before this epoch, in 1818, in a letter addressed to Humboldt, Gay-Lussac had investigated the causes of the formation of storm clouds. According to him, the electricity constantly diffused in the air suffices to explain the phenomena presented by this kind of cloud. When the storm clouds are of great density they possess the properties of solid bodies; the electricity originally disseminated in their masses rises to the surface where it has considerable tension, by virtue of which it can overcome at times the pressure of the air and dart forth in long flashes, either from one cloud to another, or over the surface of the earth. It will be seen how greatly these views differ from those of Volta, the master of everything connected with electricity. Whatever be the opinion pronounced upon the rival theories, it must be acknowledged that in the discussion of what Gay-Lussac calls his conjectures he has shown himself a very skillful logician and perfectly familiar with the most subtle properties of the electric principle.

Among the researches of our friend, designed to throw light upon the nicest points of meteorology, we must also mention those which concern vaporization and the dissemination of vapors, either on empty spaces or in spaces containing aeriform fluids.

I perceive that I shall scarcely be able to say even a few words about Gay-Lussac's views with regard to volcanic phenomena. These opinions were published in 1823 under the title of *Réflexions,* in a memoir inserted in the twenty-second volume of the *Annales de chimie et de physique.* The author does not believe that the central heat of the earth, if that heat exists, contributes at all to the production of volcanic phenomena. These phenomena, according to him, are owing to the action of water, probably sea water, on combustible substances. According to this hypothesis, the torrents of gaseous matter which issue from the craters of volcanoes should contain a great deal of hydrogen and hydrochloric acid. The manner in which the author explains the absence of hydrogen in these aeriform emanations, and the processes which he points out to such men as Montecelli, Cavelli, and other scientific observers, suitably placed to ascertain the existence of hydrochloric acid, must be sought in the original memoir. I do not think that this memoir, in spite of its ingenuity, has solved the so much controverted question of volcanic phenomena. But I will in this case simply imitate the reserve of Gay-Lussac, who modestly said in beginning his memoir, "I do not possess the extent of information (in geology) required to treat such a subject. I shall merely skim lightly over its surface."

.   .   .

It has pleased some to divide the career of our colleague into two distinct phases: the first devoted to the speculative study of natural phenomena, the second entirely confined to the applications from which he was to realize substantial benefits. In this second phase, which they claim fades into insignificance if it is not diminished in importance by comparison with the first, Gay-Lussac, enjoying the favor of the government, was selected in succession to aid by his scientific knowledge in the manufacture of gunpowder; to act as adviser in the administration of the excise; to manage the assay office become vacant by the death of Vauquelin, etc. The invention of new processes, characterized by exactness, simplicity, and elegance, proves what a slave Gay-Lussac was to his duties and that the government could not have bestowed its confidence more judiciously.

.   .   .

As fertile in the invention of industrial methods as in the discovery of scientific truths, one after the other as if by enchantment Gay-Lussac created chlorometry, invented methods for determining the richness of the alkalis of commerce, contrived ingenious means by which the manufacture of sulphuric acid has become less expensive and has no longer need to be brought from unfrequented places. And he crowned this series of important works by the discovery of a process which has been substituted in all civilized countries for cupellation, an ancient and defective method for analyzing alloys of silver and copper. Truly, I ask myself, with what theoretical speculations could Gay-Lussac have better filled the second phase of his career, since phase there is, than by producing works which to their scientific merits add the advantage of being susceptible of positive and multiplied applications, which serve as safe guides to the natural industries and to enlighten the public authorities? To pretend to confine men of genius to the path of pure abstraction, and to forbid discoveries which may be useful to the human race, would be to yield to the most erroneous ideas, in my opinion.

.   .   .

I am going . . . to take the liberty of introducing you into those amphitheaters where our colleague delighted with his eloquence a large and brilliant audience. We will then pass into his laboratory. . . . Gay-Lussac on all occasions showed his profound dislike for those ostentatious phrases into which his first titular professor, notwithstanding his well-merited celebrity, often allowed himself to be drawn, and in which the most pompous words were found side by side with such technical expressions as ammonia, azote, carbon. His language and style were grave, correct, nervous, always perfectly adapted to the subject and characterized by the mathematical spirit which he had imbibed in his youth at the Polytechnic School. He had the power, as others had, of exciting astonishment in his audience by presenting himself before it without any manuscript notes in his hand, but he would have run the risk of using erroneous figures, and exactness was a merit which touched him most nearly.

Gay-Lussac's knowledge of foreign languages, Italian, English, and German, enabled him to enrich his lectures with erudition of the purest kind and drawn from the original sources. He it is who has initiated our own chemists and physicists into several theories originating on the right bank of the Rhine. In brief, Gay-Lussac, who has not been surpassed by any contemporary chemist in the importance, novelty, and brilliancy of his discoveries, has also indisputably occupied the first rank among the professors of the capital upon whom devolved the task of teaching the sciences at the Polytechnic School. On entering Gay-Lussac's laboratory everyone was struck at the first glance with the intelligent order which reigned everywhere. The machines and different utensils, for the most part prepared by his own hands, were remarkable for the most careful conception and execution. . . . When the chemist operates upon new substances and combinations with unknown reactions, he is exposed to real and almost inevitable dangers. Gay-Lussac realized this but too truly. During his long and glorious scientific campaigns he was seriously wounded on several different occasions: the first time, June 3, 1808, by potassium, prepared in large quantities by a new method. Humboldt and Thénard led our friend with his eyes bandaged from the laboratory of the Polytechnic School, where the accident occurred, to his house, Rue des Poules, which, by the way, it would be well to call Rue Gay-Lussac. In spite of the prompt attention of Dupuytren, he lost the lachrymal glands and thought himself perfectly blind for a month. This disheartening prospect for a man of thirty was borne by our friend with a calmness and serenity that the stoics of antiquity might have admired.

"For nearly a year," said Madame Gay-Lussac (in a note she had the goodness to send me), "the reflection from a small night lamp before which I placed myself to read to him was the only light he could endure. During the rest of his life his eyes remained red and weak."

The last explosion of which Gay-Lussac was the victim took place at a period of his life when misinformed individuals declared him to be idle. Our friend was busy with the study of the carbureted hydrogens proceeding from the distillation of oils. The glass balloon containing the gases, which had been set aside for several days, was taken by Larivière, a young chemist, to be submitted to Gay-Lussac's inspection. While our colleague was absorbed in the minute examination necessary to give the projected experiments the desirable precision, a frightful explosion took place, the cause of which even to this day is not perfectly understood, which completely shattered the balloon. Such was the velocity of the fragments of glass that they made in the windowpanes of the laboratory clear holes without the trace of a fissure, as if by projectiles from firearms. Gay-Lussac's eyes, which were but a few centimeters (not more than an inch) from the balloon, this time escaped all injury, but one of his hands was seriously wounded and required long and painful treatment. Some persons saw in this terrible wound the original cause of the painful disease to which our friend succumbed a few years afterward. The members of the Academy, who went daily to visit him on his bed of suffering, heard him with emotion congratulate himself that the wounds of his young friend and assistant, Larivière, were insignificant, and on this occasion his own life alone had been endangered.

Some have desired to regard these accidents as the consequences of negligence and thoughtlessness; say, rather, by a comparison whose appropriateness will be recognized by all who know our friend, that if he was often wounded it was because he was often under fire, and that he did not hesitate to examine things very closely even when there was great danger in doing so. It has been thought the successes of Gay-Lussac in his scientific researches afforded him only that calm satisfaction which the discovery of some new truths must naturally produce. Appearances were deceitful. To protect himself from the dampness of the laboratory, which was on the ground floor, Gay-Lussac usually wore sabots over his shoes. Pelouze, one of his favorite pupils, told me that after the success of an important experiment he had frequently seen him through the half-open door of his study give signs of the liveliest pleasure, and even dance in spite of his clumsy wooden shoes.

. . .

There was in Gay-Lussac's laboratory, by the side of furnaces, retorts, and apparatus of every kind, a small white wooden table, on which our friend recorded the results of his experiments as they progressed. It was, if I may be allowed the comparison, the exact bulletin written during battle. It was on this little table that were also traced the articles concerning different points of doctrine or questions of priority.

It would be impossible, in relating the life of a man whose chief works date back to the beginning of this century, the period of an entire renewal in chemistry, that we should not have to mention discussions of this kind. These scientific polemics took place especially between Gay-Lussac, Dalton, Davy, Berzelius, etc. You see our friend dealt with doughty antagonists, with adversaries worthy of him. In these discussions our old friend marched straight forward, regardless of anyone, with the vigor, let us say more, with the dryness, of a mathematical demonstration. Rarely do we find in them phrases like the balm applied to freshly made wounds. But how is it that no one has remarked that Gay-Lussac treated himself with a want of ceremony quite equal to that which he used toward others?

The following lines are quoted literally from one of his writings: "The results that I have given," said he, in the *Memoirs* of Arcueil, "of the different combinations of azote and oxygen are not exact." Should not he who criticizes his own works so frankly be excusable for being so exclusively preoccupied with the interests of truth in examining the works of others?

Those who only knew Gay-Lussac slightly fancy there could have been no romance in his private life. Perhaps they will change their opinion after hearing this recital:

There was in Auxerre at the beginning of our first revolution a musical artist who was attached to the four large societies and to the college of that city. The suppression of these establishments in 1791 brought great pecuniary troubles upon this respectable family. The artist did not, however, lose courage and devoted the small fortune of his wife to the education of his three daughters, whom he wished to fit for the honorable position of governess. But the eldest of these young girls, Josephine, becoming aware of the narrowness of the means of her parents and of the sacrifices they would have to endure before attaining their object, earnestly begged to be placed in a mercantile establishment in Paris, to remain there until the ages of her sisters and their education should enable them to realize the hopes entertained for them by their parents.

It was at a linen draper's (the usual refuge of women of all conditions and ages whose lives had been disturbed by revolutions, where Josephine had placed herself) that Gay-Lussac made her acquaintance. He saw with curiosity a young girl of seventeen seated behind the counter holding in her hand a small book which seemed to fix her attention deeply. "What are you reading, miss?" he said. "A work, perhaps, beyond my comprehension; it interests me much, however—a treatise on chemistry." This singularity excited the interest of our young friend; from that moment an unusual necessity for linenware brought him constantly to the draper's, where he entered repeatedly into conversation with the young reader of the chemical treatise; he loved her and was loved in return and obtained from her a promise of marriage. Our illustrious colleague, as a future marriage dower, placed Josephine in a boarding school to complete her education and especially to learn English and Italian. Some time after, she became his wife. I would not venture to advise this rash fashion of choosing a wife, although our celebrated chemist perfectly succeeded in it. Beautiful, sparkling with wit, brilliant, and admired in society—for which nevertheless she cared but little—for the grace and distinction of her manners, Madame Gay-Lussac constituted for more than forty years the happiness of her husband.

From the beginning, they adopted the amicable custom, the consequence of some slight mutual concession, of merging their thoughts, desires, or sentiments into one thought, one desire, one sentiment common to both. This identification in everything was such that they ended by so entirely having the same handwriting that an amateur of autographs might readily believe that a memoir copied by Madame Gay-Lussac had been written by the celebrated academician. Three days before his death, touched by the infinite solicitude lavished upon him, Gay-Lussac said to his wife, "We will love each other to the last; the sincerity of attachments is the only happiness." . . . Gay-Lussac's demeanor was always very grave; he entered frankly into the bursts of merriment that a well-chosen anecdote created in societies where he was surrounded by his friends, but he never provoked them himself.

. . .

A single fact will suffice to show that Gay-Lussac gave himself up enthusiastically to the honest inspirations of his soul when necessary, even at his own risk and peril, to baffle an intrigue or defend a friend. At the second restoration it had been decided in high places, it was said, to remove a professor, whose liberal sentiments had rendered him an object of suspicion, from the Polytechnic School. But how effect this dismissal without exciting great opposition? The professor was zealous, respected, and even, I must say, beloved by all his pupils. The case was embarrassing when it was discovered that this victim of public animosity had during the hundred days signed the additional act. The professor of literature . . . undertook to make every use of this discovery. In a meeting of the corps of instruction he declared that in his opinion those who gave their support to the usurper, that Corsican ogre, whatever might be their motives, were not worthy to lecture before the youth to whom the future of the country was to be confided; they should themselves decline to officiate. The member of the corps of professors against whom this attack was directed asked permission to explain himself, when Gay-Lussac arose impetuously, interrupted his friend, and announced in a sonorous voice that he also had signed the additional act, that he would not hesitate in the future to sustain the government, whatever it might be, even the government of Robespierre, when the enemy threatened the frontiers; that if the patriotic sentiments which guided him were a subject of reprobation, he formally demanded that the proposed reformation should begin in his person. The professor of literature saw therefore that his proposition would be followed by consequences which would far exceed the limit within which he wished to confine it, and no more was said.

.   .   .

Gay-Lussac saw his end approach with the resignation which a pure conscience must inspire. He faced not only death with calmness, but even the *act of dying,* as Montaigne might have said. When the sad news fell like a thunderbolt upon Paris that the health of our colleague was a cause of great solicitude, one of his friends immediately wrote to the afflicted family who surrounded him to learn the truth. Gay-Lussac desired to reply himself. The following were the words of the dying man:

My dear Arago: My son has just told me of your letter to him. It is but too true; I have one foot in the grave, which must very soon close over me; but I gather all my strength to thank you for the interest you take in me, and to tell you that the mutual affection of our two families has been a source of great happiness to me all my life. Adieu, my dear Arago.

.   .   .

The forebodings of Gay-Lussac, his family, and the public yielded every moment to more encouraging anticipations. Our colleague Magendie,* who had hastened to his old friend with his scientific skill, was for a short time himself deluded by this general hope. Gay-Lussac was removed to Paris, where his condition for some days seemed to improve. He spoke to us then of his future work and of the regret he felt at a time when there seemed no possibility of prolonging his life, at having given an order to his son to burn his treatise, *Philosophie chimique,* the first chapters of which were nearly finished. But he was soon forced to abandon all hope. The dropsy, with which he had been suddenly attacked, made rapid progress, and our friend expired quietly and bravely

* See Flourens, "Memoir of François Magendie," *A.R.,* 1866, pp. 91–125.

on the 9th of May, 1850, at the age of seventy. He might have said with one of ancient times, "If it were given me to live my life over again, I would on all occasions do as I have done."

The obsequies of the learned academician were solemnized May 11, in the midst of a large concourse, including nearly the entire body of his early associates of the Academy of Sciences and some of the most distinguished members of other academies; the entire Institute testified in this manner that it could not at that time have suffered a greater loss. The early pupils of the Polytechnic School, the entire body of the two present classes of the school, the friends of science, and many grateful auditors of the two excellent courses of the Sorbonne and the Jardin des Plantes, also joined in the funeral procession.

The various political opinions which unhappily divided our country were blended together in this mournful train, and who could, indeed, say to which of these parties Gay-Lussac belonged? What party could flatter itself to have numbered the illustrious scientist in its ranks? The compatriots of our colleague once intrusted him with the honor of representing them in the Chamber of Deputies. . . . Louis Philippe made him peer of France; but he approached the tribunes of these two assemblies very rarely and only to discuss special questions relating to his favorite studies. Should this reserve be attributed to timidity, or can it be simply explained by Gay-Lussac's desire not to introduce any disturbing elements into the even current of his life? If this last supposition be correct, he was perfectly successful. Never did the foulest of all calumnies, political calumny, attack the scientific career of our associate. His works have escaped the daily criticisms of those hireling writers who, before taking up the pen, ask themselves, not what are the real merits of the memoirs whose analysis they are about to publish, but what are the supposed opinions of their authors upon the exciting and yet perplexing questions of social organization. The discoveries of our colleague have always been appreciated in France at their just value. We can, therefore, say of him, in the words of Voltaire, written under a portrait of Leibnitz, "Even in his own country he lived respected."

The recollections of the profound friendship which bound me to Gay-Lussac for more than forty years have perhaps tempted me into too minute details in writing his biography. However that may be, I will sum up the history of this beautiful life in these few words: Gay-Lussac was a good father, an excellent citizen, an honest man in every event of his life, an ingenious physicist, and a peerless chemist. He honored France by his moral qualities, and the academy by his discoveries. His name will be uttered with admiration and respect in every land where science is cultivated. Finally, the illustrious academician will live forever in the hearts and memories of all who had the happiness to rejoice in his friendship.

Michael Faraday *

1791–1867

———◆———

ARTHUR AUGUSTE DE LA RIVE †

SCIENCE HAS just lost one of its most eminent and faithful representatives. Faraday died on Sunday, the 25th of August, 1867, at Hampton Court. He was born on the 24th of September, 1791, at Newington Butts, near London. In 1804 at the age of 13 he was apprenticed to a bookbinder, in whose workshop he remained eight years. So many books passed through his hands that he could not resist the temptation of opening and reading some of them. These readings, performed in the evenings after the work of the day was finished, gave him a taste for study, and in particular for that of the sciences. The *Encyclopædia Britannica* first of all introduced him to some notions of electricity; and it was afterwards, from the works of Mrs. Marcet, that he derived his first knowledge of chemistry. His labors received their permanent direction from this opening; their essential objects were electricity and chemistry.

Do not fancy [he said to me in a letter of the 2nd of October, 1858, in which he gives me these details] that I was a profound thinker or a precocious child; I had merely a good deal of life and imagination, and the tales of the Thousand and One Nights pleased me as much as the *Encyclopædia Britannica*. But what saved me was the importance I early attached to facts. In reading Mrs. Marcet's book on chemistry, I took care to prove every assertion by the little experiments which I made as far as my means permitted; and the enjoyment which I found in thus verifying the exactitude of the facts contributed essentially to give me a taste for chemical knowledge. You may therefore easily im-

* A.R., 1867, pp. 227–245. Translated from the *Bibliothèque Universelle,* Oct. 25, 1867, *Arch. des Sci.,* pp. 131–176.
† Swiss physicist (1801–1873), a eulogy of whom by Jean Baptiste Dumas, appeared in *A.R.,* 1874, pp. 184–205.

agine the pleasure I experienced when I subsequently made the personal acquaintance of Mrs. Marcet, and how delighted I was when my thoughts went backward to contemplate in her at once the past and the present. Whenever I presented her with a copy of my memoirs I took care to add that I sent them to her as a testimony of my gratitude to my first instructress.

I have the same sentiments towards the memory of your own father [adds Faraday] for he was, I may say, the first who encouraged and sustained me, first at Geneva, when I had the pleasure of seeing him there, and afterwards by the correspondence which I regularly maintained with him.

Faraday here alludes to a journey in which he accompanied Davy to Geneva in 1814, and in which, during a stay which he made with his illustrious master at my father's, the latter quickly discerned the merits of the young assistant and formed relations with him which were interrupted only by death. At the time when he travelled with Davy, Faraday was his assistant at the Royal Institution in London; and I must say that he has more than once expressed to me, both by letter and *viva voce,* his thankfulness to the eminent chemist who had admitted him to one of his courses, and consented, after running through the notes of this course prepared by the young pupil, to take him for his assistant.

After the journey just referred to, Faraday, with the exception of rare and short absences, never again quitted the Royal Institution, where he had his laboratory and his residence. Married to a lady worthy of him and who shared and understood all his impressions and all his sentiments, he passed a life equally peaceful and modest. He refused all the honorary distinctions which the government of his country wished to confer upon him; he contented himself with a moderate salary and with a pension of £300 sterling which fully sufficed for his wants; and accepted nothing supplementary to this except the enjoyment, during the summer in the latter years of his life, of a country house at Hampton Court, which the Queen of England graciously placed at his disposal. Without children, a complete stranger to politics or to any kind of administration except that of the Royal Institution, which he directed as he would have directed his own house, having no interest but that of science, and no ambition but that of advancing it, Faraday was of all savants the one most completely and exclusively devoted to the investigation of scientific truth of which the present century offers us an example.

One may easily understand what must be produced under such circumstances by a life thus wholly consecrated to science, when to a strong and vigorous intellect is joined a most brilliant imagination. Every morning Faraday went into his laboratory as the man of business goes to his office and then tried by experiment the truth of the ideas which he had conceived overnight, as ready to give them up if experiment said *no,* as to follow out the consequences with rigorous logic if experiment answered *yes.* His everyday labor experienced no interruption except the few hours which he devoted from time to time to the exposition in the theater of the Royal Institution, before an audience equally numerous and select, of certain parts of physics and chemistry. Nothing can give a notion of the charm which he imparted to these improvised lectures, in which he knew how to combine animated and often eloquent language with a judgment and art in his experiments which added to the clearness and elegance of his exposition. He exerted an actual fascination upon his auditors; and when, after having initiated them into the mysteries of science, he terminated his lecture, as he was in the habit of doing, by rising into regions far above matter, space, and time, the emotion which he experienced did not fail to communicate itself to those who listened to him, and their enthusiasm had no longer any bounds.

Faraday was, in fact, thoroughly religious, and it would be a very imperfect sketch of his life which did not insist upon this peculiar feature which characterized him. His Christian convictions occupied a great place in the whole of his being, and he showed their power and sincerity by the conformity of his life to his principles. It was not in arguments derived from science that he sought the evidences of his faith; he found them in the revealed truths at which he saw that the human mind could not arrive by itself alone, even though they are in such great harmony with that which is taught by the study of nature and the marvels of creation. Faraday had long and justly perceived that scientific data, so movable and variable, cannot suffice to give to man a solid and impregnable basis for his religious convictions; but he at the same time showed by his example that the best answer which the man of science can give to those who assert that the progress of science is incompatible with these convictions, is to say to them, *And yet I am a Christian.*

The sincerity of his Christianity appeared in his actions as much as in his words. The simplicity of his life, the rectitude of his character, the active benevolence which he displayed in his relations with others, gained him general esteem and affection. Always ready to render services, he could quit his laboratory when his presence elsewhere was necessary to a friend or useful to humanity. We see him putting his knowledge under contribution both for inquiries upon questions of public health or industrial applications, and to give practical advice to an artisan or examine the discovery of a *débutant* in the scientific career. Only, as I have already said, with these exceptions, he made it a rule not to allow himself to be turned aside from the labors to which he had consecrated his life by occupations of another kind, or by those pretended duties of society which waste time, abridge intellectual life (already so short), and very often leave nothing behind them but emptiness and regret. It was not that he could not be eminently sociable when necessary, or that he did not allow himself some relaxations when, fatigued with work, he needed some repose. But these were only accidental circumstances in his life, which was so exclusively devoted to his laboratory. The scientific career of Faraday was equally fortunate and complete. Named as early as 1823 a correspondent of the Academy of Sciences of Paris, he was called in 1844 by this same Academy to occupy one of its eight foreign associateships, after having been associated successively with all the learned bodies of Europe and America. He was by no means insensible to these scientific honors, which he accepted with genuine satisfaction, while he constantly refused every other kind of honorary distinction.

But it is time to commence the more important part of this notice, that which is to be devoted to the examination of the works of Faraday. Only I may, perhaps, be allowed, before speaking of the works themselves, to say a few words of the manner in which Faraday worked.

Is it true that the man of science who wishes to interrogate nature must set himself face to face with his apparatus, make them act to derive facts from them, and wait until these facts have appeared, in order to deduce their consequences, and all without any preconceived idea? Most certainly the philosopher who could advance such an opinion has never experimented, and in any case this method has never been that of discoverers; it was assuredly not the one adopted by Faraday. There is a second method also which was not his, although it is truly worthy of attention, and often fertile of results. This consists in taking up known phenomena and studying them with great precision, carefully determining all the elements and numerical data, so as to deduce therefrom the laws which govern them, and often also to show the inexactitude of the laws to which they were supposed to be subjected. This method requires great previous study, great practical talent in the construction of apparatus, remarkable sagacity in the interpretation of the results furnished by experiment, and, lastly, much perserverance and patience. It is true that it leads with certainty to a result; and this is its good side; but the difficult conditions which it imposes are so many obstacles which prevent its being generally followed except by the highest intellects.

A third method, very different from the last mentioned, is that which, quitting the beaten track, leads as if by inspiration to those great discoveries which open new horizons to science. This method in order to be fertile requires one condition—a condition, it is true, which is but rarely met with—namely, genius. Now this condition existed in Faraday. Endowed, as he himself perceived, with much imagination, he dared to advance where many others would have recoiled; his sagacity, joined to an exquisite scientific tact, by furnishing him with a presentiment of the possible, prevented him from wandering into the fantastic. Still always wishing for facts and accepting theories with difficulty, he was nevertheless more or less directed by preconceived ideas, which, whether true or false, led him into new roads, where most frequently he found what he sought, sometimes, indeed, what he did not seek, but where he constantly met with some important discovery.

Such a method, if indeed it can be called one, although barren and even dangerous with mediocre minds, produced great things in Faraday's hands—thanks, as we have said, to his genius, but thanks also to that love of truth which characterized him, and which preserved him from the temptation so often experienced by every discoverer of seeing what he wishes to see and not seeing what he dreads.

The works which have issued from his brain, so well organized, are numerous and varied; they relate essentially, as we have already stated, to chemistry and electricity. Those on the latter subject are by far the most numerous and important; we shall, therefore, devote to them the greater part of this notice, after giving a summary exposition of the others.

I. In 1816 Davy received a specimen of native caustic lime from Tuscany. He gave it to Faraday for analysis and found that the account given was so perfect that he had it printed and accompanied it with some observations. This success, by giving Faraday confidence in his own strength, encouraged him to attempt other original researches. He published (in 1817 and 1818) an investigation of the passage of gases through narrow tubes, from which it appeared that the velocity of the flow of elastic fluids does not depend upon their density alone, but also upon their individual nature. Various other points of chemistry and physics, besides those which had electricity and magnetism for their object, attracted his attention from time to time throughout the whole of his scientific career. Now we have a note upon the combustion of the diamond; then an investigation of the sounds produced by the combustion of gases, or by the superposition of a strongly heated iron rod upon a mass of copper at the ordinary temperature (Trevelyan's experiment); and then, again, researches upon the limit of vaporization or upon the evaporation of mercury at low temperatures. We may notice two important memoirs—one upon the explanation of certain optical illusions produced by bodies in motion, the other describing some new acoustic figures proceeding from the vibrations of the stratum of air in contact with the surface of vibrating plates. His elegant discovery of *regelation* (that is to say, of the power possessed by two fragments of ice when brought together to become amalgamated by the fact of their simple contact at a temperature above 32° Fahrenheit), followed into its consequences as it has been by Tyndall, has had a much greater influence than perhaps he ever expected. In all these notices, even the least important of them, we find an original idea, a new and striking point of view, which enables us at once to recognize Faraday. And in connection with this, how can we omit to mention his simple and clear explanation of table-turning and the ingenious experiment by which he so clearly shows the muscular efforts made unconsciously by the persons who, by laying their hands upon the table, cause its movement?

Let us now dwell for a few moments upon some researches of longer duration, the publication of which preceded, and also in great part accompanied, his great works on electricity. In 1820 Faraday described two new compounds of chlorine and carbon. One of them was solid, transparent, and colorless; it crystallizes in little prisms and in laminæ and is obtained by exposing to the direct action of the sun bicarbonated hydrogen gas with a large proportion of chlorine. The other contains less chlorine; it is liquid and colorless, possesses great density, and is prepared by passing the former through an incandescent tube, from which chlorine is set free. The discovery of these two compounds filled up an important gap in the history of chemistry.

Subsequently (in 1825) by the compression of the gas obtained from coal, Faraday obtained a new compound, which, no less interesting than the preceding from a scientific point of view, had besides a great industrial importance. This was a bicarburet of hydrogen in a liquid state, which was found to be a mixture of several compounds endowed with various degrees of volatility, and which could be separated by distillation. Everyone knows the advantage in the production of colors derived from this by the illustrious chemist Hofmann, when he extracted aniline from it.

The discovery of this bicarburet of hydrogen was only an incident in the researches which Faraday had undertaken in 1823, upon the condensation of gases into liquids. His mode of operation in this investigation consisted in placing in one extremity of a recurved tube, closed at both ends, the necessary ingredients for the production of the gas, and plunging the other extremity in a freezing mixture. The gas, evolved in a closed space, speedily condensed into a liquid state in the refrigerated extremity of the tube. In this way chlorine, sulphurous acid, sulphuretted hydrogen, carbonic acid, protoxide of nitrogen, cyanogen, ammonia, and hydrochloric acid were successively reduced to a liquid state. With the exception of chlorine, all these liquefied gases were colorless and perfectly transparent; and all of them had a refractive power superior to that of water. The attempts made to reduce the other gases, especially hydrogen, oxygen, and nitrogen, to a liquid state were fruitless. Twenty years later (in 1844) Faraday resumed these experiments by directly condensing the gases by mechanical processes in very strong and hermetically sealed tubes, refrigerating them by means of the mixture of ether with solid carbonic acid produced by Thilorier's method. The condensation could be brought to fifty atmospheres, and the lowering of temperature to $-166°F$, or $110°C$ below $0°$. In this way Faraday succeeded in liquefying, besides the gases which I have already mentioned, olefiant gas, phosphuretted hydrogen, and arseniuretted hydrogen, as also fluosilicic acid; but he did not succeed in solidifying them. On the other hand, by applying his new process to the gases which he had previously liquefied, he brought them not only to a liquid state, but even to that of transparent and crystalline solids; hydrochloric gas alone of these latter would not become solid, whilst hydriodic and hydrobromic gas were successively liquefied and solidified.

It is easy to understand all the importance of an investigation the result of which was to modify completely the received ideas as to the constitution of the permanent gases by causing them to enter into the category of simple vapors; this was to introduce into molecular physics a new and important notion, the consequences of which have gradually unfolded themselves. It is also to a question of molecular physics that we must refer the memoir on the relations of gold and the other metals to light, published by Faraday in 1857. Among other interesting facts that this memoir contains, we shall cite that of a leaf of beaten gold, which, when placed upon a plate of glass, becomes perfectly transparent and colorless when it is brought to a high temperature, and which, when seen by transmitted light, resumes its green color when it is subjected to strong pressure. A great number of experiments upon the pulverulent deposits of various metals obtained by electrical discharges transmitted through very fine wires led to remarkable results as to the variations of color arising from change in the molecular state of the same body. We also find in this memoir a detailed investigation of the various colors presented by different solutions of gold, and especially of the fine ruby-red tinge obtained by the solution of a quantity of gold which, if agglomerated into a single mass, would not occupy the seven-hundred-thousandth part of the volume of water which it colors. It is not necessary to dwell upon the interest presented by researches having for their object the study of the influence, still so imperfectly known, of the molecular structure of bodies upon their relations to light and especially upon their transparency.

Among the numerous works of Faraday relating to the applications of science to the arts, we shall confine ourselves to citing his researches upon the manufacture of steel and of glass for optical purposes, these being the most important. It was by the analysis of the Indian steel called *wootz* that he was led, in concert with Stodart, to compose an alloy which had all the properties of this, by combining aluminum with iron and carbon. In a letter addressed in 1820 to Professor De la Rive he relates all the attempts made by his collaborator and himself during two years of persevering labor to discover the most satisfactory alloys. He indicates, as one of the best, that of rhodium and steel, and, as presenting curious peculiarities, that of steel and silver; this last alloy does not become a true combination unless the silver only forms one five-hundredth part of it. Platinum, on the contrary, combines in all proportions with steel, but it does not furnish so good an alloy as rhodium and silver for the construction of cutting instruments.

Although interesting in many respects, the results which Faraday obtained in his great investigation of the alloys of steel were not proportionate in their importance to the time and trouble which they cost him. We may say the same of the laborious researches upon the manufacture of glass for optical purposes, which he made a few years afterwards (in 1829). It was upon the initiative taken in 1824 by the Royal Society of London, which named a committee for the study of the improvement of glass with a view to its optical use, that Faraday was called upon to occupy himself with it. Whilst he pursued the chemical part of these investigations, Dollond worked up the glass, and Herschel subjected it to the test of experiment. At the end of long and difficult experiments, Faraday ascertained that the greatest difficulty in the way of the fabrication of a good flint glass (that is to say, a very refractive glass) was the presence of streaks and striæ proceeding from a want of homogeneity, due in its turn to differences of composition between the contiguous portions of the same glass. The employment of oxide of lead in the composition of flint glass was the cause of this defectiveness, which could not be avoided even by making use of the most efficacious means of rendering the mixture perfect while in a state of fusion. Among the combinations tried, that of borate of lead and silica furnished a glass endowed with optical properties still more strongly marked than those of flint glass and at the same time presenting a very uniform structure. This glass, which on account of its great density (double that of flint glass) has been named heavy glass, is found, unfortunately, to have a slight yellowish coloration, which renders it unfit for optical purposes; but the labor which Faraday devoted to its fabrication has not been lost; for, as we shall see hereafter, this same glass in the hands of the talented experimenter became the instrument of one of his most beautiful discoveries.

In the long and curious memoir which he published upon the fabrication of optical glass Faraday gives a minute description of all the processes employed by him—of the construction of furnaces, selection of crucibles, means of heating, various artifices, such as the injection of platinum in powder into the fused glass to cause the disappearance of bubbles, etc. It is a genuine instruction in chemical manipulation, and, as it were, a complement to his treatise on this subject, which was published in 1827, and has since gone through three editions. Only those who are called upon to experiment in the domains of physics and chemistry can appreciate the immense service which this treatise has rendered to them by teaching them a multitude of processes of detail so valuable for them to know, and of which a description was previously nowhere to be found, so that everyone was obliged to undergo an apprenticeship to them on his own account. It was necessary that a savant who for so many years had been struggling with the difficulties of experimentation and who had been able to surmount them in so ingenious a manner should give himself the trouble to describe the means which he had employed, so that his experience might be of service to others. Faraday was this savant, and his object was completely attained.

Here, perhaps, before proceeding to another set of subjects, we ought to speak of certain of Faraday's theoretical ideas relating to general physics, and more especially to the nature of the forces and their correlation to each other and to the essence of matter; but we prefer not to discuss the opinions emitted by him upon these questions until after the exposition of his works on electricity and magnetism. We must, however, at once admit that his views on these matters are very contestable, and that, if they inspired him to make experimental researches of the highest interest, this is a proof that in the hands of a man of genius even a bad theory may be the origin of the most beautiful discoveries.

II. I pass now to the examination of those works of Faraday which relate to electricity and magnetism. It is not without embarrassment that I approach this examination; for these researches are so numerous that it would be necessary to extend this notice beyond all bounds in order to give only a simple analysis of them; and they are at the same time so varied that it is impossible to explain them in the chronological order of their publication without confusion being the result. Thus, for example, the researches on induction are interrupted by others on electrochemical decompositions, to be afterwards resumed and completed. Each memoir certainly forms a complete whole; but one memoir is most frequently followed by another the subject of which is quite different. It seems as if the author, after having treated one question, found it necessary to recollect himself before resuming it, and to divert his mind from it, so to speak, by taking up some other kind of work.

It has therefore appeared to me that the best thing for me to do was to group all these various works under a few distinct heads, so as to be able to give their essence without requiring to enter into too many details. The first would include all the researches relating to electrochemistry; the second those which have for their object induction, whether electrodynamic or electrostatic; and the third the phenomena relating to the action of magnetism and dynamic electricity upon light and upon natural bodies in general. It is true that there are some works which elude this classification, as they will not enter into any one of our three divisions. But these are less important works and such as were produced as occasions offered, that is to say, they are the fruit of some particular circumstance which attracted Faraday's attention to some special point. Such is, for example, the memoir which has for its object the investigation of the electrical properties of the *Gymnotus*—and that devoted to the evolution of electricity by the friction exerted against solid bodies by the globules of water or other substances carried up by vapor—experiments undertaken in consequence of the invention of Armstrong's machine. Lastly, there are others which only contain the more or less indirect consequences of the fundamental discoveries, which will be explained in one of the three subdivisions under which we have grouped them. We shall not dwell upon any of these, thinking that we may give a more exact and complete idea of all the progress which Faraday caused the science of electricity and magnetism to make by confining ourselves to pointing out in some detail the most prominent parts of his researches upon these subjects.

Faraday commenced with chemistry in his scientific career; it is therefore not surprising that he approached electricity by the study of electrochemistry. It was, moreover, towards electrochemistry that his attention must have been first directed in that laboratory of the Royal Institution which had witnessed the magnificent discoveries of Davy in chemical decompositions effected by the pile, and especially in the production of the alkaline metals. In taking up this subject Faraday only followed the traditions left to him by his predecessor.

His researches upon the electrical conductibility of bodies constitute a first step in this path. The business was to ascertain whether, as was previously supposed, the presence of water is necessary to render solid bodies conductors, and whether solid non-metallic (and consequently compound) bodies can conduct electricity without being decomposed. Commencing with water, which is an insulator when solid and a good conductor in the liquid state, Faraday shows that a great number of compound substances are in the same case. Such are many oxides, some chlorides and iodides, and a multitude of salts, which do not conduct electricity in the solid state, but, without any intermixture of water, become excellent conductors when liquefied by heat, and are not decomposed by electricity with separation of their elements in the same way as aqueous solutions. To the list of these compounds Faraday adds that of those substances, either simple like sulphur and phosphorus, or compound, such as the periodides and perchlorides of tin, and many others, which continue insulators when fused as well as in the solid state. In this first investigation, notwithstanding a great number of experiments in which he employed the influence of heat and of electricity of high tension in the study of the conductive power of solid bodies, he did not succeed in determining very accurately the conditions of electrical conductibility; he only ascertained that with one exception, which he justly regards as only apparent, there is not a solid body which, on becoming conductive by its passage to a liquid state, is not decomposed by the electrical current. We may add, so as not to return to the subject, that Faraday sometimes had doubts upon this point and that he even thought that water could conduct electricity without being decomposed. Now experiment shows that in all cases, even those which appear most favorable to this opinion, electricity cannot be transmitted under any form through a compound liquid body without this body undergoing electrochemical decomposition.

As to the causes of conductibility, they are still far from being known; when we see bodies, such as the gases, becoming conductors when greatly rarefied, whilst under the ordinary pressure they are perfect insulators, we are compelled to come to the conclusion that the impossibility that we find of explaining this difference, as well as so many others presented in this respect by solid and liquid bodies, is due to the fact that we have not yet a correct notion of the molecular constitution of bodies. Perhaps the recent theories of several physicists, particularly that of Clausius, who regards the particles of bodies as being in a constant state of movement, may succeed in elucidating this subject, which is still so mysterious. Faraday himself had fully foreseen this relation between electrical conductibility and the ideas which we may form as to the nature of matter. In a remarkable article published in 1844 he showed, upon an experimental basis, that in the theory according to which a body is regarded as consisting of atoms possessing weight separated from each other by larger or smaller intermolecular intervals, there are a multitude of facts, some of which can only be explained by assuming that the atoms are the conductors and the molecular space an insulator, and the others by supposing that the intermolecular space is the conductor and the atoms insulators—a contradiction which is inadmissible. He concluded from this that we must imagine matter to be continuous, or rather imagine the atoms to be simply centers of force, and consequently replace the atomistic by the dynamical theory. We shall often find traces of these ideas in the subsequent works of Faraday; for ourselves we cannot take this view. We are convinced that it is not by denying the existence of matter, properly so called, and admitting only that of forces, that we shall succeed in solving the difficulties under consideration and many others, but rather, following the example of Clausius and others, by modifying the ideas hitherto accepted as to the mode of constitution of bodies, and replacing them by others more in accordance with recent discoveries.

But we must return to electrochemistry. I have already said that Faraday first occupied himself with chemical decompositions effected by the electrical current. He commences by effecting the decomposition of water and of solutions by means of a jet of ordinary electricity, rendered as continuous as possible by leaving a stratum of air interposed between the metallic points which convey and carry off the electricity from a machine, and a strip of moistened paper which this electricity traverses. He observes that the deposition of the elements, separated from the decomposed liquid, takes place against the surface of the air which is in contact with the paper. Then, investigating the decompositions effected by the pile, he examines the various explanations which have been given of this phenomenon and concludes that it is much rather a chemical phenomenon than a truly electrical one. In other words, it is a peculiar form of affinity which, under the influence of electricity, is exerted between the neighboring molecules, so that the decomposition is the easier in proportion as the affinity is stronger. He shows that the transfer of the elements can only take place between bodies the constituent parts of which have an affinity for each other; and if these elements separate in a free state against the surface of the metallic poles of the pile, this is because they cannot combine with the substance of these poles; for whenever this combination is possible, they are no longer set free. Water in some cases, air in others, as we have already seen, may serve as poles just as well as solid bodies. Faraday justly rejects the old idea of certain physicists who attributed electrochemical decompositions to the ordinary electrical attractions and repulsions exerted upon the elements of a conductive liquid by the voltaic poles immersed in it. The metallic wires or other conductors which transmit electricity into a liquid are merely, according to him, the roads by which the electric current passes into the liquid; therefore, to exclude any idea of electrical tension, which is more or less implied in the name *pole,* Faraday proposed to substitute for the denomination poles that of *electrodes.* He likewise applied the term *electrolysis* to the chemical decomposition effected by electricity, reserving that of *analysis* for the ordinary chemical decompositions in which electricity does not assist. Lastly, he gives the name of *electrolytes* to those compound bodies which are capable of being decomposed by the electric current.

After this preliminary and general study of the subject, Faraday enumerates the results which he obtained by submitting to electrochemical decomposition a very great number of compounds, some of them simple acids or simple bases, others saline combinations. He dwells particularly on the secondary effects often manifested in these decompositions, especially in the case of aqueous solutions, in which decomposition of the water and of the substance dissolved takes place at the same time. But the essential point of his researches is the law at which he arrived as to the definite nature of electrochemical decomposition. He demonstrates, relying solely upon experiment, that the quantity of chemical action exerted by an electrical current is proportionate to the quantity of electricity constituting this current; and, further, that the same quantity of electricity, or the same current, decomposes chemically equivalent quantities of all the compound bodies through which it is passed. Thus, if we place one after the other in the circuit of a voltaic pile several pieces of apparatus arranged for the decomposition of water and for collecting the gaseous products of this decomposition, we find that in all, even when the degree of acidity of the water and the form and size of the electrodes are different in each, the same current traversing them for a given time produces the same quantity of gas and consequently decomposes the same quantity of water. The quantity of water decomposed in a given time, estimated by the quantity of gas evolved, is therefore the exact measure of the quantity of electricity which has produced this effect. Hence, like Faraday, we give the name of *voltameter* to the very simple apparatus which holds acidulated water destined to be decomposed by the current, and by means of which the volume of gases set free by this current in a given time may be exactly measured.

The second principle, that the same quantity of electricity decomposes chemically equivalent quantities of all compound bodies, was demonstrated by Faraday by placing several different electrolytes one after the other in the same circuit, as, for example, acidulated water in a voltameter, and protochloride of tin and chloride of lead in a state of fusion; and he obtains quantities of tin, lead, chlorine, hydrogen, and oxygen, which are chemically equivalent. Then, rising from the effect to the cause, he comes to the conclusion that there is a perfect equality between the electricity which decomposes a body and that which is generated by the chemical action which produces the direct decomposition of an equal quantity of the same, or of a chemically equivalent quantity of some other body. He is thus led to pay attention to the theory of the pile and to recognize that the power of this apparatus originates in chemical action and not in the contact of two heterogeneous metals—a contact which is not necessary either to produce a spark or to cause a chemical decomposition.

He establishes in the first place that either to effect a decomposition or to produce a spark a plate of zinc immersed in acidulated water is sufficient without its being necessary to bring the zinc into contact with any other metal. He shows that in every pile the presence of an electrolyte (that is to say, a liquid susceptible of being decomposed) is indispensable for the evolution of electricity. Then, distinguishing in the electricity generated the intensity (or the tension) and the quantity, he studies the circumstances, depending either on the nature of the chemical action or on the number of voltaic pairs associated, which exert an influence on these two characters of the current. In a word, he establishes such a correlation between that which occurs in the interior of a pile and that which takes place in the electrolyte interposed between the poles of this pile, that it is impossible not to admit (with him) that electrolytic decomposition is nothing but a form of chemical affinity transferred from the pile into the electrolyte decomposed.

Wishing to obtain an idea of the quantity of electricity which is associated with the particles of which matter is composed, he endeavors to estimate that which is necessary for the decomposition of a grain of water, regarding it, as he is justified in doing, as equivalent to that produced by the direct chemical action (of the acidulated water upon the zinc) which decomposes this grain of water. He arrives at this incredible result, namely: that this quantity of electricity, estimated by the heat evolved by it in traversing a fine platinum wire, is superior to that manifested in 800,000 discharges of a battery of Leyden jars charged by thirty turns of a powerful plate-machine, and consequently equivalent to that constituting a violent flash of lightning.

The researches of which I have been speaking were made in 1833, 1834, and 1835. I had previously paid attention to the same questions, and had arrived by somewhat different methods at the same conclusion with Faraday, namely: that it is in chemical action that resides the origin of the evolution of electricity in the voltaic pile. Faraday frequently alludes to my investigations in a very kind manner; and subsequently (in 1840) he wrote me a letter in which he said that, being a thorough adherent of the chemical theory, he had just attacked the question directly, as I had already done, by demonstrating that contact alone, if not accompanied by chemical action, is not a source of electricity. The memoir in which he probes this question to the bottom is the last which he devoted to this department of electricity. In it, by means of a multitude of ingenious experiments, he demonstrates that the presence of an electrolyte (that is to say, of a liquid which is at once a compound and a conductor of electricity) is indispensable for the production of electricity in a voltaic couple; he varies his experiments in a thousand ways, sometimes by exhausting the number of chemical compounds employed as electrolytes, sometimes by the intervention of temperature or of other agents; and he concludes by showing by general considerations the improbability of the existence of a force of contact.

We may say that this last work, a precious supplement to the preceding ones, has rendered perfectly evident the truth of the chemical theory. This theory, foreseen by Wollaston and Fabbroni, but opposed by most of the physicists of the early part of the present century, had found a powerful argument in its favor in the beautiful experiments of the elder Becquerel upon the electricity developed by chemical action. It was then (from 1825 to 1835) that, profiting by these experiments, and seeking on my own part to make others of the same kind although in a slightly different direction, I published several memoirs to support and render more precise the chemical theory of the voltaic pile. But I cannot but admit that we are indebted to Faraday for having based this theory upon irrefutable proofs, not only by the great number and variety of his researches, but especially by his beautiful discovery of the definite decomposing action of the electric current—a discovery which established between the external chemical action of the voltaic pile and the chemical action which takes place in the interior of this apparatus a relation so intimate that it is impossible not to see in the latter the cause of the former.

III. In 1831 Faraday discovered electrical induction; it is the most important, although perhaps not the most brilliant of his discoveries. Ten years before (in 1821) he had observed a perfectly new phenomenon in the science of electrodynamics—that science which issued complete, as we may say, from the brain of

Ampère after Oersted's discovery. Struck by the experiments of the great French physicist upon the mutual attractions and repulsions of electrical currents and magnets, Faraday was led by theoretical ideas which were rather disputable and not very comformable to the principles of mechanics to assume that an electric current must turn round the pole of a magnet with a continuous movement, and reciprocally that the pole of a magnet must in like manner turn round an electric current. He verified this double result by experiment, and Ampère soon showed its accordance with his theory, adding to it other facts of the same nature. It is not the less true that the discovery of a continuous movement of rotation due to the combined action of a magnet and an electric current was quite unforeseen and at the same time very important, for up to that time there was no example of any such action in physics. It was a first step in the course which was to lead to the finding of a relation between mechanical movement and the molecular forces.

Arago (in 1824) was the first who directly established this relation by his beautiful discovery of magnetism by rotation; for he showed that simple mechanical movement could render a body, in itself non-magnetic, capable of acting upon the magnet. Faraday advanced still further in 1831 by discovering that it was sufficient to bring towards, or remove from, a metallic wire forming a closed circuit another parallel wire traversed by an electric current, or simply a magnet, in order to develop in the former wire an electric current. He discovered induction—that phenomenon which so many others had sought in vain, although suspecting its existence, but which he alone had succeeded in producing.

Let us dwell for a moment upon his fundamental experiment. Two metal wires covered with silk are rolled together round a cylinder of glass or wood; the two wires are thus isolated and have all their spirals approximate and parallel. An electric current is passed into one of these wires; immediately a current is manifested in an opposite direction in the neighboring wire, the extremities of which are united by a galvanometer; but this current only lasts for a moment. The current passing through the first wire is interrupted; immediately another current is developed in the second wire, which is momentary, as in the former case, but directed in the same way as the producing current instead of in the contrary direction. The momentariness of these two currents and the fact of their alternately opposite directions constitute the two important characters of this new mode of production of electricity.

Faraday did not stop at this. Starting from Ampère's idea that a magnet is only an assemblage of electric currents arranged round an axis in a manner very analogous to the circulation of an electric current through a metallic wire rolled into a coil, he tried the replacement, in his fundamental experiment, of the wire traversed by the current by a simple magnet. For this purpose he twisted a single wire instead of two into a coil round a glass or wooden tube; then he introduced a magnet into this tube and ascertained that at this moment a momentary current is developed in the coil of wire, and that a second, equally momentary but in an opposite direction, is developed at the moment when the magnet is withdrawn. Here therefore was realized that production of electricity by magnetism which Faraday had long been seeking, convinced as he was that as electricity produces magnetism, magnetism in its turn must produce electricity. Is it necessary to follow Faraday in the multiplied experiments by which he demonstrates that the electricity developed by induction possesses all the properties of voltaic electricity and of the ordinary electricity produced by machines—that it heats fine metallic wires, gives shocks, and even produces the spark? To produce an electric spark by means of the action of a simple magnet is one of those striking facts which give to the discovery leading to such a result a popularity, if I may venture so to express myself, which is reflected upon its author.

Faraday soon showed that terrestrial magnetism, like that of a magnet, can develop electric currents by induction in a metallic wire rolled into a coil or a circle, and actuated by a movement of oscillation in a plane perpendicular to that of the magnetic meridian. He found that it was not even necessary to employ metallic wires to ascertain the influence of the terrestrial magnetism upon the production of induced currents, but that it sufficed to set a metallic disk (of copper, for example) in rotation in a plane perpendicular to the direction of the inclination needle to find that it is traversed by electric currents passing from the center to the circumference, or from the circumference to the center, according to the direction of the rotation. Still more readily does the vicinity of a magnet to a similar disk set in rotation in any plane under the influence of this magnet develop in it induced currents, the presence of which, directly ascertained, explains in a perfectly satisfactory manner the phenomena of magnetism by rotation discovered by Arago.

These currents, although difficult to perceive, must nevertheless possess considerable power, since they can drag a rather heavy magnet by the action which they exert upon it. It is probable that this power is due less to their individual intensity than to their number, which appears to be very considerable. We may cite two examples which prove in a striking manner the energy which this mode of production of induced currents may acquire. The first is furnished by a curious experiment of Faraday's, in which, on causing a cubical mass of copper suspended by a thread between the poles of an unmagnetized electromagnet to turn upon itself, he saw this mass stop suddenly the moment he magnetized the electromagnet, in consequence of the magnetic action exerted by the currents which induction had set up in the copper. We find the second example in the fact observed by Foucault of the sudden stoppage which is likewise experienced by a thick disk of copper set in rotation between the poles of an electromagnet the moment the latter is magnetized. This stoppage is such that it can only be surmounted by a considerable effort, and the disk itself becomes very strongly heated if the rotation be continued in spite of the resistance it meets with. In order that such a heating effect should be produced in a mass of such considerable size and that we should experience an attractive action so strong on the part of the electromagnet, the induced currents thus produced must be of very great power—a power which they owe essentially to the excessive rapidity of the movement generating them.

I shall not follow Faraday through all his works upon induction which accompanied his fundamental discovery. I shall only refer to the fact that in 1834 he discovered a new important fact, namely: the production of an induced current in the very wire that conducted the inductive current, and which takes place at first at the moment when the latter current begins to circulate, and then at that when it ceases passing. If this wire is rolled in a coil round a cylinder of soft iron, the effect produced acquires great intensity by the fact of the alternate magnetization and demagnetization of the iron which accompanies the passage and interruption of the current in the wire. We all know the advantage that has been taken of this combination in the construction of very powerful apparatus. We also know how, from one improvement to another, we have come to find in induction, and consequently in the simple mechanical movement which gives birth to it, the most simple and economical principle for obtaining electricity, especially with regard to its application to therapeutics and illumination.

The discovery of electrodynamical induction (that is to say, the production of a current by the influence of an exterior current) led Faraday to examine more closely than had previously been done into the phenomenon of statical induction—that is to say, the development at a distance of tension electricity in an isolated conductor by the influence of an electrified body. He ascertained what no one had previously suspected, that the nature of the body interposed between the source of electricity and the conductor submitted to the action of this source had a great influence upon the effect produced—that of the various bodies some facilitated the development of electricity at a distance, whilst others completely stopped it. He named the former *dielectrics;* and he proved that these dielectrics, which are essentially resins, sulphur, shellac, oils of turpentine and naphtha, etc., enjoy this property of transmitting electricity by influence in different degrees, whilst there is not in this respect any difference between the gases, which have the same dielectric power, whatever their nature or their density may be. On the other hand, none of the metals are dielectric; they are subject to the electrical influence but do not transmit it.

From the investigation which we have just summarized, Faraday drew the conclusion that induction does not take place at a distance, but that it is effected by the intermediation of the particles interposed between the inductor and the inducted body. He assumed that these particles are polarized one after the other, which Matteucci afterwards demonstrated directly by experiment; that consequently the mode of propagation of electricity is the same in insulating as in conducting bodies; and that the various substances only differ from each other by the greater or less facility or rapidity with which this polarization, necessary for the transmission of electricity, takes place in them. Then, passing from this to the analysis of the different modes in which electrical discharges take place, some obscure, others luminous, some electrolytic (that is to say, accompanied by the chemical decomposition of the conducting body), others disruptive (that is to say, effected by the mechanical disjunction of the particles of the interposed substance), he applied himself more particularly to the study of the various forms displayed by the electric spark in more or less rarefied gases. I should never have done if I were to attempt to describe all the experiments which he made to elucidate these different points and to arrive at an idea of the actual nature of the electric current. The identity of the current, whatever may be its origin—that its production is due to polar forces which may exert a transverse action, as is the case in electrodynamical phenomena— that these polar forces emanate from contiguous particles; such are the principles which Faraday endeavored to establish as the consequences of his experimental researches, at the same time that he rejected the idea of action at a distance, referring all electrical manifestations to the presence of ponderable matter.

Whether or not we completely admit all Faraday's ideas, it is impossible not to acknowledge the immense advance which he caused the theories of electricity to make, either by demonstrating by experiment the falsity of certain conceptions generally accepted up to his time, or by opening up perfectly new points of view as to the actual nature of electrical phenomena. We have just had the proof of this in the consequences to which he was led by his investigations on statical induction. His discoveries in electrodynamical induction have had still more important consequences, by introducing the notion of mechanical movement into the essence of electrical movement, and thus enabling Weber to combine, in an equally ingenious and satisfactory manner, the mechanical phenomena of electrodynamics, discovered by Ampère, with the electrical phenomena due to mechanical movement, discovered by Faraday.

Ampère and Faraday: two names which will always be united by the intimate relation of their works to the history of the science of electricity, in which they have opened such new and vast horizons; and yet minds as dissimilar in their mode of proceeding as similar in the power of their genius. Both eminently endowed with that faculty of divination which generates great discoveries, but one of them, Faraday, arriving at them by impression, by a kind of instinct which never deceived him, the other, Ampère, advancing with a more certain step, having as his instrument those calculations which he handled with such remarkable ability, and thus arriving at results which he hardly required experiment to confirm, so certain was he that this would not contradict him.

IV. I now pass to the last great series of Faraday's works. I have said and I think proved that induction was the most important of his discoveries; I must now say that the action of magnetism and electricity upon light was the most brilliant. Often the attempt had been made to see whether magnetism and electricity exerted any direct influence upon light, but these attempts had always failed. Investigators had operated upon luminous rays travelling in the air or in liquids and endeavored to act upon them, sometimes by strong magnets, sometimes by electric currents or by statical electricity; but these attempts had led to nothing, absolutely nothing. All these negative investigations have never been published, but they have nevertheless been made.

Guided by theoretical considerations upon the mutual correlation of the forces of nature, Faraday, after many fruitless attempts, succeeded in finding the connection which exists between light and the magnetic and electric forces. Instead of taking an ordinary ray, he operated with a polarized ray; instead of acting directly upon this ray by means of a magnet, he submits it to the influence of magnetism while it is traversing a glass prism in the direction of its length. This prism, terminated by two square and parallel bases, the surfaces of which are well polished, and which are those by which the polarized ray penetrates and issues from the prism, is placed between the poles of an electromagnet in such a manner that its length and, consequently, the direction of the transmitted ray are parallel to the line joining the magnetic poles. Lastly, the polarized ray on issuing from the glass prism only reaches the eye after passing through a Nicol's prism, which serves as an analyzer. It is also by traversing a Nicol's prism before penetrating into the glass prism that the ray of light is polarized, but this may be effected in any other manner.

It is well known that by turning the analyzing prism to a certain angle the polarized ray is extinguished in such a manner that the brilliant spot is replaced by a black spot. If, after this operation has been effected, a strong electric current is passed through the wire surrounding the electromagnet, the black spot disappears and the bright one again makes its appearance. Then by turning the analyzing prism a little further in the same direction, the luminous ray is again extinguished; but this extinction ceases as soon as the magnetic action is suppressed by the interruption of the current which magnetized the electromagnet. The action of magnetism therefore consists simply in causing the plane of polarization to turn by a certain angle and to give artificially to the glass, while it is under the magnetic influence, a property which certain substances, such as quartz and essence of turpentine, possess naturally.

Any transparent substance except gases may serve, although in different degrees, as the *medium* for magnetism to act upon the polarized ray. But that by means of which this influence is best manifested is the yellowish heavy glass (borosilicate of lead) which Faraday obtained in his experimental researches upon the fabrication of glass for optical purposes. He happened to have at hand several specimens of this glass, and it was by using one of these for performing the experiment just described that he discovered the magnetic rotation of the plane of polarization, a phenomenon which would probably have escaped him if he had made use of ordinary glass at first starting. Thus the long and painful labors to which he had formerly devoted himself without any great success, in order to discover a glass fitted for the fabrication of lenses, were not lost to science, since they facilitated his enriching it with one of his finest discoveries.

Let us now study the new phenomenon a little more closely, the better to show all its importance. Some substances, we have said, naturally possess the property of causing the plane of polarization of a polarized ray traversing them to rotate through a larger or smaller angle; some cause it to turn to the right and others to the left of the observer. The discovery of Faraday was that the influence of magnetism or of electric currents develops this same property in nearly all transparent substances, but with this difference, that the direction of rotation of the plane of polarization depends only upon the position of the magnetic poles or the direction of the currents with relation to the transparent substance. The law is that if the north pole of the electromagnet is placed on the same side as the observer who receives the ray into his eye, and consequently the south pole on the side by which the polarized ray enters into the substance, the rotation of the plane of polarization takes place, to the observer, from left to right. It takes place from right to left if the direction of the current, and consequently that of the magnetization, be changed. The action of the magnet may be replaced by that of a coil in the axis of which the transparent substance is placed. In this case, again, the rotation of the plane of polarization is very well observed when a rather strong current is transmitted through the wire of the coil; and the direction of the rotation is always the same as that of the current.

Thus, whilst in substances naturally endowed with circular polarization the rotation of the plane of polarization always takes place according to the nature of the substance, either to the right or left of the observer, in Faraday's experiment the direction of this rotation only depends upon the direction of electric currents or the relative position of the magnetic poles, since it is completely independent of the position of the observer. These two kinds of action are therefore not identical, and we cannot say that by the influence of the magnet or of electricity we produce in all transparent bodies exactly the same property that certain substances naturally possess. Faraday well shows this difference by an experiment which consists in producing, by an ingenious artifice, the internal reflection of the polarized ray upon the extreme surfaces of the prism. This may be done once or several times before the ray is allowed to escape, and doubles, triples, or quadruples the angle of rotation of the plane of polarization, according as the ray is reflected once, twice, or three times. But when, instead of the magnetic, we have to do with the natural rotary polarization, the result is quite different, the return of the reflected ray neutralizing the effect which the direct ray had undergone while travelling in an opposite direction. In this case the angle of rotation of the plane of polarization reflected twice, and which consequently has three times traversed the transparent substance, is no greater than that of a ray which has only traversed it once.

The general phenomenon so unexpectedly discovered by Faraday has hitherto remained unexplained, notwithstanding many investigations, and especially the persevering and remarkable researches of Verdet. It has not even been possible to connect it with some other property of bodies, although each substance has its specific magnetic rotatory power. Faraday, however, drew from it a general consequence which led him to another discovery, namely: that magnetism acts upon all bodies, since all transparent bodies may be modified under its influence sufficiently to acquire, in different degrees indeed, a power which they do not possess of themselves. The discovery to which I have just alluded is that as the magnet acts by attraction upon magnetic bodies, it acts also by repulsion upon all other bodies in nature. From this it results that whilst a rod of iron or of some other magnetic substance, suspended between the poles of an electromagnet, places itself *axially* (that is to say, parallel to the line which joins the poles), a prism of heavy glass (the same, for example, which served for the experiments on light) places itself equatorially (that is to say, transversely to this line). A rod of bismuth is in the same case; and this metal and heavy glass are the substances on which this repulsive action of the magnet is most distinctly exerted. But all bodies in nature which are not magnetic (and these are by far the most numerous) present the same property, although in various degrees. In this way Faraday comes to class all bodies under two heads: those which are magnetic or *paramagnetic,* as he calls them, such as iron, nickel, etc.; and those which are *diamagnetic,* such as bismuth, antimony, heavy glass, etc. The character of the former is to be attracted by the magnet, that of the latter to be repelled by it. It is true that this repulsion, to become sensible, requires an enormous magnetic power even in the case of bodies of which the diamagnetism is most strongly marked, whilst a very weak magnet is sufficient to betray its action upon the magnetic bodies, such as iron, steel, nickel, etc.

It therefore required very powerful means such as Faraday employed for the discovery of diamagnetism. Nevertheless, a distinguished amateur in science, Lebaillif of Paris, had shown as early as 1828 that a fragment of bismuth or antimony very evidently repels a delicately suspended magnetized needle when brought as near as possible to one of the poles of the needle but without touching it. Faraday was ignorant of this circumstance when he published his first work on diamagnetism. I immediately informed him of it, at the same time indicating the journal in which I had published Lebaillif's experiment, which I had witnessed at the time. He accepted my claim in the most amicable manner and at once with his usual good faith recognized the priority of Lebaillif with regard to bismuth and antimony.

In the numerous researches which Faraday devoted (from 1845 to 1855) to diamagnetism and at the same time to magnetism, there are some important points which I must indicate. He discovered the remarkable influence exerted upon this kind of properties by the molecular constitution of bodies, and especially by crystallization. He showed, for example, that a crystallized lamina of bismuth or antimony can place itself axially between the poles of an electromagnet like a magnetic body, as well as equatorially, and that the position which it takes depends on the manner in which it is suspended relative to the direction of its cleavage. He endeavored to investigate the force which comes into play in facts of this order, which he names *magnetocrystalline* force; whilst Plücker, on his part, widened its field by his beautiful and numerous researches on the manner in which crystals place themselves between the poles of an electromagnet; and Tyndall, the worthy successor of Faraday at the Royal Institution, by his ingenious experiments analyzed the phenomenon in its generality and succeeded in connecting it in a perfectly satisfactory manner with the laws which govern magnetism and diamagnetism. Subsequently Tyndall succeeded also in demonstrating by a decisive experiment that diamagnetism, like magnetism, is due to a polarity caused by the influence of the magnet in the diamagnetic body, but with this difference, that instead of opposite poles homonymous poles are developed by the poles of the magnet. Thus fell to the ground all the other more or less rash attempts at explanation which had been given of diamagnetism.

Another point which deserves attention is the investigation which Faraday made of the magnetism and diamagnetism of gases. He arrived at this curious result (observed likewise by Edmond Becquerel at the same time): that of all gases oxygen alone is magnetic, and this in a very marked degree, while all the other gases are diamagnetic. Considering the great part taken by oxygen in the composition of our atmosphere, he attempted to explain, by the magnetic properties of this gas combined with variations of temperature, the phenomenon of the diurnal variations of the magnetic needle which he traced over all parts of the surface of the globe. It is impossible for us not to regret a little the considerable time which he devoted to this investigation, especially as it appears to us very probable that it is not in the action of the atmosphere, but much rather in that of the earth itself, or perhaps even in that of the sun, that we must seek the cause of all the phenomena presented by the magnetic needle.

Lastly, a third point remains to be noticed, namely, that which relates to the investigation of the magnetic field and of what Faraday denominates the lines of magnetic force. According to him, as we have already had occasion to remark, there is no such thing as action at a distance; consequently the magnetic field (that is to say, the space included between two approximated magnetic poles, such as those of a horseshoe magnet) is a medium from which, in every one of its points, forces emanate, the distribution and direction of which are indicated by the very regular arrangement effected by fine iron filings placed in this space. The lines which he calls lines of magnetic force thus become visible and even tangible. But they exist none the less even when we cannot see them, and it is the displacements or modifications which they experience by the presence of a ponderable body in the medium in which they occur that give rise to all the remarkable effects of which the magnetic field is the scene. Such is, in a few words, Faraday's view upon this particular question.

We pass in silence over a multitude of interesting details upon diamagnetic polarity, upon the distinction to be set up between magnetic and diamagnetic bodies, and upon the possible relation between gravity and electricity. In 1850 Faraday reverted to this question, which he had previously attempted, but without success. We see that it is with regret that he is obliged to relinquish the discovery of this relation, which he had twice sought after; but with his usual good faith he admits that, although convinced that it exists, he was unable to find any fact to establish it. If experiment, which he knew so well how to employ constantly, gave him a negative response, would not this be because his point of view was not correct? And did not his error arise from his forming too vague ideas as to the transformation of forces, not taking sufficiently into account that it is the work effected by the force, and not the force itself, that must be considered in questions of this kind?

V. We have passed in review the principal labors of Faraday, and it only remains for us, in order to complete this notice, to endeavor to form an idea of the special character of these labors and of the influence which they have exerted on the progress of science. The first character that strikes us is their number. What Faraday published in the form of memoirs from 1820 to 1855 is incredible. And what would it have been if, side by side with the multitude of experiments which he has made known, we placed in a parallel series those which he never published? It is true that if he has left them buried in his journal, it is because they gave him negative results; but from how many fruitless essays and erroneous attempts he would have preserved scientific men if he had not been so discreet!

A second character is the exactitude of the results obtained. I do not think that Faraday has once been caught in a mistake, so precise and conscientious was his mode of experimenting and observing. It must be admitted that in him the hand marvellously seconded the head. He was of remarkable dexterity and possessed a practical talent, rare and precious in men of science, which enabled him when necessary to construct and modify his apparatus for himself, with the view of attaining with more certainty the desired result.

A third character, of quite a different kind and of much greater value, is the originality of the works of Faraday. A disciple of Davy, he undoubtedly shows traces of the school from which he came, especially in the choice of the subjects of which he treats; but he does not blindly follow either the method or the steps of his master, and, soon quitting the beaten track, he strikes out a path for himself. What is this path? I shall be asked. This is not easy to say, but I will nevertheless attempt it.

At the commencement of the present century, thanks to the important works of which it had been the subject, the science of physics had acquired a character of precision and clearness which seemed almost to make of it a mathematical science. The fine treatise in four volumes, on *Experimental and Mathematical Physics,* published in 1816 by Biot, gives the most correct and complete idea of the point at which this science had arrived. To the confusion which still reigned in the middle of the eighteenth century between the various departments of the science, to the ignorance which then still prevailed upon a great number of these departments, succeeded a clear and substantial analysis of all the phenomena, brought under simple and rigorous laws. Heat, light, electricity, and magnetism were regarded in it as so many distinct agents, having their special properties and obeying their own laws. Calculation was admirably fitted to these clear and precise conceptions; hence we find it greatly used, as witness the very title of Biot's treatise.

The great discovery of Oersted (in 1820) upon the relations existing between electricity and magnetism began to diminish confidence in this mode of considering the phenomena, a confidence which was already a good deal shaken by the researches of Fresnel and Arago upon light. The breach once opened, the fortress was soon entered; and among the most intrepid assailants Faraday figures in the front rank. By his researches on the condensation of gases, he shows that there is nothing absolute in the laws of Mariotte and Gay-Lussac and in the distinction so generally accepted between vapors and permanent gases. By his investigations upon voltaic electricity he establishes between chemical affinity and the production of electricity a relation so intimate that it seems as if the one was only a form of the other. By his discovery of induction he brings in mechanical movement as an important element in the production of electrical phenomena. By his experiments on the influence of the magnet and of electricity on polarized light and by those which were the consequence of it he opens to science a new path which no one had foreseen. He succeeds thus in establishing between the natural agents which we name light, heat, electricity, magnetism, chemical affinity, and molecular attraction such intimate relations, such a connection, that it is impossible not to think that we shall one day succeed in demonstrating that they are only different forms of the same agent. No doubt he is not the only one that has followed this path. Many others have brought their quota to this work of demolition and reconstruction; but he was one of the first, most active and most persevering. Therefore his works, I have no doubt, will always be regarded as cornerstones in the new edifice which we are now endeavoring to construct.

I designedly say *which we are endeavoring to construct;* for we must carefully avoid thinking that it is already constructed. Since the fine discovery of the mechanical equivalent of heat, it seems as if everything had been said and everything were easily explained by means simply of a ponderable matter, an imponderable ether, and a mechanical impulse. Vulgarizers of science, more anxious to produce an effect than to remain faithful to scientific truth, proclaim a molecular system of the world destined to form a counterpart to the *Mécanique Céleste* of Laplace. According to them, nothing is more simple, nothing clearer; attraction itself, which has been the object of the study of so many superior minds, is merely the effect of an impulse easy to understand. A dangerous illusion! which, if it succeeded in propagating itself, would be as fatal to the true progress of science as opposed to its useful diffusion; for it is especially upon those who take to themselves the high mission of popularizing science that it is imperiously incumbent to spread none but correct and well-founded ideas. Let us not, however, exaggerate anything, or refuse to recognize in the too positive ideas which we have just combatted that portion of truth which they may contain. With this purpose let us try, in conclusion, to lay down in few words the point at which in our opinion in the present state of science the important question of the unity of forces has arrived.

After having for a long time arrested the progress of science by abstract and general considerations upon the phenomena of nature, the philosophers finished by adopting, with Galileo, the experimental method, the only one that can lead with certainty to the discovery of the truth. A rigorous and profound analysis, placed at the service of this method, furnished certain and fundamental results. Reverting to a synthetic phase, many superior minds now seek by means of these tediously and painfully collected materials to reconstruct the edifice of which the raising was formerly attempted in vain. No doubt science has thus entered upon a fertile course, but only on condition of advancing with sure and consequently with slow steps. We speak of the unity of force and of the transformation of forces one into the other; but do we know what are forces? Do we know their nature? We have certainly proved transformations of movement and shown that one form of energy may change into another form, mechanical motion into heat, and heat into mechanical motion. These are, without doubt, the most important points gained by science and enable us to get a glimpse of the existence of a single cause manifesting itself in various forms. But it is a long way from this to the discovery of this cause, this single force. Shall we some day arrive at it? It is possible and even probable, and in this case the name and the works of Faraday will always remain associated with one of the greatest problems the human mind can entertain.

Lambert Adolphe Quetelet *

1796–1874

———◆———

NICOLAS ÉDOUARD MAILLY †

LAMBERT ADOLPHE QUETELET was born at Ghent on the 22nd of February, 1796. He was educated at the lyceum of his native town and early showed that nature had endowed him not only with a vivid imagination and a mind of power, but also with the precious gift of indomitable perseverance. He carried away all the prizes of his school and at the same time wrote poetry which attracted considerable attention. He also manifested a talent for art, and a drawing of his gained the first prize at the lyceum of Ghent in 1812.

Having lost his father when only seven years of age, and his family not being able to support him, he was obliged as soon as he had completed his course at the lyceum to enter as a teacher the institution for public instruction at Audenarde. Here he remained a year, teaching mathematics, drawing, and grammar; he was then given a mastership in his native town. In 1815 the lyceum at Ghent, by order of the municipal council, was converted into a university, and Quetelet was appointed professor of mathematics. He received his nomination on his nineteenth birthday. There was nothing brilliant in the lot which had thus far fallen to him, but it secured the means of existence and left him at liberty to devote himself to art, literature, and science.

His most intimate companion, with whom he shared all his tastes, was G. Dandelin, who had been his fellow pupil at the lyceum. The two friends at one time appear to have been seized with a dramatic furor and with the assistance of a distinguished

---

* *A.R.,* 1874, pp. 169-183. From *Annuaire de l'Académie Royal* (Belgique), 1875.
† Belgian historian of science, Secretary of the Royal Academy of Belgium, (1810–1891).

246

musician composed a grand prose opera in one act called *John the Second, or Charles the Fifth, in the Walls of Ghent.* It was presented in the theater of Ghent on the 18th of December, 1816. Its success appears to have been moderate, since it was only played twice and was withdrawn on the plea that it excited the galleries too much. Be this as it may, with it ended the dramatic careers of the authors. They had, however, in preparation, two other pieces, *The Two Troubadours* and *The Jester,* but before the completion of these Dandelin was appointed second lieutenant of engineers and ordered to Namur, while Quetelet was won back to the pursuit of science through the influence of his associate, Professor Garnier.

In 1819 he passed his examination and received the degree of Doctor of Science, the first conferred by the new university. In honor of the event he gave a banquet, which was attended by many of the public functionaries as well as the professors and pupils of the university. His inaugural address gave brilliant promise of his future success. It was divided into two parts: in the first he showed that the locus of the centers of a series of circles, tangents to two given circles of position, is always a conic section; in the second he exhibited a new curve of the third degree, the *focale,* the locus of the foci of all the conic sections, determined by a transversal plane, revolving around a certain point upon the surface of a vertical cone. The discovery of this curve was an important addition to mathematics, and the term *focale* is as inseparably connected with the name of Quetelet, as *cycloid* with that of his favorite author Pascal. Among the themes he submitted to the university in addition to his address was a Latin essay upon the question whether aerolites are projected from the moon.

On the occasion of the laying of the cornerstone of the university buildings, a banquet was given, preceded by a literary meeting, at which was read a poem by Quetelet upon the death of Grétry. This production, full of beautiful versification and expressions of exquisite sensibility, procured for him an introduction to Falk, minister of public instruction, who, with the interest excited by a young man at once a poet and a geometer, a man of letters and of science, caused him to be nominated to a professorship at the Athenæum of Brussels.

His first act on arriving at Brussels was to pay his respects to Commandant Nieuport, then in his seventy-third year, and who might be said to be the only representative of the exact sciences in Belgium. He had read the inaugural address of the young doctor and appreciated as it deserved the discovery of the *focale*. Stimulated by the encouragement he received, Quetelet continued his labors in this direction and published in 1819 in the *Annales Belgique* an article under the title of "Some New Properties of the Focale and of Some Other Curves." This was favorably noticed by Garnier, his former preceptor at Ghent, and procured his election as a member of the Belgian Academy on the 1st of February, 1820. He was then twenty-four years of age.

He soon won the high regard of his associates in the Academy, among whom were the talented Cornelissen and the renowned chemist Van Mons, whose niece he afterward married. The first use he made of his influence was to procure the election of his friend Dandelin and of Baron Reiffenberg, third regent of the Athenæum, afterward professor of philosophy at the University of Louvain. The latter lodged in the same house with Quetelet and soon became ardently attached to him. He was in intimate intercourse and a great favorite with the French refugees then in Brussels and introduced to them his new friend. Among them were such men as David, Arnault, Bory de Saint Vincent, Berlier, Merlin, etc. who, if they had been won by the ready and brilliant wit of Reiffenberg, were equally attracted by the more solid qualities of Quetelet. His relations with the refugees did not, however, prevent him from forming other associations; he sought out and made friends of the artists of the city, joined a literary society which had just been formed, and became a member of the reading committee for the royal theaters. In the latter capacity he had free access to a stage which was favored each year by Talma, Mlle. Mars, and the principal French comedians of the day.

The literary society published annually a poetical almanac, the twentieth and last volume of which appeared in 1825, when the society quietly ceased to exist. Quetelet was a contributor, and as his poetical life seems also to have ended about this time it may be well to notice here some of the pieces published by him since the *Eulogy on Grétry*. The article entitled "The Last Moments" resembles somewhat, but is inferior to, the "Farewell of the Poet to His Lamp," one of his best pieces. "The 19th of January, or The Night Watch of the Ladies," contains some charming lines. An ode to Tollens is in the style of Horace, the favorite poet of Quetelet. An ode to Odevare, a painter greatly admired in 1821 although now but little known, is much more elevated in character. The investiture of the principality of Orange, given by Charlemagne to William the Cornet was also ably treated in verse by our associate. Works of the imagination, whether in prose or verse, greatly interested Quetelet. His "Essay upon Romance," published in 1823 in *Belgian Annals,* has lost none of its interest and, with his poetry, ought to be reprinted. He studied the romances of different nations, translated into verse Schillers tale, "The Knight of Toggenburg," and into prose various Spanish and English ballads.

He had no predilection for the classical in literature or art, and says of modern painting:

The pictures of antiquity, full of life and genius as they are, can never produce in our minds the illusive effect they had upon the Greeks and the Romans. Flora, Zephyr, Venus, so charming in their pictures, are seldom so in ours. It is no doubt good to be the echo of antiquity, but only those can understand the sounds repeated who can go back to past ages and assume for the moment their religion and national character. Let us imitate the Greeks in their simplicity and in their admirable portraiture of nature, but let us have, as they did, our own heroes, our groves, and our religion. What would the age of Pericles have said if Euripides and Sophocles had represented only Osirus or the mysterious *fêtes* of the Egyptians?

"The Lords of the Castle" and "The Countess Ida" (fables), "My Little Boat," an allegorical ballad dedicated to Falk, an elegy upon the death of Adolph Delemer, an ode to Orion translated from the Dutch of Nieuland, a translation of a portion of Byron's "Siege of Corinth," and the "Scald and Lysis," a romance, are among others of his poetical pieces worthy of mention. The last was commended by Raoul in the *Mercure Belgique.* He says in reference to it, "Quetelet, with whom poetry is only a relaxation, writes verse with great facility. He is of the number of those who illustrate the truth that the muses are sisters."

We have endeavored to give some idea of Quetelet as a poet, a man of letters, and a geometer, and before proceeding to consider him as a physicist, astronomer, and statistician we shall see how he filled the office of professor. When first appointed to the Athenæum of Brussels he occupied only a very subordinate position as professor of elementary mathematics, but he was soon promoted and his duties much extended. In 1824 we find him teaching at the Athenæum the descriptive geometry of Menge, the theory of shades and perspective, the calculation of probabilities of La Croix, higher algebra, and analytical geometry, while he was also giving a public course of lectures at the museum upon experimental physics, the elements of astronomy, and of differential and integral calculus.

He was very highly esteemed by his pupils. There was something about him at once imposing and amiable, while there was a complete absence of anything like pedantry or haughtiness. Although marked with smallpox, his physiognomy was refined and impressive. It was only necessary to fix his large dark eyes, surmounted with heavy black brows, upon the refractory, to insure at once silence and submission. On account of the inefficiency of his assistants he was obliged each year to commence arithmetic, algebra, and geometry. He separated his pupils according to their ability into two classes occupying adjoining rooms, and he would pass from one to the other apartment, experiencing no difficulty in preserving silence in both. He was as simple and natural in his teaching as in everything else. He reduced arithmetic to a few general principles, and as soon as he had initiated his pupils in the notation of algebra showed how this admirable instrument could be used to resolve all ordinary questions relating to numbers. His talent for drawing was displayed by the geometrical figures he formed with chalk upon the blackboard to illustrate his teaching. At the Athenæum his courses attracted numerous auditors from all classes of society. He had a special talent for exposition and knew how to use to advantage the few instruments he had at command. He disliked to make experiments with complicated apparatus, which he said was apt to divert the attention from the results exhibited; he considered that only indispensable articles, such as the scales, an electric machine, a voltaic pile, and a few other simple instruments, need be provided.

For the use of his public courses he published several elementary works. The first, upon astronomy, appeared in Paris in 1826. It has been reprinted many times in France and Belgium and translated into several languages. It was followed by one upon natural philosophy, which was intended to enable his pupils at the museum to correct the notes hurriedly taken at the time of the lecture and often erroneous. We have said that he disliked complicated apparatus in teaching the elements of physics, and he accordingly prepared a small volume, the object of which was to describe observations and experiments which could be easily made by any one. This was published in 1832, and the author intended to follow it with other works of the same kind upon magnetism, electricity, light, etc. In 1828 he published a review of the lectures given at the museum upon the calculus of probabilities, as an introduction to his course of physics and astronomy.

The public lectures of Quetelet were such a success that the government considered it advisable to institute other courses of the same kind, and on the third of March, 1827, was installed the Museum of Science and Letters, with a corps of efficient professors in the various branches of science and literature. In the review of the lecture with which three days later Quetelet opened his course we find one of his favorite ideas: "The more progress physical sciences make, the more they tend to enter the domain of mathematics, which is a kind of center to which they all converge. We may even judge of the degree of perfection to which a science has arrived by the facility with which it may be submitted to calculation." The Museum continued to exist for eight years. After suffering with all the other educational establishments of the country from the effects of the revolution, it was absorbed into the free university in 1834, and Quetelet ceased his public instruction after twenty years of service. He soon commenced again, however, having been appointed professor of astronomy and geodesy to the military school, by a royal decree, on the 6th of January, 1836. Among his pupils at the Athenæum were the Duke of Saxe-Coburg-Gotha and the late Prince Consort of England, who always retained a warm affection for his preceptor.

We have said that Quetelet was only twenty-four years of age when made a member of the Brussels Academy. His first contribution, "A Memoir upon a General Formula for Determining the Surface of a Polygon, Formed on a Sphere, by the Arcs of Great or Little Circles, Disposed in Any Manner Whatever," was an admirable production. Garnier said of it that its elegant simplicity and the symmetry of the formula lent interest to a subject which would otherwise have appeared very dry. His second memoir, "A New Theory of Conic Sections Considered in the Solid," did him great honor. His third paper was upon the paths followed by light and elastic bodies. We have now come to a subject which occupied much of his attention, to which he devoted three memoirs presented to the academy, and numerous articles in the *Correspondance mathématique et physique*—that is, caustic curves. In one of those articles he gives the following theorem, which in importance is worthy to be ranked with the discovery of the *focale:*

The caustic by reflexion, or by refraction, for any curve whatever, illuminated by a radiant point, is the development of another curve, which has the property of being the envelope of all the circles, which have their centers upon the reflecting or directing curve, and of which the radii are equal to the distances of the centers from the radiant point in the first case, and proportional to these same distances in the second case; the constant relation being that of the sine of incidence to the sine of refraction.

It was easy to extend this theorem to surfaces, considering spheres enveloped instead of circles. The memoirs presented to the Academy were: February 3, 1823, "Upon Circular Conchoids"; November 3, 1825, "Review of a New Theory of Caustics Followed by Different Applications to the Theory of Stereographic Projections." These researches attracted the attention of Gergonne and other distinguished geometers and were particularly noticed by the illustrious French mathematician, Chasles, after *La Corréspondance mathématique et physique* had given them notoriety. We mention two other papers read before the Academy. One, "A Memoir upon Some Graphical Constructions of the Planetary Orbits," and the other, "Upon Different Subjects of Geometry of Three Dimensions," presented October 28, 1826.

In 1823 commenced the efforts to found an observatory in Belgium. The especial aptitudes of Quetelet pointed him out as the best person to complete the enterprise, and thanks to Falk, then minister of the interior, he was commissioned to go to Paris to study the practice of astronomy. His own account of his first visit to the observatory may not be uninteresting:

I arrived at Paris near the close of the year 1823, with the prospect of founding an observatory in Belgium, but at the same time with a thorough conviction of my want of knowledge of practical astronomy. I went immediately to the royal observatory, but on entering this building, distinguished by historical associations, I was more than ever oppressed with a sense of my deficiencies. I had not even a letter of introduction to relieve the embarrassment of a first visit. I mounted with sufficient assurance the grand staircase, but when I found myself before the doors of Arago and Bouvard I stood for some time irresolute. I was about to knock at the first, when Bouvard opened his and came out, on his way to the observing-halls. He asked me what I wanted. I at once told him my history, to which the excellent man seemed to listen with interest. He then introduced me to the observing-rooms, into the presence of the great astronomical instruments, to me a novel and wonderful sight. With great kindness he explained their purpose and use, and gave me permission to observe whenever I chose to do so. I availed myself of this permission that very evening, and to my surprise was allowed access, freely and alone, to the instruments and records of the observatory. I came day after day, and always with the same confidence accorded! From time to time the kind Bouvard examined my observations and always with encouraging words. He gradually manifested more and more affection for me, offered to initiate me into the practical calculus of astronomy, and from that time directed all my studies, with a care truly paternal. Not content with these manifestations of kindness, he invited me to his house, presented me to his friends, among others to Laplace and Poisson, admitted me to his Friday dinners, and I became in some sort a member of his household.

Quetelet remained in Paris several months and had the honor of being presented to the Institute by Alexander von Humboldt. He returned to Brussels on the first of March, 1824. To fit himself still further for the office of director of the new observatory, he was sent to the principal establishments of the kind in Europe, and on this tour he was accompanied by his wife. He had married on the 20th of September, 1825, the daughter of a French physician, the niece of the chemist Van Mons. To an intimate acquaintance with the usages of polite society this lady united a ready wit and not inconsiderable literary attainments. She was also an excellent musician. Obliged at an early age to preside in the house of her father, where was congregated the best society of Brussels, she acquired ease and grace of manner and was well prepared to assist her husband when in after years he had arrived at distinction and exercised a generous hospitality toward the distinguished strangers of every country who visited the observatory. During his journey Quetelet made the acquaintance of some of the most distinguished men of the age, of Herschel, Schumacher, Gauss, Olders, and others, and at Weimar he had the pleasure of assisting in the celebration of the eightieth birthday of Goethe, with whom he remained eight days. The great poet showed him his experiments in optics, and entertained him with his theory of colors. He was also present at the conference of German naturalists held at Heidelberg on the 18th of September.

While awaiting the completion of his plans in regard to the observatory, in conjunction with M. Garnier, he established the periodical *La Correspondance mathématique et physique,* to which the most eminent men of the age were willing contributors. This publication continued without interruption till 1839, when Quetelet was obliged to resign its supervision on account of the pressing nature of his engagements as permanent secretary to the Academy, to which office he had been elected in 1834.

The erection of the observatory was decided upon on the 8th of June, 1826. It was constructed according to the plans of Quetelet, but was not finished till after many vicissitudes, occasioned principally by the political events of 1830. He had been appointed to the directorship in 1828, but the observatory was not completed until 1832. He then immediately commenced his labors, of which it would occupy too much space to give even a list. They included meteorology, terrestrial physics, astronomy, the collection of materials for the *Annales* of the observatory, and the other special works in which he has brought together the results of his researches. In the early days of the observatory all the attention of Quetelet was directed toward meteorology and terrestrial physics. The elements of these two sciences had been almost totally neglected in Belgium, and his first desire was to correct this grave error, a task in which he perfectly succeeded. He has given the results of his persevering observations in his works *Upon the Climate of Belgium,* and *Upon the Physics of the Globe,* and thus the basis of the meteorology of Belgium was established. The meteorological observations were commenced in 1833 and also the observations for the determination of the latitude and longitude of the establishment. At that time Quetelet possessed only very few and very inferior astronomical instruments. In the month of July 1835 the meridian telescope and the mural circle were put in position, but the equatorial was not mounted until June of the following year. Quetelet was anxious to have the turning dome for the equatorial ready in time to observe Halley's comet, the return of which was looked for with great interest by all Europe, but in spite of all his efforts and the good will of the government, he was disappointed and was obliged to follow the course of this eccentric wanderer with only his telescope.

The determination of the difference of longitude between the observatories of Brussels and Greenwich was later a source of great anxiety as well as interest to him, when in 1853 a trial was made of the new electrical telegraph for this purpose. Two successful attempts of the kind had been made in America, but the distance between the two places, the intervention of the sea, the great reputation of the director of the observatory of Greenwich, and the responsibility assumed before the world rendered Quetelet very solicitous as to the result of his cooperation, and his anxiety did not cease until the two sealed packets, containing the observations made simultaneously at Greenwich and Brussels, which were by common consent opened on the same day in both places, proved the result to be entirely satisfactory. A similar attempt was made in 1868 between Brussels and Leyden.

At the time the observatory was erected clocks and watches throughout the country were regulated only by sundials, and as these were often defective and liable to get out of order, it frequently happened that there would be a difference in time of from 20 to 25 minutes between the clocks of different towns and even between those of the same city. The establishment of railroads necessitated more precision, and on the 22nd of February, 1836, a royal decree enacted that a meridian should be traced and an instrument of observation be established in forty-one of the principal cities of the kingdom. The execution of this work was entrusted to Quetelet.

From 1841 to 1845 the observatory of Brussels was the center of a vast meteorological network which comprised more than eighty stations in Europe and in the north of Asia. Its director published the results of this great enterprise with a large number of plates showing the course and rapidity of the movements of the atmospheric waves. He also made many observations upon the temperature of the earth and an uninterrupted series of observations of the elements of terrestrial magnetism. But perhaps the most remarkable works of Quetelet were the papers he published on his observations of the periodical phenomena of plants and animals. These gave an impulse to similar studies throughout the whole of Europe, and he may on this account be considered as the founder of a new science.

As a class for the study of the fine arts had been added to the Academy, and other changes made, it was deemed advisable to form a new institution, and on the 16th of December, 1845, was established The Royal Academy of Science, Letters, and Fine Arts of Brussels. The first communication made by Quetelet to the new establishment was upon the history of art in Belgium, the manners and customs of the people at different ages, their habitations, ornaments, furniture, the instruments they used to supply the needs of life, etc. He recommended the formation of an ethnological museum to assist in the study of various types of the human race as well as of their habits, and in 1847 through his instrumentality was formed the Museum of Antiquities of Belgium.

In 1853 Quetelet was appointed president of the maritime conference held at Brussels on the suggestions of Lieutenant (afterward Captain) Maury. Its purpose was to establish a system of uniform observations at sea.

The regular astronomical observations of the Brussels Observatory commenced in 1836, although the small corps of the establishment and the attention given to meteorological observations did not permit of a great field of work. The observations made from 1837 to 1839 furnish in the *Annals of the Observatory* a catalogue of 666 stars. From 1848 these observations were carried on with renewed ardor, but all the regularity Quetelet desired could not be secured until 1857. From this year a great work has been continued up to the present day. We refer to the catalogue of 10,000 stars, still in preparation, but which will soon be published, completing the monument raised to astronomical science by Adolphe Quetelet, and his son Ernest Quetelet, who during nearly eighteen years has shared the work of the observatory and whose labors have not been interrupted by his father's death.

Adolphe Quetelet contributed greatly to the progress of the study of shooting stars, about the nature of which little was then known. His attention was first turned to them in 1819, when he wrote his thesis upon the origin of aerolites, and a few years later he gave in the first number of the *Correspondance* a method for determining the height of a meteor from two observations in different places. In 1826 simultaneous observations were organized by his efforts at Brussels, Gand, and Liége. He then abandoned the subject and did not take it up again until ten years later, when he resumed his observations and continued them for the rest of his life. He first called attention to the periodicity of the star showers of the 10th of August and stimulated astronomers of his own and other countries to make numerous observations, which taken together have prepared the way for the remarkable theories now formed as to the character of these interesting meteors. We are indebted to him for very valuable catalogues of their appearances and also for conscientious and precise researches on their frequency and on the several peculiarities they present.

The direction of the establishment confided to his care did not hinder him from devoting himself to studies of another order which show the variety of his powers and the habitual industry of his life. We refer to the statistical works, which obtained for him a high place in the world of science. His first memoir upon this subject, *"The Laws of Birth and Mortality in Brussels,"* was read before the Academy on the 4th of June, 1825. "The establishment of the life insurance companies in our provinces," says the author, "and the desire to see these laudable and, if well conducted, benevolent institutions continued among us has induced me to make some researches into the laws of birth and of mortality."

After showing that during the preceding year the births and the deaths had followed almost exactly in the same proportion the variations of the thermometer, only in contrary directions, he gives some tables of mortality and population, with distinction of sex, and shows how they might be made of use in the speculations of the life insurance companies. Two important remarks appear in the memoir. One, that the annual number of births and of deaths corresponds to a sinusoid, of which the abscissas represent the different times of the year and the ordinates the number of births or of deaths at these seasons. The other verifies the observation of Malthus, that the number of births increases when through any accidental cause an unusual loss of life has been sustained by a population. Another memoir, in 1827, upon the births, deaths, prisons, and poorhouses of the Pays-Bas was intended to complete and develop the preceding. It contained another table of mortality for the lower provinces, but without distinction of sex. *Researches upon Population* next appeared and in 1828 *Statistical Researches in the Kingdom of the Netherlands.* In the importance of the facts given, in breadth of view and novelty of deduction this memoir is superior to the two preceding. A short introduction gives the origin, aim, resources, and use of statistics, the degree of probability which may be obtained in deductions from them, the uncertainty, which can never be entirely overcome, and the objections of ignorance and false knowledge. The author divides the subject as follows: extent of the Kingdom of the Netherlands; population; imposts and commerce; libraries and daily papers; educational and benevolent institutions; crimes and delinquencies; comparative examination of the different parts of the kingdom. Some of the results obtained are very striking. Thus, in comparing the fecundity of marriage with us and with the English, he says:

Great Britain produces less than our country, but her fruit is more durable. She gives birth to fewer citizens, but she preserves them better. If her fecundity is less, her useful men are more numerous, and generations are not as often renewed to the detriment of the nation. Man during his early years lives at the expense of society. He contracts a debt which he ought some time to pay, and if he fails to do so, his existence has been a loss instead of a gain to his fellow citizens.

Speaking of criminals and delinquents, he says:

The proportion condemned to the number accused in the criminal and police courts is the same in Belgium and in France; but in the courts of assize the proportion of the condemned to the accused in Belgium is 84 to 100, while in France and England it is only 65; a fact due to the want of the jury in Belgium at the time the observations were made. When that institution was restored, the number of the condemned was reduced to that of France.

The author then gives a table indicating the number of crimes committed at different ages and also giving the amount of what he calls the tendency to crime.

What is very remarkable [he observes] is the frightful regularity with which crimes are repeated. Year after year are recorded the same crimes, in the same order, with the same punishments; in the same proportions. Sorrowful condition of the human race! The number condemned to the prison, irons, and the scaffold is as certain as the revenue of the state. We can tell in advance how many individuals will poison their fellows, how many will stain their hands with human blood, how many will be forgers, as surely as we can predict the number of births and of deaths.

During the years 1831 and 1832 Quetelet devoted most of his time to statistical researches, and the five following memoirs were the fruit of his labors: "Upon the Law of the Growth of Man"; "Upon the Tendency to Crime at Different Ages"; "Upon the Weight of Man at Different Ages"; "Upon Reproduction and Mortality"; and "Statistics of the Courts of Justice of Belgium from the Years 1826 to 1831." The researches in regard to the size and weight of man were new at the time. Quetelet found that the law of growth, at least from birth until the thirteenth year, could be represented by a hyperbola. Twenty years later Bravais and Martins adopted a hyperbola as the curve of the diametrical increase of the Norway pine, which is at least a singular coincidence. In the memoir upon the tendency to crime he enlarges upon the ideas already given, passes in review the different causes which lead to the development or suppression of this tendency, and denies the favorable influence ordinarily attributed to education.

We too often [he says] confound moral instruction with the merely learning to read and write, which in many instances only provides new instruments for the commission of crime. On the other hand, as to the injurious moral effects of poverty, some of the provinces of France reputed to be poorest are also the most virtuous.

In connection with these two memoirs he says:

Man, without knowing it, and supposing that he acts of his own free will, is governed by certain laws from which he cannot escape. We may say that the human species, considered as a whole, belongs to the order of physical phenomena. The greater the number, the more the individual will is subordinated to the series of general results which proceed from general causes that control the social condition. These causes ought to be sought out, and only observation can discover them.

Man, as the author considers him, is analogous to the center of gravity in a body.

If the average man were determined for a nation, he would represent the type of that nation; if he could be determined for an assembly of all men, he would represent the type of an entire human species. Although his will is restrained within very narrow limits, man contains within him moral forces which distinguish him from the animal, and by which he can, to some extent, modify the laws of nature. These perturbing forces act so slowly that the modifications they produce may be called secular perturbations, since they are analogous to those astronomical variations in the systems of the world which require centuries for their investigation. The study of the natural and perturbing forces of man, in other words *social mechanics,* would develop laws as admirable as those which govern celestial and inanimate bodies. As to the accusation of materialism, to which these results are said to lead, it has been made so often whenever science has essayed a new step into the unknown regions of nature, that it is not worth while to answer it; especially at the present day, when it can no longer be followed by the rack or imprisonment. Who can justly accuse us of insulting the Divinity, when we exercise the most noble faculties He has given us in meditating upon the sublime laws of the universe, or in endeavoring to make manifest the admirable economy and infinite wisdom which presided over their formation? Or who can regard with indifference the sciences which have substituted for the narrow, insignificant world of the ancients, our magnificent solar system, and so extended our starry vault that we cannot attempt to fathom its depths without a feeling of religious awe? Certainly a knowledge of the marvelous laws which govern the universe gives a much grander idea of the power of the Divinity than that which blind supersitition would impose upon us. If the material pride of man is humbled by the thought of the small space he occupies even upon the grain of dust he calls his world, how much he should rejoice in his intelligence, which allows him to penetrate so far into the secrets of the heavens. If science has advanced thus in the study of worlds, may we not look for equal progress in the study of man? Is it not absurd to suppose that, while all else is controlled by admirable laws, the human race alone is abandoned to blind chance, and possesses no principle of conservation? Such a belief is surely more injurious to the Divinity than the research we propose.

In 1832–1833, appeared an article "Upon the Possibility of Measuring the Influence of the Causes which Modify Social Elements," and one "Upon the Influence of the Seasons upon the Faculties of Man." As soon as Quetelet obtained a new result he hastened to make it known, often before his idea was sufficiently matured or the fact at all certain, which accounts for the repetition in his articles. This mode of working has some advantages; it excites interest and parallel efforts, but it occasions loss of time and renders the coordination of the researches more difficult. In 1835 appeared the admirable work, *Man and the Development of his Faculties,* or *An Essay upon Social Physics.* It is a review of all his previous works on statistics, "a sketch," he calls it, "of a vast picture, the details of which can only be supplied by patient investigation." It is divided into four volumes: the first two are devoted to the physical qualities of man, the third to his moral and intellectual qualities, and the fourth treats of the properties of the average man and of the social system. The author considers first the determination of the average man in general, second, with respect to the physical qualities. He then proceeds to examine all that relates to the life of man—his birth, death, strength, height, agility, etc. We give some extracts:

The appreciation of the physical qualities of the average man is by no means difficult, either when measured directly or through their effects; it is quite otherwise with the moral and intellectual qualities, though they also, to some extent, may be judged of through the effects they produce.

Man possesses at his birth the germ of all the qualities which are successively developed, to a greater or less degree; prudence predominates in one, imagination in another, avarice in a third. We sometimes observe great size in proportion to age, or a precocious imagination, or unusual vigor in old age, and the fact alone that we notice these exceptional cases proves that we are conscious of a general law of development, and even make use of it to form our judgment.

The author successively considers the average man, first with reference to letters and the fine arts, second, in relation to the medical or natural sciences:

The consideration of the average man is so important in medical science that it is almost impossible to judge of the condition of an individual without comparing it with that of a fictitious being, supposed to be in the normal state; in fact, the average man we have been considering.

Third, in relation to philosophy and morals; and fourth, in relation to politics. It is quite curious to see how he regards political systems. He is opposed to the system which consists, when there are two dominant ideas in a country, in taking a kind of mean between the two, but would found a system upon the elements common to all parties; or, where there is divergence, upon the ideas held by the largest number.

Governments have their states of equilibrium, which may be either stable or unstable. The stable equilibrium exists when, after action and reaction of every kind, a government constantly returns to its normal condition. If, on the contrary, from any cause whatever, a government tends to diverge more and more from its normal condition, changing constantly, without sufficient motive, its form and institutions, its end is near. Revolutions are only the reactions of the people, or a party, against abuses, real or supposed, and would not take place if the provocation did not exist. The liberty of the press, singularly enough, by facilitating these reactions, renders great revolutions almost impossible, for it does not allow forces to accumulate. The reaction is manifested immediately after the action, sometimes almost before the action has time to propagate itself.

This essay gave its author a high place in the scientific world. It was translated into both English and German. We have not space to notice other papers upon statistics, which appeared in 1845, 1846, and 1848. He was happy in his application of mathematics to statistical questions. He formulated the now well-known *binomial theorem* and insisted, more especially in his last years, on its remarkable generality. He organized the first statistical congress, which was held in Brussels in 1853, and was appointed its president. He was also president of the commission of statistics of the Kingdom of Belgium. On account of his works on social statistics he was made in 1872 an associate of the section of moral and political sciences of the Institute of France. He had long been a corresponding member of this Academy.

He was a member of the Royal Academy of Belgium, as we have said, from 1820, and held the presidency of this learned body from 1832 to 1835, and then succeeded Dewez as perpetual secretary of its three divisions, science, literature, and the fine arts. We have been able to notice only a few of the memoirs inserted in the publications of the Academy. The bulletins of each *séance* are, so to speak, crowded with his articles. One can see by their inspection with what care he registered all the remarkable phenomena which presented themselves during his long career. Thanks especially to him, they, as well as the *Annuaires* and *Annales* of the Observatory, will always be consulted with profit by those who wish closely to study the aurora borealis, shooting stars, bolides, storms, earthquakes, and such phenomena, upon which attention is drawn so strongly at the present time, and of which for the most part a complete theory has not yet been formed. The correspondence which Quetelet had with the official heads of science in different countries contributed greatly to extend the relations of the Academy and to enrich its bulletins.

The revolution of 1848 was not a surprise to Quetelet. He foresaw that the opposition of Louis Philippe to reforms, not in themselves to be feared, would cause some such catastrophe, but he did not anticipate the effect it would produce all over Europe. His attention of course at such a time was turned to politics, and in the month of March he presented to the Academy a paper upon the nature of constitutional states and some principles which may be derived from the consideration of them. Several other articles were also written by him on political subjects. We know that while other governments were falling, Belgium remained intact, and while distress and terror were reigning elsewhere, she prepared to celebrate the anniversary of her independence. The *fête* in honor of the occasion was organized by Quetelet as head of the artistic and literary circle, and never was a more brilliant entertainment given in Brussels. It evinced not only the good taste of Quetelet but the extent of his influence.

As to the private life of Quetelet, we have said that in 1825 he married Mademoiselle Crulet, niece of Professor Van Mons. Two children, a boy and a girl, were the fruit of this union. His mother and a young half-sister, who married the artist Madou, formed the rest of his household. The children were educated at home. Madame Quetelet herself taught them to read, and they had a master for writing. Every Sunday a few friends were invited to dinner, and in the evening the house was open to visitors. There were conversation, music, and charades. The latter were in great favor, and Quetelet himself often took part in them. Those who knew Quetelet only through his works or when enfeebled by age and disease can have no idea of his gayety, wit, and cordiality. He thoroughly enjoyed a laugh, and Rabelais was almost as much of a favorite with him as Pascal. His conversation was admirable, bright, merry, witty, condescending to the most trivial as well as embracing the most extended subjects in letters, science, and art. It was marked occasionally by a vein of severity, which, however, never wounded anyone, and only served to bring into stronger relief the amiable traits of his character. He possessed the very rare faculty of nowing when to listen and always managed to make his guests feel at ease. As the years passed, he attained more and more a position of distinction. The husband of his sister became a painter of eminence; his daughter married a promising young artist, and his son, one of the best pupils of the military school, quitted the engineer corps of the army when he had attained the rank of lieutenant, to enter the observatory. Death soon deprived him of his mother, whom he loved tenderly, but his wife remained his companion for thirty years.

In the last years of his life, when his age warned him in vain to take repose, he undertook a series of works which he intended to be an epitome of the labor of his life. In 1864 appeared *The History of Mathematical and Physical Science in Belgium;* in 1866, *Mathematical and Physical Science in Belgium from the Commencement of the Nineteenth Century;* in 1867, *The Meteorology of Belgium, Compared with That of the World;* in 1869, *Social Physics, or an Essay upon the Development of the Faculties of Man;* in 1870, *Anthropometry, or Measure of the Faculties of Man.* If death had not overtaken him he would have completed the series by a new edition of his *Physics of the Globe,* published in 1861, and by a treatise on astronomy.

We will not attempt to enumerate the learned societies of which Quetelet was a member; the list would be too long. He was elected an associate of the Royal Astronomical Society on January 11, 1828.

Notwithstanding the numerous occupations which claimed every moment of his time, Quetelet always gave the kindest reception to those who wished to speak with him on subjects connected with his studies. He could discern and would encourage merit, and many learned men will remember the support they received from him in the commencement of their careers with feelings of profound gratitude.

Eighteen months before his death he undertook the fatiguing journey to St. Petersburg, at the pressing invitation of the Grand Duke Constantine, under whose auspices a statistical congress had been called. Neither the fear of cholera nor the entreaties of his friends deterred him. He was much gratified by the reception given him and appeared to have been benefited in health by the journey. On Monday, the 2nd of February, he fulfilled exactly his duties as secretary of the Academy, although suffering from the disease of the lungs of which he died fifteen days later. And he also assisted at the session of the class of letters. He died on the 17th of February, 1874, and Belgium deplored the loss of her greatest scientific luminary. "Academy" was the last word on his lips as he sank into unconsciousness.

Joseph Henry *

1797–1878

———◆———

ASA GRAY †

THE REGENTS of the Smithsonian Institution, on the day following the obsequies of their late Secretary, resolved to place upon record, by the hands of their committee, a memorial of their lamented associate. The time has arrived when this should be done, now that the Institution enters upon another official year, and its bereavement is brought freshly to mind.

Although time may have assuaged our sorrow, as time will do, and although the recollection that a well-spent life was well appreciated and not prematurely closed should temper regret, yet they have not dulled our sense of loss, nor lessened our estimate of the signal services to science, to this Institution, and to the general good which remarkable gifts and a devoted spirit enabled this man to render.

If we would fit this memorial to the subject of it, we must keep in mind Professor Henry's complete and transparent, but dignified simplicity and modesty of character, in which a delicate sense of justice went along with extreme dislike of exaggeration, and aversion to all that savored of laudation.

Yet it is not for ourselves, his associates—some of few, some of many years—that this record is made; nor need we speak for that larger circle of his associates, the men of science in our land, who will, in their several organizations, recount the scientific achievements of their late leader and Nestor. And nothing that we can say will enhance the sentiments of respect, veneration, and trust with which he was regarded here in Washington by all who new him, whether of high or humble station. Even those, here or

———

* A.R., 1878, pp. 143–177. Supplementary Note III (Scientific Papers), pp. 170–77, is omitted.
† See pp. 340–363.

elsewhere, who came only into occasional intercourse with him will remember that thoughtful and benignant face—certainly it will be remembered by those who, in that recourse to him which it was always easy to gain, have seen the mild seriousness of a somewhat abstracted and grave mien change into a winning smile, sure precursor of pleasant words, cheerful attention, and, if need were, wise counsel and cordial help. But we are all passing, as he has passed, and the tribute to his memory which it is our privilege to pay is a duty to those who are to come after us.

Joseph Henry was of Scotch descent. His grandparents, paternal and maternal, landed at New York from the same vessel on the day before the battle of Bunker Hill. The Henrys settled in Delaware County, the Alexanders in Saratoga County, New York. Of his father, William Henry, little is known. He died when his oldest son, Joseph, was eight or nine years old. His mother lived to a good age. He was born at Albany very near the close of the last century. His boyhood was mostly passed with his maternal grandmother in the country at Galway. His early education was such as a country common school would furnish to a lad of inquisitive mind but no aptness for study. The fondness for reading came early, but in a surreptitious way.

One day, in the pursuit of a pet rabbit, he penetrated through an opening in the foundation wall of the village meetinghouse. A glimmer of light enticed him through the broken floor into a room above, in which an open bookcase contained the village library. He took down a book—Brookes's *Fool of Quality*—was soon absorbed in the perusal, returned again and again to this, which he said was the first book he ever opened voluntarily, and to all the works of fiction which the library contained. Access in the regular way was soon granted to him.

The lad at this time was a clerk or office boy in the store of a Mr. Broderick. He returned to Albany at the age of fourteen or fifteen. We may count it as a part of his education that he there served a brief apprenticeship to a silversmith, in which he acquired the manual dexterity afterward so useful to him. Opportunely perhaps, the silversmith soon failed in business, and young Henry was thrown out of employment. His powers were now developing, but not in the line they were soon to take. To romance-reading was now joined a fondness for the theater. Not content with seeing all the plays he could, he found his way behind the scenes and learned the methods of producing stage effects. He joined a juvenile forensic and theatrical society called the Rostrum and soon distinguished himself in it by his ingenuity in stage arrangements. He was made president, and having nothing else to do at the time, he gave his whole attention to the Rostrum. He dramatized a tale, wrote a comedy, and took a part in its representation. Unusually comely in form and features and of prepossessing address, our future philosopher was in a fair way to become an actor, perhaps a distinguished one.

But now a slight illness confined him for a few days to his mother's house. To while away the hours he took up a small book which a Scotchman, who then occupied a room in the house, had left upon his mother's table. It was *Lectures on Experimental Philosophy, Astronomy, and Chemistry,* intended chiefly for the use of young persons, by G. Gregory, an English clergyman. It is an unpretending volume, but a sensible one. It begins by asking three or four questions, such as these:

You throw a stone, or shoot an arrow into the air; why does it not go forward in the line or direction that you give it? Why does it stop at a certain distance, and then return to you? . . . On the contrary, why does flame or smoke always mount upward, though no force is used to send them in that direction? And why should not the flame of a candle drop toward the floor when you reverse it, or hold it downward, instead of turning up and ascending into the air? . . . Again, you look into a clear well of water and see your own face and figure, as if painted there. Why is this? You are told that it is done by reflection of light. But what is reflection of light?

Young Henry's mind was aroused by these apt questions and allured by the explanations; he now took in a sense of what knowledge was. The door to knowledge opened to him, that door which it thence became the passion of his life to open wider. Thenceforth truth charmed him more than fiction. At the next meeting of his dramatic association he resigned the office of president and took his leave in a valedictory address, in which he assured his comrades that he should now prepare to play his part on another stage, with nobler and more impressive scenes. The volume itself is preserved in Professor Henry's library. On a flyleaf is the following entry:

This book, although by no means a profound work, has, under Providence, exerted a remarkable influence upon my life. It accidentally fell into my hands when I was about sixteen years old, and was the first work I ever read with attention. It opened to me a new world of thought and enjoyment; invested things before almost unnoticed with the highest interest; fixed my mind on the study of nature, and caused me to resolve at the time of reading it that I would immediately commence to devote my life to the acquisition of knowledge.

The pursuit of elementary knowledge under difficulties and privations now commenced. At first he attended a night school, where he soon learned all the master could teach. At length he entered Albany Academy, earning the means at one time by teaching a country district school, later by serving as tutor to the sons of General Stephen Van Rensselaer the patroon. Then he took the direction of a road survey across the southern portion of the State, from West Point to Lake Erie, earning a little money and much credit. He returned to Albany Academy as an assistant teacher but was very soon, in 1828, appointed professor of mathematics. He had already chosen his field and began to make physical investigations.

It is worth noticing that just when Henry's youthful resolution to devote his life to the acquisition of knowledge was ready to bear fruit, another resolve was made in England by another scientific investigator, James Smithson, in his will, executed in October, 1828, wherein he devoted his patrimony "TO FOUND AT WASHINGTON AN ESTABLISHMENT FOR THE INCREASE AND DIFFUSION OF KNOWLEDGE AMONG MEN." Who could have thought that the poor lad who resolved to seek for knowledge as for hidden treasure, and the rich man of noble lineage, who resolved that his treasure should increase and diffuse knowledge, would ever stand in this interesting relation; that the one would direct and shape the establishment which the other willed to be founded!

The young professor's position was an honorable but most laborious one. Although Albany Academy was said by the distinguished president of Union College in those days to be "a college in disguise," it began its work low down. Its new professor of mathematics had to teach seven hours of every day and for half of this time to drudge with a large class of boys in the elements of arithmetic. But he somehow found time to carry on systematically the electromagnetic researches which he had already begun. In the very year of his appointment, 1828, he described in the *Transactions* of the Albany Institute a new application of the galvanic multiplier, and throughout that year and the next he carried on those investigations which, when published at the beginning of the ensuing year, January 1831, in that notable first paper in the *American Journal of Science and the Arts,* at once brought Henry's name to the front line among the discoverers in electromagnetism.

Sturgeon may be said to have first made an electromagnet; Henry undoubtedly made the electromagnet what it is. Just after

Barlow in England had declared that there could be no electric telegraph to a long distance, Henry discovered that there could be, how and why it could be; he declared publicly its practicability and illustrated it experimentally by setting up a telegraph with such length of wire as he could conveniently command, delivering signals at a distance by the sounding of a bell.

Previous to his investigations the means of developing magnetism in soft iron were imperfectly understood (even though the law from which they are now seen to flow had been mathematically worked out by Ohm),* and the electromagnet which then existed was inapplicable to the transmission of power to a distance. Henry first rendered it applicable to the transmission of mechanical power to a distance. He was the first actually to magnetize a piece of iron at a distance and by it to deliver telegraphic signals. He showed what kind of battery must be employed to project the current through a great length of wire and what kind of coil should surround the magnet used to receive this current and to do the work.†

For the telegraph and for electromagnetic machines what was now wanted was not discovery but invention, not the ascertainment of principles but the devising of methods. These, the proper subjects of patent, have been supplied in various ways, and as to the telegraph with wonderful efficiency—in Europe by the transmission of signs through the motion of a magnetic needle; in America by the production of sounds or records by the electromagnet. Morse was among the first to undertake the enterprise, and—when directed to the right way through Professor Gale's acquaintance with Henry's published researches—he carried the latter mode into practical and most successful execution. If Henry had patented his discovery, which he was urged but declined to do, Morse could have patented only his alphabetical mode of signaling and perhaps the use of relay batteries, the latter indispensable for long lines upon that system.

The scientific as well as popular effect of Professor Henry's first paper in *Silliman's Journal* was immediate and great. With the same battery that Sturgeon used he developed at least a hundred times more magnetism. The instantaneous production of magnets lifting four hundred and twenty times their own weight, of those which with less than a pint of dilute acid acting on two hands' breadths of zinc would lift seven hundred and fifty

---

* See Eugene Lommel, "Scientific Work of George Simon Ohm," *A.R.*, 1891, pp. 247–256.
† See pp. 279–280, Supplementary Note I.

pounds, and this afterward carried up to a magnet lifting thirty-three hundred pounds, was simply astonishing. Yet it was not these extraordinary results nor their mechanical applications which engaged Professor Henry's attention so much as the prospect they opened of a way to which to ascend to higher discovery of the laws of nature. In other hands his discoveries furnished the means by which diamagnetism, magnetic effects on polarized light, and magneto-electricity—now playing so conspicuous a part—soon came to be known. In his own hands the immediate discovery of the induction of a current in a long wire on itself* led the way to his next fertile field of inquiry, the following up of which caused unwise tardiness in the announcement of what he had already done. For it is within our knowledge that the publication of the paper which initiated his fame had been urged for months by scientific friends and at length was hastened by the announcement of some partly similar results reached in a different way by Moll, of Utrecht. In a letter not long afterward written to one of us Professor Henry had occasion to declare: "My whole ambition is to establish for myself *and to deserve* the reputation of a man of science." Yet throughout his life ardor for discovery and pure love of knowledge were unattended by corresponding eagerness for publication. At the close of that very year, 1832, however, he did announce the drawing of a spark from a magnet, that first fact in magneto-electricity and, as he supposed, a new one. But he had been anticipated.

In May 1830 Professor Henry married his cousin, Harriet L. Alexander of Schenectady, who with three daughters survives. Two earlier children died in infancy and a son in early manhood.

Pleasant in most respects as his situation at Albany was, it was not an unwelcome invitation which in the summer of 1832 it became the duty and the privilege of the most venerable of our number, then vice-president of the College of New Jersey, to give to Professory Henry, offering him the chair of Natural Philosophy at Princeton. By this early call that college secured him for her own during the years most prolific for science. It was on a later occasion that Sir David Brewster wrote: "The mantle of Franklin has fallen upon the shoulders of Henry." But the aureole was already visible to his fellow workers in science; and Silliman, Renwick, and Torrey urged his acceptance of the new position and congratulated Princeton upon the acquisition.

The professorship came to him unsought. In his last address

* Announced in *American Journal of Science and the Arts* in 1832. [Original note]

to one of the learned societies over which he presided Professor Henry mentions that the various offices of honor and responsibility which he then held, nine in number, had all been pressed upon him; that he never occupied a position for which he had of his own will and action been made a candidate. It did not occur to him at that moment to make one exception. When a pupil in Albany Academy he once offered himself as a teacher of a country district school. The school trustees thought him too young, but took him on trial at eight dollars a month. At the beginning of the second month they raised his pay to fifteen.

At Princeton Professor Henry found congenial companions and duties well suited to his powers. Here he taught and investigated for fourteen fruitful and happy years; here he professed the faith that was in him, entering into the communion of the Presbyterian Church, in which he and his ancestors were nurtured; and here he developed what might not have been expected—a genius for education. One could count on his being a clear expositor, and his gifts for experimental illustration and for devising apparatus had been already shown. But now as a college professor the question how to educate came before him in a broader way. He appreciated and he made his associates and pupils appreciate the excellence of natural philosophy for mental discipline, for training at once both the observing and the reasoning faculties. A science which rises from the observation of the most familiar facts and the questioning of these by experiment, to the consideration of causes, the ascertaining of laws, and to the most recondite conceptions respecting the constitution of matter and the interplay of forces offers discipline to all the intellectual powers and tasks the highest of them. Professor Henry taught not only the elementary facts and general principles from a fresh survey of both, but also the methods of philosophical investigation and the steps by which the widest generalizations and the seemingly intangible conceptions of the higher physics have been securely reached. He exercised his pupils in deducing particular results from admitted laws and in then ascertaining whether what was thus deduced actually occurred in nature, and if not, why not. Though very few of a college class might ever afterward undertake a physical or chemical investigation, all would or should be concerned in the acquisition of truth and its relations; and by knowing how truth was won and knowledge advanced in one field of inquiry, they would gain the aptitude which any real investigation may give, and the confidence that springs from a clear view and a sure grasp of any one subject.

He understood as few do the importance of analogy and hypothesis in science. Premising that hypothesis should always be founded on real analogies and used interrogatively, he commended it as the prerequisite to experiment, and the instrument by which in the hands of sound philosophers most discoveries have been made. This free use of hypothesis as the servant and *avant-courier* of research—as means rather than end—is a characteristic of Henry. His ideas on the subject are somewhat fully and characteristically expounded by himself in his last presidential address to the Philosophical Society of Washington—one which he evidently felt would be the last.

How Henry was valued, honored, revered at Princeton, the memorial published by his former associates there feelingly declares. What he did there for science in those fourteen years would be long to tell and difficult to make clear without entering into details, here out of place. Happily the work has been done to our hand by the Professor himself, several years ago, in a communication which is printed in the index volume of the Princeton Review, and reprinted in the Princeton Memorial. This careful and conscientious, though cursory, analysis of the principal researches of that period we propose to append to the record.* . . .

One of these, of the Princeton period, ought to be mentioned. It is upon the origin of mechanical power and its relations to vital force. It is a characteristic example of Professor Henry's happy mode of treating a scientific topic in an untechnical way. It also illustrates his habit of simply announcing original ideas without putting them prominently forward in publication, as anyone who was thinking of himself and of his own fame would be sure to do. The doctrine he announced was communicated to the American Philosophical Society in 1844 in brief outline. He developed it further in an article published in the *Patent Office Report* for 1856, twelve years later, a medium of publication which was naturally overlooked. Only at a friend's desire was the paper reproduced in 1860 in the *American Journal of Science,* where it would be noticed. The attention of Professor Henry was turned to the topic (as we happen to know) by an abstract which was given to him of Dumas' celebrated lecture in 1841 on "The Chemical Statics of Organized Beings." If he had published in 1844 with some fullness, as he then wrought them out, his conception and his attractive illustrations of the sources, transformation, and equivalence of mechanical power, and given them fitting publicity,

* See Supplementary Note II, pp. 281–295.

Henry's name would have been prominent among the pioneers and founders of the modern doctrine of the conservation of energy.

In the year 1837 Professor Henry first visited Europe and came into personal communication with the principal men of science of England, Scotland, and France. One of us had the pleasure, a few years afterward, of hearing Faraday speak of Henry in terms of hearty regard and admiration. The two men were in some respects alike, wholly alike in genuine simplicity of character and in disinterested devotion to scientific discovery. They were then rival investigators in the same line; and the race for a time was not unequal, considering how Henry was weighted with onerous professional work. For Faraday, while that most acute mind retained its powers, there was the congenial life of pure research, undistracted by cares of administration or of instruction beyond a few popular lectures; supplied with every means of investigation; stimulated by the presence or proximity of many fellow workers; rewarded by discovery after discovery, and not unconscious of the world's applause—such was the enviable life of the natural philosopher favorably placed. But in this country, where fit laborers are few, duty rather than inclination must determine their work. Midway in his course Professor Henry was called to exchange a position which allowed the giving of considerable time to original researches for one of greater prominence, in which these had practically to be abandoned. Not, indeed, that this was assuredly expected, but it was contemplated as probable. And the event justified the apprehension, while it opened other fields of not inferior usefulness.

In August 1846 the act of Congress establishing the Smithsonian Institution was passed and approved. On the 7th of September ensuing the Regents held their first meeting. On the 3rd of December following they resolved:

That is essential for the advancement of the proper interests of the trust that the Secretary of the Smithsonian Institution be a man possessing weight of character and a high grade of talent; and that it is further desirable that he possess eminent scientific and general acquirements; that he be a man capable of advancing science and promoting letters by original research and effort, well qualified to act as a respected channel of communication between the Institution and scientific and literary individuals and societies in this and foreign countries; and, in a word, a man worthy to represent before the world of science and letters the Institution over which this Board presides.

Immediately following the adoption of this resolution, Professor Joseph Henry of Princeton was elected Secretary. On the 14th of

December a letter was read from him accepting the appointment. At the meeting a week later he appeared and entered upon the duties of his office. From this time the biography of Professor Henry is the history of the Institution. That history is set forth in the Secretary's annual reports, presented by the Board of Regents to Congress, and it need not be recapitulated. A few words may give some idea of the deep impression he made upon the Institution while it was yet plastic.

Some time before his appointment he had been requested by members of the Board of Regents to examine the will of Smithson and to suggest a plan of organization by which the object of the bequest might in his opinion best be realized. He did so, and the plan he drew was in their hands when he was chosen Secretary. As he himself summed it up, the plan was based on the conviction "that the intention of the donor was to advance science by original research and publication; that the establishment was for the benefit of mankind generally, and that all unnecessary expenditures on local objects would be violations of the trust." The plan proposed was in the leading feature, "to assist men of science in making original researches, to publish them in a series of volumes, and to give a copy of these to every first-class library on the face of the earth."

His "Plan of Organization," filled out in its details and adjusted to the conditions prescribed by the law and by the action of the Regents, was submitted to the Board in the following year, was adopted as its "governing policy," and it has been reprinted in full or in part in almost every annual report. All would understand, therefore, that Profesor Henry's views were approved and that they would be carried into effect as far and as fast as they commended themselves to the judgment of the Regents and as opportunity made them practicable.

If the Institution is now known and praised throughout the world of science and letters, if it is fulfilling the will of its founder and the reasonable expectations of the nation which accepted and established the trust, the credit is mainly due to the practical wisdom, the catholic spirit, and the indomitable perseverance of its first Secretary, to whom the establishing act gave much power of shaping ends which, as roughhewn by Congress, were susceptible of various diversion. For Congress in launching did not shape the course of the Institution except in a general way. And in intrusting its guidance to the Regents the law created only one salaried and permanent officer, the Secretary, on whom, by its terms and by the conditions of the case, it devolved great responsibility and commensurate influence. Some of us are old enough to remember the extreme diversity of opinion in Congress over the use to be made of Smithson's legacy. One party, headed by an eminent statesman and ex-President, endeavored to found with it an astronomical observatory, for which surely the country need not be indebted to a foreigner. A larger party strove to secure it for a library, not probably because they deemed that use most relevant to the founder's intention, but because rival schemes might fritter away the noble bequest in popular lecturing, itinerant or stationary, of which the supply and the quality are in this country equal to the demand; or in the dissemination of elementary knowledge by the printing press, as if that were beyond the reach of private enterprise; or in setting up one more college, university, or other educational establishment on half an endowment; or in duplicating museums and cabinets, which, when supported by a fixed capital, necessarily soon reach the statical condition in which all the income is absorbed in simply taking care of what has been accumulated.

Congress rejected one after the other the schemes for making of the Institution an observatory, a library, a normal school, and a lecturing establishment, with professors at Washington. It created a Board of Regents, charged it with the care of the collections and museums belonging to the United States; authorized the expenditure, if the Regents saw fit, of a sum not exceeding twenty-five thousand dollars annually for the formation of a library; and in all else it directed them to make such disposal of the income "as they shall deem best suited for the promotion of the purpose of the testator."

Under this charter and with the course of the Institution still to be marked out, it is not surprising that the official adviser and executive of the Board should look to the will of Smithson for the controlling interpretation of the law. He knew, moreover, that in an earlier will Smithson had bequeathed his fortune to the Royal Society of London, an institution expressly for the furtherance of scientific research; and that he changed, as we may say, the trusteeship for a purely personal reason. Henry took his stand on the broad and simple terms of the bequest, "for the increase and diffusion of knowledge among men." And he never—

Narrowed his mind,
And *to locality* gave what was meant for mankind.

He proposed only one restriction, of obvious wisdom and necessity, that in view of the limited means of the Institution it ought not to undertake anything which could be done, and well done, by other existing instrumentalities. So as occasion arose, he lightened its load and saved its energies by giving over to other agencies some of its cherished work—meteorology, for instance, in which a most popular bureau now usefully expends many times more than the whole Smithsonian income. He has in these last years signified his desire to go still further in this direction and to have the Institution relieved from the charge of the National Museum, now of imperial dimensions and importance. His reasons were summed up in few words in his last report, along with his synopsis of the appropriate functions of the Institution, which he prays may not be merged in or overshadowed by any establishment of the Government, but may stand "free to the unobstructed observation of the whole world, keeping in perpetual remembrance the will of its founder." Its true functions he declares are:

First: To enlarge the bounds of human thought by assisting men of science to make original investigations in all branches of knowledge; to publish these, and to present copies to all the principal libraries of the world. Second: To institute investigations in various branches of science, and explorations for the collection of specimens in natural history and ethnology, to be distributed to museums and other establishments. Third: To diffuse knowledge by carrying on an extended international series of exchanges by which the accounts of all the original researches in science, the educational progress, and the general advance of civilization in the New World are exchanged for similar works of the Old World.

The plan which our late Secretary originated has commended itself to the judgment of successive Boards of Regents, and, we may be permitted to add, is now approved wherever it is known and understood.

Professor Henry took his full share of the various honorable duties to which such men are called. He was in his turn President of the American Association for the Advancement of Science in the year 1849; of the Society for the Advancement of Education in 1855; a Trustee of Princeton College and of Columbian College also of the Corcoran Gallery of Art, in which the Smithsonian Institution deposits its art collections; Visitor of the Government Hospital for the Insane; President of the Philosophical Society of Washington; President of the National Academy of Sciences at Washington. For many years a member of the Lighthouse Board, to which he gave gratuitous and invaluable services as Chairman of its committee on experiments, he added for the last seven years the chairmanship of the Board itself, in his administration no sinecure. Advice and investigation were sought from him from time to time by every department of Government. All were sure that his advice was never biased by personal interest; and his sound judgment, supported by spotless character, was greatly deferred to.

We have said that in coming to Washington a career of investigation was exchanged for a life of administration. It should rather be said that his investigations thereafter took a directly practical turn, as his mind was brought to bear upon difficult questions of immediate importance which were referred to him by Government or came in the course of official duty. In the Lighthouse service alone his timely experiments upon lard-oil lighting, and the firmness with which he pressed his conclusions into practice when sperm oil became dear, has already saved more than a million of dollars; the adaptation of mineral oil to the lesser lights made another great savings; and the results reached by his recent investigations of the conditions which influence the transmission of sound and their application to acoustical signaling are not to be valued by the saving of money only.

It was in the prosecution of these last investigations over a year ago, and probably in consequence of exposure in them, at the lighthouse station on Staten Island, that an intimation of the approaching end of these labors was received. Yet a few months more of useful life were vouchsafed to him, not free from suffering, but blessed with an unclouded mind and borne with a serene spirit; and then, at midday on the 13th of May last, the scene was closed. At the sepulture of his remains (on the 16th) and afterward, it was generally remarked at Washington that never before had the funeral of a private citizen called forth such sense of loss, such profound demonstrations of respect and affection.

It is not for us to assign Professor Henry's place among the men of science of our tiime. Those who do this will probably note that his American predecessors were Franklin and Rumford; that all three were what we call self-made men; that all three, after having proved their talents for original investigation in physics, were called in their mature years to duties of administration and the conduct of affairs. There are interesting parallels to be drawn from their scientific work, if one had time to trace them.

Not often is a great man of science a good man of business. Henry's friends at Princeton, who besought him not to abandon the peaceful academic life which he was enjoying and the quiet pursuits which had given him fame, were surprised when in another sphere he developed equal talents for organization and administration. We have seen how he always developed the talent to do wisely and well whatever he undertook. His well-poised spirit, at once patient and masterful, asserted itself in the trials he encountered in the early years of the Institution, and gave assurance that he could deal with men as well as with the forces of nature. Again, not often is a man of science free from the overmastering influence of his special pursuit. More or less his "nature is subdued to what it works in, like the dyer's hand." Now Henry's mind was uncolored by the studies of his predilection. His catholic spirit comes out in his definition of science: "Science is the knowledge of the laws of phenomena, whether they relate to mind or matter." It appears in his choice of the investigations to be furthered and memoirs to be published by the Institution. These nowhere show the bias of a specialist.

Then he was a careful, painstaking man, very solicitous—perhaps unduly anxious—about the particulars of everything for which he felt responsible. Therefore he was sometimes slow in making up his mind on a practical question. May we here condescend to a trivial anecdote of his early boyhood, which he amusingly related to one of us many years ago and pleasantly recalled at one of our latest interviews? It goes back to the time he was first allowed to have a pair of boots and to choose for himself the style of them. He was living with his grandmother in the country, and the village Crispin could offer no great choice of patterns; indeed, it was narrowed down to the alternative of round toes or square. Daily the boy visited the shop and pondered the alternatives, even while the manufacture was going on, until at length the shoemaker, who could brook no more delay, took the dilemma by both horns and produced the most remarkable pair of boots the wearer ever had: one boot round-toed, the other square-toed.

Deliberate as Henry was in after years, taught by this early lesson he probably never again postponed decision till it was too late to choose. One result of due deliberation was that he rarely had to change his mind. When he had taken his course, he held to it. His patience and kindness under demands upon his time were something wonderful. Some men are thus patient from easy good nature; Henry was so from principle. A noticeable part of the Secretary's correspondence was with a class of men—more numerous than would be supposed—who thought they had discovered new laws of nature or new applications of them, and who appealed to him to make their discoveries known. The Secretary never returned a curt answer to such appeals or inquiries, whether made personally or by letter. Many are the hours which he would conscientiously devote to such paradoxical schemes—sometimes of wonderful ingenuity—and to the dictation of elaborate replies to them. Detecting far down in the man's mind the germs of the fallacy which had misled him, he would spare no pains to present it and its consequences so plainly to his bewildered correspondent that he could find his own way out of it; while at the same time he awarded credit and encouragement for whatever was true, probable, or ingenious.

Although of sensitive spirit and with a just sense of what was due to himself, Professor Henry kept free from controversy. Once he took up the pen, not because his discoveries were set at naught, but because his veracity was impliedly assailed. His dignified recital of undeniable facts (in his *Annual Report* for 1857) was all that was necessary, and not even a word of indignant comment was added.

He left his scientific work to form its part of the history of science and to be judged by scientific men. The empiric he once sententiously defined to be "one who appeals his cause to an incompetent tribunal." He never courted publicity; not from fastidious dislike, still less from disdain of well-earned popular applause, but simply because he never thought of it. His disinterested devotion to this Institution was shown in many ways; among others in successive refusals to accept increase of salary lest it should be thought that the office he held was lucrative. Twice or thrice, moreover, while cumbered with anxieties, he promptly declined calls to positions of greater emolument, less care, and abundant leisure of the pursuits he loved.

We cannot here continue these delineations, and it may be that the character of the man has portrayed itself in general outlines as the narrative proceeded. But one trait may not be wholly omitted from the biography of one who has well been called "the model of a Christian gentleman," and who is also our best example of a physical philosopher. His life was the practical harmony of the two characters. His entire freedom from the doubts which disturb some minds is shown in that last letter which he dictated, in which he touches the grounds of faith both in natural and revealed religion; also in his sententious declaration upon some earlier occasion, that the person who thought there could be any real conflict between science and religion must be either very young in science or ignorant of religion.

The man for whom this memorial is placed was a veteran in both; was one of that noble line of natural philosophers for whom we may in all sincerity render to Almighty God hearty thanks, not only for the good example and fruit of their lives, but also that, having finished their course in faith, they do now rest from their labors.

SUPPLEMENTARY NOTES

NOTE I

SEQUENCE OF DISCOVERY AND INVENTION RESULTING IN THE ELECTROMAGNETIC TELEGRAPH

The following appear to be the main points in the order of discovery which led to the electromagnetic telegraph. They are here condensed from Professor Henry's "Statement," in the "Proceedings of the Regents," published in the *Smithsonian Report* for the year 1857, and from a note appended by Mr. William B. Taylor to his "Memoir of Joseph Henry and His Scientific Work," read before the Philosophical Society of Washington.

1819-1820. Oersted showed that a magnetic needle is deflected by the action of a current of galvanic electricity passing near it. It appears that this discovery had already been made as early as the year 1802, by Romagnesi, and published in 1805.

1820. Arago discovered that while a galvanic current is passing through a copper wire it is capable of developing magnetism in soft iron.

1820. Ampère discovered that two wires through which currents are passing in the same direction attract, and in opposite directions repel, each other; and thence he inferred that magnetism consists in the attraction of electrical currents revolving at right angles to the line joining the two poles of the magnet, and is produced in a bar of steel or iron by induction from a series of electrical currents revolving in the same direction at right angles to the axis of the bar.

1820. Schweigger in the same year produced the galvanometer.

1825. Sturgeon made the electromagnet by bending the bar, or rather a piece of iron wire, into the form of a horseshoe, covering it with varnish to insulate it, and surrounding it with a helix of wire the turns of which were at a distance.

1829-1830. Henry, in accordance with the theory of Ampère, produced the intensity or spool-wound magnet, insulating the wire instead of the rod or bar, and covering the whole surface of the iron with a series of coils in close contact. He extended the principle to the full by winding successive strata of insulated wire over each other, thus producing a compound helix formed of a long wire of many coils. At the same time he developed the relation of the intensity magnet to the intensity battery, and their relations to the magnet of quantity. He thus made the electromagnet capable of transmitting power to a long distance, demonstrated the principle and perfected the magnet applicable to the purpose, was the first actually to magnetize a piece of iron at a distance, and to demonstrate and declare the applicability of the electromagnet to telegraphy at a distance. Using the terminal short-circuit magnet of quantity and the armature as the signaling device, he was the first to make by it acoustic signals, sounding a bell at a distance by means of the electromagnet.

1833. Weber discovered that the conducting wires of an electric telegraph could be left without insulation except at the points of support.

1833. Gauss ingeniously arranged the application of a dual sign in such manner as to produce a true alphabet for telegraphy.

1836. Daniel invented and brought into use a constant galvanic battery.

1837. Steinheil discovered that the earth may form the returning half of the circuit, so that a single conducting wire suffices for telegraphy.

1837. Morse adopted, through the agency of Dr. Gale, the principle of the Henry electromagnet, and the armature made of a recording instrument.

1838. Morse devised his "dot and dash" alphabet, a great improvement upon the Gauss and Steinheil alphabets.

1844. Morse suggested and brought into use the system of relay-magnets, and relay-circuits, to re-inforce the current.

NOTE II

LETTER FROM PROFESSOR HENRY TO THE REV. S. B. DOD, GIVING A
SKETCH OF SCIENTIFIC RESEARCHES AT PRINCETON

[From the Princeton *Memorial of Professor Henry*]

My dear Sir: In compliance with your request that I would give an account of my scientific researches during my connection with the College of New Jersey, I furnish the following brief statement of my labors within the period mentioned:

I. Previous to my call from the Albany Academy to a professorship in the College of New Jersey, I had made a series of researches on electro-magnetism, in which I developed the principles of the electro-magnet and the means of accumulating the magnetic power to a great extent, and had also applied this power in the invention of the first electro-magnetic machine; that is, a mechanical contrivance by which electro-magnetism was applied as a motive power.

I soon saw, however, that the application of this power was but an indirect method of employing the energy derived from the combustion of coal, and, therefore, could never compete, on the score of expense, with that agent as a means of propelling machinery, but that it might be used in some cases in which expense of power was not a consideration to be weighed against the value of certain objects to be attained.

A great amount of labor has since been devoted to this invention, especially at the expense of the Government of the United States, by the late Dr. Page, but it still remains in nearly the same condition it was left in by myself in 1831.

I also applied, while in Albany, the results of my experiments to the invention of the first electro-magnetic telegraph, in which signals were transmitted by exciting an electro-magnet at a distance, by which means bells were struck in succession, capable of indicating letters of the alphabet.

In the midst of these investigations I was called to Princeton, through the nomination of Dr. Jacob Green, then of Philadelphia, and Dr. John Torrey, of New York.

I arrived in Princeton in November, 1832, and as soon as I became fully settled in the chair which I occupied, I recommenced my investigations, constructed a still more powerful electro-magnet than I had made before—one which would sustain over 3,000 pounds—and with it illustrated to my class the manner in which a large amount of power might, by means of a relay-magnet, be called into operation at the distance of many miles.

I also made several modifications in the electro-magnetic machine before mentioned, and just previous to my leaving for England, in 1837, again turned my attention to the telegraph. I think the first actual line of telegraph using the earth as a conductor was made in the beginning of 1836. A wire was extended across the front campus of the college grounds, from the upper story of the library building to the philosophical hall on the opposite side, the ends terminating in two wells. Through this wire, signals were sent from time to time from my house to my laboratory. The electro-magnetic telegraph was first invented by me, in Albany, in 1830. Professor Morse, according to his statements, conceived the idea of an electro-magnetic telegraph in his voyage across the ocean in 1832, but did not until several years afterward—1837—attempt to carry his ideas into practice; and when he did so, he found himself so little acquainted with the subject of electricity that he could not make his simple machine operate through the distance of a few yards. In this dilemma he called in the aid of Dr. Gale, who was well acquainted with what I had done in Albany and Princeton, having visited me at the latter place. He informed Professor Morse that he had not the right kind of a battery nor the right kind of magnets, whereupon the professor turned the matter over to him, and with the knowledge he had obtained from my researches, he was enabled to make the instrument work through a distance of several miles. For this service Professor Morse gave him a share of his patent, which he afterwards purchased from him for $15,000. At the time of making my original experiments on electro-magnetism in Albany, I was urged by a friend to take out a patent, both for its application to machinery and to the telegraph, but this I declined, on the ground that I did not then consider it compatible with the dignity of science to confine the benefits which might be derived from it to the exclusive use of any individual. In this, perhaps, I was too fastidious. In briefly stating my claims to the invention of the electro-magnetic telegraph, I may say I was the first to bring the electro-magnet into the condition necessary to its use in telegraphy, and also to point out its application to the telegraph, and to illustrate this by constructing a working telegraph, and, had I taken out a patent for my labors at that time, Mr. Morse could have had no ground on which to found his claim for a patent for his invention. To Mr. Morse, however, great credit is due for his alphabet, and for his perseverance in bringing the telegraph into practical use.

II. My next investigation, after being settled at Princeton, was in relation to electro-dynamic induction. Mr. Faraday had discovered that when a current of galvanic electricity was passed through a wire from a battery, a current in an opposite direction was induced in a wire arranged parallel to this conductor. I discovered that an induction of a similar kind took place in the primary conducting wire itself, so that a current which, in its passage through a short wire conductor, would neither produce sparks nor shocks, would, if the wire were sufficiently long, produce both these phenomena. The effect was most strikingly exhibited when the conductor was a flat ribbon, covered with silk, rolled into the form of a helix. With this, brilliant deflagrations and other electrical effects of high intensity were produced by means of a current from a battery of low intensity, such as that of a single element.

III. A series of investigations was afterward made, which resulted in producing inductive currents of different orders, having different directions, made up of waves alternately in opposite directions. It was also discovered that a plate of metal of any kind, introduced between two conductors, neutralized this induction, and this effect was afterward found to result from a current in the plate itself. It was afterward shown that a current of quantity was capable of producing a current of intensity, and, *vice versa,* a current of intensity would produce one of quantity.

IV. Another series of investigations, of a parallel character, was made in regard to ordinary or frictional electricity. In the course of these it was shown that electro-dynamic inductive action of ordinary electricity was of a peculiar character, and that effects could be produced by it at a remarkable distance. For example, if a shock were sent through a wire on the outside of a building, electrical effects could be exhibited in a parallel wire within the building. As another illustration of this, it may be mentioned that when a discharge of a battery of several Leyden jars was sent through the wire before mentioned, stretched across the campus in front of Nassau Hall, an inductive effect was produced in a parallel wire, the ends of which terminated in the plates of metal in the ground in the back campus, at a distance of several hundred feet from the primary current, the building of Nassau Hall intervening. The effect produced consisted in the magnetization of steel needles.

In this series of investigations, the fact was discovered that the induced current, as indicated by the needles, appeared to change its direction with the distance of the two wires, and other conditions of the experiment, the cause of which for a long time baffled inquiry, but was finally satisfactorily explained by the discovery that the discharge of electricity from a Leyden jar is of an oscillatory character, a principal discharge taking place in one direction, and immediately afterward a rebound in the opposite, and so on forward and backward, until the equilibrium is obtained.

V. The next series of investigations related to atmospheric induction. The first of these consisted of experiments with two large kites, the lower end of the string of one being attached to the upper surface of a second kite, the string of each consisting of a fine wire, the terminal end of the whole being coiled around an insulated drum. I was assisted in these experiments by Mr. Brown, of Philadelphia, who furnished the kites. When they were elevated, at a time when the sky was perfectly clear, sparks were drawn of surprising intensity and pungency, the electricity being supplied from the air, and the intensity being attributed to the induction of the long wire on itself.

VI. The next series of experiments pertaining to the same class was on the induction from thunder clouds. For this purpose the tin covering of the roof of the house in which I resided was used as an inductive plate. A wire was soldered to the edge of the roof near the gutter, was passed into my study and out again through holes in the window-sash, and terminated in connection with a plate of metal in a deep well immediately in front of the house. By breaking the continuity of that part of the wire which was in the study, and introducing into the opening a magnetizing spiral, needles placed in this could be magnetized by a flash of lightning so distant that the thunder could scarcely be heard. The electrical disturbance produced in this case was also found to be of an oscillatory character, a discharge first passing through the wire from the roof to the well, then another in the opposite direction, and so on until equilibrium was restored. This result was arrived at in this case, as well as in that of the Leyden jar, before mentioned, by placing the same, or a similar needle, in succession, in spirals of greater and greater numbers of turns; for example, in a spiral of a single turn the needle would be magnetized *plus,* or in the direction due to the first and more powerful wave. By increasing the number of coils, the action of the second wave became dominant, so that it would more than neutralize the magnetism produced by the first wave, and leave the needle *minus.* By farther increasing the number of turns, the third wave would be so exalted as to neutralize the effects of the preceding two, and so on. In the case of induction by lightning, the same result was obtained by placing a number of magnetizing spirals, of different magnetizing intensities, in the opening of the primary conductor, the result of which was to produce the magnetization of an equal number of needles, plus and minus, indicating alternate currents in opposite directions.

VII. In connection with this class of investigations a series of experiments was made in regard to lightning-rods. It was found that when a quantity of electricity was thrown upon a rod, the lower end of which was connected with a plate of metal sunk in the water of a deep well, that the electricity did not descend silently into water, but that sparks could be drawn from every part of the rod sufficiently intense to explode an electrical pistol, and to set fire to delicate inflammable substances. The spark thus given off was found to be of a peculiar character, for while it produced combustion and gave a slight shock, and fired the electrical pistol, it scarcely at all affected a gold-leaf electroscope. Indeed, it consisted of two sparks, one from the conductor and the other to it, in such quick succession, that the rupture of the air by the first served for the path of the second. The conclusion arrived at was, that during the passage of the electricity down the rod, each point in succession received a charge analogous to the statical charge of a prime conductor, and that this charge, in its passage down the rod, was immediately preceded by a negative charge; the two in their passage past the point at which the spark was drawn, giving rise to its duplex character. It was also shown by a series of experiments in transmitting a powerful discharge through a portion of air, that the latter, along the path of discharge, was endowed for a moment with an intense repulsive energy. So great is this that in one instance, when an electrical discharge from the clouds passed between two chimneys through the cockloft of a house, the whole roof was lifted from the walls. It is to this repulsive energy, or tendency in air to expand at right angles to the path of a stroke of lightning, that the mechanical effects which accompany the latter are generally to be attributed.

In connection with this series of investigations an experiment was devised for exhibiting the screening effect, within a space inclosed with a metallic envelope, of an exterior discharge of electricity. It consisted in coating the outside of a hollow glass globe with tinfoil and afterward inserting, through a small hole in the side, a delicate gold-leaf electrometer. The latter, being observed through a small opening in the tinfoil, was found to be unaffected by a discharge of electricity passed over the outside coating.

VIII. Another series of investigations was on the phosphoro-genic emanation from the sun. It had long been known that, when the diamond is exposed to the direct rays of the sun, and then removed to a dark place, it emits a pale blue light, which has received the name of phosphorescence. This effect is not peculiar to the diamond, but is possessed by a number of sub-stances, of which the sulphuret of lime is the most prominent. It is also well known that phosphorescence is produced by ex-posing the substance to the electric discharge. Another fact was discovered by Becquerel, of the French Institute, that the agent exciting phosphorescence traverses with difficulty a plate of glass or mica, while it is transmitted apparently without impediment through plates of black quartz impervious to light.

My experiments consisted, in the first place, in the reproduc-tion of these results, and afterward in the extension of the list of substances which possess the capability of exhibiting phospho-rescence, as well as the effects of different interposed media. It was found that, among a large number of transparent solids, some were permeable to the phosphorescing agent, and others impermeable, or imperfectly permeable. Among the former were ice, quartz, common salt, alum. Among the latter class, mica, tourmaline, camphor, etc. Among liquid permeable substances were water, solutions of alum, ammonia; while among the im-permeable liquids were most of the acids, sulphate of zinc, sul-phate of lead, alcohol, etc.

It was found that the emanation took place from every point of the line of the electric discharge, but with more intensity from the two extremities; and also, that the emanation producing phosphorescence, whatever be its nature, when reflected from a mirror, obeys the laws of the reflection of light, but no reflection was obtained from a surface of polished glass. It is likewise re-fracted by a prism of rock salt, in accordance with the laws of the refraction of light. By transmitting the rays from an electrical spark through a series of very thin plates of mica, it was shown that the emanation was capable of polarization, and, conse-quently, of double refraction.

IX. The next series of investigations was on a method of de-termining the velocity of projectiles. The plan proposed for this purpose consisted in the application of the instantaneous trans-mission of electrical action to determine the time of the passage of the ball between two screens, placed at a short distance from each other in the path of the projectile. For this purpose the observer is provided with a revolving cylinder moving by clockwork at a uniform rate, and of which the convex surface is divided into equal parts indicating a fractional part of a second. The passage of the ball through the screen breaks a galvanic circuit, the time of which is indicated on the revolving cylinder by the terminal spark produced in a wire surrounding a bundle of iron wires. Since the publication of this invention various other plans founded on the same principle have been introduced into practice.

X. Another series of experiments was in regard to the relative heat of different parts of the sun's disk, and especially to that of the spots on the surface. These were made in connection with Prof. S. Alexander, and consisted in throwing an image of the sun on a screen in a dark room by drawing out the eyepiece of a telescope. Through a hole in the screen the end of a sensitive thermo-pile was projected, the wires of which were connected with a galvanometer. By slightly moving the smaller end of the telescope different parts of the image of the sun could be thrown on the end of the thermo-pile, and by the deviation of the needle of the galvanometer the variation of the heat was indicated. In this way it was proved that the spots radiated less heat than the adjacent parts, and that all parts of the sun's surface did not give off an equal amount of heat.

XI. Another series of experiments was made with what was called a thermal telescope. This instrument consisted of a long hollow cone of pasteboard, lined with silver leaf and painted outside with lampblack. The angle at the apex of this cone was such as to cause all the parallel rays from a distant object entering the larger end of the cone to be reflected on to the end of a thermo-pile, the poles of which were connected with a delicate galvanometer. When the axis of this conical reflector was directed toward a distant object of greater or less temperature than the surrounding bodies, the difference was immediately indicated by the deviation of the needle of the galvanometer. For example, when the object was a horse in a distant field the radiant heat from the animal was distinctly perceptible at a distance of at least several hundred yards. When this instrument was turned toward the celestial vault the radiant heat was observed to increase from the zenith downward; when directed, however, to different clouds, it was found to indicate in some cases a greater and in others a less degree of radiation than the surrounding space. When the same instrument was directed to the moon a slight increase of temperature was observed over that of the adjacent sky, but this increase of heat was attributed to the reflection of the heat of the sun from the surface of the moon, and not to the heat of the moon itself. To show that this hypothesis is not inconsistent with the theory that the moon has cooled down to the temperature of celestial space, a concave mirror was made of ice, and a thermo-pile placed in the more distant focus. When a flame of hydrogen, rendered luminous by a spiral platinum wire, was placed in the other focus, the needle of the galvanometer attached to the pile indicated a reflection of heat, care being taken to shade the pile by a screen with a small opening introduced between it and the flame.

XII. Another series of experiments connected with the preceding may be mentioned here. It is well known that the light from a flame of hydrogen is of very feeble intensity. The same is the case with that of the compound blowpipe, while the temperature of the latter is exceedingly high, sufficiently so to melt fine platinum wire. It is also well known that by introducing lime or other solid substance into this flame its radiant light is very much increased. I found that the radiant heat was increased in a similar ratio, or, in other words, that in such cases the radiant heat was commensurate with the radiant light, and that the flame of the compound blowpipe, though of exceedingly high temperature, is a comparatively cool substance in regard to radiant heat. To study the relation of the temperature of a flame to the amount of heat given off, four ounces of water were placed in a platinum crucible and supported on a ring-stand over a flame of hydrogen; the minutes and seconds of time were then accurately noted which were required for the raising of the water from the temperature of 60° to the boiling point. The same experiment was repeated with an equal quantity of water, with the same flame, into which a piece of mica was inserted by a handle made of a narrow slip of the same substance. With this arrangement the light of the flame was much increased, while the time of bringing the water to the boiling point was also commensurately increased, thus conclusively showing that the increase of light was at the expense of the diminution of the temperature. These experiments were instituted in order to examine the nature of the fact mentioned by Count Rumford, that balls of clay introduced into a fire under some conditions increase the heat given off into an apartment. From the results just mentioned it follows that the increase in the radiant heat, which would facilitate the roasting of an article before the fire, would be at the expense of the boiling of a liquid in a vessel suspended directly over the point of combustion.

XIII. Another investigation had its origin in the accidental observation of the following fact: A quantity of mercury had been left undisturbed in a shallow saucer, with one end of a piece of lead wire, about the diameter of a goose-quill, and six inches long, plunged into it, the other end resting on the shelf. In this condition it was found, after a few days, that the mercury had passed through the solid lead, as if it were a siphon, and was lying on the shelf still in a liquid condition. The saucer contained a series of minute crystals of an amalgam of lead and mercury. A similar result was produced when a piece of the same lead wire was coated with varnish, the mercury being transmitted without disturbing the outer surface.

When a length of wire of five feet was supported vertically, with its lower end immersed in a vessel of mercury, the liquid metal was found to ascend, in the course of a few days, to a height of three feet. These results led me to think that the same property might be possessed by other metals in relation to each other. The first attempt to verify this conjecture was made by placing a small globule of gold on a plate of sheet-iron and submitting it to the heat of an assaying furnace, but the experiment was unsuccessful, for, although the gold was heated much beyond its melting point, it showed no signs of sinking into the pores of the iron. The idea afterward suggested itself that a different result would have been obtained had the two metals been made to adhere to each other, so that no oxide could form between the two surfaces. To verify this a piece of copper, thickly plated with silver, was heated to near the melting point of the metals, when the silver disappeared, and, after the surface was cleaned with diluted sulphuric acid, it presented a uniform surface of copper. This plate was next immersed for a few minutes in a solution of muriate of zinc, by which the surface of copper was removed and the surface of silver again exposed. The fact had long been observed by workmen in silver-plating that, in soldering the parts of plated metal, if care be not taken not to heat them unduly, the silver will disappear. This effect was supposed to be produced by evaporation, or the burning off, as it was called, of the plating. It is not improbable that a slow diffusion of one metal into the other takes place in the case of an alloy. Silver coins slightly alloyed with copper, after having lain long in the earth, are found covered with a salt of copper. This may be explained by supposing that the alloy of copper at the surface of the coin enters into combination with the carbonic acid of the soil, and, being thus removed, its place is supplied by a diffusion from within, and so on; it is not improbable that a large portion of the alloy may be removed in progress of time, and the purity of the coin be considerably increased. It is known to the jeweler that articles of copper plated with gold lose their brilliancy after a while, and that this can be restored by boiling them in ammonia. This effect is probably produced by the ammonia acting on the copper and dissolving off its surface so as to expose the gold, which by diffusion had penetrated into the body of the metal.

The slow diffusion of one metal into another at ordinary temperatures would naturally require a long time to produce a perceptible effect, since it is probably only produced by the minute vibrations of the particles due to variations of temperature.

The same principle is applied to the explanation of the phenomenon called segregation—such as the formation of nodules of flint in masses of carbonate of lime; or, in other words, to the explanation of the manner in which the molecular action, which is insensible at perceptible distances, may produce results which would appear, at first sight, to be the effect of attraction acting at a distance.

XIV. Another series of experiments had reference to the constitution of matter in regard to its state of liquidity and solidity, and they had their origin in the examination of the condition of the metal of the large gun constructed under the direction of Captain Stockton, by the explosion of which several prominent members of the United States Government were killed at Washington. It was observed in testing the bars of iron made from this gun, that they varied much in tensile strength in different parts, and that, in breaking these bars, the solution of the continuity took place first in the interior. This phenomenon was attributed to the more ready mobility of the outer molecules of the bars, the inner ones being surrounded by matter incapable of slipping, and hence the rupture. A similar effect is produced in a piece of thick copper wire, each end, when broken, exhibiting, at the point of rupture, a cup-shaped surface, showing that the exterior of the metal sustained its connection longer than the interior. From these observations the conclusion was drawn that rigidity differs from liquidity more in a polarity which prevents slipping of the molecules, than in a difference of the attractive force with which the molecules are held together; or that it is more in accordance with the phenomena of cohesion to suppose that, in the case of a liquid, instead of the attraction of the molecules being neutralized by heat, the effect of this agent is merely to neutralize the polarity of the molecules, so as to give them perfect freedom of motion around any imaginable axis. In illustration of this subject, the comparative tenacity of pure water and water in which soap had been dissolved was measured by the usual method of ascertaining the weight required to detach from the surface of each the same plate of wood, suspended from the beam of a balance, under the same condition of temperature and pressure. It was found, by this experiment, that the tenacity of pure water was greater than that of soap and water. This novel result is in accordance with the supposition that the mingling of the soap and the water interferes with the perfect mobility of the molecules, while at the same time it diminishes the attraction.

XV. A series of experiments was also made on the tenacity of soap in films. For this purpose sheets of soap-water films were stretched upon rings, and the attempt made to obtain the tenacity of these by placing on them pellets of cotton until they were ruptured. The thickness of these films was roughly estimated by Newton's scale of the colors of thin plates, and from the results the conclusion was arrived at that the attractive force of the molecules of water for those of water is approximately equal to that of the molecules of ice for those of ice, and that the difference in this case of the solidity and liquidity is due to the want of mobility in the latter, which prevented the slipping of the molecules on each other. It is this extreme mobility of the molecules of water that prevents the formation of permanent bubbles of it, and not a want of attraction.

The roundness of drops of water is not due to the attraction of the whole mass, but merely to the action of the surface, which in all cases of curvature is endowed with an intense contractile power.

This class of investigation also included the study of soap bubbles, and the establishment of the fact of the contractile power of these films. The curvature of the surface of a bubble tends to urge each particle toward the center, with a force inversely as the diameter. Two bubbles being connected, the smaller will collapse by expelling its contents into the larger. By employing frames of wire, soap bubbles were also made to assume various forms, by which capillarity and other phenomena were illustrated. This subject was afterward taken up by Plateau, of Ghent. Another part of the same investigation was the study of the spreading of oil on water, the phenomenon being referred to the fact that the attraction of water for water is greater than that of oil for oil, while the attraction of the molecules of oil for each other is less than the attraction of the same molecules for water; hence the oil spreads over the water. This is shown from the fact that when a rupture is made in a liquid compound, consisting of a stratum of oil resting on water, the rupture takes place in the oil, and not between the oil and water. The very small distance at which the attraction takes place is exhibited by placing a single drop of oil on a surface of water of a considerable extent, when it will diffuse itself over the whole surface. If, however, a second drop be placed upon the same surface, it will retain its globular form.

XVI. Another contribution to science had reference to the origin of mechanical power and the nature of vital force. Mechanical power is defined to be that which is capable of overcoming resistance; or, in the language of the engineer, that which is employed to do work.

If we examine attentively the condition of the crust of the earth, we find it, as a general rule, in a state of permanent equilibrium. All the substances which constitute the material of the crust, such as acids and bases, with the exception of the indefinitely thin pellicle of vegetable and animal matter which exists at its surface, have all gone into a state of permanent combination, the whole being in the condition of a burnt slag of a furnace, entirely inert, and capable itself of no change. All the changes which we observe on the surface of the globe may be referred to action from without, from celestial space.

The following is a list which will be found to include all the prime movers used at the present day, either directly or indirectly, in producing molecular changes in matter:

Class I. { Water power. Tide power. Wind power. } Immediately referable to celestial disturbance.

Class II. { Steam and other powers developed by combustion. Animal power. } Immediately referable to what is called vital action.

The forces of gravity, cohesion, electricity, and chemical attraction tend to produce a state of permanent equilibrium on our planet; hence these principles in themselves are not primary, but secondary, agents in producing mechanical effects. As an example, we may take the case of water-power, which is approximately due to the return of the water to a state of stable equilibrium on the surface of the ocean; but the primary cause of the motion is the force which produced the elevation of the liquid in the form of vapor—namely, the radiant heat of the sun. Also, in the phenomena of combustion, the immediate source of the power evolved in the form of heat is the passage from an unstable state into one of stable combination of the carbon and hydrogen of the fuel with oxygen of the atmosphere. But this power may ultimately be resolved into the force which caused the separation of these elements from their previous combination in the state of carbonic acid—namely, the radiant light of the sun. But the mechanical power exerted by animals is due to the passage of organized matter in the stomach from an unstable to a stable equilibrium, or as it were from the combustion of the food. It therefore follows that animal power is referable to the same source as that from the combustion of fuel—namely, developed power of the sun's beams. But according to this view what is vitality? It is that mysterious principle—not mechanical power—which determines the form and arranges the atoms of organized matter, employing for this purpose the power which is derived from the food.

These propositions were illustrated by different examples. Suppose a vegetable organism impregnated with a germ—a potato, for instance—is planted below the surface of the ground in a damp soil, under a temperature sufficient for vegetation. If we examine it from time to time, we find it sending down rootlets into the earth and stems and leaves upward into the air. After the leaves have been fully expanded we shall find the tuber entirely exhausted, nothing but a skin remaining. The same effect will take place if the potato be placed in a warm cellar. It will continue to grow until all the starch and gluten are exhausted, when it will cease to increase. If, however, we now place it in the light, it will commence to grow again, and increase in size and weight. If we weigh the potato previous to the experiment and the plant after it has ceased to grow in the dark, we shall find that the weight of the latter is a little more than half that of the original tuber. The question then is, what has become of the material which filled the sac of the potato? The answer is, one part has run down into carbonic acid and water, and in this running down has evolved the power to build up the other part into the new plant. After the leaves have been formed and the plant exposed to the light of the sun, the developed power of its rays decomposes the carbonic acid of the atmosphere, and thus furnishes the pabulum and the power necessary to the further development of the organization. The same is the case with wheat and all other grains that are germinated in the earth. Besides the germ of the future plant, there is

stored away around the germ the starch and gluten to furnish the
power necessary to its development and also the food to build it
up until it reaches the surface of the earth and can draw the
source of its future growth from the power of the sunbeam. In the
case of fungi and other plants that grow in the dark, they derive
the power and the pabulum from surrounding vegetable matter in
process of decay or in that of evolving power. A similar arrangement is found in regard to animal organization. It is well known
that the egg continually diminishes in weight during the process of
incubation, and the chick when fully formed weighs scarcely more
than one-half the original weight of the egg. What is the interpretation of this phenomenon? Simply that one part of the contents
of the shell has run down into carbonic acid and water, and thus
evolved the power necessary to do the work of building up the
future animal. In like manner when the tadpole is converted into
a frog the animal for a while loses weight. A portion of the organism of its tail has been expended developing the power necessary
to the transformation, while another portion has served for the
material of the legs.

What, then, is the office of vitality? We say that it is analogous
to that of the engineer who directs the power of the steam-engine
in the execution of its work. Without this, in the case of the egg,
the materials, left to the undirected force of affinity, would end in
simply producing chemical compounds—sulphuretted hydrogen,
carbonic acid, etc. There is no special analogy between the process
of crystallization and that of vital action. In the one case definite
mathematical forms are the necessary results, while in the other
the results are precisely like those which are produced under the
direction of will and intelligence, evincing a design and a purpose,
making provision at one stage of the process for results to be attained at a later, and producing organs intended evidently for
locomotion and perception. Not only is the result the same as that
which is produced by human design, but in all cases the power
with which this principle operates is the same as that with which
the intelligent engineer produces his result.

This doctrine was first given in a communication to the American Philosophical Society in December, 1844, and more fully developed in a paper published in the Patent Office Report in 1857.

The publication in full of three of the series of investigations
herein described was made in the Transactions of the American
Philosophical Society. Others were published in Silliman's Journal,
and both these are noticed in the Royal Society's Catalogue of
Scientific Papers; but the remainder of them were published in

the Proceedings of the American Philosophical Society, and are not mentioned in the work just referred to.

In 1846, while still at Princeton, I was requested by members of the Board of Regents of the Smithsonian Institution, which was then just founded, to study the will of Smithson, and to give a plan of organization by which the object of the bequest might be realized. My conclusion was that the intention of the donor was to advance Science by original research and publication; that the establishment was for the benefit of mankind generally, and that all unnecessary expenditures on local objects would be violations of the trust. The plan I proposed for the organization of the Institution was to assist men of science in making original researches, to publish these in a series of volumes, and to give a copy of these to every first-class library on the face of the earth.

I was afterward called to take charge of the Institution and to carry out this plan, which has been the governing policy of the establishment from the beginning to the present time.

One of the first enterprises of the Smithsonian Institution was the establishment of a system of simultaneous meteorological observations over the whole United States, especially for the study of the phenomena of American storms.

For this purpose the assistance of Professor Guyot was obtained, who drew up a series of instructions for the observers, which was printed and distributed in all parts of the country. He also recommended the form of instruments best suited to be used by the observers, and finally calculated, with immense labor, a volume of meteorological and physical tables for reducing and discussing observations. These tables were published by the Institution, and are now in use in almost every part of the world in which the English language is spoken. The prosecution of the system finally led to the application of the principles established to the predictions of the weather by means of the telegraph.

JOSEPH HENRY.

Washington, D.C., *December* 4, 1876.

Alexander Dallas Bache *

1806–1867

JOSEPH HENRY

ALEXANDER DALLAS BACHE, whose life and character form the subject of the following eulogy, was the son of Richard Bache, one of eight children of Sarah, the only daughter of Dr. Benjamin Franklin. His mother was Sophia Burret Dallas, daughter of Alexander J. Dallas, and sister of George M. Dallas, whose names are well known in the history of this country, the former as Secretary of the Treasury, and the latter as Vice-President of the United States, and subsequently as minister to the Court of St. James.

The subject of our sketch was born in Philadelphia on the 19th of July, 1806. At an early age he became a pupil of a classical school and was distinguished by an unusual aptitude in the acquisition of learning. Shortly before arriving at the age of fifteen he was appointed a cadet at the National Military Academy at West Point. Here, though the youngest pupil, he soon attained a high grade of scholarship, which he maintained during the whole of his course, and was finally graduated in 1825 at the head of his class. His merit was in this case the more conspicuous, inasmuch as the class is shown to have been one of unusual ability, by having numbered no less than four successful candidates for the honor of adoption into the Corps of Engineers. It has been mentioned as a solitary instance in the history of the Academy, noted for its rigid discipline, that young Bache passed through the entire course of four years without having received a mark of actual demerit, and, what is perhaps not less uncommon, without having called forth the least manifestation of envy on the part of his fellow-pupils. On the contrary, his superiority

* A.R., 1870, pp. 91–116. The list of Bache's published scientific papers originally appended to this memoir (pp. 108–116) is omitted.

296

in scholarship was freely acknowledged by every member of his class, while his unassuming manner, friendly demeanor, and fidelity to duty secured him the affection as well as the respect not only of his fellow-pupils, but also of the officers of the institution. It is also remembered that his classmates, with instinctive deference to his scrupulous sense of propriety, forbore to solicit his participation in any amusement which in the slightest degree conflicted with the rules of the Academy. So far from this, they commended his course, and took pride to themselves, as members of his class, in his reputation for high standing and exemplary conduct. His roommate, older by several years than he was, and by no means noted for regularity or studious habits, constituted himself, as it were, his guardian and sedulously excluded all visitors or other interruptions to study during the prescribed hours. For this self-imposed service, gravely rendered as essential to the honor of the class, he was accustomed jocularly to claim immunity for his own delinquencies or shortcomings. But whatever protection others might require on account of youth and inexperience, young Bache needed no guardian to keep him in the line of duty. Impressed beyond his years with a sense of the responsibility which would devolve upon him as the eldest of his mother's family, entertaining a grave appreciation of the obligations involved in his education at the National Academy, he resolved from the first to exert his energies to the utmost in qualifying himself for the duties which he might be called upon to discharge, whether in professional or private life. Nor was he uninfluenced in this determination by a consciousness that as a descendant of Franklin he was in a certain degree an object of popular interest, and that on this account something more than an ordinary responsibility rested upon him. On a mind constituted like his an influence of this kind could not but exert a happy effect.

The character which he established for gentleness of manner and evenness of temper was not entirely the result of native amiability, for when a child he is said to have been quick-tempered, and at later periods of his life, when suddenly provoked beyond his habitual power of endurance, he sometimes gave way to manifestations of temper which might have surprised those who only knew him in his usual state of calm deportment. These ebullitions were, however, of rare occurrence and always of short duration. His marked characteristic was the control which he had acquired over his passions and feelings, and it was this which enabled him to suppress all tendency to self-indulgence, to pursue with unremitting perseverance the course he had marked out, to observe an undeviating regard for truth and justice, and to cherish habitually all that would tend to exemplify the kindlier affections of the heart.

Although young Bache was perhaps predisposed, from hereditary influence, to form correct habits and adopt high moral principles, yet these dispositions might have remained dormant had it not been for the early training and the watchful care of his noble mother. From his earliest days she checked with gentle reproof every indication of childish revolt against wholesome restraint and steadily carried out her system of discipline so gently and yet so effectually that it met with scarcely any opposition, and left the conviction that she was always in the right. Her maternal solicitude did not end with his being placed under military rule but was continued through his whole course by means of a ready pen. In the language of one who was permitted to read her letters to her son while at West Point, "nothing could be more admirable than the way in which, amid pleasant gossip and family news, she would inspire her son with high sentiments and encourage him to persevering industry."

As an illustration of his persistency of purpose, it is related that when a recitation of more than common length or difficulty was to be prepared for the morrow, it was no unusual practice of his to place himself on a seat of unstable equilibrium, which by giving way when volition was about to lose its power recalled his flagging attention to the allotted task.

After graduating he was selected on account of his scholarship to remain at the Academy as an assistant professor. In this position, which gave him an opportunity to review his studies and extend his reading, he continued one year, when at his own request he was assigned to engineering duty under the late General, then Colonel, Totten, at Newport, Rhode Island. Here he remained two years, engaged in constructing fortifications, devoting his extra hours to the study of physics and chemistry and as a recreation collecting and labeling the shells of that region. But the most important event of this period of his life and that which doubtless contributed in a large degree to his future success was his becoming acquainted with and subsequent betrothal to Miss Nancy Clarke Fowler, the daughter of an old and highly respected citizen of Newport. With the stinted pay of a lieutenant of engineers, out of which his mother and her younger offspring were to be provided for, marriage was not to be thought of excepting as an event in the remote distance. Fortunately as unexpectedly, however, a change now took place in his circumstances which enabled him to gratify the earnest wish of his heart and to secure to himself a companion and helpmate who lavished upon him all her affections and through his life ardently devoted all her thoughts and energies to sustain, assist, and encourage him. The change alluded to, and which opened to him an uninterrupted career of usefulness during the whole of his active life, was the result of an invitation to the chair of natural philosophy and chemistry in the University of Pennsylvania at Philadelphia. He accepted the position with that unaffected diffidence which is the usual concomitant of true but untried merit, though as might have been anticipated, his eventual success was commensurate with the industry and ability which had marked his previous progress. Having already had some experience as a teacher, he the more readily gained the entire confidence of the authorities of the university and the affection of his pupils. He did not, however, rest satisfied with the occupation of teacher or with merely imparting knowledge obtained by the labors of others, but sought to enlarge the bounds of science by discoveries of his own. As auxiliary to this he became a member of the Franklin Institute, a society then newly established for the promotion of the mechanical arts. This society, which still maintains a vigorous existence, was well calculated to exhibit his talents and develop his character. It brought him into intimate association with the principal manufacturers, engineers, and artisans of the city, and into relations of friendship with a large number of young men destined in more advanced life to exert an extended influence on public affairs. He was appointed chairman of one of the most important of its committees and was chosen as the expounder of the principles of the Institute at its public exhibitions. Facilities were thus afforded him for the prosecution of science which he could not have well commanded in any other position. Workshops were thrown open to him, and skillful hands yielded him ready assistance in realizing the conceptions of his suggestive mind. His descent from the illustrious statesman and philosopher whose name the Institute bears and who is almost regarded as the tutelar saint of Philadelphia no doubt contributed to a prepossession in his favor, but the influence which he acquired and maintained was due to his own learning, industry, ability, and courtesy. To these he owed the favor and distinction of having conferred upon him the principal directorship of the scientific investigations of the Institute and the opportunity which it afforded him of so greatly contributing to the usefulness of the society and to the advancement of his own reputation.

For a full account of the labors in which he was engaged in his connection with the Franklin Institute we must here be content with referring to the volumes of its journal from 1828 to 1835 inclusive. We may pause a moment, however, to notice the investigations relating to the bursting of steam boilers, of which he was the principal director. The public mind had at that epoch been so frequently and painfully called to this subject that the Institute was induced to organize a series of systematic researches in regard to it, the importance of which was soon recognized by the general government in the form of an appropriation for defraying the attendant expenses. In the prosecution of these inquiries a large amount of information relative to explosions and suggestions as to their causes was first collected by correspondence, and on this was based a series of well-devised experiments, which were executed with signal address and the results interpreted with logical discrimination. The conclusions arrived at were embodied in a series of propositions which after a lapse of more than thirty years have not been superseded by any others of more practical value. The most frequent cause of explosion was found to be the gradual heating of the boiler beyond its power of resistance, and next to this, the sudden generation of steam by allowing the water to become too low and its subsequent contact with the overheated metal of the sides and other portions of the boiler. The generation of gas from the decomposition of water as a cause of explosion was disproved, as was also the dispersion of water in the form of spray through superheated steam. These experiments were not unattended with danger and required in their execution no small amount of personal courage. Accidents were imminent at almost every stage of the investigation; and in some instances explosions were produced which alarmed the neighborhood. So true is it that in the pursuit of science dangers are oftentimes voluntarily encountered, exacting no less courage or firmness of nerve than that which animates the warrior in the more conspicuous but scarcely more important conflicts of the battlefield.

The attention of Mr. Bache at this period was not exclusively devoted to his labors in connection with the Franklin Institute. He was also a member of the American Philosophical Society and as such in association with [Robert] Hare, [James] Espy, and others interested in the pursuit of various branches of physics and chemistry. He erected an observatory in the yard of his dwelling, in which with the aid of his wife and of his former pupil, John F. Fraser, he determined with accuracy, for the first time in this country, the periods of the daily variations of the magnetic needle, and by another series of observations the connection of the fitful variations of the direction of the magnetic force with the appearance of the aurora borealis.

Again, in connection with his friend Espy, he made a minute survey of a portion of the track of a tornado which visited New Brunswick, in New Jersey, on the 19th of June, 1835, and from the change of place and relative position of the trees and other objects, as left by the wind, he succeeded in establishing the fact, in accordance with the hypotheses of Mr. Espy, that the effects of the storm were due to an ascending and progressive column of air, by which all objects within the influence of the disturbance, on either side the track, were drawn inward, and not due, as had been supposed, to a horizontal rotation at the surface, which would tend to throw them outward by centrifugal projection. In co-operation with Professor Courtenay he also made a series of determinations of the magnetic dip at various places in the United States. Indeed, terrestrial magnetism was with him a favorite subject, to which he continued to make valuable contributions at intervals during his whole life. The phenomena of heat likewise engaged much of his attention, and he was the first to show, contrary to generally received opinion, that the radiation and consequent absorption of dark heat is not affected by color. His investigations in this line were suddenly brought to a close by an accident, which we may be allowed to mention as furnishing an illustration of his self-control and considerate regard for the feelings of others. After an expenditure of money which he could ill afford, and of time withdrawn from the hours due to repose, he had procured and arranged on a stand a series of delicate instruments intended for a long-meditated experiment on radiant heat. During his temporary absence his mother, in hurriedly passing through the apartment, accidentally caught in her dress the support of the apparatus and brought the whole to the floor, a mass of mingled fragments. The author of this disaster was so painfully affected by the destruction, of which she had been the unintentional cause, as to be obliged to leave to his wife the task of breaking the unwelcome tidings to her son. On receiving the information he stood for a moment perfectly silent, then hurried out into the open air to conceal his emotion and tranquilize his feelings. After a short interval he returned, calm, affectionate, and apparently cheerful, and neither by word nor look gave any indication of the pain and disappointment he had so severely experienced.

It should not be forgotten that the labors to which we have alluded were performed in hours not devoted to his regular duties as a professor in the university. To these he was obliged to give three hours a day, besides other time to the preparation of illustrations for his lectures, while several evenings of the week were claimed by committees of the Franklin Institute and the Philosophical Society. He was enabled to execute these multifarious labors by a division of his time into separate periods, to each of which was allotted its special occupation. By a rigid adherence to this system he was always prompt in his engagements, was never hurried, and found time, moreover, to attend to the claims of friendship and society. He was a zealous and successful teacher, to whom the imparting of knowledge was a source of unalloyed and inexhaustible pleasure. His pupils could not fail to be favorably impressed by his enthusiasm and influenced by his kindness. He always manifested an interest not only in their proficiency in study, but also in their general welfare. They regarded him with affection as well as respect, and while in other classrooms of the university disorder and insubordination occasionally annoyed the teachers, nothing was to be witnessed in his but earnest attention and gentlemanly deportment.

His success as an instructor affords a striking confutation of the fallacy which has not unfrequently been advocated in certain quarters, that men devoted to original research and imbued with habits of mind which it generates are not well qualified for the office of instructors. So far is the proposition from having any foundation in fact, that it is precisely among the most celebrated explorers of science of the present century that the most successful and noted teachers have been found. In proof of this the illustrious names of Priestley, De Candolle, Dalton, Davy, Oersted, Faraday, and a host of others immediately occur. At the same time it cannot be denied that it is questionable economy to devote to the drudgery of drilling youth in the elements of knowledge a mind well qualified by nature and training to enlarge the boundaries of thought and increase the stores of knowledge. But it is equally clear that the practice of teaching is to a certain extent not incompatible with the leisure and concentration of mind requisite for original research; that the latter must, in fact, act beneficially alike on the instructor and instructed, the former gaining in clearness of conception in the appreciation of the new truths he is unfolding by imparting a knowledge of their character to others, while the latter catch, by sympathy, a portion of the enthusiasm of the master and are stimulated to exertions of which they would otherwise be incapable.

In 1836, when Professor Bache had just attained the thirtieth year of his age, his attention and energies received a new direction, constituting, as it were, a new epoch in his life. This change was caused by a movement on the part of the trustees of the Girard College for Orphans, an institution munificently endowed by a benevolent citizen of Philadelphia. Preparatory to organizing this institution it was thought desirable to select a suitable person as president and to send him abroad to study the systems of education and methods of instruction and discipline adopted in Europe. The eyes of the entire community were with one accord directed to our professor as the proper man for this office. He had, however, beome enamored with the pursuit of science, and it was with difficulty that he could bring himself to regard with favor a proposition which might tend to separate him from this favorite object. The consideration of a more extended field of usefulness at length prevailed, and he accepted, though not without some lingering regret, the proffered position. No American ever visited Europe under more favorable circumstances for becoming intimately acquainted with its scientific and literary institutions. His published researches had given him a European reputation and afforded him that ready access to the intelligent and influential classes of society which is denied the traveler whose only recommendation is the possession of wealth. It cannot be doubted that he was also favored in this respect by the admiration which in Europe still attaches to the name of his renowned ancestor. He was everywhere received with marked attention and from his moral and intellectual qualities did not fail to sustain the prepossessions in his favor and to secure the friendship and esteem of the most distinguished savants of the Old World.

He remained in Europe two years and on his return embodied the results of his researches on education in his report to the trustees of Girard College. This report forms a large octavo volume and is an almost exhaustive exposition of the scholastic systems and methods of instruction in use at the time in England, France, Prussia, Austria, Switzerland, and Italy. It has done more perhaps to improve the theory and art of education in this country than any other work ever published, and it has effected this not alone by the statement of facts derived from observation, but also by the inferences and suggestions with which it abounds. The accounts which are given of the different schools of Europe are founded on personal inspection, the results being noted down at the time with the writer's habitual regard to accuracy.

After completing his report he was prepared to commence the organization of the Girard College, but the trustees, partly on account of the unfinished condition of the building, and partly from a delay in the adjustment of the funds of the endowment, were not disposed to put the institution into immediate operation. In the meantime Professor Bache, desirous of rendering the information he had acquired of immediate practical use, offered his services gratuitously to the municipal authorities of Philadelphia, to organize on an improved basis a system of public education for that city. This offer was gladly accepted, and he commenced the work with his usual energy and with the cordial support of the directors and teachers of the common schools. At the end of the year, finding that the trustees of the college were still unprepared to open the institution, he relinquished the salary but retained the office of president and devoted his time mainly to the organization of the schools. He was now, however, induced to accept from the city, as the sole and necessary means of his support, a salary much less than the one he had relinquished. The result of his labors in regard to the schools was the establishment of the best system of combined free education which had at that time been adopted in this country. It has since generally been regarded as a model and has been introduced as such in different cities of the Union.

In 1842, having completed the organization of the schools, and Girard College still remaining in a stationary condition, he resigned all connection with it and yielding to the solicitations of the trustees of the university, returned to his former chair of natural philosophy and chemistry in order that he might resume the cultivation of science. Not that it is to be inferred that in his devotion to the advancement of education he had relinquished or deferred the scientific pursuits to which the habit of his mind and the bent of his genius continually impelled him, for during his travels in Europe he had been careful to provide himself with a set of portable instruments of physical research, and as a relief from the labors imposed by the special object of his mission he instituted a connected series of observations at prominent points on the Continent and in Great Britain relative to the dip and intensity of terrestrial magnetism. These observations were made with the view of ascertaining the relative direction and strength of the magnetic force in Europe and America by the comparison of parallel series of observations in the two countries with the same instruments. They also served in most instances to settle with greater precision than had previously been attained the relative magnetic condition of the points at which they were made.

Though the organization of the schools of such a city as Philadelphia might seem sufficient to absorb all this energy and self-devotion, yet even in the midst of this labor we find our late colleague actively co-operating in the great enterprise of the British Association to determine by contemporaneous observations, at widely separated points, the fluctuations of the magnetic and meteorological elements of the globe. This co-operation, in which no doubt a feeling of national pride mingled itself with his ardor for the advancement of science, consisted primarily in the establishment of an observatory, to which the trustees of Girard College contributed a full series of instruments combining all the latest improvements, and which was supported by the American Philosophical Society and a number of liberal and intelligent individuals. The observations which were here continued at short intervals, both by day and night for five years form a rich mine of statistics, from which until within the last few years of his life the professor drew a highly interesting series of results without exhausting the material. In addition to these observations, he made during his summer vacations a magnetic survey of Pennsylvania.

He was not destined to remain long in his old position in the university. Before he had become fairly settled in it and had renewed his familiarity with its duties, he was called in November 1843, on the occasion of the death of [Ferdinand] Hassler, Superintendent of the United States Coast Survey, to fill the important sphere of public duty thus rendered vacant. His appointment to this position was first suggested by the members of the American Philosophical Society and the nomination [was] fully concurred in by the principal scientific and literary institutions of the country. In this movement he himself took no part and indeed regarded the position as one not to be coveted; for while it opened a wide field for the exercise of talent and the acquisition of an enviable reputation, it involved responsibilities and presented difficulties of the gravest character. Professor Bache was not one of those who, abounding in self-confidence, imagine themselves equal to every exigency or who seek the distinctions and emoluments of office without any regard to the services to be rendered or the duties to be discharged. On the contrary, though early and continued success must have tended to increase his self-esteem, each new position to which he was called was entered upon with feelings of solicitude rather than of exultation. He rightly judged that the proper moment for self-congratulation is not at the beginning of an arduous and precarious enterprise, but at the time of its full and successful accomplishment. Nor can it be necessary to add that this characteristic contributed largely to his success. In civil service as in the camp the leader to whom all look with confidence is not he who with blind and arrogant self-reliance disdains caution as unworthy of courage, but he who, sensitively alive to the dangers to be encountered, exerts every faculty in calling to his aid every resource which may tend to secure victory or facilitate retreat.

With whatever misgivings Professor Bache may have undertaken the task to which he was assigned, it may be truly said that no living man was so well qualified as himself to secure the results which the nation and its commercial interests demanded. His education and training at West Point, his skill in original investigations, his thorough familiarity with the principles of applied science, his knowledge of the world, and his gentlemanly deportment were all in a greater or less degree essential elements in the successful prosecution of the Survey. It would appear as if the training and acquisition of every period of his life and the development of every trait of his character had been especially ordained to fit him in every respect to overcome the difficulties of this position. Besides the qualifications we have enumerated, he possessed rare executive ability, which enabled him to govern and guide the diverse elements of the vast undertaking with consummate tact and skill. Quick to perceive and acknowledge merit in others, he rapidly gathered around him a corps of men eminently well qualified for the execution of the tasks to which he severally assigned them.

The Coast Survey had been recommended to Congress by President Jefferson as early as 1807, but it was not until ten years afterward that the work was actually commenced under the superintendence of Professor Hassler, an eminent Swiss engineer, whose plans had been previously sanctioned by the American Philosophical Society. Though the fundamental features of the Survey had been established on the most approved scientific principles, yet so frequent were the changes in the policy of the Government, and so limited were the appropriations, that even up to the time of Professor Bache's appointment in 1843 little more than a beginning had been made. The Survey, so far as accomplished, extended only from New York Harbor to Point Judith on the east coast, and southward to Cape Henlopen. The new Superintendent saw the necessity of greatly enlarging the plan so as to embrace a much broader field of simultaneous labor than it had previously included. He divided the whole coast line into sections and organized under separate parties the essential operations of the Survey simultaneously in each. He commenced the exploration of the Gulf Stream and at the same time projected a series of observations on the tides, on the magnetism of the earth, and the direction of the winds at different seasons of the year. He also instituted a succession of researches in regard to the bottom of the ocean within soundings, and the forms of animal life which are found there, thus offering new and unexpected indications to the navigator. He pressed into service for the determination of the longitude the electric telegraph; for the ready reproduction of charts, photography, and for multiplying copperplate engravings, the new art of electrotyping. In planning and directing the execution of these varied improvements, which exacted so much comprehensiveness in design and minuteness in detail, Professor Bache was entirely successful. He was equally fortunate, principally through the moral influence of his character, in impressing upon the Government, and especially upon Congress, a more just estimate of what such a survey required for its maintenance and creditable prosecution. Not only was a largely increased appropriation needed to carry out this more comprehensive plan, but also to meet the expenses consequent upon the extension of the shore line itself. Our seacoast, when the Survey commenced, already exceeded in length that of any other civilized nation, but in 1845 it was still more extended by the annexation of Texas, and again in 1848 by our acquisitions on the Pacific. Professor Bache was in the habit of answering the question often propounded to him by members of Congress, "When will this survey be completed?" by asking, "When will you cease annexing new territory?" a reply not less significant at the present day than when it was first given, and which may continue long to be applicable under the expansive tendencies of our national policy.

When Professor Bache took charge of the Survey it was still almost in its incipient stage, subjected to misapprehension, assailed by unjust prejudice, and liable, during any session of Congress, to be suspended or abolished. When he died, it had conquered prejudice, silenced opposition, and become established on a firm foundation as one of the permanent bureaus of the executive Government. The importance of the work, which was always highly appreciated by the mariner, because strikingly obvious to the general public through the service which it rendered during the late war in furnishing accurate charts and sailing directions for the guidance of our squadrons along the southern coast. Nor was this alone; an active participation was also borne by the officers of the Survey in the attack of the United States Navy on Sumter, Port Royal, Fort Fisher, Mobile, New Orleans, and other strongholds, while constant aid was rendered by them in the navigation of the inlets and channels and in the avoidance of hidden rocks or shoals with which one could be more minutely acquainted. Though the value of the Survey was signally conspicuous on these occasions, it needs but little reflection to be convinced of its essential connection with the general prosperity of the country. Whatever diminishes the danger of departure from or an approach to our shores facilitates commerce and thus renders more valuable the products of our industry, even in portions of our land most remote from the seaboard. But the Survey should not be viewed alone in its economical relations, since as an enlightened and liberal people we owe it to the great community of nations and the cause of humanity to supply the world with accurate charts of our precarious coast, as well as to furnish it with all the other aids to safer navigation which the science and experience of the age may devise.

Professor Bache, with his enlightened appreciation of the value of abstract science, kept constantly in view the various problems relative to the physics of the globe which are directly or even incidentally connected with the survey of the coast, and ever cherished the hope of being permitted to complete his labors by their solution. Among these was a new determination of the magnitude and form of the earth and the variations in the intensity of terrestrial gravity at various points on the continent of North America; the discussion of the general theory of the tides; the magnetic condition of the continent; and the improvement of the general map of the United States by determining its relation to the coast line and the precise geographical positions of the most important points in the interior. Though his hopes in regard to these problems were not destined to be realized by himself, fortunately for the cause of science they have been left in charge of a successor in the person of his ardent friend and collaborator. Professor [Charles S.] Peirce, to whose genius and industry we may confidently look for that full exposition of the work which, while it entitles him to the highest approbation of the scientific world, will render ample justice to the labors and sagacity of his lamented predecessor.

Besides having charge of the Coast Survey, Professor Bache was Superintendent of Weights and Measures and in the exercise of this function directed a series of investigations relative to the collection of excise duties on distilled spirits and likewise superintended the construction of a large number of sets of standard weights and measures for distribution among the several states of the Union. He was also appointed one of a commission to examine into the condition of the lighthouse system of this country and to report upon any improvements calculated to render it more efficient. In the investigations pertaining to this subject, involving as they do a knowledge of a wide range of applied science, he took a lively interest and rendered important service in the organization of the admirable system which was adopted and still remains in operation. This commission of investigation was afterward merged in the present Lighthouse Board, of which he continued a member until the time of his death.

In 1846 he had been named in the act of incorporation as one of the Regents of the Smithsonian Institution and by successive reëlection was continued by Congress in this office until his death, a period of nearly twenty years. To say that he assisted in shaping the policy of the establishment would not be enough. It was almost exclusively through his predominating influence that the policy which has given the Institution its present celebrity was after much opposition finally adopted. The object of the donation, it will be remembered, had been expressed in terms so concise that its import could scarcely be at once appreciated by the general public, though to the cultivators of science, to which class Smithson himself belonged, the language employed failed not to convey clear and precise ideas. Out of this state of things it is not surprising that difference of opinion should arise respecting the proper means to be adopted to realize the intentions of the founder of the Institution. Professor Bache with persistent firmness, tempered by his usual moderation, advocated the appropriation of the proceeds of the funds principally to the plan set forth in the first report of the Secretary, namely, of encouraging and supporting original research in the different branches of science. Unfortunately this policy could only be partially adopted, on account of the restrictions of the enactment of Congress, by which provision was to be made for certain specified objects. He strenuously opposed the contemplated expenditure of a most disproportionate sum in the erection and maintenance of a costly edifice, but failing to prevent this, he introduced the resolution adopted by the board as a compromise, whereby the mischief which he could not wholly avert might at least be lessened. This resolution provided that the time of the erection of the building should be extended over several years, while the fund appropriated for the purpose, being in the meantime invested in a safe and productive manner, would serve in some degree to counterbalance the effect of the great and unnecessary outlay which had been resolved on. It would be difficult for the Secretary, however unwilling to intrude anything personal on this occasion, to forbear mentioning that it was entirely due to the persuasive influence of the Professor that he was induced, almost against his own better judgment, to leave the quiet pursuit of science and the congenial employment of college instruction to assume the laborious and responsible duties of the office to which through the partiality of friendship he had been called. Nor would it be possible for him to abstain from acknowledging with heartfelt emotion that he was from first to last supported and sustained in his difficult position by the fraternal sympathy, the prudent counsel, and the unwavering friendship of the lamented deceased.

His demeanor in the broad was quiet and unobtrusive, and his opinions sought no support in elaborated or premeditated argument, but when a topic likely to lead to difficulty in discussion was introduced, he seldom failed, with that admirable tact for which he was always noted, to dispose of it by some suggestion so judicious and appropriate as to secure ready acquiescence and harmonious action. The loss of such a man in the councils of the Institution, when we consider the characteristics which it had been our aim to portray, must indeed be regarded as little less than irreparable.

As a vice-president of the United States Sanitary Commission his influence was felt in selecting proper agents and suggesting efficient means for collecting and distributing the liberal contributions offered for ameliorating the condition of our soldiers during the war. But the services which he rendered the Government during the recent struggle were not confined to this agency or to the immediate operations of the Coast Survey. He was called into consultations to discuss plans of attack on the part of the Navy and for its co-operation with the Army. He acted also as a member of a commission to which various projects professing to improve the art of war were referred, and in this capacity it is not too much to say that his judicious counsel contributed to save the Government millions of dollars by preventing the adoption of plausible though impracticable propositions from which nothing but failure and loss could have resulted.

One of the last acts of his life was an exemplification of the devoted affection which he had always borne to his native city, whither it was his cherished intention to return when he should be at last released from official duty. At the request of the Governor of Pennsylvania, although overwhelmed with other public labors, he planned lines of defenses for Philadelphia and to a certain extent personally superintended their construction. Unaccustomed for many years to direct exposure to the sun, this work proved too much for his physical strength and brought on the first indications of that malady which terminated his life. Though apparently of a vigorous constitution and capable under the excitement of official life of bearing an unusual amount of bodily fatigue, yet he was subject at intervals to "sick headaches," a disease which seems to have been hereditary and which perhaps conspired with other causes in terminating his useful and distinguished career. Previous to the war he had spent the warmer part of each summer in a tent at some point of the primary triangulation of the Survey, whence he directed the various parties in the field by correspondence, and as the point was usually at the top of a mountain or at some elevated position from which other stations of the Survey could be seen, he did not want for invigorating air. With this and the exercise of measuring angles he laid in a store of health sufficient to enable him to carry on without interruption the arduous duties of the remaining portion of the year. But after the commencement of the war his presence was continually required in Washington to give advice and information as to military and naval operations and to attend the meetings of the scientific commission to which we have previously referred. He was therefore no longer able to avail himself of the recuperating influence of mountain air, and in view of this his valuable life may be said to have been one of the sacrifices offered for the preservation of the Union.

The first indications of the insidious disease which gradually sapped the citadel of life were numbness in the fingers of his right hand and on one occasion, for a short time only, loss of memory. Though these symptoms gave him some uneasiness, they did not diminish his exertions in the line of his duty. Other symptoms, however, exhibited themselves which, though awaking anxiety, did not much alarm his friends until he was suddenly deprived in a considerable degree of the power of locomotion and of the expression of ideas, the result, it was supposed, of a softening of the brain. But though the power of expression was paralyzed, his memory appeared to retain all the impressions of the past, and he evidently took much pleasure in having recalled to him scenes and events of years gone by. For several months he was very anxious as to the business of the Coast Survey, and it was with difficulty he could be restrained from resuming in full the duties of his office, but as the malady increased his perception of external objects diminished. He took less and less interest in passing events and finally seemed to withdraw his attention from the exterior world, with which he almost ceased thenceforth to hold any active communication. It was hoped that a voyage to Europe, through the excitements of shipboard and the revival of old associations, would be of service to him, but, notwithstanding an occasional manifestation of his wonted spirit of social and intellectual enjoyment at the encounter of a friend of former times or distinguished associate in the walks of science, he returned from a sojourn abroad of eighteen months without having experienced any permanent abatement in the progress of his malady. He lingered for a short time longer and finally resigned his breath at Newport, Rhode Island, on the 17th of February, 1867, in the sixty-first year of his age.

It would be impossible to name an American distinguished on purely scientific grounds to whom the enlightened sentiment of his own countrymen and of foreign nations has awarded more emphatic marks of admiration and esteem. The degree of Doctor of Laws was conferred on him by the principal universities of this country, and few of our leading societies were willing to forego the honor of numbering him among their associates. He was elected in succession president of the American Philosophical Society, of the American Association for the Advancement of Science, and of the National Academy of Sciences established by Congress. Nor were foreigners less forward in acknowledging his merit. He was a member of the Royal Society of London, of the Imperial Academy of Sciences at St. Petersburg, of the Institute of France, the Royal Society of Edinburgh, the Royal and Imperial Geographical Society of Vienna, the Royal Academy of Turin, the Mathematical Society of Hamburg, the Academy of Sciences in the Institute of Bologna, the Royal Astronomical Society of London, and of the Royal Irish Academy of Dublin. In addition to these testimonies of appreciation, several medals were awarded to him by foreign governments for his distinguished services in the Coast Survey and in the cause of science generally.

The life we have here sketched is eminently suggestive, both from a philosophical and a practical point of view. It presents an unbroken series of successful efforts, with no interruptions in its sustained and constantly ascending course. All parts follow each other in harmonious continuity, and not only is each stage of its progress in advance of the one which preceded it, but it furnishes the means of education for that which succeeded. It is not merely curiosity, laudable as that might be, but a sense of the importance of the inquiry which prompts us to ask, What were the mental and moral characteristics of the mind which produced such results? And we say intentionally, the *mind which produced these results,* for although it be true that accident has in many cases a determining influence on the fortunes of an individual, it will be clear from what precedes, or we shall have greatly failed in the task which we proposed to ourselves, that the element of casualty had but little to do with the success which crowned the life to which the question at present relates.

From long acquaintance with him and critical study of the events of his life and the distinctive manifestations of his moral and intellectual nature, we venture, though not without hesitation, to present the following analysis of the character of one who has performed so conspicuous a part and in whose memory so many are deeply interested.

Alexander Dallas Bache possessed, or we may perhaps say originally inherited, a mind of strong general powers, with no faculty in excess or in deficiency, but as a whole capable of unusual expansion or development in any direction which early training or the education of life might determine. He also possessed strong passions, which, instead of exerting an unfavorable effect on his character by their indulgence, became under the restraining influence to which they were in due season subjected, a reserved energy, as it were, ready to manifest itself spontaneously and at any time in the vindication of truth and justice. He was likewise endowed with a power of *will* which, controlling all his faculties and propensities, rendered them subservient to those fixed purposes which had once received the sanction of his deliberate judgment. Eminent also among his characteristics and perhaps most conspicuous of all, was the social element of refined humanity, a regard for his fellow-man, which craved as an essential want of his nature fraternal sympathy, not only with those within the wide circle of his daily associations, but with those from whom he could expect no reciprocation of the sentiment, the entire brotherhood of mankind. These characteristics, with a nice perception of right and a conscience always ready to enforce its mandates, are, we think, sufficient to explain the remarkable career we have described.

They were perhaps indicated by himself, though with an admission not to be accepted without some reserve, in a conversation with the writer of this sketch in reference to his entrance at West Point. "I knew," he said, "that I had nothing like genius, but I thought I was capable by hard study of accomplishing something, and I resolved to do my best, and if possible to gain the approbation of the teachers, and, above all, to make myself loved and respected by my classmates."

To illustrate the progressive development of the individual traits of his character, we may be allowed to dwell for a moment on a few analytical details. The early period of his life, including that which preceded his first call to Philadelphia, was almost wholly devoted to the improvement of the mechanical or the "doing" faculties of his mind, and but little attention was given to invention, or the exercise of original thought. His final examination at the Academy, perfect as it was in its kind, only exhibited his capacity for the acquisition of knowledge, not the power to originate or apply it. When his efforts were first turned in the latter direction, he evinced, as I well remember, no especial aptitude for it that would indicate future success, but in a short time, and under the stimulus of the associations into which he was thrown in Philadelphia, the faculties of investigation and of generalization were rapidly developed, and had he not been partially turned aside from such pursuits, I doubt not but that he would have still more highly distinguished himself in the line of experimental research. Again, the change in the circumstances and relations of his life produced by his election to the presidency of Girard College introduced him to a familiarity with an entirely new class of ideas which served to exercise and expand another faculty of his mind, that, namely, which observes and appreciates moral truths, though without impairing his aptitude for physical research. In like manner his foreign mission with reference to popular education, by bringing him into intimate and friendly association with minds of the first order in the principal cities of Europe, afforded him an opportunity for enlarging the sphere of his sympathies, as well as of studying men under a great variety of social and mental peculiarities.

Again, his long residence and high social position at the seat of Government, his intimate acquaintance and friendly intercourse with statesmen and politicians imbued him with a thorough knowledge of the working of the Government such as few have ever possessed, while his exertions to sustain the Coast Survey and improve its condition served to call into active operation his power to appreciate character, to discern motives, and therefore to convince, persuade, and control men. His ability in this latter respect was remarkable; a personal interview with an opponent of the Survey scarcely [if] ever failed to convert perhaps an active enemy into an influential friend. His success in this respect often astonished those who frequently harassed Congress with propositions covertly designed to promote their own interest at the expense of public utility. Hence the exclamation was not unfrequently heard, "Bache is certainly a wonderful manager." If that which is unusual constitutes an element of wonder, then the exclamation was not without truth, though not in the sense of those by whom it was uttered, for he never advocated any measure that was not just, expedient, and proper, either as concerned the interests of the country or the welfare of his species.

On the whole, if we would seek the real secret of his influence over his fellow-men, it would be found no doubt to have consisted in the singular abnegation of self which pervaded his whole conduct, his great practical wisdom, his honesty of purpose, and his genial though quiet and unobtrusive manner. In the exercise of these characteristics he was so far from the least appearance of dissimulation, that no one ever approached him without feeling that it was equally impossible to doubt the purity of his intentions as it was to elude the penetration of his quiet but thorough scrutiny. His calmness served as a shield from within and without and as a guard against himself as well as a protection against others. It enabled him to weigh the motives and observe the character of those who consulted him with the view of securing his influence or gaining his patronage. His genial nature enabled him to descend gracefully from the heights of science and to enter fully and frankly into the feelings of any company with which he might be thrown. In this he was aided by a playfulness of fancy and a quiet humor which banished any reserve that might have been produced by a knowledge of his superior talents and attainments. He was, though by no means gifted with those attractions of person which influence at first sight, a favorite with all ages and particularly with the sex whose discrimination of character is said to be least fallible. It seems almost superfluous to say of such a man that his friendship was open and unwavering, that his confidence once bestowed could be shaken by no mere difference of opinion or conflict of personal interests. Severe to himself under the responsibility of duty and in the punctual observance of his engagements, his indulgence was reserved for the weak and the erring. Though his outer life was free from disappointments or reverses, and though he walked as it were in perpetual sunshine, all was not so within. Besides the anxiety and solicitude incident to the responsible duties of his position, occasions of trial and profound sorrow were not spared him. He was called to mourn the untimely loss of a beloved brother, who fell a victim to his zeal for the professor's service in the survey of the Gulf Stream; of another brother, the youngest and last, also an officer of the Navy, and a general favorite, who was drowned on the coast of California; and lastly of a sister, whom he had adopted and cherished as a child. In these seasons of affliction he found consolation in the steadfast convictions of religious faith. Nurtured in the forms and principles of the Episcopal Church, he was a devout worshiper in the sanctuary, though not bigoted in his attachment to the peculiar ordinances of that communion. He fully recognized the union of science and religion and held with unwavering constancy the belief that revelation properly interpreted and science rightly understood must ultimately join in perfect accord in reference to the great truths essential to the wellbeing of man.

As an evidence of his high appreciation of abstract science derived from original investigation, he left his property in trust to the National Academy of Sciences, the income to be devoted to the prosecution of researches in physical and natural science by assisting experimentalists and observers, and the publication of the results of their investigations.

I here close this imperfect sketch, in which I am conscious of having passed in silence many admirable traits of character and conduct, and of having very inadequately portrayed others, with the remark that, though our companion and brother has departed, his works and his influence still remain to us; that, sorrow as we must for his loss, we can still recall with pride and satisfaction the example he has left us of all that, in heart, in spirit, and in life, the true man of science ought to be.

Charles Darwin *

1809–1882

———◆———

AUGUST WEISMANN †

FORTY-ONE years ago, when I delivered my inaugural address as a professor of this university, I took as my subject "The Justification of the Darwinian Theory." It is a great pleasure to me to be able to lecture again on the same subject on the hundredth anniversary of the birth of Darwin. This time, however, I need not speak of justifying the theory, for in the interval it has conquered the whole world. Yet there remains much that may be said—much, indeed, that ought to be said at the present time. In my former lecture I compared the theory of descent or evolution to the Copernican cosmogony in its importance for the progress of human knowledge, and there were many who thought the comparison extravagant. But it needs no apology now that the idea of evolution has been thoroughly elaborated, and has become the basis of the science of life.

You know that Darwin was not the only one and was not even the first to whom the idea of evolution occurred; it had arisen in several great minds half a century earlier, and it may therefore be thought an injustice to give, as we now do, almost all the credit of this fruitful discovery to Darwin alone. But history is a severe and inexorable judge. She awards the palm not to him in whose mind an idea first arises, but to him who so establishes it that it takes a permanent place in scientific thought, for it is only then that it becomes fruitful of, and an instrument for, human progress. The credit for thus establishing the theory of evolution is

———

* A.R., 1909, pp. 431–452. From an address delivered at the University of Freiburg on the occasion of the Centenary of Darwin, published in the *Contemporary Review*, July 1909.
† German biologist (1834–1914).

shared with Charles Darwin only by his contemporary, Alfred
Russel Wallace, of whom we shall have to speak later.

Nevertheless, a reflection of the discoverer's glory falls upon
those who about the end of the eighteenth and the beginning of
the nineteenth century were able to attain to the conception of
evolution, notwithstanding the incomparably smaller number of
facts known to them. As one of these pioneers we must not omit
to mention our own poet, Goethe, though he rather threw out
premonitory hints of a theory of evolution than actually taught it:
*Alle Gestalten sind ähnlich, doch keine gleichet der andere, und
so deutet der Chor auf ein geheimes Gesetz.*

The "secret law" was the law of descent, and the first to define
this idea and to formulate it clearly as a theory was, as is well
known, also a Darwin, Charles Darwin's grandfather, Erasmus,
who set it forth in his book, *Zoonomia,* in 1796. A few years later
Treviranus, a botanist of Bremen, published a book of similar
purport, and he was followed in 1809 by the Frenchman Lamarck, and the German Lorenz Oken. All these disputed the venerable Mosaic mythos of creation, which had till then been
accepted as a scientific document, and all of them sought to show
that the constancy of species throughout the ages was only an appearance due, as Lamarck in particular pointed out, to the short-
ness of human life. But Cuvier, the greatest zoologist of that time,
a pupil of the Stuttgart *Karlsschule,* would have none of this idea
and held fast to the conception of species created once for all,
seeing in it the only possible explanation of the enormous diversity of animal and plant forms. And there was much to be said
for this attitude at that time, when the knowledge of facts was not
nearly comprehensive enough to afford a secure and scientific
basis for the theory of descent. Lamarck alone had attempted to
indicate the forces from which in his opinion the transmutation
of species could have resulted.

It was not, however, solely because the basis of fact was insufficient that the theory of the evolution of organic nature did
not gain ground at that time. It was even more because such foundation as there was for it was not adhered to. All sorts of vague
speculations were indulged in, and these contributed less and
less to the support of the theory the more far-reaching they became. Many champions of the *Naturphilosophie* of the time, especially Oken and Schelling, promulgated mere hypotheses as
truths. Forsaking the realm of fact almost entirely, they attempted
to construct the whole world with a free hand, so to speak, and
lost themselves more and more in worthless phantasy. This na-

turally brought the theory of evolution and with it *Naturphiloso-phie* into disrepute, especially with the true naturalists, those who patiently observe and collect new facts. The theory lost all credence, and sank so low in the general estimation that it came to be regarded as hardly fitting for a naturalist to occupy himself with philosophical conceptions.

This was the state of the matter onward from 1830, the year in which the final battle between the theory of evolution and the old theory of creation was fought out by Geoffroy Saint-Hilaire and Cuvier in the Paris Academy. Cuvier triumphed, and thus it came about that an idea so important as that of evolution sank into oblivion again after its emergence and was expunged from the pages of science so completely that it seemed as if it were forever buried beyond hope of resurrection. Scientific men now turned with eagerness toward special problems in all the domains of life, and the following period may well be characterized as that of purely detailed investigation.

Great progress was made during this period: entirely new branches of science were founded, and a wealth of unexpected facts was discovered. The development of individual organisms, of which little had previously been known, began to be revealed in all its marvelous diversity: first, the development of the chick in the egg; then of the frog; then of insects and worms; then of spiders, crustaceans, starfishes, and all the classes and orders of mollusks, as well as of backboned animals from the lowest fish up to man himself. Within this period of purely detailed investigation there falls also the discovery in animals and plants of that smallest microscopically visible building stone of the living body, the cell, and this discovery paved the way for the full development of the newly founded science of tissues, histology.

In botany the chief progress in this period was in regard to the reproduction and development of the lower plants, or cryptogams, and the discovery of alternation of generations, a mode of reproduction that had previously been known in several groups of the animal kingdom, in polyps and medusæ, in various worms, and later in insects and crustaceans. At the same time it was found that the proposition, which had hitherto been accepted as a matter of course, that an egg can only develop after it has been fertilized, is not universally valid, for there is a development without previous fertilization—parthenogenesis, or virgin birth.

Thus, in the period between the Napoleonic wars and 1859 an ever-increasing mass of new facts was accumulated, and among these there were so many of an unexpected nature that further

effort was constantly being put forth to elucidate detailed processes in every domain. This was desirable and important—was,
indeed, indispensable to a deeper knowledge of organic nature.
But in the endeavor to investigate details naturalists forgot to inquire into the deeper causes and correlations which might have
enabled them to build up out of the wealth of details a more general conception of life. So great was the reaction from the unfortunate speculations of the so-called *Naturphilosophie* that there
was a tendency to shrink even from taking a comprehensive survey
of isolated facts, which might lead to the induction of general
principles.

How deep was the oblivion into which the philosophical conceptions of the beginning of the century had sunk by the middle of
it may be gathered from the fact that in my own student days in
the fifties I never heard a theory of descent referred to, and I
found no mention of it in any book to which I had access. One of
the most famous of my teachers, the gifted anatomist, J. Henle,
had written as a motto under his picture, "There is a virtue of renunciation, not in the domain of morality alone, but in that of intellect as well." This sentence was entirely obscure to me as a
student, because I knew nothing of the intellectual excesses of the
Naturphilosophie, and I only understood later, after the revival
of interest in general problems, that this insistence upon the virtue of intellectual renunciation was intended as a counteractive
to the over-speculations of that period. This was one-sided, but it
was a necessary reaction from the one-sidedness in the opposite
direction which had preceded it.

The next swing of the pendulum was brought about by Charles
Darwin in 1859 with his book, *The Origin of Species.* Let us now
consider the development of this remarkable man, and note the
steps by which he attained to his life work. Charles Darwin was
born on the 12th of February, 1809, the same year in which
Lamarck published his *Philosophie Zoologique.* But he had not
sucked in the doctrines of that evolutionist or of his own grandfather, Erasmus Darwin, with his mother's milk. His youth fell
within the period of the reaction from philosophical speculation,
and he grew up wholly in the old ideas of the creation of species
and their immutability. His birthplace was the little town of
Shrewsbury near the border of Wales, where his father was a
highly respected physician, well-to-do even according to English
standards.

If we think of Charles Darwin's later achievements we are apt
to suppose that the bent toward natural science must have been

CHARLES DARWIN 321

apparent in him at a very early age, but this was not the case, at least not to a degree sufficient to attract the attention of those about him. It is easy now of course to say that the pronounced liking for ranging about wood and field and collecting, quite unscientifically, plants, beetles, and minerals, foreshadowed the future naturalist. Even as a boy Darwin was an enthusiastic sportsman and an excellent shot, and the first snipe he brought down excited him so much that he was hardly able to reload. But he must have been not merely a sportsman but an eager observer, especially of birds, for at that time he wondered "in his simplicity" that every gentleman was not an ornithologist, so much was he attracted by what he observed of the habits of birds.

The school which he began to attend at Shrewsbury in his ninth year was probably very similar to our earlier *gymnasia*. Darwin himself maintained that nothing could have been worse for his intellectual development than this purely classical school, in which nothing was taught, in addition to the ancient languages, except a little ancient history and geography. Darwin had no talent for languages and no pleasure in them. So he remained a very mediocre scholar, and his father therefore removed him from school in his sixteenth year and sent him to the University of Edinburgh to study medicine.

The condition of the British universities at that time must have left much to be desired, for Darwin characterizes the majority of the lectures as terribly dull and the time spent in attending them as lost. Moreover, anatomy disgusted him, and the tedium of the geological lectures repelled him so that he vowed never again to open a book on geology, a resolution which, happily, he did not adhere to. In his student days, as in his school time, he roamed about in the open air, sometimes shooting, sometimes riding, sometimes making long expeditions afoot. But even then he was not a conscious observer of nature, not a naturalist, but rather a lover of the beauty of nature and a collector of all sorts of natural objects, though he collected still, as he had done at school, rather from the collecting impulse frequently characteristic of youth than from any real scientific interest. If he had had that interest his chief passion would not have been the shooting of birds. His friends even found him one day making a knot in a string attached to his buttonhole for every bird he succeeded in bringing down! Thus he must have been mainly a sportsman, a hunting fanatic whose chief desire was to bring down as many birds as possible in a day. However, this devotion to sport must have stood him in good stead later, especially on his great journey, for through it he not only acquired the technique of shooting but sharpened his naturally acute powers of observation.

He remained two years at Edinburgh and then entered the University of Cambridge. His father, who had observed his disinclination for medicine, proposed that he should study theology, and Darwin knew himself so little that he was quite willing to agree to the proposal. He examined himself very conscientiously to see whether he was able to subscribe to the dogmas of the Anglican Church, and he came to the conclusion that he could accept as truth every word that the Bible contained. This was certainly remarkable and proves that the *Zoonomia* of his grandfather and the doctrines of Lamarck, as far as he was acquainted with them, had not taken very deep root. So he proceeded to study theology. But he did it in much the same way as he had studied medicine in Edinburgh, he listened only to what pleased him, and that cannot have been very much, for here, too, he complained of the dullness of official lectures. Nevertheless, at the end of three years he passed his examination quite creditably and received the degree of B. A. Of the greatest advantage to him in Cambridge was his intercourse with two distinguished teachers of the university, and this intercourse probably guided him imperceptibly toward the real work of his life. One of these teachers was Professor Henslow, a theologian who afterwards accepted a living, but who had a comprehensive knowledge not only of entomology but of chemistry, botany, mineralogy, and geology. By Henslow, Darwin was introduced to the professor of geology, Sedgwick, and he, too, interested himself greatly in the young man, taking him with him on his longer geological excursions and thus giving him a most valuable introduction to the science. This proved of the greatest use to Darwin on his travels and probably enabled him to make his numerous geological observations.

Other older men also admitted Darwin to their friendship, so that it is obvious that there must have been something about him even then which distinguished him from others of his age. His interests now began to widen; he came under the educative influence of art and studied the picture gallery in Cambridge and later the National Gallery in London. He gained entrance to a musical circle and derived great pleasure from music, though, curiously enough, as he tells us, he was almost destitute of "ear" and could not even whistle "God Save the King" correctly. He was thus one of those rare persons who are exceedingly sensitive to the emotional effect of music and yet possess little or nothing of its physical basis, the sense of tone.

In addition to all this, Darwin retained his passion for beetles and collected with such ardor that twenty years later he recognized at sight small rare species he had found under bark or moss at that time. His powers of observation had thus been awakened, although as yet they were employed mainly to minister to his zeal for collecting. But collecting is not a mere amusement for the young naturalist; it is a necessary discipline in surveying a definite range of forms, and it cannot well be replaced by anything else. One who has never collected and thus never made himself thoroughly acquainted with a limited circle of forms will find it difficult to fill up the gap in his attainments in later life.

In vacation time toward the autumn of each year Darwin turned again with enthusiasm to sport, either at his home in Shrewsbury or on his uncle Wedgwood's large estate of Maer. He did not lose a possible day from this amusement, for as he says in his autobiography, "I should have thought myself mad to give up the first days of partridge shooting for geology or any other science." Thus, notwithstanding his interest in geology and beetle collecting, in pictures and music, the old passion for the chase was still the dominant one; one pleasure crowded upon another, and the whole made his life a joyous symphony, so that he could say of that period, "The three years which I spent at Cambridge were the most joyful in my happy life." But in the midst of all the joyousness of life he was undergoing an inward preparation for the seriousness of it. We can gather from his own account of that time that the strongest impulse toward the study of natural science came from reading two works which aroused his interest, Humboldt's *Personal Narrative* and Herschel's *Introduction to the Study of Natural Philosophy*. Darwin says of these: "No other book influenced me so much as these two." He used to copy long passages from Humboldt about Teneriffe and read them aloud to Henslow. He was very anxious to go to Teneriffe and even made inquiries in London about a ship to take him there, when an event happened which overthrew that project but at the same time opened up the way to a naturalist's career—the only one really suited to him—in a much more satisfactory manner. He received a proposal to make a voyage round the world.

It must appear to us singular that a young man who had just finished his university course and had done no scientific work of any kind should be invited to accompany as a naturalist a naval vessel which was being sent round the world by the government for the purpose of making nautical observations. It proves that Darwin's older friends must have had very high expectations in regard to his future. Captain Fitzroy of the English navy was looking for a young man who would go with him as naturalist, on a voluntary footing, on his voyage in the *Beagle*. Darwin himself was at once eager to accept, but his father objected very decidedly, seeing no reasonable object in spending five years ranging over the globe. But he concluded his letter with the sentence, "If you can find any man of common sense who advises you to go, I will give my consent." The necessary adviser was found in his uncle Wedgwood, who, as soon as he heard of the matter, immediately drove the 40 miles from Maer to Shrewsbury and persuaded the elder Darwin that he must allow his son to go.

Thus it happened that Darwin made the journey which he speaks of later as "the most important event of my life," as it undoubtedly was. It was only later that he learned that even then his going was not a certainty, for Captain Fitzroy, after seeing him, was in doubt as to whether he should accept him—for a reason not easy to guess: because of the shape of his nose! Fitzroy was an enthusiastic disciple of Lavater, whose doctrine of physiognomy was then widespread. He believed that the shape of Darwin's nose proclaimed a lack of energy, and he was doubtful about taking anyone deficient in that quality on such a journey. Happily, Darwin's friends were able to reassure Fitzroy on this point, and he must often enough afterwards have had opportunity to convince himself of Darwin's energy.

Thus it was apparently by mere chance that Darwin got the opportunity to develop actually into the great naturalist we now know that he must have been potentially. But I do not believe that this is a correct judgment. His inward impulse would certainly have forced a way after he had been led to perceive through Humboldt and Herschel what the way for him was to be. And even at that time no serious obstacle would be likely to stand in the path of a young Englishman of fortune who wished to explore foreign lands and seas. But undoubtedly this manner of traveling for five years through the seas and countries of different zones was particularly advantageous. And Darwin used his opportunities to the full. On board ship he studied the best books, especially Lyell's *Principles of Geology,* but he also collected certain kinds of natural objects and investigated all that came in his way, keeping a detailed journal of everything that struck him as worthy of note in what he observed. Thus he became a well-informed and many-sided naturalist. But he valued much more highly than any other result of the voyage the habits of energetic industry and concentrated attention to whatever he had in hand that he then acquired.

And thus he became the great naturalist for which nature had designed him.

Darwin published his journal later; it fills a closely printed volume of 500 pages. Like all his books, it is characterized by simplicity and straightforwardness of expression; there is absolutely no striving after sensational effect, but an innate enthusiasm and truth pervades it, and I have always found it most enjoyable reading. Other people must have found it so, too, for by 1884 16,000 copies of the English edition had been sold. I cannot here give even a brief account of the voyage of the *Beagle;* I can only say that its work lay chiefly on the southern coast line of America, and the journey included the east coast of Bahia to Tierra del Fuego, and the inhospitable Falkland Islands, and the western coast to Ecuador and Peru.

This occupied several years, and thus the young explorer had a chance to make himself thoroughly acquainted with a great part of the South American continent, for while the ship lay at anchor taking soundings in some bay or other Darwin ranged over the country on horseback, in a boat, or on foot. In Brazil, on the plains of the La Plata River, and in Patagonia he made excursions into the interior which lasted for weeks, and he was thus able to see and investigate everything that interested him.

In all his descriptions of what he saw his keen appreciation of the beauty and grandeur of nature are manifest. Thus he writes from Bahia on the first day of his arrival in South America: "The day has passed delightfully. Delight itself, however, is a weak term to express the feelings of a naturalist who for the first time has wandered by himself in a Brazilian forest. The elegance of the grasses, the novelty of the parasitical plants, the beauty of the flowers, the glossy green of the foliage, but above all the general luxuriance of the vegetation, filled me with admiration. A most paradoxical mixture of sound and silence pervades the shady parts of the wood. The noise from the insects is so loud that it may be heard even in a vessel anchored several hundred yards from the shore; yet within the recesses of the forest a universal silence appears to reign. To a person fond of natural history such a day as this brings with it a deeper pleasure than he can ever hope to experience again."

Not less delightful are his descriptions of the monotonous and almost endless plains of Patagonia and the La Plata River, over which, accompanied by Gaucho Indians, he rode for many days; or his account of the wild mountain scenery of Tierra del Fuego, with its gloomy evergreen woods, broken into by deep inlets and bays in which whales disported themselves, and its mountains whose dark cloud-laden summits are swept by the most violent storms. A different picture is called up by Darwin's description of his ascent from the "Vale of Paradise" (Valparaiso) up the Cordilleras to a height of 13,000 feet, and the view from there down upon the coast region and the Pacific Ocean far beneath him. And how many other passages might be cited!

He cared, however, not only for what was beautiful, but for what was most interesting from a scientific point of view. Thus he discovered in a pass in the Cordilleras a stratum of fossil shells, a proof that this place was at one time a part of the sea floor, and that therefore it had been raised in the course of ages more than 13,000 feet. His journal contains a wealth of observations about plants and animals as well as about man, and many detailed accounts of the geological structure of the countries visited. We see how well his Cambridge studies and the excursions he made there had prepared him for this work.

I cannot enter into any details of his observations, but I must at least mention those which deal with the facts that led him gradually to change his previous views in regard to the nature and origin of species. When he first began his explorations in South America he was, as he expressly says, still completely under the influence of the dogma of the creation of species once for all, and their immutability, and he regarded it as unassailable. But very soon he was struck by certain facts which seemed to him difficult to reconcile with this dogma, and these increased in number in the course of his journey, till finally they led him to the conviction that the old position was untenable and that the organic world had not been created immutable, but had slowly evolved.

I select two of these phenomena: first, the occurrence of the fossil remains of gigantic mammals in the diluvial strata of the great plains of La Plata and Patagonia. Darwin found a gigantic armadillo (*Dasypus gigas*), and he was led to ask how it happened that small armadillos now live in South America, whereas they do not occur, either living or fossil, anywhere else in the world. The answer was easy, if it was possible to assume that the present-day species were descended from the diluvial forms or from other smaller, still undiscovered forms from the same period.

But he was especially impressed by the fauna and flora of the Galapagos Islands, which lie under the equator, 500 nautical miles to the west of the South American coast. On these isolated and comparatively barren volcanic islands there live many animals which could not fail to arrest the attention of the naturalist—land birds which are like those of the neighboring continent and are of purely American type, yet are not identical but closely related species. Most of them are so-called "endemic" species, that is, species which occur in no other part of the world. This was striking enough, but the matter proved even more remarkable on closer investigation, for several of the fifteen islands of which the archipelago consists possess species of the same genus peculiar to themselves—mocking thrushes, for instance, which are represented in the other islands by similar but not identical species.

What inference is possible from these facts except that at some earlier period bird migrants from the neighboring continent had landed on these volcanic islands and in the course of thousands of years had varied, that is to say, had become distinct species on each island? These and other phenomena aroused in Darwin's mind the idea of evolution, and he resolved to devote his attention to this problem after he returned home, for he was persuaded that he could attain to certainty in regard to it by patiently collecting facts. Thus he set himself the task of his life. It may be well to inquire here whether, or to what extent, Darwin had taken over the idea of evolution from his predecessors at the beginning of the century, and especially from his grandfather Erasmus. It is certain that at 16 he had read the *Zoonomia,* and that he admired it. He relates in his autobiography that during his student days in Edinburgh Doctor Grant, afterwards a professor at University College, London, spoke to him in the course of a walk in the most enthusiastic manner of Lamarck and his views on evolution. Darwin listened to these views with interest, but was in no way impressed or convinced by them. The same is true of the *Zoonomia,* and when he reread it fifteen years later he was disappointed in it, "the proportion of speculation being so large to the facts given." Thus Darwin was quite familiar with the views of his grandfather and of Lamarck, but it was not these that incited him to follow in the same paths; it was rather his own observations of nature that led him to abandon his old opinions, and it was only after long years of investigation, study, and doubt that he gained sufficient certainty to venture on giving his ideas to the world.

I must refrain from saying more about this journey, which was so fruitful for Darwin himself and for science; the two groups of facts of which I have spoken were undoubtedly decisive in their effect on his conception of nature. In December 1836, with a wealth of great impressions and rich experiences in all the domains of natural science, his mind concentrated on the new idea of evolution, Darwin returned to England after an absence of five years.

Two years after his return he married, bought the estate of Down in the county of Kent and retired there to spend the whole of the rest of his life in constant work, but also in constant fellowship and personal touch with the most prominent naturalists of the day, who were readily accessible in London. He gradually came to have correspondence also with many naturalists in other countries. His "chief pleasure and constant occupation" was his work, which sometimes even enabled him to forget the daily discomfort due to his health, which had been bad ever since his voyage. From the very beginning of the voyage he had suffered from severe and persistent seasickness, and his constitution had apparently suffered lasting injury, for in his autobiography he often speaks of being unable to work because of illness, and sometimes of having lost days and weeks, and on one occasion two whole years, from this cause.

In dealing with his work it is impossible for me to speak of all the important volumes he published in the course of his life. The first were the results of his voyage, various geological observations, and a new theory of the origin of coral islands. Up till that time it had been believed that the so-called atolls, or lagoon reefs, had been simply built up by the coral polyps from the ocean floor until they finally reached the surface, where they formed flat islands. Darwin recognized that the process could not be quite so simple, because the polyps cannot live at great depths. He therefore assumed that a secular subsidence of the ocean floor must have played a part, and this hypothesis not only explains in the most beautiful way the details of the structure of an atoll, but it has been brilliantly corroborated by later investigations, especially by borings on one of the islands, and the theory is now a permanent possession of science. After the completion of this volume he worked for eight years on the rich material he had brought from the coast of Chile, of that remarkable group of sedentary crustaceans, the *Cirripedes,* usually known as barnacles and acorn shells. Two thick volumes on this subject appeared in 1851 and later two other quarto volumes on fossil species of the same group. Even here, in this apparently dry and purely systematic province, the true spirit of the investigator revealed itself, for he did not neglect what was unintelligible to him and therefore inconvenient for his theory, but devoted the most persistent attention to obscure points until he had found a solution of the difficulty. Thus he discovered that within the group there are species which, like all *Cirripedes,* are hermaphrodite but which possess in addition small degenerate-looking males of different structure attached as parasites to the hermaphrodite animals. It is, however, only in our own day that it has become possible to understand the deeper significance of this important discovery.

In addition to these special pieces of work Darwin collected with untiring energy facts which had any bearing on the theory of transmutation, having begun in 1837, just after his return to England, a large collecting notebook, in which he entered all the facts referring to the variability of animals and plants, in particular of those which are under the care of man. By means of printed lists of questions, of conversations with expert breeders of animals and plants, and of wide reading in books and journals, he sought to lay the foundation of fact which he required in order to attain to clearness in regard to the supposed transformation of organisms.

He was very soon led to the conviction that the essential factor in the artificial modification of an animal or plant form was selection for breeding. But how could such selection take place in free nature? For a long time he was unable to find the answer to this question, until chance made him acquainted with the work of the economist Malthus on *Population,* and the ideas developed in this book suggested to him the solution of the problem. Malthus showed that the human population multiplied much more rapidly than the means of subsistence could increase and that therefore catastrophes must occur from time to time to diminish the excessive number of human beings. Darwin said to himself that in the rest of nature, among other forms of life also, an enormous number of individuals must perish, since all that were born could not survive, and since the greater part of a species furnishes food for some other species. Thus the ceaseless "struggle for existence" became clear to him and suggested the question whether it was merely a matter of chance which of the many born should survive and which should perish. He concluded that the answer to this question was evidently that favorable variations would have more prospect of survival than unfavorable, and thus he discovered the principle of natural selection—that principle at once so simple and so powerful, which alone enables us to understand the transmutation of organisms in adaptation to the conditions of their life. But it was a long time before Darwin ventured to publish this luminous idea. For his own satisfaction he wrote quite a short sketch of it in 1842, and in 1844 he expanded this to 230 pages; but it was not till the fifties that, urged by his friends Lyell and Hooker, he resolved to give his ideas to the world. Even then he might have delayed publication but that in the meantime the same idea had occurred to Alfred Wallace, in Ternate, in the Malay Archipelago, and had been communicated by him, first to Darwin, and then through Darwin to Lyell and Hooker. Then followed the memorable meeting of the Linnaean Society, London, in July 1858 at which two papers were read, one written by Darwin, the other by Wallace, both setting forth the same far-reaching idea of evolution based upon the principle of selection—a beautiful example of the unenvying magnanimity of two great discoverers.

This private communication to a scientific society made no great stir. But the publication in the end of 1859 of Darwin's book, *The Origin of Species by Means of Natural Selection,* attracted great attention. A new edition was called for on January 2, 1860, and during the twenty-two years between that time and 1882, the year of Darwin's death, one English edition followed another, and more than 24,000 copies were printed. During the same period one German edition succeeded another, and it is doubtful whether any other purely scientific book has ever attained to such a circulation. Yet the book is simple and straightforward, never sensational in style, but advancing quietly and concretely from one position to another, each supported by a mass of carefully sifted facts. Every possible objection is duly considered, and the decision is never anticipated, but all the arguments on both sides are carefully and impartially discussed in a manner that is apt to seem to the impatient reader almost too conscientious and cautious.

To readers who were acquainted with the scientific results of the time, who were aware of the numerous important facts that had been discovered, but missed the unifying idea which should gather them all together into a harmonious picture of life, the book came as a revelation. I myself was at the time in the stage of metamorphosis from a physician to a zoologist, and as far as philosophical views of nature were concerned I was a blank sheet of paper, a *tabula rasa.* I read the book first in 1861, at a single sitting and with ever-growing enthusiasm. When I had finished it I stood firm on the basis of the evolution theory, and I have never seen reason to forsake it.

This must have been the case with many. You know that the generation at the beginning of the century, satiated with speculation, threw itself wholly into detailed research, and its whole endeavor was to acquire new facts. Darwin furnished the unifying idea for these: it was evolution. Almost the whole younger generation of naturalists ranged themselves at once on his side; the

older generation gradually followed, first zoologists, then botanists; even my excellent friend, Anton de Bary, was only converted to the new views in 1880, and from that time onward there
was little further opposition, even on the part of the botanists.
Although Darwin's book was straightforward and simple, its
effect was nothing less than revolutionary; it upset the old deep-
rooted doctrine of creation just as completely as Erasmus Darwin,
Lamarck, and Oken had desired. The book raised a conflagration
like lightning in a full barn. This was soon so wide spread
that people read only "against" or "for" Darwin, especially
in Germany, but later also in England. At first the opponents
had the upper hand; the church regarded the new doctrine
as dangerous to religion, because the old Mosaic mythos of creation could no longer be regarded as the basis of belief, and many
of the older naturalists did not care to give up their inherited
opinions without a struggle and therefore strove to depreciate the
new theory, either by serious argument or by satire and ridicule.
The first to publish a work "for" Darwin was the German naturalist, Fritz Müller (1864), in Brazil. His book contained the
first important deduction from the Darwinian theory; it went further than Darwin himself and contained the germ of what Ernst
Haeckel called in his suggestive *Generelle Morphologie* (1866)
the "fundamental biogenetic law." I myself was probably the
third champion of Darwin's views when in 1867 I delivered my
academic inaugural address on "The Justification of the Darwinian Theory."

At that period almost every special study in the domain of
embryology and comparative anatomy revealed fresh facts which
were only intelligible on the assumption that the theory of descent
was valid; much was now observed that had formerly been overlooked, simply because it was not understood, and much of the
work done in the period of detailed investigation had to be done
over again, because the points that were now most important
had previously been disregarded. In this no reproach is implied
to the many excellent observers of that period. No one can possibly observe everything that takes place; for instance, in the
development of an animal, each notes only what seems to him to
have some significance, whether he is able to interpret it or not.
We do not work with our eyes alone; we must think at the same
time.

But I need not dwell longer on the manner in which the Darwinian theory gained over the scientific workers of all countries
and penetrated deeply even among the laity. We have all had

some personal experience of it, for the triumph of the theory of evolution has not long been won. A few words may be necessary as to why it was won so easily and so completely. This was due in part to the enormous and increasing mass of facts in support of it, but mainly to Darwin's discovery of a principle capable of explaining transformations, in so far at least as these are "adaptations"— the principle of selection. Lamarck, too, had thought out a principle of explanation—the use or disuse of parts—but it was obviously insufficient to explain evolution as a whole, since it could only apply to actively functional organs. The discovery of the principle of selection is the greatest achievement of Charles Darwin and his contemporary, Alfred Wallace, and it alone, in my opinion at least, affords a secure basis for the theory of evolution. It reveals to us how the apparently impossible becomes possible, how what is adapted to its purpose can have arisen without the intervention of a directing power.

The principle of selection shows us how the thousands of adaptations in living beings which arouse our constant admiration may have arisen in a purely mechanical way. And they must necessarily have done so if the evolution of the living has resulted from the same forces and laws as the not living; in other words, if, in explaining natural phenomena, we can leave out of account altogether any forces outside of or beyond nature. The principle of selection enables us to do this, and therein lies its far-reaching significance. It is, I believe, the discovery of this principle that will make the name of Darwin immortal. Wallace, too, deserves a full share of the credit, although he did not base his theory on such a broad foundation of facts and did not apply it in so many directions. This principle is fully developed in *The Origin of Species by Means of Natural Selection*, as, indeed, the title of the book shows.

It might be thought that the publication of this book finished the labors of the hermit of Down, but this was not the case; it was followed by the richest creative period of his life. Between 1860 and his death in 1882 he issued a whole series of works, small and large, each of them based upon numerous observations and experiments, and most of them containing wholly fresh associations of ideas, usually connected directly or indirectly with the theory of evolution, and sometimes extending and corroborating it more fully. I must at least give a few indications as to the nature of these different books.

In 1862 Darwin published his book, *The Various Contrivances by Which Orchids Are Fertilized by Insects.* Orchids often exhibit the most special and diverse adaptations to the visits of insects, and they help to make clear to us how flowers may have been developed in all their manifoldness in relation to the needs of their insect visitors. In the same year and those following there appeared several treatises on *Dimorphism in the Flowers of Primula*. Darwin had discovered minute differences in the length of the stamens in the same species, and he demonstrated that these differences are not mere chance variations, but are adaptations which secure the crossing of individuals and prevent self-fertilization. He obtained the proof of this through many careful experiments.

This was followed in 1864 by a treatise on *The Movements and Habits of Climbing Plants,* showing the different ways in which they climb—another study in plant adaptations. In 1868 appeared the great work begun in 1860, *The Variation of Plants and Animals under Domestication,* and this book greatly extended and strengthened the basis of his theory of selection. The phenomena and laws of variation and heredity are discussed and illustrated by a wealth of examples, and the work concludes with a theory of heredity which he called "Pangenesis."

The Descent of Man appeared in 1870. Up till that time Darwin had made no definite pronouncement upon this subject, though of course he must from the very first have deduced from the variability of species that man also was a product of evolution. He now discussed this view in detail in a two-volumed work, which also contained a fuller treatment of an aspect of the theory of selection only briefly sketched in *The Origin of Species*. Here the phenomena of "sexual selection" are traced throughout all the animal groups in which preferential mating plays a part. The principle is illustrated by a positively overwhelming mass of detailed facts and is shown to have been a factor even in the differentiation of the sexes in the human race.

Closely associated with this work is the one which followed it in 1872 on *The Expression of the Emotions in Man and in Animals*. The birth of Darwin's first child in 1839 had induced him to record in a special notebook all his observations on the gradual awakening of the sensations and their expression on the features of the child, for he was convinced that even the most complex and delicate emotional expressions of man had their natural roots in animals, just in the same way as the parts of the body and the mental faculties. For thirty-two years he followed out this idea, experimenting, observing, collecting facts, until finally he was able to write his remarkable and fascinating book, the first English edition of which consisted of 5,000 copies.

Darwin's next book appeared in 1875, and this also had been a long time in course of preparation. In ranging about the country during a summer holiday in 1860 he had noticed a dainty little plant, the "sundew" (*Drosera rotundifolia*), to the viscous leaves of which several small insects were usually found adhering. Many other collectors had noticed this, because of the difficulty of procuring a clean specimen for the herbarium. Darwin took a few of the plants home with him and soon discovered that certain parts of the leaves exhibit movement as soon as small insects are brought into contact with them. This led him to the discovery of *Insectivorous Plants,* and his book bearing that title was published fifteen years later.

In 1876 Darwin published a work on *Different Forms of Flowers on Plants of the Same Species,* and in 1880, jointly with his son Francis, *The Movements of Plants.* Finally, in 1881, the year before his death, there appeared *The Formation of Vegetable Mould through the Action of Worms.* This last book, like some of the earlier short treatises, had no direct connection with the theory of evolution, but it illustrates in a very characteristic manner Darwin's eminently scientific mood, which led him to note everything that seemed unusual or interesting in the most ordinary things and to follow it out till it led him on to new discoveries. How many hundreds of people and even of naturalists had seen the little earthcastings that cover the damper parts of our garden paths on summer mornings! These are due to earthworms and are the remains of the decaying leaves on which they feed. The earthworms cover the whole land with fertile mold, and through their agency in the course of time the surface of the ground is raised, and bad soil is transformed into good. But no one had deemed the phenomenon worthy of attention. It is a case parallel with that of the sundew, which hundreds of botanists had passed by without ever suspecting that the adherence of the insects was more than a matter of chance.

The fruitful discovery of the "struggle for existence," too, was due to this vision of the true naturalist, who sees in what lies before him much that others pass by unheeding. It was certainly no chance that the "struggle for existence" first revealed itself to men who had spent the greater part of their lives in the open air; no chance that it was two travelers like Darwin and Wallace who first perceived the dependence of one species upon another and the competition between them.

From the little that I have been able to tell you of Darwin's life in Down you can gather what a rich, full life it was. You will now wish to hear something of the man himself and his character. . . . He was tall, nearly 6 feet in height, and his most striking features, the high forehead, the large, prominent and bushy eyebrows, the blunt nose, and energetic mouth are well known. No one interested in Darwin's personality should fail to read both Francis Darwin's account of him and his autobiography. Taken together they give a picture of the man which could not be more truthful and could hardly be more complete.

Add to this picture what we can gather from his scientific works, and especially from the accounts of his journey, and we find that he had a great and comprehensive mind, concerned in the main with general conceptions, yet possessing in a high degree the faculty of becoming sympathetically absorbed in detail. He took pleasure in small things as in large and was able alike to study with the most painstaking minuteness the structural details of a flower or a crustacean, or to draw far-reaching conclusions from an enormous number of isolated facts. He possessed the fundamental qualities of a naturalist: great powers of observation and absolute accuracy; the most extreme caution in judgment is revealed in all his writings, and his presentation of his ideas is always simple and entirely free from arrogance or vanity, for a great natural modesty was one of the main features of his character. But his theories clearly show that he was not lacking in imagination, for they could never have been thought out without it. He was not a keen critic, grasping a thing quickly and illuminating it at once; he was, on the contrary, rather inclined to take too favorable a view of the work of others and had a tendency, by no means very common, to acknowledge the achievements of strangers and to take a positive delight in them. His mind was of the penetrating order which worked persistently at any problem until he began to see light on it. He was not concerned with practical aims; he was an idealist who desired knowledge for its own sake and not for any utilitarian end; a naturalist who worked for pleasure in the work itself and rejoiced in the advancement of science his work brought about. He was not lacking in ambition, but it was ambition on a large scale, not to gain fame and position, but to create works which should seem to him worthy. Fame came unsought, and, as he tells us, it was a satisfaction to him to feel that he was held in esteem by those whom he himself esteemed.

He has sometimes been called an amateur, and in a certain sense this is true, in as far as he worked in several different scientific provinces, each of which requires a man's whole strength. But he had full command over these different provinces, at least as far as was necessary for the end he had in view. He was certainly not a restricted specialist. The zoologists accepted him as a zoologist, the botanists as a botanist, perhaps also the geologists as a geologist. But he was not an expert in any, or rather, it would be more correct to say that he was so wherever he himself had done productive work. For he was essentially self-taught and had passed through no normal school of zoology or botany, but with his great energy and unflagging industry he had acquired a profound knowledge from books and from personal intercourse with specialists, and every piece of work he did added to this store of knowledge. He was perhaps the last not merely to survey but to do productive work in every domain of biological science. Yet I will not assert this, for we have all been convinced in recent times through the evolution theory that it is not enough to be at home in a single science; it is necessary also to have at least a general acquaintance with the essentials of allied branches.

Darwin has sometimes been accused of being one-sided, of caring for nothing but his science. But this was not the case; it is less true of him than of many specialists in natural science. He had a wide knowledge of English literature, Milton and Shakespeare having been his favorite reading in his youth. In later life he had novels, historical works, and books of travel read aloud to him every day. He was fond of music, too, though, as we have said, he had no musical ear. Darwin was a man not only of lofty, noble spirit, but of the tenderest feeling. Let anyone who doubts this read the touching pages in memory of his little daughter Annie, who died young; they form one of the most beautiful memorials ever dedicated by a father to his child. His son's picture of him, too, reveals the beautiful and intimate relations that prevailed between them, and the whole quiet and joyous life of the Darwin family testifies to the cheerful and affectionate disposition of its head.

It remains to estimate the influence of Darwin's theories on his time and on the future. But this is a task for which a whole book would not be too much, and a task, moreover, which could be better accomplished on the two hundredth than on the one hundredth anniversary of his birth. We can at least say, however, that the influence was a great and many-sided one, and that it will endure throughout all time. All who know the position of science before 1859 will be ready to admit this; the younger generation have grown up so thoroughly under the influence of Darwin's ideas that it must be difficult for them to realize the state of affairs before his day.

Let us speak of biology first. But was there a biology then?

Strictly speaking, there was not; there was a zoology, botany, and even anthropology. Each of these sciences consisted of a very large and well-arranged mass of facts, but with no intrinsic coherence among them. This was supplied by the theory of evolution. The different departments of science were not even then regarded as complete; it was well known that there were many gaps in our knowledge, but we were only seeking for missing details, whereas in reality it was the main thing that was lacking—the unifying idea which Goethe had sought for and tried to supply in his theories of the plant prototype and of the skull.

The science of embryology, or, as we now call it, ontogenesis, at that time consisted of a great number of observations, interesting enough but without any recognized unity; it was not a harmonious structure but a collection of finely-cut building stones. But what a change when the luminous idea of evolution was added! Life seemed to be infused into the stones and almost spontaneously they formed a magic edifice. The ovum, now at last recognized as a cell, was seen to be a reminiscence of the descent of all higher animals from unicellular organisms; rudimentary organs, such as the rudimentary eyes of blind cave animals, were found to be signposts indicating the racial history of these animals and pointing back to their sight-endowed ancestors. This evolutionary view illuminated the whole science, and not embryology alone, but also comparative anatomy, the understanding of the structure of animals. It became plain why the New Zealand kiwi should have little rudimentary wings under its skin, although it does not fly. It is not in order that it may conform to an ideal of a bird, as was previously thought, but because its ancestors had possessed wings that were used in flight.

Physiology also gained much, especially the theory of reproduction, of heredity, of organs, of the cell, and especially of the cell nucleus. I do not mean to say that all these were the direct result of the idea of evolution, but they have an indirect connection with it.

Anthropology gained quite a new interest after it was recognized that man, too, was a product of evolution. A vast number of problems presented themselves; it was necessary to investigate the gradual becoming not only of the body but of the mind, the evolution of the psyche and all that flows from it. Before that time there had been a history of language, of law, of religion, of art, and so on, but it now became necessary to carry these further back—beyond Adam and Eve to the animal ancestors. Undoubtedly a study of the psychology of animals is one of the essential tasks of the future! I can here only give a few hints without elaborating them, but I must emphasize the fact that the idea of evolution, in the form in which Darwin presented it to us, has given an impulse to new life and further development in every department of human knowledge and thought. Everywhere it acts as the yeast in cider—it sets up fermentation. This has already borne rich fruit, and we may hope for much more in the future.

Our greatest gain from the theory of evolution has, however, been the evidence it affords of the unity of nature, the knowledge that the organic world must be referred back to the same great everlasting laws which govern the inorganic world and determine its course. Even if formal proof of this be still wanting, the probability is now so strong that we can no longer doubt it. It is not only the theory of evolution as a whole, but the active principle in it, the principle of selection, that is transforming and illuminating all our old conceptions. It is teaching us to understand the struggle, silent or clamant, among human races, their rivalry for the possession of the earth, and to understand, too, the composition of human society, the unconscious division of labor among the members, and the formation of associations. The development of classes and their union in a state appears in a new light when looked at from this point of view. In this department a good deal has been already accomplished. The study of human health must be particularly influenced by the theory of evolution, and a beginning has already been made in this department also.

But there is another and very important point in regard to which the theory of selection must be our guide. If we take a survey of the evolution of the world of life as we know it, we see that on the whole it has been an ascending evolution, beginning with the lowest organisms and advancing through higher and higher to the highest of all, man himself. It must be admitted that at certain stages in this evolutionary series we find retrograde steps (as, for instance, parasites and sedentary animals), but on the whole the direction of evolution has been an ascending one.

I see no ground for assuming that this will be otherwise in the future. According to the principle of selection the best will survive in the future as in the past, and mankind will ascend. I do not believe we are likely to undergo any essential changes in a crude physical sense; we are not likely to grow wings, and even our mental powers may not be capable of much further improvement, but ethical improvement seems to me not only possible but probable, on the principle of selection. Mankind will never consist of wholly selfless saints, but the number of those who act in accordance with the ideals of a purer, higher humanity, in whom the care for others and for the whole will limit care for self, will, it is my belief, increase with time and lead to higher religions, higher ethical conceptions, as it has already done within the period of human existence known to us. But here again I can only indicate without following out my ideas. I wished to express them, because the principle of selection has so often been applied in an inverted sense, as if the brutal and animal must ultimately gain the ascendency in man. The contrary seems to me to be true, for it is the mind, not the body, that is decisive in the selection of the human race.

Thus we see the principle of evolution intervening, transforming, re-creating in every department of human life and thought and endeavor. We owe this principle, which has been so fruitful in results, mainly to Charles Darwin, though he was not the only one nor the first to think it out. But it was he, with Wallace, who secured it its place in science and made it a common possession of mankind by working it out in all directions and supporting it with another principle, that of selection, which explains the riddle of the automatic origin of what is suited to its purpose in nature. Thus he cleared away the obstacle which would otherwise have stood in the way of the acceptance of the theory of evolution.

By all this he has earned enduring fame in the annals of science. His own country has not been ungrateful to him. A colossal statue of him in marble decorates the British Museum; from the background of the entrance hall he looks down on the passers-by with the calmness of the sage. His mortal remains lie in Westminster Abbey beside those of Newton. Fate, too, was kind to him. He could truly say that his life was a happy one, for it was filled with a great idea, and he was supported by the consciousness that Goethe expresses through his Faust: *Es kann die Spur von meinen Erdentagen nicht in Aeo nenuntergehen.* This is true of Darwin, and we may think of him as one of the great immortals among men.

Asa Gray *

1810–1888

———◆———

WILLIAM GIBSON FARLOW †

ASA GRAY was born on November 18, 1810, in Sauquoit Valley in the township of Paris, Oneida County, New York, and died on January 30, 1888, at Cambridge, Massachusetts. On the paternal side he was descended from a Scotch-Irish family who emigrated to this country in the early part of the eighteenth century. His grandfather, Moses Wiley Gray, was born at Worcester, Massachusetts, December 31, 1745, and was married in 1769 to Sallie Miller. He went in 1787 to Vermont, where his wife soon afterwards died; and when their son Moses, the father of Asa Gray, was eight years old, the father and son moved still farther west to Sauquoit Valley, then almost a frontier settlement. Sixteen years later Moses Gray was married to Roxana Howard, a daughter of Joseph Howard, of English descent, who, leaving his home in Massachusetts, had settled in Sauquoit Valley the same year as the Gray family. Of their family of eight children, five sons and three daughters, Asa was the first-born.

When a boy he assisted his father in the smaller duties connected with his farm and tannery; but at an early age he showed a much greater fondness for reading than for farm work, and the father soon came to the conclusion that his son would make a better scholar than farmer. Until he was about twelve years old the only education he received was what could be obtained for a part of the year in the small district school and in the small private school at

* *A.R.*, 1888, pp. 763–783, Memorial address before the American Academy of Arts and Sciences, June 13, 1888. See also: "List of the Writings of Asa Gray," *A.R.*, 1888, pp. 785–825; "Memoir of Asa Gray," by James D. Dana, *A.R.*, 1888, pp. 745–762.

† American botanist (1844–1919), whose reports on progress in botany appeared in *A.R.*, 1880, pp. 313–329; 1881, pp. 391–408; 1882, pp. 551–563; 1883, pp. 681–698.

340

Sauquoit taught by the son of the parish pastor. He was then sent to the grammar school at Clinton, New York, where he remained for two years; and when in the autumn of 1825 his teacher, Charles Avery, accepted a place in Fairfield Academy, young Gray followed his instructor to that place, where for four years he pursued elementary mathematical and classical studies. Connected with the Fairfield Academy was a medical school which enjoyed a high reputation and was attended by two hundred students, a large number for that time. Dr. James Hadley, the Professor of Materia Medica and Chemistry in the Medical School, also gave some instruction in the Academy, and it was probably through his influence that Gray's attention was first strongly drawn towards natural science. Apparently he was not at first so much interested in plants as in minerals, and it was not until towards the close of his course in the academy that his passion for plants was aroused by reading the article on botany in the *Edinburgh Encyclopedia*. His delight the following spring at being able to make out with the aid of Eaton's *Manual* the scientific name of the common *Claytonia* is now a well-known story.

Following his father's wish, which probably was in accord with his own inclination, he decided to study medicine and formally entered the Fairfield Medical School in 1829, although for two years previously, while a student in the Academy, he had attended some of the medical lectures. The sessions of the Medical School, like those of the academy, hardly occupied more than six months of the year, and the remainder of the time was spent in study with different physicians in the neighborhood of Sauquoit, one of whom, Dr. John F. Trowbridge, of Bridgewater, was a man of good scientific attainments. He was thus in an excellent position for collecting, and even before he graduated he had brought together a considerable herbarium and had entered into correspondence with Dr. Lewis C. Beck of Albany and Dr. John Torrey* of New York, who aided him in the determination of his plants. He received his doctor's degree at Fairfield on February 1, 1831. He never, however, entered upon the practice of medicine, but after receiving his degree he became instructor in chemistry, mineralogy, and botany in Bartlett's High School at Utica, New York, and taught those subjects for a part of the year, from the autumn of 1831 to 1835.

The first actual record of any public lectures on botany given by him is found in a circular of the Fairfield Medical School, dated January 1832, in which the following statement is made: "Asa

* See Asa Gray, "Sketch of the Life and Labors of John Torrey," *A.R.*, 1873, pp. 211–218.

Gray, M.D., will give a course of lectures and practical illustrations on botany, to commence [in June] and continue the same
time with the lectures on chemistry [six weeks]. Fee, $4." This
course was attended apparently by ten persons, for he states that
he spent the $40 earned from these lectures in making a botanical
excursion to Niagara Falls. It appears to be the case, however, that
in the previous year, just after graduation, he had given a few
lectures on botany in the Medical School in the absence of the
regular instructor, Dr. Beck; and a little later he gave another
course of lectures on mineralogy and botany at Hamilton College,
Clinton. During other intermissions of his work at Bartlett's School
he made mineralogical and botanical excursions to different parts
of New York and New Jersey; and it was while living at Utica that
he published in the *American Journal of Science* of October 1833
his first scientific paper on new mineral localities in northern New
York, written in collaboration with Dr. J. B. Crawe.

In the autumn of 1833, having leave of absence from Bartlett's
School, he accepted the position of assistant to Prof. John Torrey,
in the chemical laboratory of the Medical School of New York.
His time was here mainly occupied in botanical studies, and besides aiding Dr. Torrey in his botanical work he prepared and
published several original papers of his own, of which his memoir
on *Rhynchospora* may be said to be his first contribution to descriptive botany. His connection with Bartlett's School ended early
in 1835, and although the financial condition of the New York Medical School did not permit his continuing as assistant of Dr. Torrey,
he returned to New York in the autumn of 1835 and accepted the
position of curator and librarian of the Lyceum of Natural History, a position which gave him leisure for continuing his botanical
studies and to prepare his first textbook, *Elements of Botany*,
which appeared in 1836.

About this time a Government expedition, since known as the
Wilkes Exploring Expedition, was fitting out, and the position of
botanist of the expedition was offered to Dr. Gray in the summer
of 1836. The expedition did not sail, however, until two years
later; and meanwhile, wearied by the numerous delays and uncer-
tainties about the management of the expedition, Dr. Gray resigned his position and settled in New York, where, in company
with Dr. Torrey, he worked energetically on the preparation of
the earlier parts of the *Flora,* of which the first two parts appeared
in October 1838. While occupied in this work, a new state university had been founded in Michigan, and Dr. Gray accepted the
chair of botany which was offered to him, with the understanding

that he should be allowed to spend a year abroad in study before beginning his official duties.

The elaboration of the new *Flora* made it necessary for him to examine the types of American plants in foreign herbaria; and in November 1838 he started on the journey which was not only to give him the means of clearing up much of the existing confusion with regard to the identity of previously described North American species, but, what was more important, was to bring him into close scientific and social relations with the botanical lights of a generation now long past and with those who were then the young men of promise—a brilliant group, of which Sir J. D. Hooker* and A. De Candolle are now almost the only survivors.

He returned to America in November 1839 but never assumed the duties of professor at Michigan. He was absorbed in his work on the *Flora,* and refreshed and stimulated by what he had seen and heard abroad, he was pushing rapidly ahead with the second volume, of which he wrote the greater portion, and at the same time printing a *Botanical Text-Book,* which was to form the basis of his many subsequent textbooks, when he was invited to Cambridge to fill the newly endowed chair of the Fisher Professorship of Natural History in Harvard College.

He accepted and in 1842 took up his residence in Cambridge. The second volume of the *Flora* was completed the following year. He was at once favorably received in learned and social circles of Cambridge and Boston, and, when delivering a course of lectures at the Lowell Institute, he first became acquainted with Miss Jane Lathrop Loring, daughter of Mr. Charles Greely Loring of Boston, to whom he was married on May 4, 1848. From this time his energies were devoted to building up a botanical establishment at Cambridge—for what was in existence before 1842 hardly deserves mention—and to the completion of a *Flora of North America.* The number of collectors and explorers had by this time greatly increased, and the material they had brought together contained so much that was new, that it was plain that the original plan of the *Flora* must be changed, for the two volumes already published had hardly appeared when a revision seemed necessary. It was not until many years later, in 1878, that the first part of the new *Flora* appeared, and he continued to labor toward the completion of his great work until death forced him to relinquish the unfinished task.

He continued in the exercise of the active duties of lecturer and

* See pp. 418–435 this volume; also, D. Prain, "Sir Joseph Dalton Hooker," *A.R.,* 1911, pp. 659–671.

instructor until 1872, when he was relieved of this charge by the appointment of a colleague, Prof. G. L. Goodale, but he gave occasional lectures in the college for a few years longer. In 1873 he resigned his office of Director of the Botanic Garden, and Prof. C. S. Sargent was appointed his successor. He retained the title of Fisher Professor and Director of the Herbarium until his death, although he was in part relieved of the responsibilities of the latter position by the appointment of Mr. Sereno Watson as Curator of the Herbarium in 1874.

His long residence and arduous labors at Cambridge were varied and relieved by several journeys, some of which were of considerable extent, and all of which were made to contribute to the advancement of the work on the *Flora,* either by enabling him to examine in the field the plants which he was studying or by examination of foreign herbaria and consultations with leading foreign botanists. He made three trips to California, in 1872, in 1877 (when he was in company with Sir J. D. Hooker), and in 1885 (when he visited not only southern California and the great Colorado Canyon but journeyed into Mexico as far as Orizaba and Cordoba. He was once in Florida, in 1875, and made, besides, several trips to the mountains of North Carolina, where he botanized at different times with his botanical friends, Sullivan, Carey, Engelmann, Canby, and Redfield.

He made in all six journeys to Europe, including the journey already mentioned and a short business trip of six weeks to Paris in the summer of 1855. On the other journeys he was accompanied by Mrs. Gray. When abroad he always spent much of his time with the English botanists, among whom he counted many warm personal friends, and he looked forward with special pleasure to his visits at Kew, where he was welcomed by the director, Sir W. J. Hooker, and by his son and successor, Sir J. D. Hooker, for forty years his intimate friend, whose opinion in botanical matters he esteemed more highly than that of any of his contemporaries. In his second journey, from June 1850 to August 1851, he traveled through France, Germany, and Holland, and spent two months with [George] Bentham at his home in Herefordshire, studying the plants of the Wilkes Expedition, upon which he was then working. The fourth journey, from September 1868 to November 1869, was undertaken at a time when he was much overworked, and he spent the winter in Egypt, that country being almost the only spot where there was nothing to tempt him to botanize, besides visiting Italy, France, Germany, and England. The event of the journey of September 1880 to November 1881 was a trip to Spain, a country where he obtained much relief from botany.

His last journey, on which he started in 1887, was a triumphant farewell, in which were heaped upon him honors bestowed on few naturalists. He visited friends in France, Austria, and Germany; stopped at Geneva to see De Candolle, his life-long friend, older by four years than himself, and sorrowfully bade him what both must have felt to be a last farewell; then hurried back from the Continent to receive the doctor's degree from the three great British universities and to attend the meeting of the British Association at Manchester. Here he saw many old friends and met for the first time three of Germany's most distinguished botanists— Cohn, Pringsheim, and the lamented De Bary, whose untimely death was to come but a few days before his own. At Manchester he was brought into contact with a large number of young botanists who were charmed with his genial manner and astonished at his well-preserved vigor of body as well as mind. He returned to America in October, apparently in perfect health, and resumed active labor on the *Flora,* but while busied with the preparation of the *Vitaceæ* for that work he was suddenly stricken with paralysis on the morning of November 28, and lingered in a partially conscious condition until the evening of January 30, when he passed calmly away.

By the death of Asa Gray this Academy has lost a member whose activity and zeal were unceasing and whose brilliant talents as a scientific writer, not surpassed by those of any of the illustrious names on our roll, added much to the reputation of the society at home and abroad. Elected a corresponding member in 1841, he became an active member in 1842 on his settlement in Cambridge and served as corresponding secretary from 1844 to 1850 and again from 1852 to 1863, and as president from 1863 to 1873. During this long membership of more than forty years his attendance was always exemplary. The storms of winter and the inclemencies of spring, which kept younger men at home, did not prevent his coming from the remote Botanic Garden regularly to attend the meetings. Although an honorary member of most of the learned societies of this country and of many of the most prominent societies of Europe, including the Royal Society of London, the French Academy, and the Imperial Academy of St. Petersburg, of which he was one of the very few Americans who have been elected corresponding members, this Academy was the society in which he felt the greatest interest and was most at home.

There are few volumes of our *Proceedings* which do not contain important communications from his pen. One of the earliest of his works, the "Chloris Boreali-Americana," was printed in the third volume of the Academy's *Memoirs* in 1846; and to subsequent volumes he contributed "Plantæ Fendlerianæ Novi-Mexicanæ," presented in November 1848; "Plantæ Novæ Thurberianæ," and "Note on the Affinities of the Genus *Vavæa,* Benth., also of *Rhytidandra,* Gray," August and October 1854; and a group of four papers, entitled "Botanical Memoirs," in 1859, including one "On the Botany of Japan, and its Relations to that of North America"—a remarkable essay on the geographical distribution of plants, which stamped the author as worthy to rank with the great botanists of the world. We need not enumerate his many papers which have appeared in the *Proceedings* of the Academy, for they alone would fill several volumes. It was his custom to embody the results of his preliminary studies on the North American flora in the form of notes on critical species, descriptions of novelties, and monographs of genera, and sometimes orders, of which by far the greater part first appeared in our *Proceedings,* usually under the heading of "Botanical Contributions," a long and very valuable series, dating from the paper "On some New *Compositæ* from Texas," presented December 1, 1846, and ending with the posthumous "Notes upon some Polypetalous Genera and Orders," presented April 19, 1888. Nor should we forget the many biographical notices in which he commemorated the lives and works of others with an appreciating discrimination, written in a manner peculiarly his own.

The botanical department of Harvard University was practically created by Asa Gray. In 1805 a small botanic garden was established at Cambridge under the auspices and by the aid of the Massachusetts Society for Promoting Agriculture, and William Dandridge Peck was appointed director and professor of botany. In 1818 he printed a *Catalogue of American and Foreign Plants Cultivated in the Botanic Garden, Cambridge,* in which one thousand three hundred and nine species were enumerated; but the list included some common Cryptogams found everywhere and a large number of Phænogamic shrubs and weeds, common natives of the region, hardly to be counted as legitimate members of a botanic garden. Professor Peck died in 1822, when, owing to the low state of the funds, a professor was not appointed, but Thomas Nuttall, the well-known botanist and ornithologist, was appointed Curator of the Garden and later

Lecturer on botany. This amiable but very reticent naturalist—
who apparently did not find his residence in Cambridge very
congenial (for he describes himself as vegetating like his plants)
—resigned his position in 1833 and returned to Philadelphia.
The Garden, such as it was, was then put under the charge of
William Carter, a gardener, and the lectures on botany were
given by T. W. Harris, the well-known entomologist and librarian of the college, and Dr. A. A. Gould of Boston. Not long
before 1842 the directorship of the Garden was offered to
George B. Emerson of Boston, who declined the position soon
afterwards accepted by Dr. Gray in connection with the Fisher
professorship.

On Dr. Gray's accession there was no herbarium, no library,
only one insignificant greenhouse and a garden all in confusion,
with few plants of value. In 1844 he moved into the house which
had been built for Professor Peck in the Garden, and with his
characteristic energy he soon brought together an herbarium
and library and arranged the Garden systematically. At the time
of his marriage a small wing was added to the house, of which
the lower story served as a study and herbarium until 1864.
But the plants soon overran the limits of the herbarium and
finally the whole house was crammed with plants—plants in the
dining-room, in the attic, in the closets, and in the bedrooms;
for whatever he could spare from a salary of $1,000 at first, and
$1,600 afterwards, was spent on his herbarium and library. In
1864, dreading the danger from fire to a collection kept in a
wooden house, he offered to present his collections to the college
on condition that a suitable building should be erected for their
reception. Through the liberality of Nathaniel Thayer of Boston,
a brick building to be used as the Herbarium and library was
erected in 1864 at a cost of $12,000; and mainly through the
agency of G. B. Emerson a further sum of $10,000 was raised,
the income of which was to be used in defraying the current
expenses of the Herbarium. From a letter by Dr. Gray to the
president of the university, dated November 20, 1864, and a
notice in the *American Journal of Science* of March 1865, we
learn that the Herbarium then contained at least 200,000 specimens, and the library about 2,200 botanical works, not including a good many pamphlets. There was also a set of 335 very
costly illustrated works contributed by John A. Lowell.

Since 1864 the Herbarium has been constantly enlarged,
principally by exchanges, of which those from the Kew Herbarium especially were of very great value so that it is now

probably twice as large as in 1864 and forms practically a
National Herbarium, for it is by far the largest and most valuable herbarium in America and is excelled in size by but few
of the older and richer herbaria of Europe, as those at Kew,
Paris, Berlin, the De Candolle Herbarium at Geneva, and possibly that at St. Petersburg. In the representation of the
Phænogams of North America outside the tropics it is probably
unequalled by any herbarium except that at Kew. The library
at the time of Professor's Gray's death was roughly estimated
to contain something over 5,000 volumes and 3,000 pamphlets,
but these figures are probably too low. Many of the additions
since 1864 are the gift of Dr. Gray. In building up this vast
collection, he gave not only much of his time and thought but
also an actual sum of money, which comes well up in the
thousands and, to crown all, manifested his devotion to the
welfare and perpetuation of the collection by bequeathing to
the University for its support the royalties on his publications.

The Garden during his administration was improved by the
addition of several greenhouses, in which were cultivated a
choice selection of exotics, and the rather limited space of the
Garden itself was filled with good representatives of the flora
of the temperate regions, the collection of *Compositæ* being
especially important. In the absence of a sufficient endowment,
activity on the part of the director had to replace the want of
money, and he, utilizing the means at hand, succeeded in making
the Garden an exceedingly important means of exchange between
foreign establishments and our own botanists and collectors.
European botanists who visited the Garden wondered how, from
such a small and ill-endowed establishment, so much had been
done in aid of other institutions. The explanation lay in the skill
and energy of Dr. Gray himself.

Gray's work as a teacher extended over a period of more than
fifty years, dating from the first lectures on botany at the Fairfield
Medical School in 1831 and 1832 and the publication of his
Elements of Botany in 1836. During that period he trained up a
whole race of botanists, now scattered through all parts of the
United States, so that wherever he went he was greeted by those
who remembered his instruction with pleasure. When at Santa
Barbara in 1885 an elderly man who seemed to be about his own
age introduced himself as a former pupil in his first class at Harvard. As a college lecturer he was not seen at his best, for his
somewhat hesitating manner when he spoke extemporaneously was
unfavorably contrasted with the fervid, almost impetuous utterance

of Agassiz, and the clear exposition and dignified address of Jeffries Wyman, his two great contemporaries at Harvard. In his public addresses he always spoke from notes, and especially in his later years his strikingly expressive face commanded the attention of his hearers from the start. In the classroom he was personally much liked, and he made a strong impression on the majority of students, although in the days when every student was forced to study botany there were of course some who would not have cared for the subject under any circumstances. The instruction, as was natural, bearing in mind his own early training and the state of botany in this country at the time when he became professor at Harvard, was confined mainly to the morphological study of flowering plants; for he recognized that until some advance had been made in that direction it was out of the question dealing adequately with the more technically complicated subjects of histology, embryology, and physiology.

For the instruction which he was obliged to give, the resources of the Garden and the Herbarium and the ordinary college lecture rooms at first sufficed, but at last it became necessary to provide a special laboratory and lecture room at the Garden. A liberal friend of Dr. Gray and the college presented a sum of money for this purpose, and in 1872 a wing was added to the Herbarium. About this time the demand for laboratory instruction and equipment increased rapidly, and the new lecture room and laboratory were soon found to be inadequate to meet the needs of the increasing calls for microscopic and physiological work, and they were at length abandoned. It is not surprising that Dr. Gray could not foresee how great the growth in this direction was to be even in his own life. Probably no person of his age could have foreseen it.

His Herbarium was at one period or another the resort of nearly all the active working botanists of the country, and thither came many young men who were afterwards to aid in the development of botanical studies in the United States. His intercourse with them was always free and unrestrained by formalities of any kind, and he seemed more like a learned friend than a teacher. Passing to and fro from his own study to the Herbarium he greeted all cordially, watching and criticizing sharply but good-naturedly the work that was going on. No one enjoyed a hearty laugh more than he, and every now and then he would brighten the work by some anecdote from the large stock which his retentive memory ever had at hand, always, however, for the purpose of emphasizing some point or illustrating some fact which he wished to bring out more clearly, but never allowing the attention of those about him to be distracted from their work. Life at the Herbarium was indeed a pleasure, and the more serious work was well seasoned and spiced in the days when the agile assistant, Charles Wright, skipped about like a squirrel, his diminutive body in Cambridge, his larger mind wandering away in his beloved Cuba and the Pacific islands —when Brewer, less continent than his teacher in the matter of anecdote, saw in every plant before him some episode of his own life in camp. The approach of Dr. Gray, heralded by his cheery laugh or perhaps by a mild anathema against the gardener, who every morning, regardless of the intentions of nature, deluged the cacti placed in the corridor, we all understood to mean business, for if joking was allowed, trifling was not. We learned something about botanists as well as about botany and often wondered whether Robert Brown were really as great as he was represented; and on the rare occasions of a visit from a man like Dr. Torrey or Dr. Engelmann we asked ourselves whether there was any chance that the younger generation of botanists would bear any comparison with the older. None who have worked under Dr. Gray at the Herbarium will forget the deep personal interest he always manifested in their work and future prospects. He always encouraged and stimulated without holding out false hopes. To those who wished to devote themselves to botany in the years still recent, when it was scarcely possible for a botanist to live by botany alone, he used to say: "Study medicine, and if you then still want to be a botanist, go ahead. Your medicine will keep your botany from starving."

Great as was the direct influence of Dr. Gray upon the students with whom he came in contact, his influence on the development of botany in this country through the medium of his numerous textbooks and manuals was even more important. His first textbook, *Elements of Botany,* written when he was only twenty-six years old, shows many of the best characteristics of his later works, being written in a smooth, graceful style, with the different topics clearly and methodically arranged. The vigorous defense of the natural system of classification, which now appears superfluous, indicates that the author of 1836 was a progressive young man who had shaken off the conservatism that prevailed among American botanists of that period. That he was young and inexperienced is occasionally shown, as in the amusing statement that "the herbarium of a diligent botanist will pass so frequently under his observation that any very extensive ravages [by insects] can hardly take place without his being aware of it in time to check the progress of the destroyers." He evidently had no conception of how large his own collection would become in a few years.

The *Elements* of 1836 developed into the *Botanical Text-Book* of 1842, in which the portion relating to systematic botany was much more fully treated than in the earlier volume. The later editions, which appeared at intervals until 1879, are familiar to everyone, for they have been the means of opening the world of botany to more than one generation of American botanists. In 1868 the *Lehrbuch der Botanike* by Sachs appeared. That work was a genuine revelation, showing the advance which had been made by experts in the science of botany, and although somewhat above the capacity of the common student it was destined to produce in a few years a revolution in the method of botanical instruction.

Recognizing the new era which had opened in botany, Dr. Gray revised the plan of the *Text-Book* with a view of bringing it into accord with the more widely developed science of the day and in 1879 issued the first volume of the revised work, in which he included the morphology of Phænogams, taxonomy, and phytography, thus covering the greater part of the ground of the original *Text-Book,* intrusting to his colleague, Professor Goodale, the volume on physiological botany (which appeared in 1885—a worthy companion of its predecessor) and to the writer the volume on Cryptogams. He hoped, but hardly could have expected, to write a fourth volume, on the Orders of Phænogamous Plants. It is deeply to be regretted that he was never able to write this volume, for it would have enabled him to present the general views on classification derived from a long and exceptionally rich experience. No better textbook on the subject had ever been written in the English language than Gray's *Text-Book* in the original form; and although botanical instruction is now very different from what it used to be, it is still true that as an introduction to the study of Phænogams, the group to which beginners naturally turn their attention, the later *Structural Botany* is likely to hold its own for some time to come. In 1887, just before he started on his last European journey, he finished a small book giving in an abbreviated form the substance of the *Structural Botany,* as well as some chapters on Cryptogams; and for this, his latest textbook, he revived the title of his earliest work, *Elements of Botany.*

The *Manual of the Botany of the Northern United States,* of which the first edition appeared in 1847, needs no words of praise here. There are probably few members of the Academy who do not own or have not at some time owned a copy of this model work. Occasionally some overwise person has discovered that certain plants grow a few inches taller or bloom a few days earlier than is stated in the *Manual;* but the botanist is yet to be born who could write a more clear, accurate, and compact account of the flora of any country. The only regret is that he could not have written manuals for all parts of the country.

Dr. Gray had the rare faculty of being able to adapt himself to all classes of readers. With the scientific he was learned, to the student he was instructive and suggestive, and he charmed the general reader by the graceful beauty of his style, while to children he was simplicity itself. The little books, *How Plants Grow* and *How Plants Behave,* found their way where botany as botany could not have gained an entrance, and they set in motion a current which moved in the general direction of a higher science with a force which can hardly be estimated. His scientific friends, especially those abroad, sometimes blamed him for spending time in popular writing, but he may have understood himself and his surroundings better than they. With him botany was a pleasure as well as a business. Few wrote as easily as he, and so long as he spent most of his time in higher work he certainly had a right to amuse himself with writings of a popular character if he chose. As it was, he interested a multitude of readers in the subjects which he had at heart, and if he was not permitted to live to see the completion of his greatest work, the *Synoptical Flora,* he at least was able to leave the work at a point where it could be continued by a trusted friend in sympathy with all his plans.

As a reviewer he was certainly extraordinary. Some of his reviews were in reality elaborate essays in which, taking the work of another as a text, he presented his own views on important topics in a masterly manner. Others were technically critical, while some were simply concise and very clear summaries of lengthy works. Taken collectively, they show better than any other of his writings the literary excellence of his style, as well as his great fertility and his fairness and acuteness as a critic. Never unfair, never ill-natured, his sharp criticism, like the surgeon's knife, aimed not to wound but to cure; and if he sometimes felt it his duty to be severe he never failed to praise what was worthy. The number of his reviews and notices written during his connection with the *American Journal of Science* as editor and assistant editor for over thirty years, and for the *North American Review, the Nation, the Atlantic Monthly,* and numerous other journals, is enormous, and it almost seems as if he must have written notices of the greater part of all the botanical works he had ever read. Those intimately acquainted with him more than half believed that he was able to write good notices of books written in languages which he could not read. He was able as if by instinct to catch the spirit and essence of what he read without any exertion on his part. One who wrote so much might have become monotonous. But he was never prosy, and his style was so easy and flowing and so constantly enlivened by sprightly allusions and pleasing metaphors, that one could read what he wrote for the mere pleasure of the reading. His was one of the rare cases where science had appropriated to herself one who would have been an ornament to any purely literary profession.

It would be presumption were we to express an opinion on the position of Gray as a scientific botanist. Fortunately for us, it is unnecessary. The greatest living systematic botanist, Sir J. D. Hooker, the one by his attainments and position fitted above all others to speak with authority on the subject, has already recorded his opinion in the following words:

When the history of the progress of botany during the nineteenth century shall be written, two names will hold high positions: those of Prof. Augustin Pyrame De Candolle * and of Prof. Asa Gray. - - - Each devoted half a century of unremitting labor to the investigation and description of the plants of continental areas, and they founded herbaria and libraries, each in his own country, which have become permanent and quasi-national institutions. - - - There is much in their lives and works that recalls the career of Linnæus, of whom they were worthy disciples, in the comprehensiveness of their labor, the excellence of their methods, their judicious conception of the limits of genera and species, the terseness and accuracy of their descriptions, and the clearness of their scientific language.

The accuracy of the resemblance of Gray and De Candolle, so admirably and justly expressed by Hooker, will be recognized by all botanists. Gray was the De Candolle of America, whose mission it was to bring together the scattered and crude works of the earlier explorers and botanists and the vast unwrought material of his own day, and to combine them with his surpassing skill into one grand comprehensive work which should fitly describe the flora of a continent. But while recognizing the resemblance between De Candolle and Gray in their mode of work and the purpose for which they strove, we can only marvel how it was

* See Flourens, "Memoir of Pyramus De Candolle," *A.R.*, 1859, pp. 271–283. His son Alphonse carried on his work (see *A.R.*, 1874, pp. 239–248; 1875, pp. 142–150).

possible for a poor farmer's boy in America, without a university education, to become the peer of one of Europe's best-trained botanists.

From his training and early surroundings we might have expected him to be energetic and original, but we should not have expected to find him highly polished and cultured. His associates at Fairfield and Clinton were persons of scientific tastes, and even if their attainments were not of the highest quality they encouraged his fondness for natural history. But it is not easy to see how he obtained the literary training which enabled him to write with the ease and elegance found even in his earlier works, for although a man may by nature be a good observer of natural objects, a finished style comes only with training and experience. From his teacher, Avery, he could not have received much in the way of training; for Dr. Gray himself says that he did not give him the sharp drilling and testing which was needed. His residence with the Torrey family in New York first placed him in a society where literary excellence as well as scientific knowledge was prized, and while he profited by the accuracy and strict scientific methods of Dr. Torrey, then the foremost American botanist, the frequent conversations and kindly criticism of Mrs. Torrey made good many of the literary deficiencies of his early training. He was also aided while in New York by the criticisms and suggestions made on some of his earlier manuscripts by the cultured botanist, Mr. John Carey. But he must have been an apt pupil, for while still with Dr. Torrey he showed that in point of clearness and accuracy he was not much inferior to his highly respected teacher, and in the second volume of the *Flora* he proved himself to be quite his equal.

The plan of the *Flora of North America* originated with Dr. Torrey, but when his pupil went to Cambridge to assume the duties of his new position, neither of them suspected the magnitude of the task which they had undertaken nor the modifications which the plan must ultimately undergo. The pupil was now in a more fortunate position than his teacher, for Gray was henceforth able to devote himself to his favorite science, while Dr. Torrey could only employ his leisure hours in botany. The two volumes of the original Torrey and Gray *Flora* will always remain a memorial of the unbroken friendship of America's two greatest botanists, alike in the spirit which animated their work and in the reverent simplicity of their characters.

The greater part of Gray's scientific work during the thirty-five years following the completion of the second volume of Torrey and Gray's *Flora* in 1843 had a more or less direct bearing on the contemplated revision and enlargement of that work. Besides the papers printed in the Academy's publications, he wrote a very large number of monographs and notes on points connected with the determination and description of new and doubtful species. They are scattered through the proceedings of different learned societies, and the columns of the *American Journal of Science,* the *Torrey Bulletin, Botanical Gazette,* the *Naturalist,* and other American as well as European journals. One of his most important works was *Genera Floræ Americæ Boreali-Orientalis Illustrata* (1848–49), in which he intended to figure and describe all the genera of the eastern states with the aid of the artist, Isaac Sprague. Of this work only two of the proposed volumes were ever published, owing to the expense entailed. Other important papers were "Plantæ Wrightianæ Texano-Neo-Mexicanæ," in the *Smithsonian Contributions* of 1852 and 1853; "Plantæ Lindheimerianæ," written in collaboration with Dr. Engelmann; "Reports on the Botany of the 32nd, 38th, 39th, and 41st Parallel Expeditions," in collaboration with Dr. Torrey; "Gamopetalæ" in Watson's *Flora in California,* etc. An examination of the complete list of his works, which will soon be printed in the *American Journal of Science,* would alone convey an adequate idea of his extraordinary fertility as a writer and the wide range of his investigations.

After this long preparation of thirty-five years, the first part of the *Synoptical Flora,* including the *Gamopetalæ* after *Compositæ,* appeared in 1878. It formed the first part of the second volume; for, on the revised plan, the first volume was to include the *Polypetalæ* and *Gamopetalæ* through *Compositæ,* and the second volume the remaining exogens and the endogens. A second part, including from *Caprifoliaceæ* through *Compositæ,* appeared in 1884, and in 1886 supplements to both parts were issued and the whole bound in one volume. He was at work on the *Polypetalæ* and had nearly finished the *Vitaceæ* when attacked by his last illness, and the unfinished volumes must now be completed by him who was his associate for many years and, after Dr. Gray himself, the best fitted for the work.

Gray's critical knowledge of the flora of North America not only placed him at the head of all American botanists, but also gave him a high reputation abroad. In his knowledge of the difficult order *Compositæ,* the largest of all the orders of flowering plants and the one in which he always felt the most interest, he probably surpassed any living botanist. He was at one time urged by Bentham and Hooker to treat that order in their classic *Genera Plantarum,* but, as the work involved a residence at Kew for a considerable time, he was obliged to decline the offer.

It was, however, more especially through his observations on the geographical distribution of plants, made incidentally during the progress of his work on our own flora, that he was recognized as a naturalist of the highest type by the scientific circles of Europe. When we consider the marked capacity for studies of this nature which he afterwards exhibited, remembering the brilliant contributions to plant geography which resulted from the explorations of Robert Brown, Darwin, and Hooker, we can only regret that Gray did not sail as botanist of the Wilkes Expedition. The collectors of the Expedition, Dr. Charles Pickering, W. D. Brackenridge, and William Rich, brought back many interesting plants, of which the Phænogams, excepting those from the Pacific coast of America sent to Dr. Torrey, were placed in his hands for description. But Gray would have been more than a collector. He would have brought back impressions and, recalling the charming narrative of the illustrious naturalist of the *Beagle,* we can imagine the pleasure with which we should have read the journal of a botanist, written with the delicate humor and the keen appreciation of the beautiful and curious in nature which Asa Gray possessed.

The study of the Wilkes plants, in which he was aided by Bentham's large experience, gracefully acknowledged in his "Memorial" of Bentham in the *American Journal of Science* of February 1885, introduced him to an exotic flora of large range. The work appeared in 1854 as a quarto volume of nearly eight hundred pages, with an atlas of a hundred folio plates.

His first paper on the distribution of plants appeared in the *American Journal of Science* of September 1856 and was followed by two other parts the next year. It bore the title of "Statistics of the Flora of the Northern United States" and was prepared at the time he was at work on a second edition of the *Manual,* partly in response to a request from Darwin for a list of American alpine plants. In this paper he gave a general view of the characteristics of the North American flora, with tables of species showing the extension of alpine plants and the comparative distribution of eastern and western species and their relation to species of Europe and Asia, although he states that he must defer making an extended comparison with the plants of northeastern Asia until he has studied some recent collections from the northern part of Japan. The most important conclusions reached in this paper may be stated in his own words:

All our strictly subalpine species (with two exceptions), which are common to us and to Europe, extend northward along the central region of the continent quite to the arctic sea-coast, while curiously enough eleven, or one-third of our strictly alpine species common to Europe—all but one of them arctic in the Old World—are not known to cross the arctic circle on this continent. This, however, might perhaps have been expected, as it seems almost certain that the interchange of alpine species between us and Europe must have taken place in the direction of Newfoundland, Labrador, and Greenland rather than through the polar regions.

Again:

The special resemblance of our flora to that of Europe, it is clear, is not owing simply either to the large proportion of genera in common, or to anything striking or important in the few genera, nearly or quite peculiar to the two. The latter, indeed, are insignificant in our flora and not to be compared, as to any features they impart, with the much more numerous and really characteristic genera which are shared by the eastern United States and eastern temperate Asia. We must look for it in the species, partly in the identical ones and partly in those which closely answer to each other in the two floras.

He accounts for such cases as the occurrence of *Phryma leptostachya* in the United States and Nepal as follows:

We should therefore look in one and the same direction for the explanation of these extraordinary no less than of the more ordinary cases of distribution, and should - - - refer such anomalous distribution to very ancient dispersion.

The plants from Japan to which he referred were collected by Charles Wright, botanist of the North Pacific Exploring Expedition, known as the Ringgold and Rodgers Expedition, of which Dr. Gray gave an account in a paper "On the Botany of Japan, and its Relations to that of North America and of other Parts of the Northern Temperate Zone," presented to this Academy December 14, 1858, and January 11, 1859, and published April 25, 1859, in the sixth volume of the *Memoirs*. This memoir raised his reputation to its highest point among scientific men, and, appealing again to the authority of Sir J. D. Hooker, "in point of originality and far-reaching results was its author's *opus magnum*." In referring to his previous paper in the *American Journal* he states with great candor from the facts there brought out, "(1) that a large percentage of our extra-European types are shared with eastern Asia, and (2) that no small part of them are unknown in western North America." Mr. Bentham was the first to state the natural conclusion that the interchange between the temperate floras even of the western part of the Old World and of the New has mainly taken place via Asia. He cites Bentham's suggestion of a continuity of territory between America and Asia "under a latitude, or at any rate with a climate, more meridional than would be effected by a junction through the chains of the Aleutian and the Kurile Islands." He then proceeds to show why a connection in a more meridional latitude need not be assumed; and fortified by the wide geological knowledge of his friend Professor James Dwight Dana, he gives a masterly account of the relations of the floras of the north temperate regions from the Cretaceous period to the present time, accounting for the present distribution by migrations of species from the arctic regions due principally to the different climatic conditions of the preglacial, glacial, and postglacial eras. The relations of the floras of eastern America and eastern Asia was a favorite topic with him, and he often spoke on the subject in public, his two most important adresses in which he referred to plant distribution being "Sequoia and its History," delivered as retiring president of the American Association for the Advancement of Science in 1872, and a lecture on "Forest Geography and Archæology," read before the Harvard Natural History Society in 1878 and afterwards translated in the *Annales des Sciences*.

The study of plant distribution necessarily involved the question of the origin of species, and this brings us to a consideration of the relations of Gray to Darwin and Darwinism. Gray first met Darwin at Westbank, the residence of Sir W. J. Hooker at Kew in 1851, and their correspondence dates from a letter of Darwin, written April 25, 1855, asking for information about the alpine plants of the United States. How intimate and frequent their correspondence became, and how deeply each was interested in the work of the other is admirably shown in the *Life and Letters of Charles Darwin*. The published letters present a vivid picture of the inner scientific life of these two men, both equally simple, earnest, remarkably free from prejudice, and anxious to do justice to the work of others. Many of the problems upon which Darwin was at work were those in which Gray was most interested, and he was often able to aid Darwin by his observations and still more by his judicious and always acceptable criticisms. While the naturalist at Down was absorbed in the study of climbing plants and cross-fertilization, the greenhouses at Cambridge were also used as nurseries for the growth of climbers and the odd, irregularly flowered plants which ought to be cross-fertilized. The writer recalls the time when Dr. Gray hardly ever passed in or out of the Herbarium without stroking—patting on the back by way of encouraging them it almost seemed—the tendrils of the climbers on the walls and porch; and when, on the announcement that a student had discovered another new case of cross-fertilization in the Garden, he would rush out bareheaded and breathless like a schoolboy to see the thing with his own critical eyes.

Darwin, in a letter dated June 20, 1856, confided to Gray that he had "come to the heterodox conclusion that there are no such things as independently created species,—that species are only strongly defined varieties." In this letter he also says: "I *assume* that species arise like our domestic varieties with *much* extinction." About a year after this (September 5, 1857) Darwin wrote to Gray the now famous letter, in which he propounded the law of the evolution of species by means of natural selection; and it was this letter, read at the Linnaean Society July 1, 1858, on the occasion of the presentation of the joint paper of Darwin and Wallace "On the Tendency of Species to Form Varieties, and on the Perpetuation of Varieties and Species by Natural Means of Selection," which fixed the date of the priority of the great discovery as due to Darwin. What were Gray's own views on the subject of evolution previous to the publication of the *Origin of Species* in November 1859 may perhaps be inferred from some remarks which he made on January 11, 1859, when he presented his paper "On the Botany of Japan" to this Academy. He then stated that "the idea of the descent of all similar or conspecific individuals from a common stock is so natural, and so inevitably suggested by common observation, that it must needs be first tried upon the problem [of distribution], and if the trial be satisfactory its adoption would follow as a matter of course." In brief, he was inclined to accept evolution but wished more proof; and nearly three years earlier, in a letter to Professor Dana written December 13, 1856, he had well expressed his own attitude by saying, "I have as yet no *opinion* whatever, and no very strong *bias*." He saw what was coming, however, and in a later letter to Professor Dana, anticipating the publication of the *Origin of Species,* he says:

You may be sure that before long there must be one more resurrection of *the development theory* in a new form, obviating many of the arguments against it, and presenting a more respectable and more formidable appearance than it ever has before.

Gray was one of the favored three, including Hooker and Lyell, to whom Darwin sent advance sheets of the *Origin of Species* prior to its publication in November 1859; and of his review in the *American Journal of Science* of the following March Darwin wrote, "Your review seems to be admirable,—by far the best I have read." The review certainly presents most accurately, succinctly, and attractively Darwin's own views; but Gray does not even here announce that he is himself a complete convert to the doctrine, as is seen by the following citation:

What would happen if the derivation of species were to be substantiated, either as a true physical theory or as a sufficient hypothesis? The inquiry is a pertinent one just now. For, of those who agree with us in thinking that Darwin has not established his theory of derivation, many will admit with us that he has rendered a theory of derivation much less improbable than before; that such a theory chimes in with the established doctrines of physical science, and is not unlikely to be largely accepted long before it can be proved.

And the similar statement in the *Atlantic Monthly* of October 1860:

Those, if any there be, who regard the derivative hypothesis as satisfactorily proved must have loose notions of what proof is. Those who imagine it can be easily refuted and cast aside must, we think, have imperfect or very prejudiced conceptions of the facts concerned and of the questions at issue.

In 1876 he brought together in a volume entitled *Darwiniana* his principal essays and reviews pertaining to Darwinism, taken from the *American Journal of Science,* the *Nation,* and the *Atlantic Monthly,* and added a chapter on "Evolutionary Teleology"; and in 1880 he published *Natural Science and Religion,* two lectures delivered to the Theological School of Yale College before a critical audience who listened with the deepest interest to what was in some points his most advanced view of natural selection. We need not dwell on a subject about which so much has lately been written by far abler pens than ours. Briefly stated, Gray was probably the best expounder of Darwinian principles—meaning thereby those actually advocated by Darwin himself and excluding the wild deductions attached to the original theory by those who deserve the name of Darwinissimists rather than Darwinists—although he himself regarded natural selection as a less efficient cause than it was assumed to be by Darwin.

His influence as an exponent of Darwinism was due partly to the admirable clearness and candor of his reviews and his interesting way of putting things; for his fertile imagination was constantly discovering apt similes to illustrate otherwise dry arguments. It was also due in part to his known caution and conservatism and his professed Christian faith. If an avowed accepter "of the creed commonly called the Nicene" saw nothing in Darwinism that implied atheism, or was opposed to the idea of design on the part of the Creator, surely one might at least listen to his account of his development theory with safety. To his hearers at New Haven in 1880 he said:

Natural selection by itself is not an hypothesis, nor even a theory. It is a truth—a *catena* of facts and direct inferences from facts. - - - There is no doubt that natural selection operates; the open question is, what do its operations amount to. The *hypothesis* based on this principle is, that the struggle for life and survival of only the fittest among individuals, all disposed to vary and no two exactly alike, will account for the diversification of the species and forms of vegetable and animal life, will even account for the rise, in the course of countless ages, from simpler and lower to higher and more specialized living beings.

He gave it as his opinion that natural selection is, on the whole, a good working hypothesis but does not explain how wholly new parts are initiated, even if the new organs are developed little by little. He repeated over and over again in different reviews his belief that natural selection could not account for variation, and he states the case particularly forcibly in his "Evolutionary Teleology":

Natural selection is not the wind which propels the vessel, but the rudder, which, by friction, now on this side and now on that, shapes the course. The rudder acts while the vessel is in motion, effects nothing when it is at rest. Variation answers to the wind. - - - Its course is controlled by natural selection. This proceeds mainly through outward influences. But we are more and more convinced that variation - - - is not a product of, but a response to, the action of the environment. Variations are evidently not from without, but from within.

But how do variations arise? According to Gray, by virtue of some inherent power imparted in the beginning by Divine agency. That granted, natural selection would in great part account for the present condition and distribution of life, so that one could be a Darwinian and Deist at the same time. Gray further believed that variation is apt to follow in certain more or less regular directions and particularly in beneficial directions. Here he differed very widely from Darwin. The one saw design where the other could not, and it must be confessed that Gray was treading on delicate ground, scientifically if not theologically speaking, when he affirmed the direction of variation in beneficial lines. For what is meant by beneficial? Beneficial to whom? Beneficial for what purpose? In one sense, any variation which tends to enable a living being to survive in the struggle for existence is beneficial; and to say that any being or structure has survived is the same as saying that the variation from which it sprang was beneficial. But Gray apparently uses the word beneficial in the sense of being foreordained to be beneficial.

Perhaps we must look to inheritance itself for an explanation of the difference in the views of Gray and Darwin. The Gray family were devout members of the Presbyterian Church, and throughout his life Dr. Gray adhered faithfully to the orthodox faith of his fathers, his own views being in harmony with those of the liberal branch rather than with those of the conservative branch of that communion. The agnostic position of Darwin may perhaps be inferred from his own description of himself and his father as belonging "nominally to [the] Church of England," an expression which leads one to believe that he was hardly to be counted a member of that or any other denomination. When a young man Gray certainly had no leanings towards evolution. In his review of *Vestiges of Creation,* in the *North American Review* of 1846 he wrote:

Although "geology fully proves" that there have been various creations, that different species were created at different periods, and that some of the humblest and simplest first appeared, while land animals, quadrupeds, quadrumana, and bimana were not introduced until after the earth was fitted for their residence, yet we are still to be convinced that they were not *then* created as perfect as they now are.

But he was convinced later, when he studied the relations of the North American flora to that of Asia, and he accepted without hesitation the view that the present species are not special creations but derived from previously existing species, at a time when the truth of the theory was scarcely recognized by any naturalists and at a date when in the public mind a belief in evolution meant atheism. He had the courage to avow openly his convictions, but on the other hand never allowed his convictions to be governed by wild speculations.

But we who have known Asa Gray so many years would now recall not the great botanist, but rather the kind-hearted, genial man, whose sympathy cheered and whose wisdom guided, whose heart was ever young, whose brain was ever active. His long life, unclouded by great sorrow and almost free from personal enmities, was inspired throughout by a faith which never faltered. Retaining to the last the energy and vivacity of youth, his intellect broadening and ripening, his character growing more and more sweet and serene, he reminds us of one of those trees which bear flowers and fruit at the same time. Industrious to an extent that few could equal, his work done, he enjoyed society with a relish, and his ready wit, his inexhaustible stock of anecdotes, and his quick and keen appreciation of the best in literature and art made him everywhere welcome. His own house was open to all, and even those who came to pay the simple tribute of staring were not often turned away. With a graceful hospitality to which wealth could have lent no greater charm, he entertained the learned of many nations and welcomed with special cordiality his brother botanists, a long array, including not only the experts in the science, but the poor and struggling student as well. He shared with all the treasures of his knowledge, and not infrequently he added something from the modest competence which his industry had amassed. The words of good cheer from his lips were re-echoed in after years, and the life so honorable was not unhonored. If the numerous honorary degrees from learned societies at home and abroad testify to the esteem in which he was held as a scientific botanist, the warm congratulations of friends from all parts of the country when the memorial vase was presented on his seventy-fifth birthday show no less clearly how much he was beloved as a man. And when, during dreary weeks, his anxious friends hoped against hope, watching to catch the sound of the loved voice which would speak but could not, all felt that the message which he sought to utter must have been a benediction. But it was not needed. His life was a benediction, and as his body was borne to its last resting place the freshly fallen snow was not more pure than his character nor the sparkling winter air more bright and clear than his intellect.

Robert Wilhelm Bunsen *

1811–1899

HENRY E. ROSCOE †

THE DEATH of Bunsen at Heidelberg on August 16, 1899, severs the last link connecting the chemists of our time with the great men of the earlier part of the century—with Berzelius, of whom Bunsen writes as "my truest friend and counsellor who, during the whole of my scientific life, has stood to me in intimate personal relationship"; with Gay-Lussac, in whose laboratory in Paris he worked in the year 1833; with Dumas, whose acquaintance and friendship he enjoyed when they both were young; with Liebig and Wöhler, who were more nearly his contemporaries, and for whom throughout their lives he entertained the warmest feelings of affectionate regard; with the Berlin chemists, Mitscherlich and the two Roses, as well as with the older physicists, Dove, Wilhelm Weber, and Magnus, all of whom he counted among his personal friends.

Moreover, living to the ripe age of 88, he was destined to witness the deaths as well as the scientific births of many distinguished colleagues and pupils—of Kirchhoff, Helmholtz, Kopp, and Hofmann; of Strecker, Kolbe, Kekulé, Pebal, Lothar Meyer; and, lastly, of his successor in the chair of chemistry at Heidelberg, Victor Meyer. So that in his later years Bunsen stood alone in his glory, like some strong oak in the forest which still holds firm root unmoved by the tempests which have smitten down both old and young around it.

Nearly twenty years ago I gave, in the columns of *Nature,* a

* "Bunsen Memorial Lecture," *A.R.,* 1899, pp. 605–644 (delivered March 29, 1900), reprinted from *Transactions of the Chemical Society,* London, vol. 77, pp. 513–554. A few passages are omitted because of length.
† Noted British chemist (1833–1915), Professor of Chemistry, Victoria University, later Vice-chancellor of the University of London.

sketch of the scientific work of him whose memory we are here assembled to honor, as being not merely one of the most distinguished of the great chemists of the century, but one of the truest and noblest of men. In introducing the subject to the readers of that journal I used the following words, which I make no apology for quoting, as I cannot find more appropriate expressions wherewith to commence the more detailed account of the life and labors of Bunsen in the memorial lecture, with the preparation of which the council of the chemical society has honored me.

The value of a life devoted to original scientific work is measured by the new paths and new fields which such work opens out. In this respect the labors of Robert Wilhelm Bunsen stand second to those of no chemist of his time. Outwardly, the existence of such a man, attached, as Bunsen had been from the first, exclusively to his science, seems to glide silently on without causes for excitement or stirring incident. His inward life however is, on the contrary, full of interests and of incidents of even a striking and exciting kind. The discovery of a fact which overthrows or remodels our ideas on a whole branch of science; the experimental proof of a general law hitherto unrecognized; the employment of a new and happy combination of known facts to effect an invention of general applicability and utility; these are the peaceful victories of the man of science which may well be thought to outweigh the high-sounding achievements of the more public professions.

Owing to the fact, not common in the annals of scientific intercourse, that I have enjoyed the privilege for nearly half a century of counting Bunsen among my most intimate friends, that we have stood in the position first of pupil and master, and afterwards of colleagues and co-workers, I am in the fortunate position of being able to present to you on this occasion something more than a description of the scientific work which he accomplished, the record of which anyone who cares to do so can gather up from his published memoirs. From my personal recollections I propose to lay before you a picture, doubtless imperfectly, but so far as my abilities go, truly drawn, of the man working in his laboratory, lecturing to his students, and enjoying simple but refined social intercourse with his friends. I shall hope to give you an idea what manner of man he was, what was his moral, as well as his scientific character, to point out why he was not only venerated as a great leader and teacher, but why he inspired all with whom he came in contact with feelings of deep attachment and regard.

But first let me shortly mention some few particulars of his life, and give you a summary of his most important investigations. Bunsen was born at Göttingen on March 31, 1811. His father,

Christian Bunsen, occupied the position of chief university librarian and professor of modern philology. After passing through the usual course in the gymnasium at Holzminden in Hanover, Bunsen entered the university in 1828, studied chemistry under Stromeyer (the discoverer of cadmium), obtained his degree in 1830, presenting for this purpose a thesis having the title *Enumeratio et descriptio hygrometrorum.* He then visited Paris; arriving there at the latter end of September 1832, he remained until the spring of 1833, meeting Reiset, Regnault, Pelouze, and Despretz. The latter proposed to Bunsen to work in common at some problem in physical chemistry. Subsequently having visited Berlin and Vienna, continuing his studies and making acquaintances with the scientific men of those cities, Bunsen returned to Göttingen where, in 1834, he was admitted by the university as *privatdozent* in chemistry. In this position he lectured for three semesters, and after Stromeyer's death in 1835 Bunsen temporarily took up his work and lectured six days a week on theoretical and practical chemistry. In January 1836 he was appointed teacher of chemistry in the Polytechnic School of Cassel as Wöhler's successor. In October 1839 he became professor *extraordinarius* of chemistry in the University of Marburg and in 1842 was advanced to the position of professor *ordinarius.* Remaining here until 1851, he went for a short period to Breslau, and in 1852 he accepted the chair at Heidelberg vacated by Gmelin, a post which he occupied until his retirement in 1889. In these several positions Bunsen labored incessantly and devotedly for fifty-six years in the furtherance of chemical science, with the result that his name will be handed down to posterity as one whose work has earned for him the very first rank among chemists of the nineteenth century.

On the present occasion it is not possible to do more than to indicate the nature and extent of Bunsen's work, so numerous are his published investigations and so wide and far-reaching their scope. To bring before you the general effect of the work, and to give you by some examples the special characteristics of that work is all that can be now attempted. And for these objects I propose to treat the matter rather by classifying his work under separate heads of subjects than by taking it in the chronological order of publication.

But before commencing a review of some of his most important researches it may be well briefly to refer to the early work by which he won his scientific spurs. The first paper was one of general interest, as recording his discovery that freshly precipitated hydrated ferric oxide acts as a powerful antidote to arsenical poisoning by rendering the arsenic insoluble both in water and in the secretions of the body. This result of the withdrawal of the whole of the arsenic from solution by this means forms a striking lecture experiment (*Journ. de Pharm.,* 1834, **20,** 567; 1838, **24,** 93).

His next communication shows the interest which in those early days Bunsen took in mineralogy and chemical geology, subjects in which he in after life became a distinguished exponent. It consisted of an exact analysis and a detailed description of a specimen of allophane from a lignite bed near Bonn (*Pogg. Ann.,* 1834, **31,** 53).

A more specially chemical subject next engaged his attention, namely, an investigation of a new series of double cyanides, in which he not only determined their composition with exactitude, but showed the relationship existing between these and other well-known members of the same class of bodies. He measured their crystalline form and proved that ammonium ferrocyanide is isomorphous with the corresponding potassium salt (*Pogg. Ann.,* 1835, **34,** 131; 1835, **36,** 404; 1836, **38,** 208).

All this work was, however, merely of the nature of what he was in the habit of calling *ein kleiner Vorversuch* when he was indicating the manner in which a pupil should commence an investigation. The first research in which Bunsen showed his power was the classical one on the cacodyl compounds—begun in Cassel in 1837 and continued in Marburg for no less than six years. The publication of this work placed Bunsen at once in the front rank of experimentalists.

.   .   .

Among the many remarkable new facts which these researches contain is that of the nonpoisonous properties of cacodylic acid, although it contains no less than 54 per cent soluble arsenic:

A solution of 8 grains of cacodylic acid injected into the *vena jugularis* of a rabbit produced no deleterious result on the health of the animal.

It is also of interest to read Bunsen's description of the properties of cacodyl cyanide, by the explosion of which he lost the sight of his right eye, was nearly poisoned, lying for days between life and death, but the investigation of which he nevertheless brought to a satisfactory conclusion.

It is obtained when cacodyl oxide is distilled with mercury cyanide, when it sublimes to a camphor-like solid; it melts at 32.5° to an oily liquid. The smell of this body produces instantaneous tingling of the

hands and feet, and even giddiness and insensibility. The cacodyl compounds appear to exert a specific action on the nervous system. It is remarkable that when one is exposed to the smell of these compounds the
tongue becomes covered with a black coating, even when no further
evil effects are noticeable.

Respecting the constitution of the radical of the cacodyl compounds, various theories have from time to time been put forward.
Bunsen himself did not give any opinion on the point, and it was
Kolbe who first suggested the view that it was arsine dimethyl,
$As(CH_3)_2$, while the experiments of Frankland, and subsequently
those of Cahours and Riche, rendered this probable. It is, however, to the researches of Adolf von Baeyer (*Annalen*, 1853,
107, 257) on the arsenmonomethyl compounds that we owe the
full explanation of the relation which these various bodies bear
to one another.

The cacodyl research claims our interest not only because, as we
have seen, it furnishes us with the first example of an isolable
radical, but also because it assisted Frankland and Kekulé in more
exactly illustrating the term "chemical valency." For it is not too
much to say that the subsequent researches of Frankland on the
organo-metallic bodies and on the so-called alcohol radicals, as
well as those of the French chemists, and, I may add, those of
Baeyer, received their first impulse from the cacodyl investigation.
This indebtedness was acknowledged by our late lamented Fellow
in the graceful and modest words which appear in the dedication
of the volume of his collected researches:

To my friend and teacher, Robert Wilhelm Bunsen, whose researches
on cacodyl, on the gases of the iron furnaces, and on the volcanic phenomena of Iceland I have always regarded as models of investigation in
pure, applied, and physical chemistry, I dedicate these pages, both as a
testimony of my regard and in gratitude for the teaching whereby he
imbued me with the necessity for thoroughness and accuracy in all scientific work. Would that they were more worthy of such a high
standard.

Thus it is seen that, although this remarkable research is the
only one of any importance which was carried out by Bunsen in
the domain of organic chemistry, it was destined to exert such an
influence on the later developments of that branch of the science
that he may with truth be regarded as one of the pioneers of modern organic chemistry.

I now pass to an investigation of a different type, but one not
less important or interesting than the last.

Up to the year 1838, when Bunsen began his investigation of the composition of the gases of the iron furnaces, the mode of measuring gaseous volumes and the methods adopted for the separation of the several gases were faulty and inaccurate in the extreme. But during the period elapsing between the above year and 1845 Bunsen had not only elaborated and perfected his well-known geometric methods, but had applied these methods with signal success to the investigation of the chemical changes which occur in the processes of a most important industry, that of the production of cast iron in the blast furnace.

The first detailed description of Bunsen's gasometric methods was published in pamphlet form by Kolbe, who was at the time one of Bunsen's assistants. To the English public these methods became known by a communication made to the meeting of the British Association at Cambridge in 1845 by R. W. Bunsen and Lyon Playfair, entitled "On the Gases Evolved from Iron Furnaces with Reference to the Smelting of Iron." Before entering upon the technical side of the question the authors give experimental proofs concerning the accuracy and reliability of the methods employed for the measurement and separation of the blast-furnace gases. One of these consisted in the analyses of a large number of samples of air. These were collected and analyzed in Marburg and gave analytical results upon which Bunsen reports as follows:

The close agreement of these experiments with one another, and with the result obtained by the careful experimental determination of the composition of air by Dumas, proves that the eudiometric examination of gases admits of a degree of exactness which is certainly not surpassed by the most minute chemical methods, and they further show that the presence of nitrogen does not exert any disturbing influence on the estimation of explosive mixtures of gases.

The report, printed in full in the British Association volume for 1845, next proceeds to discuss the experiments made by Bunsen on the composition of the gases evolved in the process of iron smelting in furnaces fed with charcoal and using cold blast at Vickerhagen in Germany. From these it appeared that in such furnaces nearly half the heat of the fuel consumed was evolved in the escaping gases.

The importance of these investigations, as being the first attempt to introduce accurate scientific inquiry into so widespread an industry as that of iron smelting, was at once appreciated by Lyon Playfair, who had made Bunsen's acquaintance at Marburg. In consequence, at Playfair's suggestion Bunsen consented to visit England and undertook to carry out a similar set of experiments for the English furnaces fed with coke and coal and worked both by hot and by cold blast, to those which he had previously made in Germany. Thus was initiated a research which may be truly said to be a model of the application of the methods of scientific investigation to the elucidation of industrial problems. For not only did it clearly reveal the nature of the chemical changes which take place throughout the furnace, but pointed out the direction in which economies to an undreamt-of extent might be effected in the processes as then carried on. Thus it proved that while about half the fuel was lost as escaping gas in the German furnaces, no less than 81.5 per cent was lost in English ones, and, what was important from the industrial point of view, it pointed out that the whole of the heat thus allowed to escape might without difficulty be utilized for the various purposes of the works. These suggestions were only slowly adopted by the ironmasters; six years elapsed before any steps in the direction indicated were taken, but gradually the importance of the proposal was appreciated, and now and for many years past the whole of the hitherto wasted heat has been utilized and economies effected of which the value may be reckoned by millions rather than by thousands of pounds.

Not only is it the lost heat which has been recovered, but also valuable by-products, the existence of which had been up to that time entirely ignored. The report points out the loss of combined nitrogen, both as ammonia and cyanogen, which the process as then carried out evolves, the upper part of the furnace being, in the words of the report, "a region of distillation and not of combustion." The amount of loss of these valuable materials was ascertained by accurate analysis and a method for recovering them suggested, "without increasing the cost of manufacture or in the slightest degree affecting the process of smelting." Apropos of the determination of the escaping cyanogen compounds, the occurrence of a singular accident to Bunsen, as related by Playfair, is found in the admirable life lately written by Wemyss Reid: "Bunsen was engaged below," at the blast furnaces at Alfreton, in Derbyshire, "and I above, passing the gases through water to collect any soluble products, when I was alarmed by being told that my friend had become suddenly ill. I ran down and saw white fumes coming out of a lateral tube, and Bunsen apparently recovering from a fainting condition. I applied my nose to the orifice and smelt the vapor of cyanide of potassium, which gave an entirely new light to the processes of the furnace."

In 1857 Bunsen collected in a volume—the only book he ever

published—the whole of his gasometric researches, and of this a second and greatly enlarged edition appeared in 1877 (*Gasometric Methods,* by R. W. Bunsen, translated by H. E. Roscoe, 1857). No better or more complete method of learning what Bunsen's work is like can be taken than that of reading this volume. For originality of conception, for success in overcoming difficulties, for ingenuity in the construction of apparatus, and for accurate work, I believe the book as a record of experiment to be unequaled.

The first part contains a description of his various processes of collecting, preserving, and measuring gases, different methods being employed for the first of these according to the source from which the gases are obtained, whether, as has been described, from blast furnaces or from fumaroles, from volcanic vents or when freely rising from mineral springs, or whether the gases are contained in solution in river or spring water. In the second part we find a full description of the methods of eudiometric analysis, giving details of manipulation, with a discussion in each case of the probable sources of error and of the means of their limitation. As a model of accurate work (his oxygen determinations in air showed differences of 0.1 per cent on the oxygen), Bunsen's eudiometric methods will always remain as the standard. More expeditious and simpler methods have been introduced of late years, but none of these equals the original processes in exactitude.

The third portion of the volume consists of a description of two new methods for determining the specific gravity of gases. The first of these, which also applies to the case of vapors, consists in weighing a tarred vessel, filled first with the gas or vapor under examination and then with air, all variations due to change of temperature and pressure being eliminated by a simple and ingenious compensating arrangement. Perhaps the most interesting portion of this section is a description of a new thermostat, by means of which perfectly constant temperatures up to a high point can be obtained. This served Bunsen for ascertaining the specific gravity of aqueous vapor at different temperatures, and closely accordant numbers were obtained, although the weight of vapor amounted to only 80 milligrams. The second method, applicable only to gases, depends on the determination of the rates of diffusion of the gases into air. Here, too, the volume of gas operated upon need not exceed 50 to 60 cubic centimeters, and yet the results obtained are extremely accurate. On this point Bunsen remarks that for technical purposes—as, for example, for the determination of the density of coal gas—the above simple method will probably be found preferable to all other processes.

The fourth part contains a series of investigations on the absorptiometric phenomena of gases in water and alcohol, the experiments having been chiefly undertaken with a view of determining the limits to which the well-known laws of pressure hold good. First he describes his absorptiometer, a new instrument by means of which it is possible to obtain accurate numbers with relatively small volumes of the gases. The absorption coefficients of no fewer than twenty-seven different gases in water and alcohol were determined by methods varying according to the nature of the case, partly carried out by himself and partly by many of his pupils, the result being that certain gases, generally those least soluble in water, are found to be in accord with Dalton's law of pressures and Dalton and Henry's law of partial pressures, whereas the more soluble gases are not always in accord with them. In the former class it is possible, from an experimental determination of the coefficient of absorption, to calculate the composition of the original gas, the composition derived from an absorptiometric analysis being found to agree exactly with that obtained by direct eudiometric measurements. It is also possible to ascertain whether a given gas consists of a single substance or is a mixture of several. Thus, while eudiometric analysis cannot decide whether the gas evolved by the action of caustic alkali on an acetate is methane or a mixture of equal volumes of ethane and hydrogen, this can readily be accomplished by absorptiometric methods.

In the fifth part of the volume he discusses the phenomena of gaseous diffusion and, although admitting the truth of Graham's law for cases of pure diffusion, he obtained results, when a stucco diaphragm of considerable thickness was used, which are not in accord with this law, the conclusion being that the pores of gypsum act upon gases, not as a series of fine openings, but rather as a series of capillary tubes, the phenomena being thus modified by those of transpiration. At the end of this chapter he describes the details of a method for ascertaining, by diffusion, whether a given gas is a mixture or not.

The sixth and last section relates to the combustion phenomena of gases. The temperature of combustion—that is, the temperature of the interior of a mixture of burning gases—can be calculated from the heat of combustion of the gaseous mixture and the specific heats of the products of combustion under the assumption that the combustion at this high temperature is perfect. This condition, however, is not fulfilled, and Bunsen therefore endeavored to determine this temperature by another means, namely, by measuring the pressure produced at the moment of explosion of an inclosed gaseous mixture.

For this purpose he constructed a wonderfully simple apparatus, by means of which he ascertained that the maximum temperature of combustion of carbon monoxide and of hydrogen with the theoretical volume of oxygen was, respectively, 3,033° and 2,844°. He likewise attempted to determine the rate at which the explosion is propagated, and came to the conclusion that for hydrogen and oxygen this was 34 meters per second. Subsequent experiments, especially those of Dixon (*Phil. Trans.*, 1893, **184**, 97), have shown that this rate referred only to the initial period of the combination before the explosion wave had attained its maximum velocity, this latter amounting in the case of hydrogen and oxygen to the high number of nearly 3,000 meters per second, the rate in other gases being of the same order in magnitude, and the ignition appearing to be propagated in somewhat the same manner as a sound wave.

One of the best known of Bunsen's discoveries is that of the carbon-zinc battery, which bears his name. The construction of this battery in 1841 (*Annalen,* 1841 **38**, 311) marks an era in the economic production of electricity. By the replacement of carbon for the platinum plates of Grove, Bunsen not only greatly reduced the initial cost but increased the length of time during which the current can be maintained at its maximum. The success of the invention depends upon a method he devised for overcoming the disintegrating action on the carbon of concentrated nitric acid. This he effected by strongly igniting the cylinders, thus foreshadowing the process adopted on a large scale for graphitizing the carbon poles now so generally used for electro-industrial purposes by ignition in the electric furnace. It is interesting to remember that it was Bunsen who so early as 1843 pointed out that the electric current could be made use of as a means of illumination. He describes how, by using a battery of 44 of his elements, a light equal in illuminating power to 1,171.3 candles can be obtained for an expenditure of 1 pound of zinc per hour, and giving a light "the brilliancy of which the eye can scarcely support." He adds that by inclosing the carbon poles in a globe of glass the wear of carbons by oxidation might be minimized. In short, he describes the first step toward the modern system of arc lighting rendered generally applicable on the large scale by the discovery of the dynamo. In his first communication respecting this battery Bunsen gave a careful estimate of the work it can accomplish. He showed that three cells will, in thirty minutes, decompose 0.6775 gram of water, yielding 1,137 cubic centimeters of mixed gas, measured at 0° and 760 millimeters. The corresponding loss of zinc in each cell was then determined, the result showing that the same weight was dissolved in each and that the weights thus found correspond closely with the zinc equivalent for the above amount of water decomposed. A few years later, in 1848, he determined the electrochemical equivalents for zinc and water. For the first of these he obtained the value 0.033 and for the latter 0.00927; in other words, in order to decompose 1 milligram of water per second a current of the absolute intensity of 106.33 is necessary. These experiments confirm Faraday's law, showing that the quantity of water decomposed is proportional to the quantity of circulating electricity, and that the nature of the poles, as well as the conducting power of the liquids decomposed, exerts no influence on the result.

We owe to Wilhelm Weber the first determination of the scientific units for electrical measurements, and in 1840 he obtained the number 0.009376 for the electrochemical equivalent of water with his unit current. The difficulties which surround the subject are: (1) the measurement of the current, and (2) the absorption of the decomposed gases by water and electrodes, and (3) the production of ozone. Bunsen improved the voltameter by evolving the mixed gases from hot acidified water, by which the second and third of these difficulties were overcome. At present voltameters depositing copper or silver are employed, and the ampere, which is now our practical unit, is one-tenth of that used by Weber and Bunsen, so that the electrochemical equivalent of water is 0.0009315 gram, meaning that 1 ampere decomposes that amount of water in one second.

This, however, was only the beginning of the work which the Bunsen battery was destined to perform. It was not until 1852 when in Breslau that Bunsen turned his attention to using the battery for electrolytic preparation of metals, some of which had not been obtained in a coherent condition, and others had only been prepared in such minute quantities that their physical and chemical properties could not be properly studied. The first of these metals he attacked was magnesium (*Annalen,* 1852, **32,** 137), the reduction of which had vainly been attempted by Davy and only with very partial success by Bussy in 1830. The difficulty which had hitherto stood in the way was the fact that the globules of molten magnesium are lighter than the fused magnesium chloride used as the electrolyte, and that on their formation they rise to the surface and burn. To avoid this Bunsen adopted the ingenious plan of cutting the carbon pole, on which the metal forms, into pockets, inside which the magnesium is deposited and from which the molten globule cannot escape. By means of the tangent galvanometer Bunsen measured in absolute units the electricity employed, finding that the quantity of magnesium reduced is 2.45 grams, while the theoretical yield of metal is 4.096 grams. Having obtained the metal in some quantity, he determined its physical and chemical properties, showed how it could be pressed out into wire, and measured the luminous intensity of the burning metal. This he found to be 500 times that of a candle flame.

Some seven years later he and I measured the actinic value of the light emitted by burning magnesium and showed that it could be used for photographic purposes. We found that a burning surface of magnesium wire which, seen from a point of the sea's level, has an apparent magnitude equal to that of the sun, effects at that point the same chemical action as the sun would do if shining from a cloudless sky at the height of $9° 53'$ above the horizon. On comparing the visible brightness of these two sources of light, it was found that the brightness of the sun's disk, as measured by the eye, is 524.7 times as great as that of burning magnesium when the sun's zenith distance is $67° 22'$, while at the same zenith distance the sun's chemical brightness is only 36.6 times as great. Hence the value of this light as a source of chemically active rays for photographic purposes is at once apparent. The application of magnesium as a source of light has become of technical importance. A burning magnesium wire of the thickness of 0.297 millimeter evolves as much light as 74 stearin candles of which five go to the pound. If this light lasted one minute, 0.987 meter of wire, weighing 0.120 gram, would be burnt. In order to produce a light equal to 74 candles burning for ten hours, whereby 20 pounds of stearin is consumed, 72.2 grams or 2½ ounces of magnesium would be needed. The light from burning magnesium has been employed for signaling and for military and naval purposes, and it is especially used in pyrotechny.

Perhaps the most interesting of these applications of the battery is that of the preparation of the metals of the alkaline earths (*Journ. de Pharm.*, 1854, **26**, 311; 1855, **28**, 155), the isolation of which had hitherto eluded pursuit, and this work he handed over to our countryman, Augustus Matthiessen, who, under Bunsen's guidance, brought the investigation to a successful issue. The conditions most favorable to a reduction were carefully worked out. It had already been pointed out by Bunsen that the density of the current (that is, the current per unit cross section) is the chief condition under which the electricity is able to overcome chemical affinities. This condition was fulfilled by using for the negative pole a very short length of thin harpsichord wire, upon which the reduced metal hangs in the form of molten beads, from which they can be quickly detached and plunged into petroleum. Another necessary condition is that the melting point of the electrolyte should be as low as possible, and this was attained by using a mixture of the chlorides of calcium and strontium and by the addition of some sal ammoniac to the mass as the electrolysis proceeds. This subject was again further elaborated in 1875, in the Heidelberg laboratory, by Hillebrand and Norton (*Pogg. Ann.*, 1875, **156**, 466), who prepared considerable quantities of cerium, lanthanum, and didymium in the coherent metallic state.

But the reduction of the metals was not the only important work which Bunsen got out of his battery, for quite early in its history it made its mark in organic chemistry. If by the electrolysis of caustic soda we obtain oxygen and a metallic radical, might not the electrolysis of an organic substance yield the corresponding organic radical? Doubtless a question of this kind presented itself to Bunsen's mind when he set his assistant, Kolbe, to work on the electrolysis of acetic and valeric acids (*Annalen*, 1847, **64**, 339; 1849, **69**, 257). The results of investigations thus commenced and carried out, both by Kolbe alone and in collaboration with Frankland, and the still more prolific researches of the latter chemist, are matters of scientific history; it is, however, not so generally recognized that they owe their origin to the Bunsen battery.

In addition to the zinc-carbon-nitric acid battery, Bunsen also constructed a powerful thermopile of copper pyrites and copper (*Pogg. Ann.*, 1864, **123**, 505); and in later years a constant zinc-carbon-chromic acid battery (*Pogg. Ann.*, 1875, **155**, 232) so arranged that the zinc and carbon plates could be lowered readily into the exciting liquid, and thus the battery was easily put in and out of action. This he used for obtaining the spark spectra of the rare earth metals.

For the purpose of measuring the intensity of the light given off by carbon poles connected with his battery, Bunsen in 1844 constructed his well-known photometer (*Berzelius Jahresber.*, 1845, **24**, 13). The essential feature of this apparatus is the "disk" of paper having a greased spot in the center, or having a greased circumference with an untouched spot in the middle.

With regard to this, Elster relates the story that when he showed this arrangement to the late Emperor Frederick, then Crown Prince, the Prince remarked: "For the first time in my life, I now know the value of a spot of grease." In the original Bunsen photometer a small flame burning in a closed box fixed on a pivot in the center of a long board illuminated the back of the disk, the relative luminous intensity of the two sources of light under examination being ascertained by moving them alternately backward and forward on each side of the disk until in each case the spot disappeared. This form of the photometer was afterwards modified by other observers—not, according to Bunsen, to its advantage—by omitting the small flame and box and simply moving the disk backward and forward between the two fixed sources of light. Recently Preece has proposed to reintroduce the principle of the original Bunsen arrangement of ascertaining the relative luminosity, by always exposing the same side of the disk and therefore eliminating the error arising from its translucency. In one form or other the Bunsen photometer has, however, for many years been in general use, but recently it has been partially replaced by the shadow photometer.

In this connection mention must be made of two important researches of a physical rather than of a purely chemical nature, and characteristic of the manipulative as well as of the intellectual power of the author. They refer to the ice and the vapor calorimeters.

As by means of his battery it was possible for Bunsen to prepare small quantities of the rare metals, so by help of his ice calorimeter (*Pogg. Ann.,* 1870, **141,** 1) he was able to ascertain one of their most important physical properties. It was constructed in order to be able to determine exactly the specific heats of substances which could only be obtained in small quantities, and to which the usual calorimetric methods were therefore inapplicable. Thus it became of the greatest theoretical importance to ascertain the specific heat of indium, of cerium, lanthanum, didymium, and germanium, and other metals which are only obtainable in small quantities. The principles of construction and mode of action of the ice calorimeter are so well known that a description of the instrument and its use is here superfluous. They were published in 1870, and by its means the atomic weight of indium and the formulæ of its compounds were rectified, while the doubts arising as to the formulæ of the compounds of other metals were eliminated. Thus Bunsen largely contributed to the confirmation and to the acceptance of the system of atomic weights now in use, and thereby to the rational classification of the elements depending on that system.

In 1887, when 76 years of age, Bunsen published the description of a new vapor calorimeter (*Ann. Phys. Chem.*, 1887, **31**, 1) upon which he had for some time been engaged. It depends on the same principle as the one previously constructed by Joly (*Proc. Roy. Soc.*, 1886, **41**, 352). The body whose specific heat has to be determined is hung by a fine platinum wire to the beam of a balance, then brought into saturated aqueous vapor at 100°, and the amount of water deposited on the body while it is being heated is weighed in the vapor, this amount being directly proportional to the specific heat. This method gives very accurate results and differs in some essential respects from that proposed by Joly. In this way Bunsen determined the specific heat of platinum at different temperatures, that of glass, and of water inclosed in glass. This latter he found to be 0.9992. (Joly obtained as a mean result 1.0062.) The originality of this idea, arrived at quite independently from Joly, and the degree of accuracy with which the whole research is worked out, must indeed be considered as a wonderful achievement of a man close upon 80 years of age.

In addition to the work which Bunsen did alone, I am bound to refer to the long and difficult series of researches on the measurement of the chemical action of light, in all of which I was associated with him (*Pogg. Ann.*, 1855, **96**, 373; *Phil. Trans.*, 1857, **147**, 355, 381, 601; 1859, **149**, 879; 1863, **153**, 139). For this reason I feel difficulty in criticizing it. This difficulty is, however, somewhat removed if for this lecture I simply quote the opinion of Richard Meyer as found in his *Nachruf* of Bunsen, with an extract from Ostwald's *Classiker,* with which he closes the notice:

The year 1855 was rendered especially memorable, as in that year the first communication appeared of the photochemical investigations which Bunsen carried out together with H. E. Roscoe. These researches are considered by Ostwald simply as the classical example for all further researches in physical chemistry.

The investigation is founded on the discovery by Gay-Lussac and Thénard of the action of light on a mixture of equal volumes of chlorine and hydrogen, in which an intense illumination produces an explosive combination, while with a less intense one the combination proceeds more slowly. So early as 1843 Draper had made use of this property for the construction of an actinometer, to which he gave the name of tithonometer. This, however, first became a reliable instrument in the hands of Bunsen and Roscoe. Equipped with this instrument, they have determined the most important laws of the chemical action of light after overcoming extraordinary experimental difficulties. Subsequently they replaced this apparatus, in consequence of the difficulties attending its manipulation, by the much more convenient chloride of silver actinometer.

The first point determined was that the chemically active rays are reflected and absorbed according to the same laws as the visible rays, and that their intensity diminishes as the square of the distance. The question as to whether energy is expended in the act of photochemical combination for which an equivalent amount of light disappears, or whether the action, like that of the liberation of a spring, is brought about by the chemical rays without any appreciable loss of light, is decided in favor of the first view. The phenomenon is termed by the authors photochemical extinction.

A second very remarkable phenomenon, first pointed out by the authors, is that of chemical induction. This refers to the fact that the action of light on the sensitive mixture of chlorine and hydrogen does not begin in its full intensity, but that it slowly increases, until after the lapse of a certain time it attains its regular and maximum rate. A satisfactory explanation, much less a theory, of induction is as yet wanting. Lastly, it was proved that photochemical action depends solely upon the quantity of the incident light, and is altogether independent of the time during which the insolation takes place.

The great and important influence which photochemical action exerts in organic nature, especially in plant assimilation, renders the application of photochemical measurements to meteorological and climatic phenomena of special interest. But the difficulties which surrounded such an application were enormous. In the first place, it was necessary to find a unit of absolute measurement for the chemically active rays. A flame of carbonic oxide which emits chemically active rays of great intensity, burning in air under carefully specified conditions, satisfied the requirement. It was found that whilst the variation of the chemical action of the light reflected from a clouded sky was subject to no recognizable law, that obtaining when the sky was cloudless and when direct sunlight was employed at once exhibited distinct relations. The curves of daily intensity thus obtained before and after noon were seen to be symmetrical throughout the day. In direct sunshine these curves, of course, rise much higher than is the case in diffuse daylight; moreover, the considerable variation due to change of latitude was precisely calculated.

The dependence of the chemical action on the wave length of the incident light was carefully studied, the result being that the most intense action was exerted by the rays between the lines G and H of Fraunhofer; the curve falls sharply toward the red end of the spectrum, whilst it extends in the more refrangible portion far into the ultraviolet. Strictly speaking, this only applies to the mixture of chlorine and hydrogen; still experiment has shown that the same thing is to some degree true of many other sensitive substances, although the distribution of the chemical activity in the spectrum is a different one.

This short account of the photochemical researches is far from doing them justice. In no other research in this domain of science do we find exhibited such an amount of chemical, physical, and mathematical dexterity, of ability in devising experiments, of patience and perseverance in carrying them out, of attention given to the minutest detail, or of breadth of view as applied to the grander meteorological and cosmical phenomena of nature.—OSTWALD.

.   .   .

Of all Bunsen's researches the one which will undoubtedly stand out pre-eminent as time rolls on is that on spectrum analysis.

The most important discovery made by Bunsen during the short duration of his residence in Breslau was the discovery of Kirchhoff,* who was then professor of physics in that university, and whose great ability the elder man at once recognized. No sooner had Joly removed to Munich in 1854 than Bunsen took care that Kirchhoff should be his successor in the Heidelberg chair of physics. And thus came about that great twin research which has made the names of these men known through the wide world. To dilate upon the importance of the discovery is unnecessary; to follow out the growth of this branch of science in its height and depth and breadth is here impossible. All that can be now done is to indicate briefly the origin of the discovery and to refer to a few points in Bunsen's work which are of special interest to chemists. To begin with, let me give you in Bunsen's own words the account of Kirchhoff's great discovery—namely, the full explanation of Fraunhofer's lines in the solar spectrum, pointing the way to a knowledge of the chemical composition of the sun and fixed stars—and then of his own application of the principles of spectrum analysis to the examination of terrestrial mater. In a letter to myself dated November 15, 1859, he writes:

At the moment I am engaged in a research with Kirchhoff which gives us sleepless nights. Kirchhoff has made a most beautiful and most unexpected discovery: he has found out the cause of the dark lines in the solar spectrum, and has been able both to strengthen these lines artificially in the solar spectrum and to cause their appearance in a continuous spectrum of a flame, their positions being identical with those of the Fraunhofer lines. Thus the way is pointed out by which the ma-

* See Robert von Helmholtz, "Memoir of Gustav Robert Kirchhoff," *A.R.*, 1889, pp. 527–540.

terial composition of the sun and fixed stars can be ascertained with the same degree of certainty as we can ascertain by means of our reagents the presence of SO_3 and Cl. By this method, too, the composition of terrestrial matter can be ascertained and the component parts distinguished with as great ease and delicacy as is the case with the matter contained in the sun. Thus I have been able to detect lithium in 20 grams of sea water. For the detection of many substances this method is to be preferred to any of our previously known processes. Thus, if you have a mixture of Li, Ka, Na, Ba, Sr, Ca, all you need to do is to bring a milligram of the mixture in our apparatus in order to be able to ascertain the presence of all the above substances by mere observation. Some of these reactions are wonderfully delicate. Thus it is possible to detect five one-thousandths of a milligram of lithium with the greatest ease and certainty, and I have discovered the presence of this metal in almost every sample of potashes.

The following letter contains the first announcement of his discovery of cæsium. It was not until one month later (May 10, 1860), that the fact of the discovery was communicated to the Berlin Academy of Sciences:

HEIDELBERG, *April 10, 1860.*

MY DEAR FRIEND: Weltzien went to Paris a week ago and pressed me to accompany him, but unfortunately I was unable to free myself from work which I had postponed until the vacation, and so I have been obliged to forego the pleasure of seeing you in Paris and to tell you how much I have been pleased with your investigation. Do not be annoyed with me, dear Roscoe, that I have done nothing with our light investigation. I have left everything untouched, because I have obtained full certainty, by means of spectrum analysis, that besides Ka, Na and Li, a fourth alkali metal must exist, and all my time has been occupied in endeavoring to isolate some compounds of the new substance. Where the presence of this body is indicated it occurs in such minute quantity that I almost give up hope of isolating it unless, indeed, I am fortunate enough to find a material which contains it in larger amount.

On November 6, 1860, Bunsen describes to me his further work on the new metal as follows:

I have been very fortunate with my new metal. I have got 50 grams of the nearly chemically pure chloro-platinic compound. It is true that this 50 grams has been obtained from no less than 40 tons of the mineral water, from which 2.5 pounds of lithium carbonate have been prepared by a simple process as a by-product. I am calling the new metal "cæsium," from *cæsius*, blue, on account of the splendid blue line in its spectrum. Next Sunday I hope to find time to make the first determination of the atomic weight.

The rare combination of mental and manual dexterity characteristic of Bunsen is nowhere more strikingly shown than in the investigation of the cæsium compounds. From these 17 grams of cæsium chloride, obtained as above described, he not only succeeded in preparing and analyzing all the more important compounds, but in crystallizing the salts in such a form that he was able to determine their crystallographic constants and then to supply all the necessary data for fixing the position of this new element and its compounds in relation to its well-known relatives, potassium and sodium.

All the world knows that shortly after his discovery of cæsium the birth of another new alkali metal, rubidium (*Berlin Monatsh.,* 1861, **6**, 273), was announced by Bunsen, and the application of spectrum analysis led, in other hands, to the isolation of thallium in 1861, indium in 1863, germanium in 1886, gallium in 1875, and scandium in 1879, but alongside of these came announcements of the discovery of other new metals whose existence was more than doubtful. Concerning these he writes to myself:

The frivolous way in which new metals are now discovered by dozens and sent forth into the world duly christened is certainly no gain to science; only later inquirers will be able to decide what remains new and serviceable out of this chaos of material.

I may here remind you that cæsium is not only interesting as being the first metal to have been discovered by spectrum analysis, but because, even before Bunsen's discovery, chemists had worked with cæsium salts which they had mistaken for potassium compounds, so closely do the properties of the two metals correspond. Plattner, in 1846, analyzing a mineral from Elba termed "pollux," could not bring his analysis to add up to 100 parts and was unable to explain the anomaly. After Bunsen had established the existence of cæsium, Pisani in 1864 took up the re-examination of the mineral and showed that the alkali metal was cæsium, with an atomic weight of 131.9, and not potassium, with one of 38.85, thus accounting for the missing percentage.

In the Christmas vacation of 1863 an extraordinary accident, illustrating in a painful manner the close analogy which exists between the properties of the potassium compounds and those of rubidium, occurred in Bunsen's laboratory. It is thus described in a letter from Bunsen to myself:

For a week I have been in a very depressed and sad state of mind owing to a fearful misfortune which has taken place in the laboratory. During my absence from Heidelberg in the Christmas holidays a man employed there in cutting wood, in spite of previous warnings, inexcusably took his little son with him into the laboratory and allowed him to run about without proper supervision. The child seems to have put into his mouth an iron tube which had been used for the reduction of metallic rubidium by heating the carbonate with charcoal, and in which the explosive compound carbonic oxide-rubidium had been formed. The result was that an explosion occurred, and although no mechanical wounding took place the child's throat and roof of its mouth were fearfully burned, so much so that it died within twelve hours. You can imagine how much I have been affected by this accident, although, heaven be thanked, no blame for want of caution can be attributed to me.

In 1875 (*Pogg. Ann.*, 1875, **155**, 230, 366) Bunsen published a long investigation upon the spark spectra of the rare earths. He had constructed, and describes there, a new and convenient form of carbon-zinc-chromic acid battery which was sufficiently powerful to give a small arc light or to work a large induction coil, and could be put in and out of action, so that it was made ready for instant use by lowering the carbons into the exciting liquid. By the help of this battery Bunsen mapped the spark spectra of the rare earths, the separation of which has proved to be a tedious and very laborious piece of work. An accident, almost pathetic in its incidents and somewhat similar to the well-known accident which happened to Newton's manuscript, occurred to Bunsen. He had just completed the above-named research, and the finished manuscript lay upon his writing table. On his return from dinner one day he found the whole reduced to ashes. It seems that a spherical water bottle stood on his desk and this, acting as a lens in the sunlight, was the cause of the disaster. Writing to me on June 3, 1874, he says:

You have good cause to be very angry with me for not having answered your sympathetic letter before this; but I have not allowed myself lately to think of anything which would remind me of the loss of my burned research. . . . I had finished the editing of a memoir on a subject which had occupied me for three years, and was about to forward it to Poggendorff for publication, when on returning home the other day I found all these papers, which had caught fire during my absence, reduced to ashes. The photographs of the apparatus, the drawings of the spark spectra of the metals of the rare earths, to separate and map which had cost me untold trouble, all are burned.

With regard to this accident, Kirchhoff writes to me on May 22:

The disaster of which you read in the papers really happened. The manuscript of a research at which he had labored for years, with maps of spectra, has been burned. He was, to begin with, much depressed, but his wonderful elasticity of mind enabled him to overcome his dejection, and he has already begun to replace what was lost.

This he continued to do, never drawing rein until the memoir was again ready for press.

The original views of Bunsen and Kirchhoff concerning the nature of the spectra of the alkali and alkaline earth metals as examined in the flame of the Bunsen burner have since their time undergone considerable modification. We now know that while the spectrum of potassium, sodium, cæsium, rubidium, and lithium, produced when any compound of these elements is brought into the flame, is that of the metal, it is quite otherwise with the similar spectra of the alkaline earths, for if a bead of calcium, strontium, or barium salt be brought into the flame bright lines and bands are seen, characteristic indeed of the individual substance, but differing altogether from the spectra obtained from the above compounds at the high temperature of the electric spark. In the first case we are dealing with the spectra of a compound, whereas in the latter instance we obtain the line spectrum of the metal itself. Nor must it be forgotten that Bunsen was the first to point out that which has only in recent years been fully recognized, namely, that change of physical condition under which a spectrum is observed may give rise to fundamental changes in the character of the spectrum itself. It was in his research on the absorption spectrum of didymium (*Pogg. Ann.*, 1866, 128, 100), carried out with minute care, that this point was made clear. In this he proved that, examined under a high dispersive and magnifying power, a crystal of didymium sulphate gives an absorption spectrum in which the dark bands vary in position and in breadth according to the position of the crystal in regard to its axes through which the light passes; that is, whether the polarized ray is ordinary or extraordinary. These changes, somewhat similar to those since shown to be effected by change of pressure under magnetic influence, or from change of temperature, have yet to receive a satisfactory explanation. To enlarge upon these matters is, however, beyond the province of the present address. Suffice it to say that Bunsen's original investigation has opened out an unbounded field for research, the cultivation of which has already yielded great results and will in future yield still greater ones.

Next let us turn to his celebrated researches on chemical geology, especially those concerning the volcanic phenomena of Iceland. The only relaxation from his scientific labors which

Bunsen throughout life allowed himself was traveling, and this he thoroughly enjoyed. During many autumn vacations I had the pleasure of accompanying him in rambles throughout Switzerland and the Tyrol. He walked well and had a keen appreciation of natural beauty, especially of mountain and woodland scenery, while he took great interest in the geology and physical characteristics of the districts through which he passed, and this it was that led him to turn his mind to chemico-geological studies. So early as 1844, in company with Pilla and Matteucci, he visited and carefully examined the carboniferous deposits occurring in the well-known fumarole districts of the Tuscan Maremma (*Annalen,* 1844, **49**, 264), and in 1846 he undertook his journey to Iceland, where he spent three and one-half months, and the outcome of which was the well-known series of investigations on the volcanic phenomena of that island (*Annalen,* 1847, **62**, 1; 1848, **65**, 70). No doubt it was the eruption of Hecla in 1845 which served as the incentive to this expedition, for he desired not only to examine the composition of the Icelandic rocks, which are entirely of volcanic origin, but especially the pseudo-volcanic phenomena, which present themselves in greater force immediately after a period of activity than at other times.

The expedition to Iceland was an official one, promoted by the Danish Government. Bunsen was accompanied by Sartorius von Waltershausen and Bergman, both colleagues at Marburg, as well as by the French mineralogist Des Cloizeaux. They left Copenhagen on May 4, 1846, reaching Reykjavik after a short but stormy passage of eleven days. The party spent ten days at the foot of Hecla, where Bunsen collected the gases emitted by the fumaroles and investigated the changes which these gases effect on the volcanic rocks with which they come into contact. Eleven more days were given to the investigation of the phenomena of the geysers, and at the end of August Bunsen left the island, having in the short space of about three months collected a mass of material the working up of which, as he writes to Berzelius, "will tax all my energies for some length of time," a prediction which was subsequently fully realized.

.   .   .

Although some of the conclusions drawn by Bunsen from his investigations on the composition of the Icelandic rocks are not generally accepted at the present day, yet geologists admit that these researches laid the foundation of modern petrology, and that the original views which he therein expressed mark an era in the history of geological theory. It is now acknowledged that the idea which he was the first to propound, namely, the necessity of examining the chemical composition of eruptive rocks taken as a whole rather than the determination of their various constituent minerals must be carried out if we wish to come to an understanding as to their mode of formation. For this purpose he made an extensive series of complete analyses of the Icelandic rocks. And from these results he drew the remarkable conclusion that in Iceland, and probably in most of the larger volcanic systems, there exist two extreme types of rocks. One of these, richest in silica, is termed the "normal trachyte"; the other, containing less silica and naturally more basic constituents, is the "normal pyroxene." All the Icelandic rocks can be classed as being either one or other of these normal silicates, or as admixtures of the two. In order to account for these well-established facts, Bunsen supposed that the two normal types were separated out from the mass of molten silicate in the interior of the earth at distinct points; and he founded this supposition on the fact of the influence of pressure on the melting point. (*Pogg. Ann.,* 1850, 81, 562.)

This had been independently pointed out by James Thomson, in 1849, as being a corollary of the mechanical theory of heat, and had also been experimentally verified by William Thomson (Lord Kelvin)* in the case of water. Bunsen developed this point further by proving that, exposed to a pressure of 156 atmospheres, the temperature of solidification of spermaceti was raised from 47.7°, under ordinary atmospheric pressure, to 50.9°. As volcanic rocks must have been subjected to varying pressures amounting to many thousands of atmospheres, it is clear that the effect of such variation on the point of solidification of the rocks must be very considerable, and that where the pressure is less the composition of the crystalline mass would be different from that of the rock formed where the pressure is greater. This remarkable theory of the existence of two distinct types of rocks separating out from the same fluid mass has recently been supplanted by other views, but the facts respecting the composition of the eruptive rocks upon which the idea was based will ever remain not only a monument to the patience and perseverance of their discoverer, but as some of the most valuable additions to our knowledge of chemical geology.

Bunsen's investigations of the pseudo-volcanic phenomena of Iceland, and especially those of the great geyser, may, indeed, be considered as models both from a physical and a chemical point

* For Lord Kelvin see pp. 466–490 of the present volume.

of view. The temperature experiments, which were both difficult and dangerous, were conducted by Bunsen in collaboration with Des Cloizeaux. He first shows that the cylindrical shaft, which is no less than 74 feet deep and 10 feet in diameter, had been built up by the deposition of the silica which the water holds in solution, so that, in Tyndall's words, "the geyser is the architect of its own tube." Bunsen determined the temperature of the water contained in the tube a few minutes before an eruption, and found that in no part of the tube did the water reach its boiling point. The situation at which the temperature of the water most nearly approached the boiling point under the superincumbent pressure was about 30 feet from the bottom, reaching there $121.8°$, whereas the boiling temperature was $123.8°$, making a difference of only $2°$. The question occurs: Why, under these circumstances, does an eruption take place? This is satisfactorily accounted for by the fact that, owing to the existence at the base of the geyser tube of volcanic vents, through which steam under pressure is passing, the whole column of heated water is lifted, so that while originally at a point 30 feet from the bottom the temperature of the water was below the boiling point, when it became raised through a height of 6 feet by the pressure of the issuing steam its temperature was $1°$ above the boiling point, the same being true for every point in the cylinder, and thus the ebullition gradually increased until at last it became eruptive. An experimental illustration of Bunsen's geyser theory is described by Tyndall in his well-known work.

The distinct shade of blue possessed by waters of the geyser led Bunsen to examine the color of distilled water (*Edin. New Phil. Journ.*, 1849, **47**, 95). For this purpose he inclosed carefully purified distilled water in a horizontal tube 2 meters long, closed by plate glass ends, the interior of which had been blackened, thus showing that the absorptive power of water is exerted less upon the blue than upon the other rays of the spectrum, and explaining the blue color of certain lakes and rivers and the color of sea water as observed in the Blue Grotto of Capri. The differences in depths of shades of blue possessed by waters in various places are doubtless due to the variation in size of the suspended particles varying in their reflective power.

Of a totally different character was the next piece of work to which I shall refer; it related to the separation of the metals of the platinum group.

In 1868 (*Annalen*, 1868, **146**, 265) Bunsen worked for some time on methods of separating the several metals contained in the residues left after the process of extracting the platinum as practiced in the imperial mint at St. Petersburg. He fully describes the somewhat complicated processes by which he effected these separations: (1) the elimination of platinum and palladium; (2) the separation of ruthenium; (3) the deposition of iridium and rhodium; and (4) the chief aim of the research, the preparation of pure rhodium and its compounds.

In the course of these experiments Bunsen met with a singular and unexplained accident, which fortunately had no serious consequences. With reference to this he writes to me as follows:

It is still difficult for me to write, as my hands are not quite healed, but I can not longer delay replying to your sympathetic letter, as I fear you may be uneasy about me. The cause of the explosion is to me still quite inexplicable. I had prepared about a pound of the mixed metals rhodium and iridium by zinc reduction, and had dried the powder at 100° in a water bath, when, on lightly touching the finely divided metal, which was not quite cold, with my finger, the whole suddenly exploded with the energy of rammed-in gunpowder. This is all the more puzzling, as I have often rubbed a powder of the same metals violently in a mortar in similar quantities without any explosion occurring. I have also heated similar preparations to a redness in vacuo without any gas, and certainly without a trace of hydrogen, being evolved. My left hand, with the first finger of which I touched the mass, saved my eyes, as my face and eyes were only superficially burned by the flames which penetrated through my fingers. My eyes are, with the exception of singed eyebrows and eyelashes, unhurt, and so the explosion will luckily leave behind no serious traces.

In the preceding communication on the platinum metals Bunsen first describes the well-known filter pump which now bears his name. But in a later publication (*Annalen*, 1868, 148, 269) he gives further particulars of its construction and use. These are so well known that it is only necessary to say that it is, in fact, a Sprengel pump in which a column of 28 inches of mercury is replaced by one of 32 feet of water. In this way a flow of water down a pipe of the above length produces a vacuum perfect up to the limit of tension of the aqueous vapor, and under the diminished pressures thus brought about all the processes of filtration and of the washing of precipitates can be carried out with much greater rapidity and perfection than is the case when working under the ordinary atmospheric pressure. Here, as in all his published work, Bunsen is precise and exact. To show the timesaving value of the process he precipitates two equal volumes of chromium sesquichloride solution of known strength by ammonia; the one portion he treats in the ordinary way, the other by the filter-pump method, whereby he demonstrates that, treated by the latter process, the precipitate is completely washed in one-thirteenth part of the time needed by the old plan, while only one-fiftieth of the volume of wash water is required. Such filter pumps, furnished with mercury pressure gauges, are now found in every well-fitted laboratory.

A somewhat simpler form of filter pump, first described by Piccard (*Zeit anal. Chem.*, 1865, 4, 45), is, however, now also very generally employed. This consists of a short glass tube at-tached to the water tap, with an inner jet for the water and an outer air tube, the rapid flow of water carrying down with it a sufficient volume of air—on the principle of the steam injector—to create a diminution of pressure, which, although by no means so great as that effected by the filter pump as described by Bunsen, is still sufficient for many purposes.

.   .   .

The invention which perhaps more than any other has popu-larized the name of Bunsen is that of his celebrated burner. The Bunsen burner, to the discovery of which I shall refer later on, is not only important from the fact of its almost universal employ-ment, but also because familiarity with its properties led Bunsen to elaborate a series of flame reactions of very wide applicability. In the communication published in 1866 (*Annalen,* 1866, 138, 257) he showed that the nonluminous flame of the burner could, with advantage, supplant the blowpipe flame for many analytical pur-poses. He first describes the constitution of the nonluminous gas flame. Next he examines the action of the high temperature of the flame on the emission of light from solid bodies placed in the flame, referring especially to the extraordinary luminous intensity of incandescent erbia, interesting as being the starting point for the enormous industry of the incandescent mantle. He also deter-mines the melting points and the rate of volatility of many salts by means of small beads of material placed at the end of a thin platinum wire in the flame, the rate of volatilization being ascer-tained by the microscopic measurement of the diminishing diam-eters, in given periods of time, of the molten globules. He next details a variety of original and most ingenious methods of detect-ing minute quantities of the metals and nonmetals by the help of reactions effected in the flame. So delicate are some of these methods, as, for instance, that of the detection of gold, that its presence can be with certainty ascertained in one centigram of a sample of a tellurium ore containing only a few tenths of a milligram of the metal.

Another most characteristic contribution to analytical chemistry is the investigation of a method of general applicability, published in 1853 (*Annalen,* 1853, **86,** 265), known as the iodometric method and consisting of the volumetric determination of free iodine by means of sulphurous acid, for which has since been substituted the more stable sodium thiosulphate. This method, as every chemist knows, is not only largely employed in commercial analyses, as, for example, for the estimation of the amount of manganese dioxide in manganese ores and Weldon mud, but it also gives valuable assistance in the determination of interesting theoretical questions, as, for instance, by Bunsen in the separation of cerium and lanthanum, and in the estimation of the atomic weight of the former metal.

Bunsen also devoted much time and labor to the perfection and systematization of the processes of mineral water analysis. In 1871 he published a detailed account (*Zeit. anal. Chem.* 1871, **10,** 391) of the methods of analysis which he adopted and their results in an investigation, made on behalf of the authorities, which had occupied him for some years, on the chemical and physical properties of the mineral waters occurring in various parts of the Grand Duchy of Baden. These results he afterwards published in pamphlet form. They certainly constitute the most complete series of mineral-water analyses existing, and serve as a model in this domain of analytical chemistry. It is interesting to remember that Victor Meyer, who acted at the time as his assistant, carried out a large part of the experimental work.

Having thus pointed out some of the main features of Bunsen's scientific achievements, I now turn to my personal recollections to give you an idea of what manner of man he was, and how he lived and worked. My reminiscences of Bunsen date as far back as the year 1852. In the autumn of that year I was introduced to him by Professor von Mohl, the father of the late Frau von Helmholtz, who was then professor of international law in the University of Heidelberg. Bunsen had just been called from Breslau to fill the chair of chemistry at Heidelberg in succession to Leopold Gmelin, best known to English chemists as the author of the great handbook translated by our late editor, Henry Watts, and published by the Cavendish Society. I shall never forget the first sight of the man who afterwards became one of my most intimate and valued friends, and to whom I owe more than I can tell. At that time Bunsen was at the height of his powers, physical and mental. He stood fully 6 feet high; his figure was well knit and powerful; his manner was one of suave dignity, while his expression was that of great kindliness and of rare intelligence. Nor did this first impression of his bearing and character ever change, much less lose force. On the contrary, the more intimate became my knowledge, the more had I cause to respect and admire him. His was a heart free from guile, guiding a temper equable and amiable. During my long and intimate friendship I never heard him set down aught in malice or express more than a mild and good-natured remonstrance—as when, for instance, one of the *Practicanten* had adopted some faulty method of analysis, the master would remark: *"Mein Gott, wie konnten Sie so was thun!"* His genial, yet quietly dignified, manner placed strangers at their ease, at once inspiring confidence and commanding respect. All saw in him a man worthy of esteem and safe to trust, while those who were favored by his more intimate friendship knew that for true modesty and greatness of heart he was excelled by none; they felt that for them he was the *chevalier sans peur et sans reproche,* and that his companionship, whether scientific or social, was something to be proud of, the recollection of which remains as one of the most fruitful as well as one of the pleasantest of their lives.

Considerate and generous toward the opinions of others, he held firmly to his own, which at times he did not fail strongly to express. Simple and straightforward, he disliked assumption and hated duplicity; single-minded and wholly devoted to his science, he abhorred vanity and despised popularity hunting. Indeed, of so retiring a disposition was he that it was difficult to get him to take part in public proceedings, and next to impossible to induce him to make any public utterance of either a scientific or of a social character.

Another and a remarkable trait in his character was his keen sense of humor. This gave a charm and a zest to his society greatly appreciated by his friends, but of all his witty sayings which passed from mouth to mouth as "Bunsen's last," none was ever tinged with ill-nature, for this was foreign to his whole being. A large and interesting collection of these "Bunseniana" might be made. . . .

His, too, was a most affectionate nature, and one may regret that this side of his character was never freely called forth by family life. For Bunsen, like Dalton, tried to explain this failing by saying that he could never find time to get married. And this loneliness, especially in later life, oppressed him, and he often felt his isolated position keenly. When bidding him good-by after my summer visits to him he would smile sadly and remark, *"Jetzt verlassen Sie mich wieder in meiner Einsamkeit."*

. . .

In 1887 the seventh century of the foundation of Heidelberg University was auspiciously celebrated. Bunsen invited me to be his guest during the ceremony. During the inaugural discourse by Kuno Fischer, which lasted more than three hours, Bunsen fell asleep, as well he might do, but a more than usually eloquent passage disturbed his rest, and he woke up with a start, and whispered to me, "I thought I had dropped a test tube full of rubidium onto the floor!"

Nothing was more distasteful to him than the etiquette of the court. Nevertheless, during these festivities at which the Grand Duke of Baden, the Prince of Prussia, and other magnificos were, of course, present, Bunsen became the cynosure of neighboring eyes. The recipient of heaps of orders of all kinds, from all quarters, he never exhibited them except when he went to court, or was invited to meet his sovereign. To be used on such occasions only, he kept an "order" coat, a "frack" or tail coat, upon the breast of which he had stitched as many of the stars and crosses as it would comfortably hold. During the jubilee the Grand Duke held a court in the castle, and presentations were made. Bunsen, who had already paid his devoirs to the Grand Duke's party, expressed his unwillingness again to go through the necessary formalities, but after some persuasion on my part he consented, hoping, as he said, to conceal himself behind the crowd of officials and dignitaries of all sorts who thronged the hall in which the royalties were assembled. So we walked together up to the castle in evening dress, as the custom is, Bunsen wearing his "orders." The streets through which the procession of magnates was to pass were filled to overflowing by a good-natured crowd, no military or even police being present to clear the way, so as the royal carriages came up the steep road leading to the castle, a block occurred, and as luck would have it, that containing the Grand Duke, the Duchess, and the Prince of Prussia came to a standstill at the exact point where Bunsen and I stood endeavoring to make our way through the crowd. The Duke at once recognized the *Geheimerath,* and beckoned him to come to the carriage, and there and then they had a friendly chat, and I had the honor of being presented. As soon as the cortege moved on I had a good laugh at

Bunsen, who, endeavoring to escape from all notice and attention, was entrapped in this amusing fashion.

Let me next endeavor to give you a picture of the master working in his laboratory. When he first came to Heidelberg in the summer of 1852, Bunsen found himself installed in Gmelin's old laboratory. This was situated in the buildings of an ancient monastery, and there we all worked. It was roomy enough; the old refectory was the main laboratory; the chapel was divided into two; one half became the lecture room and the other a storehouse and museum. Soon the number of students increased and further extensions were needed, so the cloisters were inclosed by windows and working benches placed below them. Beneath the stone floor at our feet slept the dead monks, and on their tombstones we threw our waste precipitates! There was no gas in Heidelberg in those days, nor any town water supply. We worked with Berzelius's spirit lamps, made our combustions with charcoal, boiled down our wash waters from our silicate analyses in large glass globes over charcoal fires, and went for water to the pump in the yard. Nevertheless, with all these so-called drawbacks, we were able to work easily and accurately. To work with Bunsen was a real pleasure. Entirely devoted to his students, as they were to him, he spent all day in the laboratory, showing them with his own hands how best to carry out the various operations in which they were engaged. You would find him with one man showing the new method of washing precipitates, so as to save time and labor, or with another working out a calibration table of a eudiometer, or with a third pointing out that the ordinary method of separating iron from aluminum is unsatisfactory and carrying out a more perfect process before his eyes. Often you would find him seated at the table blowpipe—the flame in those days was fed with oil— making some new piece of glass apparatus, for he was an expert glass blower, and enjoyed showing the men how to seal platinum wires into the eudiometers, or to blow bulb tubes for his iodometric analyses. Maxwell Simpson, who worked with Bunsen in the fifties, tells me that one day he saw Bunsen blow a complicated piece of glass apparatus for a pupil, who quickly broke it; Bunsen then made him a second, which at once met with a similar fate; without a murmur Bunsen again sat down to the blowpipe and for the third time presented the student (who we will trust looked ashamed of himself) with the perfect apparatus. Then he would spend half the morning in the gas-analysis room, going through all the detailed manipulation of the exact measurement of gaseous volumes, and showing a couple of men how to estimate the various constituents of a sample of coal gas, and pointing out the methods of calculating the results, and then leaving them to repeat the processes from beginning to end for themselves.

His manipulative ability was remarkable; his hands, though large and powerful, were supple and dexterous. He was amusingly proud of having a large thumb, by means of which he was able to close the open end of a long eudiometer filled with mercury and immerse it in the mercury bath without admitting the least bubble of air, a feat which those endowed with smaller digits were unable to accomplish. Then he had a very salamanderlike power of handling hot glass tubes, and often at the blowpipe have I smelt burnt Bunsen, and seen his fingers smoke! Then he would quickly reduce their temperature by pressing the lobe of his right ear between his heated thumb and forefinger, turning his head to one with a smile as the "agony abated," while it used to be a joke among the students that the master never needed a pincette to take off the lid from a hot porcelain crucible.

Accuracy of work was the first essential with him; most of us learned for the first time what this meant. Six weeks' work was spent on a single silicate analysis, but most of us contrived to keep two such analyses going at once, while an analysis of coal gas occupied a week or ten days. Not that he was averse to quick processes; indeed, many of his own investigations contain novel proposals for shortening chemical methods, but this was never done at the expense of accuracy.

After having learned his methods of quantitative work, of silicate analysis, for example, and after having gone through a course of gas analysis, those of us who had already been more or less trained elsewhere were set upon some original investigation. Lothar Meyer, who worked at the next bench to myself, being a medical student, was set to pump out and analyze the blood gases; Pauli and Carius worked on gas absorption, employing for this purpose Bunsen's recently invented absorptiometer; Russell was set to work out a new method of sulphur determination in organic bodies; Matthiessen was put on to the electrolytic preparation of calcium and strontium; Schischkoff analyzed the gaseous products of gunpowder fired under varying conditions; Landolt had to find out the composition of the gases in various portions of a flame, and I worked by myself in one of the monk's cells upstairs on the solubility in water of chlorine when mixed with hydrogen and carbonic acid, the object being to ascertain whether this gas obeys the law of Dalton and Henry.

These are only some of the investigations on a variety of subjects carried on in the old monastery by Bunsen's pupils under his supervision, and they indicate only a tithe of his activity, for at the same time he was engaged in investigations of his own. He always had two or three on hand at once.

When Bunsen accepted the chair of chemistry at Heidelberg the Baden Government agreed to build him a new laboratory. This was accordingly done, the plans having been worked out by him to the smallest detail, and in the summer of 1855 the new laboratory in the *Plöck Strasse* was opened. The rooms were by no means so lofty as those of our more modern laboratories, and as students from all parts of the world streamed in, in large and increasing numbers, the new building soon became inconveniently crowded, and many applications for working benches had to be refused.

Some short time before the opening of the new laboratory the town of Heidelberg was for the first time lighted with gas, and Bunsen had to consider what kind of gas burner he would use for laboratory purposes. Returning from my Easter vacation in London, I brought back with me an Argand burner with copper chimney and wire-gauze top, which was the form commonly used in English laboratories at that time for working with a smokeless flame. This arrangement did not please Bunsen in the very least. The flame was flickering; it was too large, and the gas was so much diluted with air that the flame temperature was greatly depressed. He would make a burner in which the mixture of gas and air would burn at the top of the tube without any gauze whatsoever, giving a steady, small, and hot, nonluminous flame under conditions such that it not only would burn without striking down when the gas supply was turned on full, but also when the supply was diminished until only a minute flame was left. This was a difficult, some thought it an impossible, problem to solve, but after many fruitless attempts and many tedious trials, he succeeded, and the Bunsen burner came to light. On the theory of the Bunsen burner I need not detain you, for it has already been brought before the society in his usual clear and masterly manner by our president (this journal, 1877 i, **31**, 627). I may, however, here remark that so general, indeed so universal, has the use of this become that its name and value must be known to and appreciated by millions of the human race. Yet how few of these have any further ideas connected with the name of its author.

Another discovery which early brought him prominently before the public was that of the Bunsen, or as he preferred to call it, the carbon-zinc battery, a description of which has already been given. The manufacture of either the battery or the burner might, had the inventor wished, have been so guarded as to bring in a large fortune. But Bunsen had no monetary ambition, although he fully appreciated the importance of applied science; and this is a fine trait in his character. He not only disliked anything savoring of money-making out of pure science, but he could not understand how a man professing to follow science could allow his attention to be thus diverted from pure research. "There are two distinct classes of men," he used to say, "first, those who work at enlarging the boundaries of knowledge, and, secondly, those who apply that knowledge to useful ends." Bunsen chose the first—perhaps one may say the higher—part, and the notion of making money out of his discoveries, or of patenting any of them, never entered into his head. As illustrating this habit of mind, I remember that once we were talking about a former pupil of his, of whose scientific ability he entertained a high opinion. "Do you know," he remarked to me, "I can not make that man out. He has certainly much scientific talent, and yet he thinks of nothing but money-making, and I am told that he has already amassed a large fortune. Is it not a singular case?" To which I replied that I did not find it so very remarkable.

In the new laboratory research work was carried on with even greater activity than it had been in the old one. My own work on photochemical measurements was first carried out in a darkened chamber under the slates, where the summer temperature was usually above blood heat, and afterwards in Bunsen's private room downstairs. Men whose names have long ago been household words with us came to work under the master. Baeyer carried out his early work under Bunsen's care, though after a time he left to work with Kekulé, who had just set up a private laboratory in the neighborhood. Lothar Meyer, Carius, and Landolt were continuing their several researches. Dexter worked on the atomic weight of antimony, Holtzmann on the cerium metals, while Pebal, Erlenmeyer, Meidinger, Lieben, Barth, Moritz Hermann, and Lotz each published interesting communications; and Bahr from Stockholm, Frapolli from Milan, Pavesi from Padua, and Lourenço from Goa, were also occupied in research. Most of this work Bunsen had initiated; all he assisted by cooperation and advice. Then, in addition, there were the beginners, to the number of 60 or 70, all of whom were looked after by the professor, and with some of whom he would spend hours showing them how to detect traces of metals by aid of the flame reactions, or how to estimate the percentage of dioxide in pyrolusite by his iodometric method. So from Bunsen all who had eyes to see and ears to hear might learn the important lesson that to found or to carry on successfully a school of chemistry the professor must work with and alongside of the pupil, and that for him to delegate that duty to an assistant, however able, is a grave error.

How, it may be asked, could a man who thus devoted himself to supervising the work of others in the laboratory—and who, besides, had a lecture to deliver every day, and much university business to transact—how could he possibly find time to carry out experimental work of his own? For it is to be noted that Bunsen never kept an assistant to work at his researches, and unless cooperating with someone else, did all the new experimental work with his own hands. It is true that in certain instances he incorporated the results of analyses, made by a student whom he could trust, into his own memoirs. Notably this was the case with the silicate analyses which he used in his chemico-geological papers, and with many of the examples given in illustration of some of his new analytical methods. Then, spending the whole day in the laboratory, he was often able to find a spare hour to devote to his own work of devising and testing some new form of apparatus, of separating some of the rare earth metals, or of determining the crystalline form of a series of salts.

Again the editing of the research, and the calculations, often complicated, which that involved, were carried on in the early morning hours. When, for four summers after the year 1857, I spent my vacations working at Heidelberg, I lived in his house, and although I rose betimes, I always found him at his desk, having begun work often before dawn.

Then, although he frequently traveled during the vacations at Easter and in the autumn, often, I am glad to remember, with myself as companion, he generally returned after a short absence to continue an unfinished, or to commence some new, research, and during these quiet days much work was done by both of us.

I will now say a few words about Bunsen as a lecturer. Bunsen lectured on general chemistry every morning in the week, from 8 to 9 in the summer, and from 9 to 10 in the winter semester. The lectures were interesting and instructive, not from any striving after oratorical effect, or by any display of "firework" experiments, but from the originality of both matter and illustration. His exposition was clear and his delivery easy, and every point upon which he touched was treated in an original fashion. No book, of course, was used or referred to; indeed, he avoided much consultation of handbooks, the only two which I have seen him occasionally turn to for the purpose of looking up some facts about which he had doubts were *Gmelin* and *Roscoe and Schorlemmer*. When occasionally one of the *Practicanten* consulted him about a passage in some manual which appeared defective, he would laughingly remark that most of what is written in books is wrong.

The illustrative lecture experiments, which he invariably performed himself, were generally made on a small scale, were often new, always strictly relevant to the matter in hand, and never introduced for mere sensational effect. He paid much attention to these experiments, and after the table had been set in order for the particular lecture by the assistant, he would regularly spend half an hour, sometimes an hour, in convincing himself that all was in readiness and in rehearsing any experiment about the success of which he was not perfectly certain.

He used few notes, but it was his habit to write up any numerical data in small figures on the blackboard, and to refresh his memory with these when needed. When I attended the lectures in the early fifties, Bunsen used the notation and nomenclature of Berzelius, writing water $\dot{H}$, and alumina $\dot{A}l_2$. Later on, he still employed the dualistic notation, writing $KOSO_3$, $HOSO_3$, for K_2SO_4 and H_2SO_4; indeed, I believe that he never adopted our modern formulæ or used Cannizzaro's atomic weights, although his determination of the atomic heat of indium and his work on cæsium and rubidium were amongst the most important contributions toward the settlement of those weights.

Bunsen did not enlarge in his lectures on theoretical questions; indeed, to discuss points of theory was not his habit, and not much to his liking. His mind was eminently practical; he often used to say that one chemical fact properly established was worth more than all the theories one could invent. And yet he did much to establish the evidence upon which our modern theories rest.

.   .   .

In conclusion, I may remark that Bunsen's constitution was a vigorous one, and it carried him fairly well through a long life; still, continuous exposure to the fumes and vitiated air of the laboratory induced bronchial troubles, from which in later life he suffered considerably. Beyond one sharp attack of peritonitis when traveling with Pagenstecher in the Balearic Islands, I do not think he ever had a serious illness. His habits were frugal, the only extravagance in which he indulged being his cigars. Of these he consumed a fairly large number, always having one or a part of one in his mouth; but as he generally allowed it to go out many times before he finished smoking it, the time it lasted was much above that of the average smoker.

Although taking no active part in German politics, Bunsen was a stanch Liberal, and no one rejoiced more than he on the consummation of the unification of the German people under the headship of the Emperor William. He was, however, no admirer of Bismarck's régime. On Mitscherlich's death Bunsen received a very pressing invitation to become Mitscherlich's successor in Berlin. On this subject, he writes to me:

Very liberal offers with regard to Mitscherlich's professorship have been made to me, but I have declined them, as I did not wish to belong to the regiment of Herr von Bismarck, or to start again from the beginning with chemistry, the position of which had there fallen so low. . . .

In 1889 Bunsen retired from active university life, resigning his professorship, and therefore his official residence, and retiring to a pretty little villa in *Bunsenstrasse,* which he had purchased, where he spent the remainder of his days in quiet repose. His chief relaxation and enjoyment throughout his life in Heidelberg was to wander with Kirchhoff or Helmholtz or some other of his intimate friends through the chestnut woods which cover the hills at the foot of which the town lies. As the infirmities of age increased and his walking powers diminished, he was obliged to take to driving through the woods along the charming roads which intersect the hills in all directions. Writing became a difficulty, and in his latter days the news of him came to me through our mutual friends Quincke and Königsberger. One of the last letters I received from him is dated June 4, 1890:

. . . I have been suffering for weeks from the after effects of influenza, and I am still so weak that I have to spend my days on the sofa, and have scarcely strength to walk the few yards to dinner at the Grand Hotel. When I think that next March I enter on my eightieth year, I must resign myself to the fact that such a state of things is inevitable. My hearing, too, becomes more and more difficult, and my eyes are worse, so I have to deny myself all social intercourse, and only see now and then one of my old friends who comes to look me up. But in spite of all this, I can still feel the humor of life. . . .

Bunsen at the time of his death had been for many years our senior foreign member, having been elected on February 1, 1842, during the first session of our society. It was not until 1858 that he became a Foreign Fellow of the Royal Society. In 1860, the Copley medal was awarded to him, and in 1877 he and Kirchhoff were presented with the Davy medal, that being the first occasion of its award, in recognition of their researches and discoveries in spectrum analysis.

.   .   .

Another English honor conferred upon him was that of the award in 1898 of the Albert medal of the Society of Arts, given for "distinguished merit in promoting art, manufacture, or commerce," in recognition of his numerous and most valuable applications of chemistry and physics to the arts and to manufactures. Almost up to the last Bunsen continued to take a vivid interest in the progress of scientific discovery and, though suffering from pain and weakness, ever preserved the equanimity which was one of his lifelong characteristics. Three days before his death . . . he lay in a peaceful slumber, his countenance exhibiting the fine intellectual expression of his best and brightest days. Thus passed away, full of days and full of honors, a man equally beloved for his great qualities of heart as he is honored for those of his fertile brain, the memory of whom will always remain green among all who were fortunate enough to number him among their friends. . . .

Karl Friedrich Wilhelm Ludwig *

1816–1895

———◆———

JOHN SCOTT BURDON-SANDERSON †

THE DEATH of any discoverer—of anyone who has added largely to the sum of human knowledge—affords a reason for inquiring what his work was and how he accomplished it. This inquiry has interest even when the work has been completed in a few years and has been limited to a single line of investigation—much more when the life has been associated with the origin and development of a new science and has extended over half a century.

The science of physiology, as we know it, came into existence fifty years ago, with the beginning of the active life of Ludwig, in the same sense that the other great branch of biology, the science of living beings (ontology), as we now know it, came into existence with the appearance of the *Origin of Species*. In the order of time physiology had the advantage, for the new physiology was accepted some ten years before the Darwinian epoch. Notwithstanding, the content of the science is relatively so unfamiliar, that before entering on the discussion of the life and work of the man who, as I shall endeavor to show, had a larger share in founding it than any of his contemporaries, it is necessary to define its limits and its relations to other branches of knowledge.

The word *physiology* has in modern times changed its meaning. It once comprehended the whole knowledge of nature. Now it is the name for one of the two divisions of the science of life. In the progress of investigation the study of that science has inevitably divided itself into two: ontology, the science of living beings; physiology, the science of living processes, and thus, inasmuch as

* *A.R.,* 1896, pp. 365–379. From a lecture delivered at the Royal Institution, Jan. 24, 1896 (printed in *Science Progress,* vol. 5, no. 25 [1896], pp. 1–21).

† English physiologist (1828–1905), Regius Professor of Medicine, Oxford.

401

life consists in processes, of life itself. Both strive to understand the complicated relations and endless varieties which present themselves in living nature, but by different methods. Both refer to general principles, but they are of a different nature.

To the ontologist, the student of living beings, plants or animals, the great fact of evolution, namely, that from the simplest beginning our own organism, no less than that of every animal and plant with its infinite complication of parts and powers, unfolds the plan of its existence—taken with the observation that that small beginning was, in all excepting the lowest forms, itself derived from two parents, equally from each—is the basis from which his study and knowledge of the world of living beings takes its departure. For on these two facts—evolution and descent—the explorer of the forms, distribution, and habits of animals and plants has, since the Darwinian epoch, relied with an ever-increasing certainty, and has found in them the explanation of every phenomenon, the solution of every problem relating to the subject of his inquiry. Nor could he wish for a more secure basis. Whatever doubts or misgivings exist in the minds of "nonbiologists" in relation to it may be attributed partly to the association with the doctrine of evolution of questions which the true naturalist regards as transcendental, partly to the perversion or weakening of meaning which the term has suffered in consequence of its introduction into the language of common life, and particularly to the habit of applying it to any kind of progress or improvement, anything which from small beginnings gradually increases. But provided that we limit the term to its original sense—the evolution of a living being from its germ by a continuous, not a gradual process—there is no conception which is more free from doubt either as to its meaning or reality. It is inseparable from that of life itself, which is but the unfolding of a predestined harmony, of a prearranged consensus and synergy of parts.

The other branch of biology, that with which Ludwig's name is associated, deals with the same facts in a different way. While ontology regards animals and plants as individuals and in relation to other individuals, physiology considers the processes themselves of which life is a complex. This is the most obvious distinction, but it is subordinate to the fundamental one, namely, that while ontology has for its basis laws which are in force only in its own province, those of evolution, descent, and adaptation, we physiologists, while accepting these as true, found nothing upon them, using them only for heuristic purposes, i.e., as guides to discovery, not for the purpose of explanation. Purposive adaptation, for example, serves as a clue, by which we are constantly guided in our exploration of the tangled labyrinth of vital processes. But when it becomes our business to explain these processes—to say how they are brought about—we refer them not to biological principles of any kind, but to the universal laws of nature. Hence it happens that with reference to each of these processes our inquiry is rather how it occurs than why it occurs.

It has been well said that the natural sciences are the children of necessity. Just as the other natural sciences owed their origin to the necessity of acquiring that control over the forces of nature without which life would scarcely be worth living, so physiology arose out of human suffering and the necessity of relieving it. It sprang, indeed, out of pathology. It was suffering that led us to know, as regards our own bodies, that we had internal as well as external organs, and probably one of the first generalizations which arose out of this knowledge was that "if one member suffer all the members suffer with it"—that all work together for the good of the whole. In earlier times the good which was thus indicated was associated in men's minds with human welfare exclusively. But it was eventually seen that nature has no less consideration for the welfare of those of her products which to us seem hideous or mischievous, than for those which we regard as most useful to man or most deserving of his admiration. It thus became apparent that the good in question could not be human exclusively, but as regards each animal its own good—and that in the organized world the existence and life of every species is brought into subordination to one purpose—its own success in the struggle for existence.

From what has preceded it may be readily understood that in physiology adaptation takes a more prominent place than evolution or descent. In the prescientific period adaptation was everything. The observation that any structure or arrangement exhibited marks of adaptation to a useful purpose was accepted, not merely as a guide in research, but as a full and final explanation. Of an organism or organ which perfectly fulfilled in its structure and working the end of its existence nothing further is required to be said or known. Physiologists of the present day recognize as fully as their predecessors that perfection of contrivance which displays itself in all living structures the more exquisitely the more minutely they are examined. No one, for example, has written more emphatically upon this point than did Ludwig. In one of his discourses, after showing how nature exceeds the highest standard of human attainment—how she fashions, as it were, out of nothing and without tools instruments of a perfection which the human artificer cannot reach, though provided with every suitable material—wood, brass, glass, india rubber—he gives the organ of sight as a signal example, referring among its other perfections to the rapidity with which the eye can be fixed on numerous objects in succession and the instantaneous and unconscious estimates which we are able to form of the distances of objects, each estimate involving a process of arithmetic which no calculating machine could effect in the time. In another discourse—that given at Leipzig when he entered on his professorship in 1865—he remarks that when in our researches into the finer mechanism of an organ we at last come to understand it, we are humbled by the recognition "that the human inventor is but a blunderer as compared with the unknown Master of the animal creation."

Some readers will perhaps remember how one of the most brilliant of philosophical writers, in a discourse to the British Association delivered a quarter of a century ago, averred on the authority of a great physiologist that the eye, regarded as an optical instrument, was so inferior a production that if it were the work of a mechanician it would be unsalable. Without criticizing or endeavoring to explain this paradox, I may refer to it as having given the countenance of a distinguished name to a misconception which I know exists in the minds of many persons, to the effect that the scientific physiologist is more or less blind to the evidence of design in creation. On the contrary, the view taken by Ludwig, as expressed in the words I have quoted, is that of all physiologists. The disuse of the teleological expressions which were formerly current does not imply that the indications of contrivance are less appreciated, for, on the contrary, we regard them as more characteristic of organism as it presents itself to our observation than any other of its endowments. But if I may be permitted to repeat what has been already said, we use the evidences of adaptation differently. We found no explanation on this or any other biological principle, but refer all the phenomena by which these manifest themselves to the simpler and more certain physical laws of the universe.

Why must we take this position? First, because it is a general rule in investigations of all kinds to explain the more complex by the more simple. The material universe is manifestly divided into two parts, the living and the nonliving. We may, if we like, take the living as our *Norma,* and say to the physicist: "You must come to us for laws; you must account for the play of energies in universal nature by referring them to evolution, descent, adaptation." Or we may take these words as true expressions of the mutual relations between the phenomena and processes peculiar to living beings, using for the explanation of the processes themselves the same methods which we should employ if we were engaged in the investigation of analogous processes going on independently of life. Between these two courses there seems to me to be no third alternative, unless we suppose that there are two material universes, one to which the material of our bodies belongs, the other comprising everything that is not either plant or animal.

The second reason is a practical one. We should have to go back to the time which I have ventured to call prescientific, when the world of life and organization was supposed to be governed exclusively by its own laws. The work of the past fifty years has been done on the opposite principle and has brought light and clearness where there was before obscurity and confusion. All this progress we should have to repudiate. But this would not be all. We should have to forego the prospect of future advance. Whereas by holding on our present course, gradually proceeding from the more simple to the more complex, from the physical to the vital, we may confidently look forward to extending our knowledge considerably beyond its present limits.

A no less brilliant writer than the one already referred to, who is also no longer with us, asserted that mind was a secretion of the brain in the same sense that bile is a secretion of the liver or urine that of the kidney; and many people have imagined this to be the necessary outcome of a too mechanical way of looking at vital phenomena, and that physiologists, by a habit of adhering strictly to their own method, have failed to see that the organism presents problems to which this method is not applicable, such, for example, as the origin of the organism itself or the origin and development in it of the mental faculty. The answer to this suggestion is that these questions are approached by physiologists only in so far as they are approachable. We are well aware that our business is with the unknown knowable, not with the transcendental. During the last twenty years there has been a considerable forward movement in physiology in the psychological direction, partly dependent on discoveries as to the localization of the higher functions of the nervous system, partly on the application of methods of measurement to the concomitant phenomena of psychical processes; and these researches have brought us to the very edge of a region which cannot be explored by our methods, where measurements of time or of space are no longer possible.

In approaching this limit the physiologist is liable to fall into two mistakes: on the one hand, that of passing into the transcendental without knowing it; on the other, that of assuming that what he does not know is not knowledge. The first of these risks seems to me of little moment; first, because the limits of natural knowledge in the psychological direction have been well defined by the best writers, as, for example, by Du Bois-Reymond in his well-known essay "On the Limits of Natural Knowledge," but chiefly because the investigator who knows what he is about is arrested by the impossibility of applying the experimental method to questions beyond its scope. The other mistake is chiefly fallen into by careless thinkers, who, while they object to the employment of intuition even in regions where intuition is the only method by which anything can be learned, attempt to describe and define mental processes in mechanical terms, assigning to these terms meanings which science does not recognize, and thus slide into a kind of speculation which is as futile as it is unphilosophical.

The uneventful history of Ludwig's life—how early he began his investigation of the anatomy and function of the kidneys; how he became just fifty years ago titular professor at Marburg, in the small university of his native State, Hesse Cassel; how in 1849 he removed to Zürich as actual professor and thereupon married; how he was six years later promoted to Vienna—has already been admirably related in these pages by Dr. Stirling. In 1865, after twenty years of professorial experience, but still in the prime of life and, as it turned out, with thirty years of activity still before him, he accepted the chair of physiology at Leipzig. His invitation to that great university was by far the most important occurrence in his life, for the liberality of the Saxon Government, and particularly the energetic support which he received from the enlightened Minister Von Falkenstein, enabled him to accomplish for physiology what had never before been attempted on an adequate scale. No sooner had he been appointed than he set himself to create—what was essential to the progress of the science—a great observatory, arranged not as a museum, but much more like a physical and chemical laboratory, provided with all that was needed for the application of exact methods of research to the investigation of the processes of life. The idea which he had ever in view and which he carried into effect during the last thirty years of his life with signal success was to unite his life work as an investigator with the highest kind of teaching. Even at Marburg and at Zürich he had begun to form a school; for already men nearly of his own age had rallied round him. Attracted in the first instance by his early discoveries, they were held by the force of his character and became permanently associated with him in his work as his loyal friends and followers—in the highest sense his scholars. If therefore we speak of Ludwig as one of the greatest teachers of science the world has seen, we have in mind his relation to the men who ranged themselves under his leadership in the building up of the science of physiology, without reference to his function as an ordinary academical teacher.

Of this relation we can best judge by the careful perusal of the numerous biographical memoirs which have appeared since his death, more particularly those of Professor His (Leipzig), of Professor Kronecker (Bern), who was for many years his coadjutor in the institute, of Professor Von Fick (Würzburg), of Professor Von Kries (Freiburg), of Professor Mosso (Turin), of Professor Fano (Florence), of Professor Tigerstedt (Upsala), of Professor Stirling in England. With the exception of Fick, whose relations with Ludwig were of an earlier date, and of his colleague in the chair of anatomy, all of these distinguished teachers were at one time workers in the Leipzig Institute. All testify their love and veneration for the master, and each contributes some striking touches to the picture of his character.

All Ludwig's investigations were carried out with his scholars. He possessed a wonderful faculty of setting each man to work at a problem suited to his talent and previous training, and this he carried into effect by associating him with himself in some research which he had either in progress or in view. During the early years of the Leipzig period all the work done under his direction was published in the well-known volumes of the *Arbeiten,* and subsequently in the *Archiv für Anatomie und Physiologie* of Du Bois-Reymond. Each "Arbeit" of the laboratory appeared in print under the name of the scholar who operated with his master in its production, but the scholar's part in the work done varied according to its nature and his ability. Sometimes, as Von Kries says, he sat on the window sill, while Ludwig, with the efficient help of his laboratory assistant, Salvenmoser, did the whole of the work. In all cases Ludwig not only formulated the problem, but indicated the course to be followed in each step of the investigation, calling the worker of course into counsel. In the final working up of the results he always took a principal part and often wrote the whole paper. But whether he did little or much, he handed over the whole credit of the performance to his coadjutor. This method of publication has no doubt the disadvantage that it leaves it uncertain what part each had taken; but it is to be re-

membered that this drawback is unavoidable whenever master and
scholar work together and is outweighed by the many advantages
which arise from this mode of cooperation. The instances in which
any uncertainty can exist in relation to the real authorship of the
Leipzig work are exceptional. The well-informed reader does not
need to be told that Mosso or Schmidt, Brunton or Gaskell,
Stirling or Wooldridge were the authors of their papers in a sense
very different from that in which the term could be applied to
some others of Ludwig's pupils. On the whole, the plan must be
judged of by the results. It was by working with his scholars that
Ludwig trained them to work afterwards by themselves and
thereby accomplished so much more than other great teachers
have done.

I do not think that any of Ludwig's contemporaries could be
compared to him in respect of the wide range of his researches. In
a science distinguished from others by the variety of its aims he
was equally at home in all branches and was equally master of all
methods, for he recognized that the most profound biological
question can only be solved by combining anatomical, physical,
and chemical inquiries. It was this consideration which led him in
planning the Leipzig Institute to divide it into three parts, experimental (in the more restricted sense), chemical, and histological.
Well aware that it was impossible for a man who is otherwise
occupied to maintain his familiarity with the technical details of
histology and physiological chemistry, he placed these departments under the charge of younger men capable of keeping them
up to the rapidly advancing standard of the time, his relations with
his coadjutors being such that he had no difficulty in retaining his
hold of the threads of the investigation to which these special lines
of inquiry were contributory.

It is scarcely necessary to say that as an experimenter Ludwig
was unapproachable. The skill with which he carried out difficult
and complicated operations, the care with which he worked, his
quickness of eye and certainty of hand were qualities which he
had in common with great surgeons. In employing animals for
experiment he strongly objected to rough and ready methods,
comparing them to "firing a pistol into a clock to see how it
works." Every experiment ought, he said, to be carefully planned
and meditated on beforehand, so as to accomplish its scientific
purpose and avoid the infliction of pain. To insure this he performed all operations himself, only rarely committing the work to
a skilled coadjutor. His skill in anatomical work was equally remarkable. It had been acquired in early days and appeared

throughout his life to have given him very great pleasure, for Mosso tells how, when occupying the room adjoining that in which Ludwig was working, as he usually did, by himself, he heard the outbursts of glee which accompanied each successful step in some difficult anatomical investigation.

Let us now examine more fully the part which Ludwig played in the revolution of ideas as to the nature of vital processes which, as we have seen, took place in the middle of the present century.

Although, as we shall see afterwards, there were many men who before Ludwig's time investigated the phenomena of life from the physical side, it was he and the contemporaries who were associated with him who first clearly recognized the importance of the principle that vital phenomena can only be understood by comparison with their physical counterparts, and foresaw that in this principle the future of physiology was contained as in a nutshell. Feeling strongly the fruitlessness and unscientific character of the doctrines which were then current, they were eager to discover chemical and physical relations in the processes of life. In Ludwig's intellectual character this eagerness expressed his dominant motive. Notwithstanding that his own researches had in many instances proved that there are important functions and processes in the animal organism which have no physical or chemical analogues, he never swerved either from the principle or from the method founded upon it.

Although Ludwig was strongly influenced by the rapid progress which was being made in scientific discovery at the time that he entered on his career, he derived little from his immediate predecessors in his own science. He is sometimes placed among the pupils of the great comparative anatomist and physiologist, J. Müller. This, however, is a manifest mistake, for Ludwig did not visit Berlin until 1847, when Müller was nearly at the end of his career. At that time he had already published researches of the highest value (those on the mechanism of the circulation and on the physiology of the kidney), and had set forth the line in which he intended to direct his investigations. The only earlier physiologist with whose work that of Ludwig can be said to be in real continuity was E. H. Weber, whom he succeeded at Leipzig and strikingly resembled in his way of working. For Weber Ludwig expressed his veneration more unreservedly than for any other man excepting, perhaps, Helmholtz, regarding his researches as the foundation on which he himself desired to build. Of his colleagues at Marburg he was indebted in the first place to the anatomist, Prof. Ludwig Fick, in whose department he began his career as prosector, and to whom he owed facilities without which he could not have carried out his earlier researches; and in an even higher degree to the great chemist, R. W. Bunsen, from whom he derived that training in the exact sciences which was to be of such inestimable value to him afterwards.

There is reason, however, to believe that, as so often happens, Ludwig's scientific progress was much more influenced by his contemporaries than by his seniors. In 1847, as we learn on the one hand from Du Bois-Reymond, on the other from Ludwig himself, he visited Berlin for the first time. This visit was an important one both for himself and for the future of science, for he there met three men of his own age, Helmholtz, Du Bois-Reymond and Brücke, who were destined to become his lifelong friends, all of whom lived nearly as long as Ludwig himself, and attained to the highest distinction. They all were full of the same enthusiasm. As Ludwig said when speaking of this visit: "We four imagined that we should constitute physiology on a chemicophysical foundation, and give it equal scientific rank with physics, but the task turned out to be much more difficult than we anticipated." These three young men, who were devoted disciples of the great anatomist, had the advantage over their master in the better insight which their training had given them into the fundamental principles of scientific research. They had already gathered around themselves a so-called "physical" school of physiology and welcomed Ludwig on his arrival from Marburg, as one who had of his own initiative undertaken in his own university *das Befreiungswerk aus dem Vitalismus.*

The determination to refer all vital phenomena to their physical or chemical counterparts or analogues, which, as I have said, was the dominant motive in Ludwig's character, was combined with another quality of mind, which, if not equally influential, was even more obviously displayed in his mode of thinking and working. His first aim, even before he sought for any explanation of a structure or of a process, was to possess himself, by all means of observation at his disposal, of a complete objective conception of all its relations. He regarded the faculty of vivid, sensual realization (*lebendige sinnliche Anschauung*) as of special value to the investigator of natural phenomena and did his best to cultivate it in those who worked with him in the laboratory. In himself this objective tendency (if I may be permitted the use of a word which, if not correct, seems to express what I mean) might be regarded as almost a defect, for it made him indisposed to appreciate any sort of knowledge which deals with the abstract. He had a disinclination to philosophical speculation which almost amounted to aversion, and perhaps for a similar reason avoided the use of mathematical methods even in the discussion of scientific questions which admitted of being treated mathematically—contrasting in this respect with his friend Du Bois-Reymond and resembling Brücke. But as a teacher the quality was of immense use to him. His power of vivid realization was the substratum of that many-sidedness which made him, irrespective of his scientific attainments, so attractive a personality.

I am not sure that it can be generally stated that a keen scientific observer is able to appreciate the artistic aspects of nature. In Ludwig's case, however, there is reason to think that æsthetic faculty was as developed as the power of scientific insight. He was a skillful draftsman but not a musician; both arts were, however, a source of enjoyment to him. He was a regular frequenter of the Gewandhaus concerts, and it was his greatest pleasure to bring together gifted musicians in his house, where he played the part of an intelligent and appreciative listener. Of painting he knew more than of music and was a connoisseur whose opinion carried weight. It is related that he was so worried by what he considered bad art, that after the redecoration of the Gewandhaus concert room he was for some time deprived of his accustomed pleasure in listening to music.

Ludwig's social characteristics can only be touched on here in so far as they serve to make intelligible his wonderful influence as a teacher. Many of his pupils at Leipzig have referred to the *"schöne gemeinsamkeit"* which characterized the life there. The harmonious relation which, as a rule, subsisted between men of different education and different nationalities could not have been maintained had not Ludwig possessed side by side with that inflexible earnestness which he showed in all matters of work or duty a certain youthfulness of disposition which made it possible for men much younger than himself to accept his friendship. This sympathetic geniality was, however, not the only or even the chief reason why Ludwig's pupils were the better for having known him. There were not a few of them who for the first time in their lives came into personal relation with a man who was utterly free from selfish aims and vain ambitions, who was scrupulously conscientious in all that he said and did, who was what he seemed and seemed what he was, and who had no other aim than the advancement of his science, and in that advancement saw no other end than the increase of human happiness. These qualities displayed themselves in Ludwig's daily active life in the laboratory, where he was to be found whenever work of special interest was going on; but still more when, as happened on Sunday mornings, he was "at home" in the library of the institute—the corner room in which he ordinarily worked. Many of his "scholars" have put on record their recollections of these occasions, the cordiality of the master's welcome, the wide range and varied interest of his conversation, and the ready appreciation with which he seized on anything that was new or original in the suggestions of those present. Few men live as he did, *"im Ganzen, Guten, Schönen,"* and of those still fewer know how to communicate out of their fullness to others.

Since the middle of the century the progress of physiology has been continuous. Each year has had its record and has brought with it new accessions to knowledge. In one respect the rate of progress was more rapid at first than it is now, for in an unexplored country discovery is relatively easy. In another sense it was slower, for there are now scores of investigators for every one that could be counted in 1840 or 1850. Until recently there has been throughout this period no tendency to revert to the old methods—no new departure—no divergence from the principles which Ludwig did so much to enforce and exemplify.

The wonderful revolution which the appearance of the *Origin of Species* produced in the other branch of biology promoted the progress of physiology, by the new interest which it gave to the study, not only of structure and development, but of all other vital phenomena. It did not, however, in any sensible degree affect our method or alter the direction in which physiologists had been working for two decades. Its most obvious effect was to sever the two subjects from each other. To the Darwinian epoch comparative anatomy and physiology were united, but as the new ontology grew it became evident that each had its own problems and its own methods of dealing with them.

The old vitalism of the first half of the century is easily explained. It was generally believed that, on the whole, things went on in the living body as they do outside of it, but when a difficulty arose in so explaining them the physiologist was ready at once to call in the aid of a "vital force." It must not, however, be forgotten that, as I have already indicated, there were great teachers (such, for example, as Sharpey and Allen Thomson in England, Magendie in France, Weber in Germany) who discarded all vitalistic theories, and concerned themselves only with the study of the time and place relations of phenomena; men who were before their time in insight and were only hindered in their application of chemical and physical principles to the interpretation of the processes of life by the circumstance that chemical and physical knowledge was in itself too little advanced. Comparison was impossible, for the standards were not forthcoming.

Vitalism in its original form gave way to the rapid advance of knowledge as to the correlation of the physical sciences which took place in the forties. Of the many writers and thinkers who contributed to that result, J. R. Mayer and Helmholtz did so most directly, for the contribution of the former to the establishment of the doctrine of the conservation of energy had physiological considerations for its point of departure; and Helmholtz, at the time he wrote the *Erhaltung der Kraft,* was still a physiologist. Consequently, when Ludwig's celebrated *Lehrbuch* came out in 1852, the book which gave the *coup de grâce* to vitalism in the old sense of the word, his method of setting forth the relations of vital phenomena by comparison with their physical or chemical counterparts, and his assertion that it was the task of physiology to make out their necessary dependence on elementary conditions, although in violent contrast with current doctrine, were in no way surprising to those who were acquainted with the then recent progress of research. Ludwig's teaching was indeed no more than a general application of principles which had already been applied in particular instances.

The proof of the nonexistence of a special "vital force" lies in the demonstration of the adequacy of the known sources of energy in the organism to account for the actual day by day expenditure of heat and work; in other words, on the possibility of setting forth an energy balance sheet in which the quantity of food which enters the body in a given period (hour or day) is balanced by an exactly corresponding amount of heat produced or external work done. It is interesting to remember that the work necessary for preparing such a balance sheet (which Mayer had attempted, but from want of sufficient data failed in) was begun thirty years ago in the laboratory of the Royal Institution by the foreign secretary of the Royal Society. But the determinations made by Dr. Frankland related to one side of the balance sheet, that of income. By his researches in 1866 he gave physiologists for the first time reliable information as to the heat value (i.e., the amount of heat yielded by the combustion) of different constituents of food. It still remained to apply methods of exact measurement to the expenditure side of the account. Helmholtz had estimated this, as regards man, as best he might, but the technical difficulties of measuring the expenditure of heat of the animal body appeared until lately to be almost insuperable. Now that it has been at last successfully accomplished, we have the experimental proof that in the process of life there is no production or disappearance of energy. It may be said that it was unnecessary to prove what no scientifically sane man doubted. There are, however, reasons why it is of importance to have objective evidence that food is the sole and adequate source of the energy which we day by day or hour by hour disengage, whether in the form of heat or external work.

In the opening paragraph of this section it was observed that *until recenty* there had been no tendency to revive the vitalistic notion of two generations ago. In introducing the words in italics I referred to the existence at the present time in Germany of a sort of reaction, which under the term *"Neovitalismus"* has attracted some attention—so much indeed that at the Versammlung Deutscher Naturforscher at Lübeck last September it was the subject of one of the general addresses. The author of this address, Professor Rindfleisch, was, I believe, the inventor of the word; but the origin of the movement is usually traced to a work on physiological chemistry which an excellent translation by the late Dr. Wooldridge has made familiar to English students. The author of this work owes it to the language he employs in the introduction on "Mechanism and vitalism" if his position has been misunderstood, for in that introduction he distinctly ranges himself on the vitalistic side. As, however, his vitalism is of such a kind as not to influence his method of dealing with actual problems, it is only in so far of consequence as it may affect the reader. For my own part I feel grateful to Professor Bange for having produced an interesting and readable book on a dry subject, even though that interest may be partly due to the introduction into the discussion of a question which, as he presents it, is more speculative than scientific.

As regards other physiological writers to whom vitalistic tendencies have been attributed, it is to be observed that none of them has even suggested that the doctrine of a "vital force" in its old sense should be revived. Their contention amounts to little more than this, that in certain recent instances improved methods of research appear to have shown that processes at first regarded as entirely physical or chemical do not conform so precisely as they were expected to do to chemical and physical laws. As these instances are all essentially analogous, reference to one will serve to explain the bearing of the rest.

Those who have any acquaintance with the structure of the animal body will know that there exists in the higher animals, in addition to the system of veins by which the blood is brought back from all parts to the heart, another less considerable system of branched tubes, the lymphatics, by which, if one may so express it, the leakage of the blood vessels is collected. Now, without inquiring into the why of this system, Ludwig and his pupils made and continued for many years elaborate investigations which were for long the chief sources of our knowledge, their general result being that the efficient cause of the movement of the lymph, like that of the blood, was mechanical. At the Berlin Congress in 1890 new observations by Professor Heidenhain of Breslau made it appear that under certain conditions the process of lymph formation does not go on in strict accordance with the physical laws by which leakage through membranes is regulated, the experimental results being of so unequivocal a kind that, even had they not been confirmed, they must have been received without hesitation. How is such a case as this to be met? The "Neovitalists" answer promptly by reminding us that there are cells, i.e., living individuals, placed at the inlets of the system of drainage without which it would not work, that these let in less or more liquid according to circumstances, and that in doing so they act in obedience, not to physical laws, but to vital ones—to internal laws which are special to themselves.

Now it is perfectly true that living cells, like working bees, are both the architects of the hive and the sources of its activity, but if we ask how honey is made it is no answer to say that the bees make it. We do not require to be told that cells have to do with the making of lymph as with every process in the animal organism, but what we want to know is how they work, and to this we shall never get an answer so long as we content ourselves with merely explaining one unknown thing by another. The action of cells must be explained, if at all, by the same method of comparison with physical or chemical analogues that we employ in the investigation of organs.

Since 1890 the problem of lymph formation has been attacked by a number of able workers, among others here in London, by Dr. Starling, of Guy's Hospital, who, by sedulously studying the conditions under which the discrepancies between the actual and the expected have arisen, has succeeded in untying several knots. In reference to the whole subject, it is to be noticed that the process by which difficulties are brought into view is the same as that by which they are eliminated. It is one and the same method throughout, by which, step by step, knowledge perfects itself—at one time by discovering errors, at another by correcting them; and if at certain stages in this progress difficulties seem insuperable we can gain nothing by calling in even provisionally the aid of any sort of eidolon, whether "cell," "protoplasm," or internal principle.

It thus appears to be doubtful whether any of the biological writers who have recently professed vitalistic tendencies are in reality vitalists. The only exception that I know is to be found in the writings of a well-known morphologist, Dr. Hans Driesch, who has been led by his researches on what is now called the mechanics of evolution to revert to the fundamental conception of vitalism that the laws which govern vital processes are not physical, but biological—that is, peculiar to the living organism and limited thereto in their operation. Dr. Driesch's researches as to the modifications which can be produced by mechanical interference in the early stages of the process of ontogenesis have enforced upon him considerations which he evidently regards as new, though they are familiar enough to physiologists. He recognizes that although by the observation of the successive stages in the ontogenetic process one may arrive at a perfect knowledge of the relation of these stages to each other, this leaves the efficient causes of the development unexplained (*führt nicht zu einem Erkenntniss ihrer bewirkenden Ursachen*). It does not teach us why one form springs out of another. This brings him at once face to face with a momentous question. He has to encounter three possibilities. He may either join the camp of the biological agnostics and say with Du Bois-Reymond *"ignoramus et ignorabimus,"* or be content to work on in the hope that the physical laws that underlie and explain organic evolution may sooner or later be discovered, or he may seek for some hitherto hidden law of organism of which the known facts of ontogenesis are the expression, and which, if accepted as a law of nature, would explain everything. Of the three alternatives Driesch prefers the last, which is equivalent to declaring himself an out-and-out vitalist. He trusts by means of his experimental investigations of the mechanics of evolution to arrive at "elementary conceptions" on which by "mathematical deduction" a complete theory of evolution may be founded.

If this anticipation could be realized, if we could construct with the aid of those new principia the ontogeny of a single living being, the question whether such a result was or was not inconsistent with the uniformity of nature would sink into insignificance as compared with the splendor of such a discovery.

But will such a discovery ever be made? It seems to me even more improbable than that of a physical theory of organic evolution. It is satisfactory to reflect that the opinion we may be led to entertain on this theoretical question need not affect our estimate of the value of Dr. Driesch's fruitful experimental researches.

Joseph Dalton Hooker *

1817–1911

———◆———

EDWIN RAY LANKESTER †

IT OFTEN happens in the progress of human thought that periods
of special importance are marked, not, as rarely occurs, by the
emergence of a solitary genius, but by the appearance of a group
of gifted men of like habit of mind and enthusiasm for a given
branch of study. Their coincidence in mental activity has been
due sometimes to family connection and local association, sometimes to the system of universities in which a professor of genius
is succeeded by his pupil and he again by his, so that a "school"
originates which may spread its members and its teaching far and
wide.

In the middle of the nineteenth century a group of naturalists
appeared in this country who were destined to bring about a
momentous change in human thought, by placing on a firm basis
the doctrine of "organic evolution"—a doctrine which includes
the gradual and "natural" development of living things from nonliving matter, and further the gradual and "natural" development
of man from an animal ancestry. The group we have in view has
Charles Lyell (born in 1797) as its starting point. Devoted from
his earliest years to the study of natural history (his father being
an accomplished botanist), Charles Lyell, when an undergraduate
at Exeter College, Oxford, was attracted to geological study by the
lectures of Canon Buckland. He was called to the bar, but fortunately his inherited property enabled him to abandon that profession when he was 30 years old, and to give all his energy to his
favorite science.

In 1830–1832 Lyell published his memorable work entitled *The*

* A.R., 1918, pp. 585–601. First published in *Quarterly Review,* Oct. 1918.
† British biologist (1847–1929).

418

Principles of Geology: An Attempt to Explain the Former Changes of the Earth's Surface by Reference to Causes Now in Operation. That book and personal friendship with its author had a commanding influence upon two younger men, Charles Robert Darwin and Joseph Dalton Hooker, the former 12 years and the latter 20 years Lyell's junior. Darwin, who had studied geology with Sedgwick of Cambridge, was away on the voyage of the *Beagle* from 1831 to 1836, when Lyell's great book was published, but came immediately under its influence on his return, and in 1838 was closely associated, as secretary of the Geological Society, with Lyell, for whom he conceived a profound admiration and lifelong regard.

Hooker left England in 1839, being then 22 years old, to accompany Captain (afterwards Sir) James Clark Ross, the experienced Arctic navigator, on the expedition of the *Erebus* and *Terror* to the Southern Hemisphere and Antarctic polar regions. The main purpose of this expedition was to make observations on terrestrial magnetism and to determine the position of the southern magnetic pole. But Ross was an ardent naturalist and anxious to observe and collect both plants and marine animals, and accordingly managed to take young Hooker as surgeon (he was M.D. of Glasgow) to the *Erebus* and botanist to the expedition. Ross not only gave his young surgeon every facility to collect plants in the various lands visited, but also employed him to work the towing net and make drawings of marine invertebrates when at sea. Some 60 years later a large portfolio of these beautiful and interesting drawings, which had never been published, was placed in the hands of the present writer by their venerable author, to ascertain whether, after so long an interval, they might have scientific value.

Young Hooker had Charles Darwin's example before him, and the recently published *Journal of a Naturalist on H. M. S. Beagle* in his cabin, when he sailed on the *Erebus*, but did not make Darwin's acquaintance until 1847, four years after his return from the Antarctic. Hooker's association with Lyell was earlier, for the Lyells of Kinnordy were intimate friends of his father; and it was from Sir Charles Lyell's father that he received the newly issued copy of Darwin's *Journal*, just in time to take it with him to the Antarctic. With Charles Lyell's great book he had early familiarity, and he had also read Robert Chambers's *Vestiges of the Natural History of Creation*, which appeared in 1832. Though not a very convincing work, it turned his thoughts, with very definite results, to the question of the mutability of species—already raised by the essential nature of Lyell's geological doctrine and widely discussed at that time in consequence of the writings of Lamarck and Saint-Hilaire.

To this group of three (Lyell, Darwin, and Hooker), who were richly stored with knowledge of living things by their explorations in many parts of the globe, there was now added a fourth, T. H. Huxley. He made Hooker's acquaintance first at the British Association meeting at Ipswich in 1851, having recently returned from the voyage of the surveying ship *Rattlesnake,* to which he had been appointed surgeon with a view to the opportunities thus provided of making studies in marine zoology. Old Sir John Richardson, the Arctic explorer, a first-rate naturalist and head of Haslar Hospital, whither in those days young naval surgeons were sent on probation, had detected Huxley's abilities and secured for him the post on the *Rattlesnake* in 1847, just as eight years earlier he had used his influence to secure for Hooker a similar position on the *Erebus.*

These four men, Lyell, Darwin, Hooker, and Huxley, were the actual "begetters" and the chief propagators, both in the more restricted world of science and among the larger public, of the vivifying doctrine of organic evolution. The close personal ties which linked the first three were strengthened by the marriage of Joseph Hooker in August 1851 to Frances Henslow, eldest daughter of the Cambridge professor of botany, the man who turned Charles Darwin to a scientific career. Huxley came to them, to use Hooker's own simile, "as steel to a magnet," and was soon admitted to the closest intimacy, giving them and receiving from them the warmest affection. A tie of fellowship between Hooker, Darwin, and Huxley was that they were all three "old salts" and had the training and "the knowledge of men" given by service in the royal navy. Huxley also met and sealed a close alliance with John Tyndall at the Ipswich gathering of the British Association in 1851, and so brought that physical philosopher into close and permanent relationship with the Darwinian "nucleus." He, too, brought Herbert Spencer into constant relation with the group; whilst young John Lubbock (afterwards Lord Avebury), who was a neighbor of Darwin's, now settled at Down in Kent, became, both by his scientific work in zoology, botany, and geology, and by his personal charm, a welcome associate.

In 1864 Huxley, Hooker, George Busk (surgeon and naturalist), Spencer, and Tyndall, who had been close friends of Huxley's ever since his return from the voyage of the *Rattlesnake,* together with Frankland, the chemist, Hirst, the mathematician, old colleagues and allies of Tyndall, and Sir John Lubbock and

Spottiswoode, friends of them all, founded the "X Club," which met once a month for dinner, its purpose being, as Mr. Leonard Huxley tells us:

. . . to afford a definite meeting point for a few friends who were in danger of drifting apart in the flood of busy lives. But it was in itself a representative group of scientific men destined to play a large part in the history of science. Five of them (there were nine in all) received the Royal medal of the Royal Society; three the Copley medal, the highest scientific award; one, the Rumford; six were presidents of the British Association, three were Associates of the Institute of France; and from amongst them the Royal Society chose a secretary, a foreign secretary, a treasurer, and three successive presidents. . . . They included representatives of half a dozen branches of science—mathematics, physics, philosophy, chemistry, botany, and biology, and all were animated by similar ideas of the high function of science and of the great Society which should be the chief representative of science in this country.

Not unnaturally the club exercised, during its 28 years of existence (it expired in 1892, owing to the dispersal of its original members and the decision not to elect new ones), a great influence on the progress of scientific organization, an influence which assuredly was not sectarian nor exercised for party purposes. While the club, though bound up with the Darwinian movement, did not comprise the originators of that new doctrine, Lyell and Darwin himself—on account of their health and absorption in special pursuits at a distance from the town—it also, for a similar reason, did not include Alfred Russel Wallace, who had lately returned to England from his long sojourn in the tropics. His name can never be forgotten as that of one who, independently of Darwin and while exploring in the tropics, conceived and stated the identical theory of the origin of species by the natural selection of favored varieties in "the struggle for existence," which had been more fully worked out, though held back from publication, by the elder naturalist. Wallace, as all the world knows, gladly gave all credit in the matter to Darwin and contributed by his original observations and arguments, and by the lucid exposition given in a series of invaluable books for a period of more than forty years, to the establishment of Darwin's doctrine of organic evolution. Wallace held himself very much aloof from the London whirlpool, finding happiness and full occupation for his long life in scientific work.

It is perhaps a mere coincidence, but in any case a very important fact, that we have a series of remarkable volumes giving in an unusually complete form the *Life and Letters* of Lyell, of Darwin, and of Huxley. Happily they wrote many letters, fortunately preserved for publication, in which their scientific work and the development of their views, as well as delightful revelations of character, of their tastes, their likes and dislikes, and of their heroic struggles and daily occupations, are recorded. These volumes can perhaps hardly be called biographies; they are the materials for considered well-balanced biography. They have been gathered by loving hands and connected by a thread of narrative and explanatory notes. Now we have a similar *Life and Letters of Hooker,* the material for which has been arranged by his widow, and presented in due order by Leonard Huxley, who had already done for his father's memory what he has here, with skill and experience, done for that of his father's closest friend. The letters here given, taken with those of Darwin and Huxley and Lyell, interweave with and complete one another, giving a remarkably close picture of the growth of a great scientific theory.

We have indicated in bald outline the place which Hooker occupied in the little group of naturalists who established, in the later half of the nineteenth century, the doctrine of organic evolution. Since we are here concerned with the story of his life and work, it is now time to state more specifically what was his actual contribution to the science of his time and then to point out, as these volumes of his *Life and Letters* enable us to do, to what native gifts of mind and character, on the one hand, and to what fortunate circumstances of training and association on the other, this contribution was due. Those are the inquiries which must always be of foremost interest when we are in possession of the detailed story of a great man's life.

Hooker was before and beyond everything else a great botanist, the greatest "knower" of plants of his day, whether we estimate the immense number and variety of plants which he knew, or the thoroughness of that knowledge, or the vast area—that of the whole earth's surface, the vegetable population of which became familiar to him, either in the dried collections of travelers or (to an extent never achieved by any earlier or contemporary botanist) in their living condition. The latter result was attained in two distinct ways: first, by his prolonged and often perilous journeys to the Southern Hemisphere, to India and the Himalayan region, to Palestine and the Lebanon, to the Atlas Mountains and to North America, and secondly, by his control of the most extensive and admirably organized botanic garden in the world, where living plants were almost daily received or were raised from seed sent from every part of the earth's surface.

Probably the greatest permanent benefit conferred on mankind by Hooker—his greatest contribution to science—was his organization, as a great and permanent state institution, of the gardens, plantations, glass houses, museums, laboratories, and the incomparable herbarium at Kew, together with its highly trained staff of all grades, its splendid and continuous series of publications, its world-wide correspondence, and close relations with botanical institutions in the colonies and India, so as to form a vast living mechanism, working under his incessant care for the increase of botanical science. The indifference, the opposition, the sheer brutality, by which his efforts were too frequently opposed, and the ultimate triumph by which his tenacity of purpose, his honesty and unworldliness of character, were rewarded, can be realized and appreciated by the reader of this book. So also can one learn with pleasure of the fine men, both among his scientific colleagues and the few intelligent officials with whom he had to deal, who sympathized with and helped him.

Here we may read the full story of the ignorant insolence of one Ayrton—an obscure politician who became a minister of the Crown and proposed to make Kew into a mere pleasure garden and to give his orders to Hooker as to a head gardener, but was, by a timely rally of wiser statesmen and lovers of science, brought to heel like a whipped dog. Here, too, we read of the mean financial tricks of the East India Company, the delays of the Admiralty, the stupid parsimony of the Treasury relieved by the generosity and friendship of Lord Dalhousie, the Governor General of India; the good-will of fine old admirals; and the enthusiasm of many high-placed officials (such as Bertram Mitford, Lord Redesdale), and well-tried friends who valued pure science and were spellbound by Hooker's abilities, persistence, freedom from all desire for personal profit, and simple-minded devotion to one noble end—the building up of what were for him two inseparables, Kew and botanical science.

Hooker's more direct contributions to scientific botany are parallel in importance to the creation of the great institution (founded by his father and completed by the loyal help of his son-in-law and successor, Sir William Thiselton Dyer), wherein he worked out during many years the enormous collections of plants brought thither by himself and amplified by official and private collections. His first scientific paper, on some new mosses, was written and published in 1837, when he was only 20 years of age;

his last in 1911, on some Indian species of the balsams (genus *Impatiens*), a large and difficult group to which he gave minute study, dissecting them under the microscope and drawing them with all the skill and assiduity of his youth, until within a few days of his death in his ninety-fifth year. The mere titles of the papers and volumes which Hooker produced in those 74 years of work occupy 20 pages in the *Life*. No mere enumeration of their number can give an idea of their bulk, of the number of drawings and often colored pictures which illustrate them, of the tireless industry which produced them, or of their scientific weight and purpose.

For the convenience of ready publication he carried on throughout his life (with the assistance in later years of other botanists, his chosen colleagues) *Hooker's Icones Plantarum*, founded by his father in 1837, and the *Botanical Magazine*, founded by William Curtis in 1787, which has appeared regularly every month during 130 years. It was edited for 40 years by Sir William Hooker, on whose death in 1865 Sir Joseph became editor and chief contributor, handing it over in 1904 to his successor as director of Kew, Sir William Thiselton Dyer. For 78 years the two Fitches, uncle and nephew, were the only artists (without rivals for the perfection of their work) employed on the production of the hundreds of plates picturing new or rare plants published in the *Botanical Magazine*. But Hooker's greatest works were published as separate volumes, usually by the aid of grants from government departments. Such were the *Flora Antarctica* (1844–1847), 2 volumes, with 198 plates; the *Flora Novæ Zælandiæ* (1853-1855), with 130 plates; the *Flora Tasmaniæ*, with 200 plates; and the *Flora of British India* (by J. D. H. assisted by various botanists), 1872–1897, 7 volumes. A great number of important papers of smaller bulk, but always of special significance, were published by him in the *Transactions of the Linnæan Society*, in the journal of the Geographical Society and other journals, and as contributions to the works of other authorities, British and foreign.

Hooker did a vast amount of work with his own hands, his own pencil and pen. The mechanical work of sorting the "hay stacks," as collections of dried plants are irreverently called, the selection of specimens for description and incorporation in the herbarium and of duplicates for distribution to other botanical institutions and individuals (a proceeding by which exchanges were obtained and the completeness of the Kew herbarium assured), was always a delight to him; the mechanical labor and the mere handling of plants being, as he tells us, a relief from closer work and yet conducive to thought and reflection bearing on his one great purpose.

Of course he had an efficient staff and distinguished botanists as volunteer assistants, attracted by the unique conveniences for study afforded by the great herbarium, the library and the working-rooms, for which by degrees, following out and developing the cherished scheme of his father, he succeeded in getting the reluctant officials of the Treasury and the Board of Works to disburse the necessary funds.

The great interest for Hooker in all this accumulation of knowledge touching the flora of every part of the world, over and above the mere record of new plants and their habitat, was the discovery of the causes which have led to the present geographical distribution of plants. The problem continually presented itself to him in his travels. Take, for instance, the following passage in a letter written to his father from the Thibet frontier in 1848:

To-day I went up the flanks of Donkiah to 19,300 feet . . . The mountains, especially Kinchin-jhow, are beyond all description beautiful; from whichever side you view this latter mountain, it is a castle of pure blue glacier ice, 4,000 feet high and 6 or 8 miles long. I do wish I were not the only person who has ever seen it or dwelt among its wonders . . . I was greatly pleased with finding my most Antarctic plant, *Lecanora miniata,* at the top of the pass; and to-day I saw stony hills at 19,000 feet stained wholly orange-red with it, exactly as the rocks of Cockburn Island were in 64° south. Is not this most curious and interesting? To find the identical plant forming the only vegetation at the two extreme limits of vegetable life is always interesting; but to find it absolutely in both instances painting a landscape so as to render its color conspicuous in each case 5 miles off, is wonderful.

How does it come about that this plant flourishes in two such widely remote regions? How can we account for hundreds of other instance of the presence of identical plants in isolated localities thousands of miles apart, and for the absence of others in regions contiguous with one in which they abound?

The great botanists preceding Hooker had believed in the "special creation" of this endless variety of species and widely differing grades and elaboration of vegetable life, as an ultimate fact. Buffon at the end of the eighteenth century had pointed out the connection of climate with the distribution of plants and argued that vegetation must have commenced where the cooling globe was first cold enough to support it—i. e., at a pole. He remarks that "the same temperature might have been expected, all other circumstances being equal, to produce the same beings in different parts of the globe both in the animal and vegetable kingdoms."

To him also we owe the recognition of the limitation of groups of species to regions separated from one another by "natural barriers." Tournefort had, still earlier, pointed out the likeness between vegetation of successive elevations, implying successive reduction of temperature, and that of successive degrees of latitude carrying the same successive change of climatic condition. Humboldt (whom Hooker met in Paris in 1845) showed that many great natural orders of plants (*Gramineae, Leguminosae, Compositae,* etc.) are subject to certain laws of increase or decrease relatively to other plants in going polewards (in both hemispheres) and skywards. The construction of the "isothermals" of the globe, which we owe to Humboldt, was a great instrument toward the advancement of geographical botany. Hooker regarded him (as he says in a letter to Darwin in 1881) as the greatest of scientific travelers; and in 1845 he writes of him (vol. i, p. 185):

He was never tired of coming to ask me questions about my voyages [the Antarctic expedition with Ross]; he certainly is still a most wonderful man, with a sagacity and memory and capability for generalizing that are quite marvelous.

Lyell had shown that distribution is not a thing of the present only or of the present condition of climates and present outline and contours of lands. He also showed that our continents and oceans had experienced great changes of surface and climate since the introduction of the existing assemblages of plants and animals; that there had been a glacial period, and long before that a warm Arctic period, as proved by the abundant fossils (brought back by Arctic travelers) of plants belonging to a warm temperate zone. But these relations of flora and climate were looked upon as the outcome of direct adaptation by sudden and inexplicable acts of creation. It was Hooker's special merit and privilege to be the first to introduce into the attempt to explain the facts of the geographical distribution of plants, the conceptions already current in the scientific world of (*a*) the *mutability* and derivative origin of species; and (*b*) the *migration* of floras. This he did independently, by his own "self-thought," as Darwin termed it. His views are apparent in his earlier publications, but are most fully set forth in his *Introductory Essay to the Flora Tasmaniae,* dealing with the Antarctic flora as a whole.

His study of Darwin's plants from the Galapagos Islands and their relation to those of other tropical islands and of the South American Continent brought him into close relation with Darwin, whom he visited in 1847. This was the beginning of their memorable intimacy and continuous exchange of letters (contained in these volumes and the similar *Life and Letters of Darwin*). These letters were really conversations as to endless botanical details—inquiries made and answered, criticisms and arguments submitted by one to the other. They form a record of surpassing interest to all future generations of biologists. Hooker's stores of knowledge of fact in every department of botanical science were of essential service to Darwin, while Darwin's marvelous fecundity in original suggestions as to the explanation and the significance of facts and his remorseless criticism of those suggestions by appeal to other facts and to experiment, were a perennial stimulus to Hooker, who was himself a theorist, a generalizer—what is sometimes called a "philosopher"—of large outlook. Lyell wrote in 1859 to Hooker of the *Introductory Essay to the Flora Tasmaniae:*

I have just finished the reading of your splendid Essay on the Origin of Species, as illustrated by your wide botanical experience, and think it goes far to raise the variety making hypothesis to the rank of a theory, as accounting for the manner in which new species enter the world.

And Darwin wrote:

I have finished your essay. To my judgment it is by far the grandest and most interesting essay on subjects of the nature discussed I have ever read.

Hooker was the earliest prominent naturalist to declare this adhesion to the theory of the origin of species by natural selection set forth by Darwin in his historic volume of 1859, but his complete adhesion to it was only arrived at by long and minute discussion with Darwin of his data, his arguments, and inferences, extending over some years both before and after 1859, in which the two naturalists were in constant communication. It must be borne in mind that Darwin's theory of the survival of favored varieties by natural selection was something additional to the hypothesis of the derivative origin of species which Hooker had supported. Darwin's theory gave an explanation of that derivation and showed it to be the necessary result of existing natural causes.

Hooker continued during the next 22 years to take a leading part in the development of an understanding of the geographical distribution of organisms on the earth's surface in the light of Darwin's great doctrine of natural selection. He was at times much perplexed by the attempt to demarcate natural phyto-geographical provinces and subprovinces, as distinct from merely topographical areas; and finally, he seems to have come to the same conclusion as that which he reached in the classification of the vegetable kingdom adopted by him in the monumental work which he produced in collaboration with Bentham, the *Genera Plantarum* (3 vols., octavo, 1862–1883). This conclusion was that, while we are still seeing a closer knowledge of the phyletic connections of the floras and faunas of the world, it is, in view of *practical* purposes (that is to say, for facilitating the accumulation and orderly arrangement of our knowledge), better to adopt a frankly arbitrary series of groups and provinces agreed upon and accepted because they are traditional and serviceable for purposes of reference, than to assume prematurely that we are in a position to define the limits and connections of all natural phyto-geographical provinces and of all phyletic groups. To do this we have not yet (he thought) sufficient knowledge, though we already see clearly much of the outlines and the needful lines of inquiry.

The means and the causes of the migration of plants were matters of extreme importance in the great problem of distribution and the closely connected problem of the changes of land and water on the earth's surface. These were the subject of speculation and inquiry by both Darwin and Hooker. Hooker had at first put forward the hypothesis of a lost circumpolar continent in order to account for the facts of plant distribution in the southern hemisphere. But Darwin favored the view of the persistence even from Silurian times of the great continental masses at present existing, and the radiation from the northern temperate and subarctic region of successive floras by spreading along the cold mountain chains which extend through the tongue-like southward projections of continental land—today traceable as South America, Africa, and Indo-Malaya. Transport of seeds, etc., by ocean currents, by wind, and by birds and other such agencies was shown experimentally by Darwin to be possible in many cases, but the emergence and submergence of large tracts of land as bridges or connections across the deep ocean beds were rejected by him. Hooker writes to Darwin in 1881:

Were you not the first to insist on this [the permanence since the Silurian period of the present continents and oceans], or at least to point this out? Do you think that Wallace's summing up of the proof of it is good? I know I once disputed the doctrine or rather could not take it in; but let that pass.

He goes on to say, in reference to the address which he was preparing for the British Association meeting at York, in which after many years' labor he expressed his final conclusions on geographical distribution:

I must wind up with the doctrine of general distribution being primarily from north to south with no similar general flow from south to north— thus supporting the doctrine which has its last expression in Dyer's essay read before the geograph. society and referred to in my last R[oyal] S[ociety] address (1879).

The conclusions at present held on this great subject, which so long occupied Hooker's attention as well as that of his friends Darwin and Wallace, are fully and admirably stated by Hooker's son-in-law and successor at Kew in his article on the "Distribution of Plants" in the last edition of the *Encyclopedia Britannica*—an essay which permanently associates the name of Sir William Thiselton Dyer with those of Hooker and Darwin as a great master in this many-sided field of scientific speculation.

While Hooker never ceased to carry on by his own individual work and that of his staff the preparation and publication of systematic "floras" of all parts of the British Empire, with a view to a full understanding of the origin of species and their geographical distribution (perhaps we should reverse the order of those terms), his botanical work was by no means limited to this. The *Life* gives a full picture of his activities, which we may briefly summarize by mentioning some of his publications, while his letters, there reproduced, to his father, to Lyell, Darwin, Harvey (of Dublin), Bentham, Bryan Hodgson, Asa Gray, Huxley, Paget, and a host of other friends and fellow-workers, reveal the methods of his scientific work as well as his aims and struggles, the steps of his official and public career, and his family life. From them, too, we can gather his views not only on scientific problems, but on art, literature, politics, education, and religion.

From the long list of his works (other than those already cited) we select first that on *The Rhododendrons of Sikkim-Himalaya* (1849–1851), edited by his father from material sent home by him while he was away collecting, drawing and mapping in the Himalayas. It is a sample of the beauty of form and color which entrances the true naturalist, however austere may be his devotion (as was Hooker's) to pure science. He writes: "It is a far grander and better book than even I expected. . . . All the Indian world is in love with my Rhododendron book."

Then we have his *Himalayan Journals, or Notes of a Naturalist in Bengal,* the *Sikkim and Nepal Himalayas,* the *Khasia Moun-*

tains, etc., (1854, reissued 1905), a book like Darwin's *Voyage of the Beagle* and Wallace's *Malay Archipelago* for all to read and enjoy; his *Students' Flora of the British Islands* (1870), which has run through three editions; and his *Primer of Botany* (1876), which has been reprinted 20 times in three editions—"the rashest and most profitable of all my undertakings," as he called it in a letter to Asa Gray. His paper "On the Diatomaceous Vegetation of the Antarctic Ocean" (*Brit. Assoc. Reports,* 1847) was the forerunner of that study of oceanic deposits which many years later became (especially in connection with the voyage of the *Challenger*) a great and important branch of research. Similarly his papers on Stigmaria and Lepidostrobi in the memoirs of the Geological Survey, 1848, were the starting point of the study of the tissues of ancient fossil plants by means of the microscope. He was the first to have sections of fossils cut sufficiently transparent for that purpose, a method which in the hands of a later generation has yielded very important results.

In the domain of physiology, besides some other contributions, there stands out his remarkable work on the attraction, capture, and digestion of insects by the pitcher plants (*Brit. Assoc. Reports,* Belfast, 1874, and *Nature,* 1870). The work was suggested by Darwin when investigating the carnivorous habits of the sundew (*Drosera*). Experiments as to the digestive ferment and microscopical investigation of the glands, etc., were made by Hooker, aided by Dyer, at Kew. In the special study and exploration of remarkable morphological characters, Hooker's investigation of the root parasites known as *Balanophoreae*—curiously simple in structure, without leaves or petals—formerly thought to be allied to the fungi, but shown by Hooker to be degenerate mistletoes, is a sample of his morphological work ("On the Structure and Affinities of the *Balanophoreae," Linnæan Society Transactions,* 1856). He made acquaintance with these strange plants both in New Zealand and in the Himalayas.

But the most striking thing which he did in this way was his description of the morphology, development and histology, and the determination of the affinities of a weird-looking South African plant discovered by Dr. Welwitsch in dry country inland from Walfisch Bay, and sent by him to Kew. Hooker named it after its discoverer; and specimens of it (since received through other travelers) have been kept in cultivation ever since in one of the hothouses at Kew ("On *Welwitschia,* a new Genus of *Gnetaceæ," Trans. Linn. Soc.,* 1863). Hooker's triumph in this investigation was that of showing, by microscopic examination of the tissues and of the reproductive structures and their development, that this strange-looking plant is one of the *Gnetaceæ,* a family including the little European Ephedra and grouped with the Cycads, the Gingko trees, and the Conifers in the great assemblage called *Gymnosperms.* In the *Life and Letters* we have a delightful picture (which will stir the sympathy of every morphologist) of his excitement, his hard work with the microscope, his reasoning, his results, and the reaction that followed. He writes (Jan. 20, 1862), to Huxley:

This blessed angola plant has proved even more wonderful than I expected—*figurez vous* a Dicotyledonous embryo, expanding like a dream into a huge broad woody brown disk, eight years old and of texture and surface like an overdone loaf, 5 feet diam. by 1½ high above the ground, and never growing higher, and whose two *cotyledons* become the two and only two leaves the plant ever has, and these each a good fathom long. From the edges of this disk above the two leaves, rise branched annual pannicles, bearing cones something like pine cones, which contain either all female flowers, or all hermaphrodite flowers; the hermaphrodite flowers consist of one naked ovule absolutely the same as of Ephedra, in the organic axis of the flower, surrounded by six stamens and a four-leaved perigone. The female flower is quite different.

Lastly, fancy my joy at discovering the key to the development of this hypertrophical embryo taking to become a plant after the fashion it does; and at my being able to show that . . . it is undoubtedly a member of the family Gnetaceae amongst Gymnosperms, as the structure of the ovule and development of the seed and embryo clearly show. It is out of all question the most wonderful plant ever brought to this country—and the very ugliest. It reopens the whole question of Gymnosperms as a class, and will (in the eyes of most) raise these, as I always said they would be raised, to equivalence in these respects with Angiosperms.

At this moment he was fortunate enough to receive five splendid specimens from a Mr. Monteiro, of Loanda, who "like a trump" sent down the coast at his request to get them. Much help, he says, was given by one of his staff, Professor Oliver, who had been examining the tissues where he had left off, making "some charming drawings that will save me a world of trouble." The completed monograph was read at the Linnæan Society in December 1862 and published in the *Transactions.* The reaction after a heavy and exciting piece of work set in, as so many ardent investigators know it has a way of doing. When it was finished he wrote to Darwin:

My wife went to Cambridge and enjoyed it; I stayed at home (and enjoyed it), working away at "Welwitschia" every day and almost every night. I entirely agree with you, by the way, that after long working at a subject, and after making something of it, one invariably finds that it all seems dull, flat, stale, and unprofitable. This feeling, however, you will observe, only comes (most mercifully) after you really have made out something worth knowing. I feel as if everybody must know more of Welwitschia than I do, and yet I can not but believe I have, ill or well, expounded and faithfully recorded a heap of the most curious facts regarding a single plant that have been brought to light for many years. The whole thing is, however, a dry record of singular structures, and sinks down to the level of the dullest descriptive account of dead matter beside your jolly dancing facts anent orchid-life and bee-life. I have looked at an orchid or two since reading the orchid book, and feel that I could never have made out one of your points, even had I limitless leisure, zeal and material. I am a dull dog, a very dull dog. I may content myself with the per contra reflection that you could not (be dull enough to) write a "Genera Plantarum" which is just what I am best fitted for. I feel that I have a call that way and you the other.

A splendid and illuminating revelation of a generous and too-modest character!

As a concluding item in our necessarily incomplete but representative selection from the long list of Hooker's varied work in and for science, we must cite his action when president of the Royal Society in 1878 in raising a fund of £ 10,000 (chiefly by subscription from wealthy friends of his own among the Fellows of the Society), by which new Fellows were relieved of the large entrance fee and all were in future to pay a reduced annual subscription of only £ 3. This admirable measure, entirely due to Hooker's initiative, had the result that, as Leonard Huxley writes, "no man henceforth need be kept outside the society on the score of money." Of the many services in economic botany, which under his direction Kew rendered and continues to render to distant parts of the Empire, we have no space to say more than that they comprise the introduction from South America to India of the quinine plant and of the rubber tree (*Hevea*), and the scientific supervision of the cultivation in the West Indies of the neglected sources of wealth—the sugar cane, tobacco, and Jamaica oranges.

When we examine, as the *Life and Letters* and our own observation of him enable us to do, the personal qualities which carried Hooker through his exceptionally long life with such splendid success, such unfailing spirit and contentment, and such lasting benefit to humanity (he was, we learn, selected by the Japanese, soon after his death, as "one of the 29 heroes of the world that modern time has produced"), we find that the emergence of those qualities was not due to heredity alone, but largely to the training which they received from a gifted and affectionate father, for whom he had profound sympathy and filial devotion. Hooker was born with a vigorous constitution and great physical endurance. He had an inborn tenacity of purpose and single-minded attitude to life, and was as remarkable for his frank honesty as for his courage. He inherited from his father and his maternal grandfather (both botanists) his aptitude for botanical science, but it was the teaching and example of his father which, from his earliest years, trained and developed that aptitude. He modestly but with characteristic insight said of himself when at the age of 70 he received the Copley medal of the Royal Society, that he had no genius, no exceptional powers or exceptional talent, but that he possessed that inward motive power—some heat, some fervor, which compels us to exercise our faculties and to ripen the fruits of our labors—which he would call "the wish to do well," expressed in the modest motto chosen for himself 400 years ago by Prince Henry the Navigator, *"talent de bien faire."*

His constant association from boyhood onwards with his father in the garden and herbarium created by the latter in Glasgow after his appointment as professor made botany a part of his very existence. At the same time the aptitude for it must have been born in him. It was not inherited by his elder brother, William, who, having the same opportunities, showed no liking for the subject, and, though more vivacious than his younger brother, displayed no scientific bent. From this point of view it is interesting to note that not one of Joseph Hooker's six sons has been attracted by botany or by scientific research. Sir William Hooker, a man of distinction in science and of influence in the official world, was able to communicate to his son his own tastes and ambitions, and to secure for him that early official employment which started him on his career as an investigator and established him for life in the great center of botanical science created by Sir William.

The intimate association of father and son and the complete devotion of the younger man to the development of the elder's cherished projects find a parallel in the lifework of Alexander Agassiz,* who realized on a magnificent scale the plans for a great museum and institution of zoological research at Cambridge, Massachusetts, designed by his father Louis Agassiz, but only in part carried into execution. Alexander Agassiz, as a young man, deliberately set to work as a mining engineer in order to procure

* See Alfred G. Mayer, "Alexander Agassiz, 1835–1910," *A.R.,* 1910, pp. 447–472.

that pecuniary independence which he decided to be necessary in the United States for one who wished to become a great zoologist. Before he was 30 years of age a copper mine in Michigan made him a millionaire and stood to him in the place of the official income and vast state-supported apparatus which awaited Joseph Hooker at Kew. Both men became great leaders in their science, and in greatly developing and completing their fathers' work, left splendid monuments of their heritage and their devotion. It is interesting to note that the sons of Alexander Agassiz like those of Joseph Hooker, though always on terms of affectionate intimacy with their father, have not become men of science.

Hooker frequently acted in younger days as examiner in botany for various boards and universities. He was a member of the senate of the University of London. Some valuable records of his views on education, which deserve special consideration at this critical moment, are to be found in these volumes. His views are of especial value because he was, above all things, a practical man, seeing his aim clearly and bringing his trained judgment and vast experience of men to bear on the means to be pursued in order to attain it. He was also absolutely frank and fearless in the expression of his conclusions. We quote below (*Life,* vol. ii, p. 329) a letters of his to his friend the Reverend J. D. La Touche, dated May 24, 1893. He says:

You must not think that I oppose education of the laboring classes, but I should like it conducted toward the future life of the average, and not to the high education of the few who can profit by the complex education of the board schools. Mind you, I am just as much against the higher school and college education of the masses of the upper classes. Surely it would be far better if much of their teaching were devoted to making them more useful members of society. . . . To return to technical education, my notion of it is that it should be begun early, at the expense of some of the board's literature, classical English, etc., and be accompanied throughout by semi-scientific teaching; i. e., the cobbler should be taught what tanning is, what bristles are, and how developed, and so forth. If any board school child shows a genius for the higher education, push him on by all means to school and college; but it is no use trying to "make silk purses out of sows' ears."

From his earliest days onwards, Hooker shrank from public speaking; he disliked lecturing, and never held a professorial post. He detested newspaper discussions as well as the pomps and vanities of official ceremony. They all seemed to him as using up the time and strength which he ought to give to his one purpose—the increase of science. His natural and strong determination was to the most thorough and strenuous work in pure scientific investigation. He desired no popularity but cared only for intimacy with and approval by the select few who were able to participate in his scientific work and thought or were bound to him by long association. He was a man of the family, not a man of society. Nevertheless his long life, his high position, and wide-reaching activities brought to him a vast number of acquaintances, inspired by admiration and affection for his kindly, frank, and energetic character. With his children and numerous family connections he found relaxation and refreshment in music and dancing and in reading works of fiction and romance. He became an enthusiastic admirer and collector of Wedgwood ware and fully indulged in the collector's joy of picking up good pieces in the shops of secondhand dealers. He retained from early life the habit of constant, regular, and uninterrupted work, and the simplest tastes in regard to food. He attributed his long life and the preservation of his health and mental power (as he said to the writer, who visited him on his ninetieth birthday) to the fact that he had made it his practice throughout his life to dine in the middle of the day, drinking only a light wine, and to take nothing but a light tea in the evening.

Hooker was, it is true, fortunate in his friends—fortunate because he merited such fortune. We read in these volumes of their passing away one by one—until he at last was left alone, but not downcast. His mind, to the end, was fully of happy memories, and he still had new plans to describe and was tended by his wife and interested in his garden. His long and fraternal association with Darwin was of vital importance to each of them. The genius and originality of his friend fed, as it were, on Hooker's immense stores of botanical knowledge; and Hooker, in turn, was stimulated by Darwin's inquiries into new lines of activity and acquired, in aiding his friend in those inquiries, a convincing proof of the decisive value of his own vast labors in building up the knowledge of plants. The *Life and Letters* forms a fascinating record of that romantic, well-nigh legendary period in the history of biological science, when great men ravished the globe of its secrets and revolutionized human thought. It was the privilege of the present writer to be personally associated—in many cases intimately so—with the heroes of this story from Lyell onwards, to grow up in their midst and to be thrilled by the daily triumphs of those mighty warriors. Many long years ago he was greeted by Hooker as "a friend and the son of a friend," and it is with those words ringing in his memory that he closes the book of that great man's life.

Hermann von Helmholtz *

1821–1894

———◆———

ARTHUR W. RÜCKER †

DEATH HAS BEEN busy lately among the ranks of German physicists. Hertz,†† Kundt, and Von Helmholtz have all been laid low within a few months, and the world is the poorer by some of the best promise of the future and the ripest experience of the past. The last-named on this sad death roll was for long regarded as the doyen of the physical sciences in Germany. He celebrated his seventieth birthday three years ago, and on that occasion the whole world (to quote his own words) "from Tomsk to Melbourne" united to do him honor. The close of his career thus lacks the element of tragedy which shocked us when we heard that Hertz, in his early maturity, before we had ceased to wonder at his first great success, was dead.

But the elder, like the younger man, died too soon, working to the last. He held one of the highest scientific posts in Germany. Long mathematical papers have quite recently been contributed by him to the *Berlin Berichte*. He was present at the meeting of the British Association at Edinburgh in 1892, at the Chicago Congress of Electricians in 1893. It was hoped that he would have attended the meeting of the British Association at Oxford in 1894.

No remarkable events distinguished the earlier years of Helmholtz from those of the majority of clever middle-class lads. His

---

* *A.R.*, 1894, pp. 709–718. From *Fortnightly Review*, Nov. 1894, vol. 56 (N.S. 135). For a systematic study of Von Helmholtz's work see Leo Koenigsberger, "The Investigations of Hermann von Helmholtz on the Fundamental Principles of Mathematics and Mechanics," *A.R.*, 1896, pp. 93–124.
† English physicist (1848–1915). See his "Territorial Magnetism," *A.R.*, 1894, pp. 173–189; and "Model of Nature," *A.R.*, 1901, pp. 171–191.
†† Hertz died in 1894, not yet 37 years old. See Helen Bonfort, "Sketch of Heinrich Hertz," *A.R.*, 1894, pp. 710–726. Articles on Hertz appeared in *A.R.*, 1892, pp. 203–227; 1889, pp. 145–203; 1894, pp. 129–139.

mother, Caroline Penn, was of English descent; his father was a professor of literature in the gymnasium at Potsdam who both in and out of school did all that he could to help his promising boy. On looking back to his youth, Von Helmholtz accused himself of a "bad memory for disconnected things," but admitted that he had an unusual power for grasping and remembering the details of a connected train of thought.

When he began the systematic study of geometry he astonished his teachers with the practical knowledge of the laws of form which he had already attained, chiefly by the aid of wooden blocks. He acquired "a great love of nature," was especially attracted by physics, and confessed that while the class was reading Cicero or Virgil he was often busy with illicit calculations under the desk.

But though he describes his interest in the special line of study to which he subsequently adhered as "amounting even to a passion," it is evident that the passion was controlled by a strong vein of common sense. Neither at that time nor for many years afterwards was a living to be made out of physics. The only influential member of the family was a military surgeon. It was therefore decided that the young man should adopt the profession of his relative and devote to his favorite science such time as he might be able to spare from more urgent duties.

It was not long before the characteristic bent of his mind displayed itself. He was the pupil of Johannes Müller, from whose laboratory came many of the most distinguished German physiologists of the last generation. The first two papers which Helmholtz published were on fermentation and muscular action, respectively, but the first effort which attracted general attention was an essay on "The Conservation of Force," published in 1847, when he was 26 years of age.

It is unnecessary to repeat the oft-told tale of how the pioneers of the great generalization, now called the conservation of energy, were for a time ignored. German physicists turned away from Mayer. England would not hear or listened in unintelligent silence to Joule. But the year 1847 was an epoch in the history of science. Joule himself for the first time claimed the full extent of the territory he had conquered. "On the 28th of April, 1847," says his biographer, "Joule gave a popular lecture in Manchester, at St. Anne's Church reading room," and chose this opportunity to deliver "the first full and clear exposition of the universal conservation of that principle now called energy." The local press would at first have nothing to do with the address. "One paper refused to give even notice of it." "The *Manchester Guardian* would, as a favor, print extracts to be selected by themselves." Finally the *Manchester Courier,* after long debate, promised to insert the whole as a special favor, not to Joule, but to his brother.

Of course no blame can attach to the newspapermen for failing to recognize the importance of views that were rejected by many of the best-known scientific authorities, but the theories which in April were hawked from one provincial editor to another found in June, when the British Association met at Oxford, an advocate who compelled attention. Joule has told the story himself. All the circumstances were depressing. An earlier paper, read some years before, had attracted little notice. The chairman, perhaps on this account, suggested that the author should be brief. No discussion was invited. In a moment the meeting would have passed to other business, and the enunciation of his views would once more have failed "if a young man had not risen in the section and, by his intelligent observations, created a lively interest in the new theory. The young man was William Thompson." The result was that the paper created a great sensation, and from that moment the tide of opinion turned.

What Thomson did in June in Oxford, Helmholtz did scarcely a month later in Berlin. His paper was read to the Physical Society of that city on the 23d of July, 1847. It was too clear, too powerful, and too convincing to be ignored. The line of thought which he had been following has been traced by his own hand. The study of medicine led to the problem of the nature of "vital force." He convinced himself that if—as Stahl had suggested—an animal had the power now of restraining, and now of liberating the activity of mechanical forces, it would be endowed with the power of perpetual motion. This led to the question whether perpetual motion was consistent with what was known of natural agencies. The essay on "The Conservation of Force" was, according to Von Helmholtz himself, intended to be a critical investigation and arrangement of the facts which bear on his point for the benefit of physiologists. In form, however, it was addressed to the physicists.

The paper was called "Ueber die Erhaltung der Kraft, eine physikalische Abhandlung." It opens with the statement, "Vorliegende Abhandlung musste ihrem Hauptinhalte nach hauptsächlich für Physiker bestimmt werden." It was communicated to the Physical Society of Berlin. The author appears to have expected that it would there be received as a mere summary of accepted facts and to have hoped that, having gained this authoritative sanction, he could thereafter appeal with greater force to his brother physiologists. To his surprise the physicists . . . showed a strong disposition to treat the essay as a fantastic speculation. The editor of Poggendorff's *Annalen* declined to publish it. On the other hand, Helmholtz was supported by his fellow-student, Du Bois-Reymond, and by mathematician Karl Jacobi. In the end they carried the Physical Society with them.

The essay itself is full of interest. The phraseology differs from that we employ, but the use of terms now regarded as archaic is not due to any mistiness of perception. Write energy here and there for "force," potential energy for "tension," as defined in the essay, assume our fuller knowledge of the results of experiment, and the whole might have been written yesterday instead of nearly fifty years ago. The author began by an argument which practically amounts to the statement that science is limited to the search for a mechanical explanation of nature and that, whatever the final result of the quest may be, it must be pushed as far as possible. Assuming that the basis of a mechanical theory must ultimately be the action of forces between material points, and implicitly assuming the Newtonian laws of motion, the conclusion is reached that the law of the conservation of energy holds good and holds good only if the forces are central; that is, if they are attractions or repulsions, the magnitudes of which depend solely on the distances between the mutually reacting particles.

The cogency of this as an *a priori* proof of the conservation of energy of course depends upon whether the premises are admitted to be axiomatic; but it was followed by an appeal to experiment. The greater part of the memoir was occupied with an elaborate discussion as to whether the law of the conservation of energy was consistent with the facts then known. This involved a survey of the application of the law to mechanics, heat, electricity, magnetism, and electromagnetics. A number of most interesting calculations and suggestions were made, and the conclusion arrived at was that "the law of the conservation of energy does not contradict any known fact in natural science, but in a great number of cases is, on the contrary, corroborated in a striking manner."

The author was acquainted with the earlier experiments of Joule only and, while employing the idea of a mechanical equivalent of heat and using symbols to represent it, dismisses the results of observation as having but "little claim to accuracy." It need hardly be said that this opinion was not afterwards extended to the later investigations, which were only just then becoming known. In a note appended, when the essay was republished in 1881, Helmholtz expressly disclaimed any right to priority as an originator of the doctrine of conservation of energy, but his essay is the more remarkable on account of his slight acquaintance with the work of his predecessors. He knew nothing of Mayer, and his information as to Joule's experiments was gained only after his work was far advanced. Enough has perhaps been said to show that he must, as Professor Tait asserts, "be classed as one of the most successful of the early promoters of the science of energy on legitimate principles." The paper on the conservation of energy was only the third or fourth which Helmholtz had published, but his remarkable abilities were now fully recognized.

His connection with the army was severed in 1848. For some months he was an assistant in the Anatomical Museum of Berlin and also teacher of anatomy at the Academy of Arts. After this he held in succession the professorships of physiology in the universities of Königsberg, Bonn, and Heidelberg, and in 1871 he was appointed professor of natural philosophy in the University of Berlin. Honors of all sorts were showered upon him. Late in life he was ennobled by the German Emperor, and the esteem in which he was held in this country was proved by the award of the Copley medal, the highest distinction in the gift of the Royal Society.

It would be impossible to follow in chronological order the work which Von Helmholtz gave to the world during these long years. The most that can be attempted is to convey some idea of its importance. He was great as a mathematician and physicist, but the direction of his most characteristic efforts was probably determined by the early necessity of seeking a livelihood by the practice of medicine. On the borderland of physics, physiology, and psychology he won a place that is all his own. This thorny region has been invaded by others from both sides, but it is not too much to say that Von Helmholtz, in his triple mastery over anatomy, mathematics, and physics, had unique qualifications for the task.

To the oculist he gave the ophthalmoscope and thus made it possible to investigate the conditions of the inmost recesses of the living eye. If the eye be illuminated a portion of the light returns from the hinder surface, is brought to a focus by the lenses of the eye itself, and forms an image of the retina in external space. To see this was no easy matter. If the patient's eye were focused on a luminous object the image would coincide with the source of light, and even if otherwise visible would be lost in the glare. If he looked elsewhere the image would move, but inasmuch as the lenses cannot be adjusted to the clear vision of any object nearer than about 10 inches, that is, the minimum distance from the eye at which it can form the image of its own retina. To see this clearly an observer without appliances must place himself at least 10 inches from the image, that is, at 20 inches from the patient. At that distance the view would be so limited that no result could be obtained.

Von Helmholtz, however, convinced himself that if these difficulties could be overcome, the image of a brightly illuminated retina could be seen. He made the observations through a small hole in the center of a mirror, which reflected light into the eye under examination. Then by means of a lens, he shifted the position of the image backward until the relative positions of the observer and the patient were such that, according to calculation, the retina should be visible. Again and again he tried and failed, but he was convinced of the validity of the theory, and at last the experiment succeeded. From that time the oculist has been able to look into the darkness of the pupil and to see through the gloom the point of entry of the optic nerve and the delicate network of blood vessels by which it is surrounded.

The great monograph on the *Sensations of Tone* appeared in 1863. The theories advanced were novel, but though some points are still open to dispute, they have as a whole been generally accepted. The aim of the work was ambitious, being nothing less than the discovery of the physical basis of the sensations which affect us when listening to consonant and dissonant musical intervals, respectively. The general nature of the solution arrived at is now well known. If two notes which differ but little from unison are produced together, throbbing alternations in the intensity of the sound are heard as beats. If the interval is gradually increased the beats become quicker, till at last they can no longer be distinguished separately. According to Von Helmholtz, however, they produce the effect of dissonance. "The nerves of hearing," he says, "feel these rapid beats as rough and unpleasant, because every intermittent excitement of any nervous apparatus affects it *more* powerfully than one that lasts unaltered. Consonance is a continuous, dissonance an intermittent sensation of tone." The disagreeable effect depends in part upon the number of beats, in part upon the interval between the notes which produce them, being greatest when the rapidity of the beats is neither very large nor very small, and when the interval between the two notes is not great. In applying this theory it is necessary to take into account not only the beats between the two fundamental notes, but also those due to two series of secondary sounds by which they may be accompanied. The presence or absence of one of these—the so-called upper harmonic partials—depends upon the way in which the note has been obtained. They produce the differences of quality which distinguish one musical instrument from another. They are also the basis of our appreciation of the closeness of the relationship between the notes they accompany. The want of perfect consonance between compound notes is attributed to beats between those members of the two groups of sound which are not very far apart on the scale. The growing importance of these beats, as the intervals become less and less consonant, was traced with wonderful ingenuity.

This theory alone would be insufficient to account for a perception of want of consonance between two pure notes unaccompanied by partials. To explain this recourse was had to a second series of attendant sounds, the most important of which had been discovered in 1745 by Sorge, a German organist, and was well known as Tartini's tone. Von Helmholtz proved that such notes would arise when the vibrating body was set in somewhat violent motion, provided that the resistances offered to equal displacements in opposite directions were unequal. Of course the air, which transmits the sounds to the ear, does not possess this property. On the other hand, the drum skin of the ear, to which the aerial vibrations are communicated, is not symmetrical, being bent inward by the little "hammer" bone. Von Helmholtz therefore concluded that it is probable that Tartini's tone is due to this membrane. From his point of view it is subjective, in the sense that it is produced within the organism, though it originates in the auditory apparatus and not in the brain. It is, if one may use the phrase, the rattling of the machinery of the ear.

Having thus accounted for the production of secondary sounds by tones that were themselves unaccompanied by partials, Von Helmholtz explained our sense of the dissonance of imperfect intervals, when produced by such pure notes, by beats due to the combinational tones. But though he maintained that these theories explained the physical "reason of the melodic relationship of two tones," the author of the *Tonempfindungen* was careful to point out that the principles he enunciated had not always determined the construction of the scale and do not determine it everywhere now. The selection of a series of notes which were *a posteriori* found to obey certain natural laws was voluntary. The scale itself is not natural, in the sense that it is not a necessary consequence of the construction of the ear. On the contrary, it is the product of artistic invention. Music is thus not a mere branch of mechanics, but an art. The architect and the composer alike deal with materials which are subject to mechanical laws, but they are alike free to fashion from these forms determined not by calculation, but by the sense of beauty.

Von Helmholtz was at work on optics while still engaged in the study of sound. The *Handbuch der Physiologischen Optik* appeared in sections in 1856, 1860, and 1866. It is, as he himself has said, a complete survey of the whole field of that science. In the first place he treated the eye as an optical instrument, traced the path of the rays through it, and discussed the mechanism by which it can be accommodated to distinct vision at different distances. To investigate the last point it was necessary to measure the images formed by reflection from the surfaces of the crystalline lens. For this purpose he invented a special instrument—the ophthalmometer—by which such measurements can be made on the living patient with great accuracy. In an interesting course of popular lectures, published in 1868, and since translated by Dr. Atkinson, Von Helmholtz insisted that far from being, as was often supposed, a perfect organ, the eye has many optical defects; and that our unconsciousness of these is due not so much to its perfection from the instrument-maker's point of view, as to the ease with which it adapts itself to different circumstances, and to the skill with which long practice enables us to interpret the messages it conveys to the brain.

The second section of the work was devoted to the sensation of sight. The theories of color and of intensity, the duration of the sensation of light, the phenomena of contrast and subjective appearances were all discussed with a fullness never before attained. The last part was devoted to such problems as our visual appreciation of three dimensions in space and binocular vision. The theory of color, originally due to Young,* was adopted and enlarged by Helmholtz. It assumes that all the sensations of color are compounded out of three fundamental sensations, which are respectively red, green, and violet or blue. Nearly if not all the phenomena of color-blindness can be explained on the hypothesis that in the case of persons so affected the power of appreciating one or other of these sensations is wanting.

It was hardly to be expected that differences of opinion would not arise as to some of the points discussed in two works so wide in their scope and so novel in their methods as the treatises on the sensations of tone and on physiological optics. Koenig, the celebrated instrument maker, has demonstrated the existence of beats

* See Arago, "Eulogy on Thomas Young," *A.R.,* 1869, pp. 111–114, especially pp. 119–125.

which in the case of compound sounds could be explained as due to the upper partials, but as they are produced when the notes are as pure as it is possible to make them, they do not appear to be accounted for by the original theory. A writer (Voigt, Wiedemann's *Annalen,* 1890, **40**, 660) who has recently examined the matter, concludes that both the combination tones of Von Helmholtz and the beat tones of Koenig can theoretically be produced without the unsymmetrical arrangement which the former regarded as essential, and that the one system or the other will tend to predominate according to circumstances. The more nearly the energies of the two vibrations approach equality the greater is the probability that the combination tones will be heard. The less nearly the condition of equal energy is fulfilled, the more important will the beat notes become. Several other points of considerable interest have been raised, but those who on one ground or another have objected to the views of Helmholtz have not been entirely in accord among themselves. It is probable that the theory will finally be accepted in its broad outlines but will require modifications of some importance in its details.

The theory of color, too, with which the name of Von Helmholtz is associated, is not without its difficulties. A new edition of his *Optics* is appearing in parts, and in this alterations have been made which prove that the author regarded the original hypothesis as capable of modification and improvement. A strong committee of the Royal Society, which has recently reported on color vision, adopted the terminology of the Young-Helmholtz theory, but pointed out that it fails to explain some curious cases of diseased vision, in which the sensation of color is confined to the blue end of the spectrum, while all the other tints appear as white. On the other hand, the rival theory of Hering also fails to account for some of the known facts. Thus the problem is not finally solved, but the importance of the contribution to its solution made in the *Physiologischen Optik* is not disputed even by those who feel that there is need for further inquiry in the future.

In these investigations on the eye and the ear, on light and sound, we see Von Helmholtz at his most characteristic work; but the shortest sketch of his scientific achievements would be incomplete without reference to his eminence as a mathematician.

He was, as might have been expected, deeply interested in the electromagnetic theory of light and developed it in a form which is even more general than that adopted by Clerk Maxwell; but it seems probable that while Von Helmholtz has indicated possibilities, Maxwell has taken account of all that is necessary to explain the facts.

Another inquiry of the first importance, and conducted with the greatest ability, was that on the laws of vortex motion. The movements of a liquid may be so complicated that it is at first sight an almost hopeless task to analyze the motion into its simplest elements. Changes of shape of the most exaggerated character may occur. A compact mass may be drawn out into long threads. Particles at one time far apart may be brought close together and again separated. If, however, instead of contemplating the final results we consider what is actually going on at a given instant at a given place it is possible to describe the facts in simple terms. A minute sphere of the liquid may be moving as a whole in some definite direction, may be changing its shape, and may be rotating about an axis. This last is the distinguishing characteristic of vortex motion. Von Helmholtz was the first to detect some of the most remarkable properties of those portions of a fluid in which it occurs. The investigation was confined to a frictionless, incompressible liquid, and the author proved that in such an ideal substance the property of vortex motion could neither be produced nor destroyed by any natural forces. If it existed in a group of particles, they would be incapable of transmitting it to others. They could not be deprived of it themselves. The laws of their motion would establish between them a curious and indissoluble fellowship.

A number of beads, strung on a ring of thread or wire and rotating about it, afford, with regard to a similarly shaped system of particles possessing vortex motion, an analogy so imperfect that it is almost dangerous to use it. But the two have at all events one property in common. The wire may be moved from place to place or bent into various forms, but wherever it goes, however it is distorted, it carries the beads with it. The connection thus artificially secured would be automatically maintained in a ring of fluid particles endowed with vortex motion. The ring might enlarge or contract, be deflected or distorted, but amid all such vicissitudes the rotating particles would move among their fellows apparently free, but in reality inseparably united.

This and other peculiarities, upon which it is unnecessary to dwell, give to vortex motion a special interest and importance. Lord Kelvin has made the profound and remarkable suggestion that the atoms of matter may be vortex rings in a frictionless liquid. Whatever the ultimate fate of this theory may be, it is justified as affording a glimpse into new possibilities. It is, at all events, not absurd to dream that we may some day regard matter as a special form of some more fundamental substance, from the comparatively simple properties of which the laws of chemistry and physics may be deduced. Apart, however, from the use which has been made of vortexes in this and in other ways, as affording a basis for the explanation of physical facts, Von Helmholtz must rank as the discoverer of a series of fundamental propositions in hydrodynamics which had entirely escaped the notice of his predecessors.

During the last years of his life Von Helmholtz was president of the *Physikalisch Technische Reichsanstalt* at Charlottenberg. In 1884 the late Werner Siemens offered £25,000 toward the foundation of a state research laboratory. The Reichstag voted the necessary additions to this sum. The institution has been established on a large scale, and the first volume of records was published in March of the present year. The preface was signed by Von Helmholtz, and thus the career of the great investigator was fittingly closed by the inauguration of a national college devoted to learning and research.

In a brief and imperfect sketch such as this it is barely possible to give an idea of the extent of the work of Von Helmholtz; it is certainly impossible to do justice to its fullness and depth. I have mapped the directions of the main streams of his thought. Only those who follow them in detail can count the fields they have fertilized. In the course of his investigations all sorts of side issues were studied, a vast number of subsidiary problems solved. The alertness of his intellect, the readiness with which he turned from one science to another, the extraordinary ease with which he handled weapons the most diverse and the most difficult to master, these are not less wonderful than the catalogue of his main achievements.

The technical merits of his work will, of course, be appreciated chiefly by experts. Special knowledge is not necessary to understand its importance. He was one of the first to grasp the principle of the conservation of energy. He struck, independently and at a critical moment, a powerful blow in its defense. He penetrated further than any before him into the mystery of the mechanism which connects us with external nature through the eye and the ear. He discovered the fundamental properties of vortex motion in a perfect liquid, which have since not only been applied in the explanation of all sorts of physical phenomena, of ripple marks in the sand and of cirrus clouds in the air, but have been the bases of some of the most advanced and pregnant speculations as to the constitution of matter and of the luminiferous ether itself.

These scientific achievements are not perhaps of the type which most easily commands general attention. They have not been utilized in theological warfare; they have not revolutionized the daily business of the world. It will, however, be universally admitted that such tests do not supply a real measure of the greatness of a student of nature. That must finally be appraised by his power of detecting beneath the complication of things as they seem something of the order which rules things as they are. Judged by this standard, few names will take a higher place than that of Hermann von Helmholtz.

Louis Pasteur *

1822–1895

———◆———

HENRY E. ROSCOE

IN ASKING myself what subject I could bring before you on the present occasion, I thought I could not do better than point out by one example what a chemist may do for mankind. And in choosing this theme for my discourse I found myself in no want of material, for amongst the various aspects of scientific activity there is surely none which, whether in its most recondite forms or in those most easily understood, have done more to benefit humanity than those which have their origin in my own special study of chemistry. I desired to show what one chemist may accomplish, a man devoted heart and soul to the investigation of nature, a type of the ideal man of science—whose example may stimulate even the feeblest amongst us to walk in his footsteps if only for a short distance, whose life is a consistent endeavor to seek after truth if haply he may find it, whose watchwords are simplicity, faithfulness, and industry, and whose sole ambition is to succeed in widening the pathway of knowledge so that following generations of wayfarers may find their journeys lightened and their dangers lessened.

Such men are not uncommon amongst the ranks of distinguished chemists. I might have chosen as an example the life and labors of your sometime townsman, Joseph Priestley, had not this theme been already treated by Professor Huxley, in a manner I cannot approach, on the occasion of the inauguration of the statue which stands hard by. Today, however, I will select another name, that of a man still living, the great French chemist, Pasteur.

As a chemist Pasteur began life, as a chemist he is ending it.

* *A.R.,* 1889, pp. 491–506. Address delivered at Birmingham and Midland Institute, Oct. 7, 1889. First published in *Nature,* Oct. 10, 1889. See also George M. Sternberg, "Pasteur," *A.R.,* 1895, pp. 781–786.

For although, as I shall hope to point out, his most important researches have entered upon fields hitherto tilled with but scanty success by the biologist, yet in his hands, by the application of chemical methods, they have yielded a most bountiful harvest of new facts of essential service to the well-being and progress of the human race. And after all, the first and obvious endeavor of every cultivator of science ought to be to render service of this kind. For although it is foolish and short-sighted to decry the pursuit of any form of scientific study because it may be as yet far removed from practical application to the wants of man, and although such studies may be of great value as an incentive to intellectual activity, yet the statement is so evident as to almost amount to a truism, that discoveries which give us the power of rescuing a population from starvation, or which tend to diminish the ills that flesh, whether of man or beast, is heir to, must deservedly attract more attention and create a more general interest than others having so far no direct bearing on the welfare of the race.

"There is no greater charm," says Pasteur himself, "for the investigator than to make new discoveries, but his pleasure is more than doubled when he sees that they find direct application in practical life." To make discoveries capable of such an application has been the good fortune—by which I mean the just reward—of Pasteur. How he made them is the lesson which I desire this evening to teach. I wish to show that these discoveries, culminating as the latest and perhaps the most remarkable of all, in that of a cure for the dreaded and most fearful of all fearful maladies, hydrophobia, have not been, in the words of Priestley, "lucky hap-hazardings," but the outcome of patient and long-continued investigation. This latest result is, as I shall prove to you, not an isolated case of a happy chance, but simply the last link in a long chain of discoveries, each one of which has followed the other in logical sequence, each one bound to the other by ties which exhibit the life-work of the discoverer as one consequent whole. In order, however, to understand the end we must begin at the beginning and ask ourselves what was the nature of the training of hand, eye, and brain which enabled Pasteur to wrest from nature secret processes of disease the discovery of which had hitherto baffled all the efforts of biologists? What was the power by virtue of which he succeeded when all others had failed; how was he able to trace the causes and point out remedies for the hitherto unaccountable changes and sicknesses which beer and wine undergo? What means did he adopt to cure the fatal silkworm disease, the existence of which in the south of France in one year cost that country more than

100,000,000 of francs? Or how did he arrive at a method for exterminating a plague known as fowl cholera, or that of the deadly cattle disease, anthrax, or splenic fever, which has killed millions of cattle, and is the fatal woolsorters' disease in man? And last, but not least, how did he gain an insight into the workings of that most mysterious of all poisons, the virus of hydrophobia?

To do more than point out the spirit which has guided Pasteur in all his work and to give an idea of the nature of that work in a few examples, I cannot attempt in the time at my disposal. Of the magnitude and far-reaching character of that work we may form a notion, when we remember that it is to Pasteur that we owe the foundation of the science of bacteriology, a science treating of the ways and means of those minute organisms called microbes, upon whose behavior the very life, not only of the animal, but perhaps also of the vegetable world depends—a science which bids fair to revolutionize both the theory and practice of medicine, a science which has already, in the hands of Sir Joseph Lister, given rise to a new and beneficent application in the discovery of antiseptic surgery.

The whole secret of Pasteur's success may be summed up in a few words. It consisted in the application of the exact methods of physical and chemical research to problems which had hitherto been attacked by other less precise and less systematic methods. His early researches were of a purely chemical nature. It is now nearly forty years since he published his first investigation. But this pointed out the character of the man and indicated the lines upon which all his subsequent work was laid.

Of all the marvelous and far-reaching discoveries of modern chemistry, perhaps the most interesting and important is that of the existence of compounds which, while possessing an identical composition (that is, made up of the same elements in the same proportions), are absolutely different substances judged of by their properties. The first instance made known to us of such isomeric bodies, as they are termed by the chemist, was that pointed out by the great Swedish chemist, Berzelius. He showed that the tartaric acid of wine-lees possesses precisely the same composition as a rare acid having quite different properties and occasionally found in the tartar deposited from wine grown in certain districts in the Vosges. Berzelius simply noted this singular fact, but did not attempt to explain it. Later on, Biot observed that not only do these two acids differ in their chemical behavior, but likewise in their physical properties, inasmuch as the one (the common acid) possessed the power of deviating the plane of a polarized ray of light to the right, whereas the rare acid has no such rotatory power. It was reserved, however, for Pasteur to give the explanation of this singular and at that time unique phenomenon, for he proved that the optically inactive acid is made up of two compounds, each possessing the same composition but differing in optical properties. The one turned out to be the ordinary dextro-rotatory tartaric acid; the other a new acid which rotates the plane of polarization to the left to an equal degree. As indicating the germ of his subsequent researches, it is interesting here to note that Pasteur proved that these two acids can be separated from one another by a process of fermentation, started by a mere trace of a special form of mold. The common acid is thus first decomposed, so that if the process be carried on for a certain time only the rarer lævo-rotatory acid remains.

Investigations on the connection between crystalline form, chemical composition, and optical properties occupied Pasteur for the next seven years, and their results—which seem simple enough when viewed from the vantage ground of accomplished fact— were attainable solely by dint of self-sacrificing labors such as perhaps only those who have themselves walked in these enticing and yet often bewildering paths can fully appreciate, and by attention to minute detail as well as to broad principles to an extent which none can surpass and few can equal. A knowledge of the action of the mold in the changes it effects on tartaric acid led Pasteur to investigate that *bête noire* of chemists, the process of fermentation. The researches thus inaugurated in 1857 not only threw a new and vivid light on these most complicated of chemical changes and pointed the way to scientific improvements in brewing and wine-making of the greatest possible value, but were the stepping-stones to those higher generalizations which lie at the foundation of the science of bacteriology, carrying in their train the revolutions in modern medicine and surgery to which I have referred.

The history of the various theories from early times until our own day which have been proposed to account for the fact of the change of sugar into alcohol or that of alcohol into vinegar under certain conditions, a fact known to the oldest and even the most uncivilized of races, is one of the most interesting chapters in the whole range of chemical literature but, however enticing, [it] is one into which I cannot now enter. Suffice it here to say that it was Pasteur who brought light out of darkness by explaining conflicting facts and by overturning false hypotheses. And this was done by careful experiment and by bringing to bear on the subject an intelligence trained in exact methods and in unerring observation, coupled with the employment of the microscope and the other aids of modern research.

What now did Pasteur accomplish? In the first place he proved that the changes occurring in each of the various processes of fermentation are due to the presence and growth of a minute organism called the ferment. Exclude all traces of these ferments and no change occurs. Brewers' wort thus preserved remains for years unaltered. Milk and other complex liquids do not turn sour even on exposure to pure air, provided these infinitely small organisms are excluded. But introduce even the smallest trace of these microscopic beings and the peculiar changes which they alone can bring about at once begin. A few cells of the yeast plant set up the vinous fermentation in a sugar solution. This is clearly stated by Pasteur as follows:

My decided opinion on the nature of alcoholic fermentation is the following: The chemical act of fermentation is essentially a correlative phenomenon of a vital act beginning and ending with it. I think that there is never any alcoholic fermentation without there being at the same time organization, development, multiplication of globules, or the continued consecutive life of globules already formed.

Add on a needle's point a trace of the peculiar growth which accompanies the acetous fermentation and the sound beer or wine in a short time becomes vinegar. Place ever so small a quantity of the organism of the lactic fermentation in your sweet milk, which may have been preserved fresh for years in absence of such organisms, and your milk turns sour. But still more, the organism (yeast) which brings about the alcoholic fermentation will not give rise to the acetous, and *vice versa;* so that each peculiar chemical change is brought about by the vital action of a peculiar organism. In its absence the change cannot occur; in its presence only that change can take place.

Here again we may ask, as Pasteur did, Why does beer or wine become sour when exposed to ordinary air? And the answer to this question was given by him in no uncertain tone in one of the most remarkable and most important of modern experimental researches. Milk and beer which have become sour on standing in the air contain living micro-organisms which did not exist in the original sound fluids. Where did these organisms originate? Are they or their germs contained in the air, or are these minute beings formed by a process of spontaneous generation from material not endowed with life?

A controversy as to the truth or falsity of the theory of spontaneous generation was waged with spirit on both sides, but in the end Pasteur came off victorious, for by a series of the most delicate and convincing of experiments he proved the existence of micro-organic forms and their spores—or seeds—in the air, and showed that while unpurified air was capable of setting up fermentative changes of various kinds, the same air freed from germs could not give rise to these changes. Keep away the special germ which is the incentive to the pathological change and that change cannot occur. In the interior of the grape, in the healthy blood, no such organisms, no such germs exist; puncture the grape or wound the animal body and the germs floating in the air settle on the grape-juice or on the wounded tissue, and the processes of change, whether fermentative or putrefactive, set in with all their attendant symptoms. But crush the grape or wound the animal under conditions which either preclude the presence or destroy the life of the floating germ, and again no such change occurs; the grape-juice remains sweet, the wound clean.

I have said that every peculiar fermentative change is accompanied by the presence of a special ferment. This most important conclusion has only been arrived at as the result of careful experimental inquiry. How was this effected? By the artificial cultivation of these organisms. Just as the botanist or gardener picks out from a multitude of wild plants the special one which he wishes to propagate, and planting it in ground favorable to its growth obtains fresh crops of the special plant he has chosen, so the bacteriologist can by a careful process of selection obtain what is termed a pure cultivation of any desired organism. Having obtained such a pure cultivation, the next step is to ascertain what are the distinctive properties of that special organism; what characteristic changes does it bring about in material suitable for its growth. This having been determined, and a foundation for the science having thus been laid, it is not difficult to apply these principles to practice, and the first application made by Pasteur was to the study of the diseases of beer and wine.

In September 1871 Pasteur visited one of the large London breweries, in which the use of the microscope was then unknown. A single glance at the condition of the yeast instantly told its tale and enabled him to explain to the brewers the cause of the serious state of things by which frequently as much as 20 per cent of their product was returned on their hands as unsalable—this being that this yeast contained foreign or unhealthy organisms. And just as pure yeast is the cause of the necessary conversion of wort into beer, so these strange forms which differ morphologically from yeast, and whose presence can therefore be distinctly ascertained, are the cause of acidity, ropiness, turbidity, and other diseases which render the beer undrinkable. It is no exaggeration to say that, whereas before Pasteur's researches the microscope was practically unknown in the brew-house, it has now become as common as the thermometer or the saccharimeter, and by its help and by the interpretations we can place upon its revelations through Pasteur's teaching, yeast—of all brewers' materials the least open to rough and ready practical discernment—becomes easy of valuation as to its purity or impurity, its vigor or weakness, and therefore its behavior during fermentation. Thus, while in former days the most costly materials were ever liable to be ruined by disease organisms unconsciously introduced into them with the yeast, at the present day the possibilities of any such vast pecuniary disasters become easily avertible.

Of all industries, brewing is perhaps the one which demands the most stringent care in regard to complete and absolute cleanliness. The brewers' materials, products, and by-products are so putrescible, there is always so vast an abundance of disease organisms in the brewery air, that the minutest amounts of these waste products lying about in vessels or pipes transform these places into perfect nests for the propagation of these micro-organisms, whence, transferred into the brewings, they inevitably ruin them, however carefully and scientifically prepared in other respects. Without the microscope, any breach of discipline in the way of the supreme cleanliness necessary is impossible of detection; with it we can track down the micro-organisms to their source, whether it be in uncleanly plant, in impurity of materials, or in carelessness of manipulation.

Among the more direct applications of Pasteur's researches, the so-called pasteurization of beer claims a place. Pasteur showed that temperatures well below the boiling point sufficed for destroying the disease organisms in alcoholic fluids, and, based on these results, enormous quantities of low-fermentation beers are annually submitted to these temperatures and thus escape the changes otherwise incident to the micro-organisms which have succumbed to the treatment. This process is, however, for several intricate reasons not suited for English beers, but if we can not keep our beers by submitting them to high temperatures, we can foretell to a nicety how they will keep by artificially forcing on those changes which would occur more slowly during storage. The application of a suitable temperature, the exclusion of outside contamination, a microscopic examination of the "forced" beer, and the knowledge which we owe to Pasteur of what the microscopic aspect means, suffice to make each brewing foretell its own future history, and thus suffice to avert the otherwise inevitable risks incident to the storage and export of beer, the stability of which is unknown.

Brewing has thus become a series of precise and definite operations, capable of control at every point. Instead of depending— as it had to depend—on intuition and experience handed down in secrecy from father to son, it now depends upon care, forethought, and the soundness of the brewer's scientific training. This change in the nature of the brewer's operations and in the persons who govern them is primarily due to Pasteur. Other men have done much to carry on his work, but it is to his example of ceaseless patience, and to his example of freely publishing to the world all the results of his work that the brewers of all countries are indebted for the connection of each phenomenon with a controllable cause, and for thus emancipating their industry from empiricism and quackery. Much the same story has to be told about Pasteur's investigation of wine and its diseases. As with the brewer, so with the wine-grower: Pasteur has pointed out the causes of his troubles, and the causes having been ascertained, the remedies soon followed, and the practical value of these researches to the trade of France and other wine-producing countries has been enormous.

The next labor of our scientific Hercules was of a different kind, but of a no less interesting or important character. The south of France is a great silk-producing district. In 1853 the value of the raw silk was represented by a sum of some £5,000,000 sterling, and up to that date the revenue from this source had been greatly augmenting. Suddenly this tide of prosperity turned, a terrible plague broke out amongst the silkworms, and in 1865 so general had the disease become that the total production of French silk did not reach £1,000,000, and the consequent poverty and suffering endured in these provinces became appalling. Every conceivable means was tried to overcome the disease, but all in vain. The population and the Government of France—for the evil was a national one—were at their wits' end, and a complete collapse of one of the most important French industries seemed inevitable. Under these circumstances the great chemist Dumas, who was born at Alais in the center of one of the districts most seriously affected, urged his friend Pasteur to undertake an investigation of the subject. Pasteur, who at this time had never seen a silkworm, naturally felt diffident about attempting so difficult a task, but at last, at Dumas's renewed entreaty he consented and in June 1865 betook himself to the south for the purpose of studying the disease on the spot. His previous training here again stood him in good stead, and in September 1865 he was able to communicate to the Academy of Sciences results of observations and experiment which, striking at the root of the evil, pointed the way to the means of securing immunity from the dreaded plague. This paper was freely criticized. Here, it was said, was a chemist who, quitting his proper sphere, had the hardihood to lay down rules for the guidance of the physician and biologist in fields specially their own. Why should his proposals be more successful than all the other nostrums which had already so egregiously failed?

In order to appreciate the difficulties which met Pasteur in this inquiry and to understand how wonderfully he overcame them, I must very shortly describe the nature of this disease, which is termed *pébrine,* from the black spots which cover the silkworm. It declares itself by the stunted and unequal growth of the worms, by their torpidity, and by their fastidiousness as to food, and by their premature death.

Before Pasteur went to Alais the presence of certain microscopic corpuscles had been noticed in the blood and in all the tissues of the diseased caterpillar, and even in the eggs from which such worms were hatched. These micro-organisms often fill the whole of the silk organs of the insect, which in a healthy condition contain the clear viscous liquid from which the silk is made. Such worms are of course valueless. Still this knowledge did not suffice, for eggs apparently healthy gave rise to stricken worms incapable of producing silk, whilst again other worms distinctly diseased yielded normal cocoons. These difficulties, which had proved too much for previous observers, were fully explained by Pasteur. "The germs of these organisms," said he, "which are so minute, may be present in the egg and even in the young worms, and yet baffle the most careful search. They develop with the growth of the worm, and in the chrysalis they are more easily seen. The moth derived from a diseased worm invariably contains these corpuscles, and is incapable of breeding healthy progeny."

This moth-test is the one adopted by Pasteur, and it is an infallible one. If the female moth is stricken, then her eggs, even though they show no visible sign of disease, will produce sick worms. If in the moth no micrococci are seen, then her immediate progeny at any rate will be sound and free from inherited taint and will always produce the normal quantity of silk. But this is not all. Pasteur found that healthy worms can be readily infected by contact with diseased ones or through germs contained in the dust of the rooms in which the worms are fed. Worms thus infected but free from inherited taint can, however (as stated), spin normal cocoons, but—and this is the important point—the moths which such chrysalids yield invariably produce diseased eggs. This explains the anomalies previously noticed. The silkworms which die without spinning are those in which the disease is hereditary— those born from a diseased mother. Worms from sound eggs which contract the disease during their lifetime always spin their silk, but they give rise to a stricken moth, the worms from which do not reach maturity and furnish no silk.

As I have said, these results were but coldly received. It was hard to make those engaged in rearing the worms believe in the efficacy of the proposed cure. Then, seeing this state of things, Pasteur determined to take upon himself the role of a prophet. Having in 1866 carefully examined a considerable number of the moths which had laid eggs intended for incubation, he wrote down a prediction of what would happen in the following year with respect to the worms hatched from these eggs. In due course, after the worms from a mixed batch of healthy and unhealthy eggs had spun, the sealed letter was opened and read and the prediction compared with the actual result, when it was found that in twelve out of fourteen cases there was absolute conformity between the prediction and the observation, for twelve hatchings were predicted to turn out diseased, and this proved to be the case. Now all these "educations" were believed to be healthy by the cultivators, but Pasteur foretold that they would turn out to be diseased by the application of the moth test in the previous year. The other parcels of eggs were pronounced by Pasteur to be sound, because they were laid by healthy moths containing none of the micrococci, and both these yielded a healthy crop. So successful a prophecy could not but gain the belief of the most obtuse of cultivators, and we are not surprised to learn that Pasteur's test was soon generally applied, and that the consequence has been a return of prosperity to districts in which thousands of homes had been desolated by a terrible scourge.

I must now ask you to accompany me to another and a new field of Pasteur's labors, which, perhaps more than his others claims your sympathy and will enlist your admiration, because they have opened out to us the confident hope of at least obtaining an insight into some of the hidden causes and therefore to the possible prevention of disease.

In the first place, I must recall to your remembrance that most infectious diseases seldom if ever recur, and that even a slight attack renders the subject of it proof against a second one. Hence inoculation from a mild case of smallpox was for a time practiced, but this too often brought about a serious if not fatal attack of the malady, and the steps taken by Jenner of vaccinating, that is of replacing for the serious disease a slight one which nevertheless is sufficient protection against smallpox infection, was one of the highest importance. But Jenner's great discovery has up to recent years remained an isolated one, for it led to no general method for the preventive treatment of other maladies, nor had any explanation been offered of its mode of action. It is to Pasteur that science is indebted for the generalization of Jenner's method and for an explanation which bids fair to render possible the preventive treatment of many—if not of all—infectious diseases. It was his experience, based upon his researches on fermentation, that led to a knowledge of the nature of the poison of such diseases and showed the possibility of so attenuating or weakening the virus as to furnish a general method of protective or preventive inoculation.

I have already pointed out how a pure cultivation of a microbe can be effected. Just as the production of pure alcohol depends on the presence of the pure yeast, so special diseases are dependent on the presence of certain definite organisms which can be artificially cultivated and which give rise to the special malady. Can we now by any system of artificial cultivation so modify or weaken the virus of a given microbe as to render it possible to inoculate a modified virus which, whilst it is without danger to life, is still capable of acting as a preventive to further attack? This is the question which Pasteur set himself to solve, nor was the task by any means an apparently hopeless one. He had not only the case of Jennerian vaccination before him, but also the well-known modifications which cultivation can bring about in plants. The first instance in which Pasteur succeeded in effecting this weakening of the poison was in that of a fatal disease to which poultry in France are very liable, called chicken cholera. Like many other maladies, this is caused by the presence of a micro-organism found in the blood and tissues of the stricken fowl. One drop of this blood brought under the skin of a healthy chicken kills it, and the same microbe is found throughout its body. And if a pure culture of these microbes be made, that culture—even after a series of generations—is as deadly a poison as the original blood. Now comes the discovery. If these cultures be kept at a suitable temperature for some weeks exposed to pure air, and the poisonous properties tested from time to time, the poison is found gradually to become less powerful, so that after the lapse of two months a dose which had formerly proved fatal now does not disturb in the slightest the apparent health of the fowl. But now let us inoculate a chicken with this weakened virus. It suffers a slight illness but soon recovers. Next let us give it a dose of the undiluted poison, and as a control let us try the action of the same on an unprotected bird. What is the result? Why, that the first chicken remains unaffected, whilst the second bird dies. The inoculation has rendered it exempt from the disease, and this has been proved by Pasteur to be true in thousands of cases, so that whereas the death rate in certain districts amongst fowls before the adoption of Pasteur's inoculation method was 10 per cent, after its general adoption it has diminished to less than 1 per cent.

We can scarcely value too highly this discovery, for it proves that the poisonous nature of the microbe is not unalterable, but that it can be artificially modified and reduced, and thus an explanation is given of the fact that in an epidemic the virus may either be preserved or become exhausted according to the conditions to which it is subjected. We have here to do with a case similar to that of Jenner's vaccine, except that here the relation between the weak and the strong poison has become known to us, whilst in Jenner's case it has lain concealed. This then is the first triumph of experimental inquiry into the cause and prevention of microbic disease, and this method of attenuation is of great importance, because, as we shall see, it is not confined to the case of chicken cholera, but is applicable to other diseases.

And next I will speak of one which is a fatal scourge to cattle and is not unfrequently transmitted to man. It is called anthrax, splenic fever, or woolsorters' disease. This plague, which has proved fatal to millions of cattle, is also due to a microbe, which can be cultivated like the rest, and the virus of which can also be weakened or attenuated by a distinct treatment which I will not here further specify. Now, what is the effect of inoculating cattle or sheep with this weakened poison? Does it act as a preventive? That the answer is in the affirmative was proved by Pasteur by a convincing experiment. Five-and-twenty sheep, chosen promiscuously out of a flock of fifty, were thus inoculated with the weak virus, then after a time all the fifty were treated with the strong poison. The first half remained healthy, all the others died of anthrax. Since the discovery of this method, no fewer than 1,700,000 sheep and about 90,000 oxen have thus been inoculated, and last year 269,599 sheep and 34,464 oxen were treated. The mortality, which before the introduction of the preventive treatment was in the case of sheep 10 per cent, was after the adoption of the method reduced to less than 1 per cent. So that now the farmers in the stricken districts have all adopted the process, and agricultural insurance societies make the preventive inoculation a *sine qua non* for insuring cattle in those districts. This is, however, not the end of this part of my story, for Pasteur can not only thus render the anthrax poison harmless, but he has taught us how to bring the highly virulent poison back again from the harmless form. This may go to explain the varying strength of an attack of infectious disease, one case being severe and another but slight, due to the weakening or otherwise of the virus of the active microbe.

Last, but not least, I must refer to the most remarkable of all Pasteur's researches, that on rabies and hydrophobia. Previous to the year 1880, when Pasteur began his study of this disease, next to nothing was known about its nature. It was invested with the mysterious horror which often accompanies the working of secret poisons, and the horror was rendered greater owing to the fact that the development of the poison brought in by the bite or by the lick of a mad dog might be deferred for months, and that if after that length of time the symptoms once make their appearance a painful death was inevitable. We knew indeed that the virus was contained in the dog's saliva, but experiments made upon the inoculation of the saliva had led to no definite results, and we were entirely in the dark as to the action of the poison until Pasteur's investigation. To begin with, he came to the conclusion that the disease was one localized in the nerve centers, and to the nerve centers he therefore looked as the seat of the virus or of the microbe. And he proved by experiment that this is the case, for a portion of the matter of the spinal column of a rabid dog, when injected into a healthy one, causes rabies with a much greater degree of certainty and rapidity than does the injection of the saliva. Here then we have one step in advance. The disease is one of the nerve centers, and therefore it only exhibits itself when the nerve centers are attacked. And this goes to explain the varying times of incubation which the attack exhibits. The virus has to travel up the spinal cord before the symptoms can manifest themselves, and the length of time taken over that journey depends on many circumstances. If this be so, the period of incubation must be lessened if the virus is at once introduced into the nerve centers. This was also proved to be the case, for dogs inoculated under the *dura mater* invariably became rabid within a period rarely exceeding eighteen days.

Next came the question, can this virus be weakened, as has been proved possible with the former poisons? The difficulty in this case was greater, inasmuch as all attempts to isolate or to cultivate the special microbe of rabies outside the animal body had failed. But Pasteur's energy and foresight overcame this difficulty, and a method was discovered by which this terrible poison can so far be weakened as to lose its virulent character, yet remain potent enough, like the cases already quoted, to act as a preventive; and dogs which had thus been inoculated were proved to be so perfectly protected, that they might be bitten with impunity by mad dogs or inoculated harmlessly with the most powerful rabic virus.

But yet another step. Would the preventive action of the weakened virus hold good when it is inoculated even after the bite? If so, it might be thus possible to save the lives of persons bitten by mad dogs. Well, experiment has also proved this to be true, for a number of dogs were bitten by mad ones or were inoculated under the skin with rabic virus; of these some were subjected to the preventive cure and others not thus treated. Of the first or protected series not one became mad; of the other, or unprotected dogs, a large number died with all the characteristic symptoms of the disease. But it was one thing to thus experiment upon dogs, and quite another thing, as you may well imagine, to subject human beings to so novel and perhaps dangerous a treatment. Nevertheless, Pasteur was bold enough to take this necessary step and by so doing has earned the gratitude of the human race.

In front of the Pasteur Institute in Paris stands a statue worked with consummate skill in bronze. It represents a French shepherd boy engaged in a death struggle with a mad dog which had been worrying his sheep. With his bare hands and with no weapon save his wooden *sabot* the boy was successful in the combat. He killed the dog but was horribly bitten in the fight. The group represents no mythical struggle; the actual event took place in October 1885; and this boy, Jupille, was the second person to undergo the antirabic treatment, which proved perfectly successful, for he remained perfectly healthy, and his heroic deed and its consequences have become historic. *"C'est le premier pas qui coute,"* and as soon as the first man had been successfully treated others similarly situated gladly availed themselves of Pasteur's generous offer to treat them gratuitously. And as soon as this cure became generally known crowds of persons of all ages, stations, and countries, all bitten by rabid animals, visited every day Pasteur's laboratory in the Rue d'Ulm, which, from being one in which quiet scientific researches were carried on, came to resemble the out-patient department of a great hospital. There I saw the French peasant, the Russian *moujik* (suffering from the terrible bites of rabid wolves), the swarthy Arab, the English policeman, with women, too, and children of every age; in all perhaps a hundred patients. All were there undergoing the careful and kindly treatment, which was to insure them against a horrible death. Such a sight will not be easily forgotten. By degrees this wonderful cure for so deadly a disease attracted the attention of men of science throughout the civilized world. The French nation raised a monument to the discoverer better than any statue, in the shape of the Pasteur Institute, an institution devoted to carrying out in practice this anti-rabic treatment, with laboratories and every other convenience for extending by research our knowledge of the preventive treatment of infectious disease. For be it remembered, we are only at the beginning of these things, and what has been done is only an inkling of what is to come. Since 1885, twenty anti-rabic institutions have been established in various parts of the world, including Naples, Palermo, Odessa, St. Petersburg, Constantinople, Rio de Janeiro, Buenos Aires, and Havana.

We in England have also taken our share, though a small one, in this work. In 1885 I moved in the House of Commons for a committee to investigate and report on Pasteur's anti-rabic method of treatment. This committee consisted of trusted and well-known English men of science and physicians—Sir James Paget, Sir Joseph Lister, Doctors Burdon-Sanderson, Lauder Brunton, Quain, Fleming, and myself, with Professor Victor Horsley as secretary. We examined the whole subject, investigated the details of a number of cases, repeated Pasteur's experiments on animals, discussed the published statistics, and arrived unanimously at the opinion that Pasteur was justified in his conclusions, and that his anti-rabic treatment had conferred a great and lasting benefit on mankind. Since then His Royal Highness the Prince of Wales, who always takes a vivid interest in questions affecting the well-being of the people, has visited the Pasteur Institute and has expressed himself strongly in favor of a movement, started by the present Lord Mayor of London, for showing to Pasteur, by a substantial grant to his Institute, our gratitude for what he has done to relieve upwards of two hundred and fifty of our countrymen who have undergone treatment at his hands, and likewise to enable poor persons who have been bitten to undertake the journey to Paris and the sojourn there necessary for their treatment. This lasts about a fortnight, it is nearly painless, and no single case of illness, much less of hydrophobia, due to the preventive treatment, has occurred amongst the seven thousand persons who have so far undergone the cure.

Now let me put before you the answer to the question: Is this treatment a real cure? For this has been doubted by persons, some of whom will, I fear, still doubt, or profess to doubt, and still abuse Pasteur, whatever is said or done! From all that can be learned about the matter, it appears pretty certain that about from fifteen to twenty persons out of every hundred bitten by mad dogs or cats, and not treated by Pasteur's method, develop the disease, for I need scarcely add that all other methods of treatment have proved fallacious; but bites on the face are much more dangerous, the proportion of fatal cases reaching 80 per cent. Now of two thousand one hundred and sixty-four persons treated in the Pasteur Institute, from November 1885 to January 1887, only thirty-two died, showing a mortality of 1.4 per cent instead of 15 to 20, and amongst these upwards of two thousand persons, two hundred and fourteen had been bitten on the face, a class of wounds in which, as I have said, when untreated, the mortality is very high; so that the reduction in the death rate seems more remarkable, especially when we learn that in all these cases the animal inflicting the wound had been proved to be rabid. The same thing occurred even in a more marked degree in 1887 and 1888. In 1887 one thousand seven hundred and seventy-eight cases were treated with a mortality of 1.3 per cent while last year one thousand six hundred and twenty-six cases were treated, with a mortality of 1.16 per cent.

Statistics of the anti-rabic treatment in other countries show similar results, proving beyond a doubt that the death rate from hydrophobia is greatly reduced. Indeed, it may truly be said that in no case of dangerous disease, treated either by medicine or surgery, is a cure so probable. Moreover, in spite of assertions to the contrary, no proof can be given that in any single case did death arise from the treatment itself. And as showing the safety of the inoculation, I may add that all Pasteur's assistants and laboratory workers have undergone the treatment, and no case of hydrophobia has occurred amongst them.

You are no doubt aware that Pasteur's anti-rabic treatment has been strongly opposed by certain persons, some of whom have not scrupled to descend to personal abuse of a virulent character of those who in any way encouraged or supported Pasteur's views, and all of whom persistently deny that anything good has come or can come from investigations of the kind. Such persons we need neither fear nor hate. Their opposition is as powerless to arrest the march of science as was King Canute's order to stop the rising tide. Only let us rest upon the sure basis of exactly ascertained fact, and we may safely defy alike the vaporings of the sentimentalist and the wrath of the opponent of scientific progress. But opposition of a much fairer character has likewise to be met, and it has with propriety been asked: How comes it that Pasteur is not uniformly successful? Why (if what you tell us is true) do any deaths at all follow the anti-rabic treatment? The answer is not far to seek. In the first place, just as it is not every vaccination which protects against smallpox, so Pasteur's vaccination against rabies occasionally fails. Then again, Pasteur's treatment is really a race between a strong and an attenuated virus. In cases in which the bite occurs near a nerve center, the fatal malady may outstrip the treatment in this race between life and death. If the weakened virus can act in time, it means life. If the strong virus acts first, prevention comes too late—it means death. So that the treatment is not doubtful in all cases but only doubtful in those which are under well-known unfavorable conditions. This it seems to me is a complete reply to those who ignorantly fancy that because Pasteur's treatment has not cured every case it must be unreliable and worthless.

One word more. I have said that Pasteur is still—as he has always been—a chemist. How does this fit in with the fact that his recent researches seem to be entirely of a biological character? This is true. They seem, but they really are not. Let me in a few sentences explain what I mean. You know that yeast produces a peculiar chemical substance—alcohol. How it does so we cannot yet explain, but the fact remains. Gradually, through Pasteur's researches, we are coming to understand that this is not an isolated case, but that the growth of every micro-organism is productive of some special chemical substance and that the true pathogenic virus—or the poison causing the disease—is not the microbe itself, but the chemical compound which its growth creates. Here once more "to the solid ground of nature trusts the man that builds for aye," and it is only by experiment that these things can be learnt.

Let me illustrate this by the most recent and perhaps the most striking example we know of. The disease of diphtheria is accompanied by a peculiar microbe, which, however, only grows outside, as it were, of the body, but death often takes place with frightful rapidity. This takes place not by any action of the microbe itself, but by simple poisoning due to the products of the growing organism, which penetrate into the system, although the microbe does not. This diphtheritic *bacillus* can be cultivated, and the chemical poison which it produces can be completely separated by filtration from the microbe itself, just as alcohol can be separated from the yeast granules. If this be done, and one drop of this pellucid liquid given to an animal, that animal dies with all the well-known symptoms of the disease. This and similar experiments made with the microbes of other diseases lead to the conclusion that in infectious maladies the cause of death is poisoning by a distinct chemical compound, the microbe being not only the means of spreading the infection, but also the manufacturer of the poison. But more than this, it has lately been proved that a small dose of these soluble chemical poisons confers immunity. If the poison be administered in such a manner as to avoid speedy poisoning, but so as gradually to accustom the animal to its presence, the creature becomes not only refractory to toxic doses of the poison, but also even to the microbe itself. So that instead of introducing the micro-organism itself into the body, it may now only be necessary to vaccinate with a chemical substance which in large doses brings about the disease, but in small ones confers immunity from it, reminding one of Hahnemann's dictum of *Similia similibus curantur.*

Here then we are once more on chemical ground. True, on ground which is full of unexplained wonders, which however depend on laws we are at least in part acquainted with, so that we may in good heart undertake their investigation and look forward to the time when knowledge will take the place of wonder.

. . . My motive has been to explain to you as clearly as I could the life work of a chemist who has in my opinion conferred benefits as yet untold and perhaps unexampled on mankind, and I may be allowed to close my discourse with the noble words of our hero spoken at the opening of the Pasteur Institute in the presence of the President of the French Republic:

Two adverse laws seem to me now in contest. One law of blood and death, opening out each day new modes of destruction, forces nations to be always ready for the battlefield. The other a law of peace, of work, of safety, whose only study is to deliver man from the calamities which beset him.

The one seeks only violent conquests. The other only the relief of humanity. The one places a single life above all victories. The other sacrifices the lives of hundreds of thousands to the ambition of a single individual. The law of which we are the instruments strives even through the carnage to cure the bloody wounds caused by this law of war. Treatment by our antiseptic methods may preserve thousands of soldiers.

Which of these two laws will prevail over the other? God only knows. But of this we may be sure, that science in obeying this law of humanity will always labor to enlarge the frontiers of life.

Lord Kelvin (William Thomson) *

1824–1907

———◆———

SILVANUS PHILLIPS THOMPSON †

ON THE 17th of December, 1907, aged 83 years, died William Thomson, Baron Kelvin of Largs. Adequately to set forth the life and work of a man who so early won and who for so long maintained a foremost place in the ranks of science were a task that is frankly impossible. The greatness of a man of such commanding abilities and such profound influence cannot rightly be gauged by his contemporaries, however intimately they may have known him. But if by the very circumstance that we have lived so near to him we are debarred from rightly estimating his greatness, we at least have the advantage over posterity that we have been able to speak with him face to face, to learn at first hand his modes of thought, to sit at his feet as students or disciples, to marvel at his strokes of genius achieved before our very eyes, to learn to love him for his single-hearted enthusiasms, for his kindliness of soul, his unaffected simplicity of life. But if we may not attempt the impossible, we may at least essay the task of setting down in simple fashion some account of those things which he achieved. Let me first set down in briefest outline a sketch of his early life. William Thomson was born on June 26, 1824, in Belfast, being the second son and fourth child of James and Margaret Thomson. James Thomson, who was at that time professor of mathematics in the Royal Academic Institute of Belfast, was the son of a small farmer at Ballynahinch, in County Down, where his ancestors had settled about the year 1641 when they migrated from the lowlands of

* *A.R.*, 1908, pp. 745–768. Kelvin Lecture, delivered April 30, 1908, published in *Journal of the Institution of Electrical Engineers* (London, 1908), vol. 41, pp. 401–423, and "abridged by request and revised for the Smithsonian Institution."
† British physicist and engineer (1851–1916).

Scotland. James Thomson had early shown a taste for mathematical studies and by study of books had mastered the art of making sundials. He had then been sent to a small school in the district to learn classics and mathematics, rising while still a youth to the position of assistant teacher. During the winters he followed the courses in the University of Glasgow, crossing back to Belfast for the summers to resume teaching at school. After thus attending Glasgow University for five years he was appointed professor of mathematics in 1815 at the Belfast Academic Institute. His eldest son, James (Lord Kelvin's elder brother), was born in 1822, and William (Lord Kelvin), as already stated, in 1824. In 1830, when William was 6 years old, his mother died. His father would never send his boys to school but taught them himself. In 1832, when William was 8 years old, Professor Thomson was offered the chair of mathematics at Glasgow, and he with his family of six children accordingly removed from Belfast. He was in many ways a remarkable man. He made several original contributions to mathematics and produced several sound textbooks, including one on the differential and integral calculus. But his range of accomplishments was wide. He was an excellent classical scholar, familiar with both Latin and Greek, and able on occasion to give lectures in the classics to the university students. After his removal to Glasgow he still kept the education of his sons in his own hands, and so it happened that in 1834 William Thomson, when in his eleventh year, matriculated as a student in the university without ever having been at school.

He early made his mark by his progress in mathematics and physical science, and in 1840 produced an essay, "On the Figure of the Earth," which won him the university medal. He also read Greek plays with Lushington, and moral philosophy. To the end of his life he was in the habit of bringing out quotations from the classic authors. His fifth year as a student at Glasgow (1839–40) was notable for the impulse toward physics which he received from the lectures of Professor J. P. Nichol and from those of David Thomson (a relation of Faraday), who temporarily took the classes in natural philosophy during the illness of Professor Meikleham. In this year William Thomson had systematically studied the *Mécanique Analytique* of Lagrange and the *Mécanique Céleste* of Laplace, both mathematical works of a high order, and had made the acquaintance—a notable event in his career—of that remarkable book, Fourier's *Théorie de la Chaleur*. On May 1 he borrowed it from the college library. In a fortnight he had read it completely through. The effect of reading Fourier dominated his whole career thenceforward. He took the book with him for further study during a three months' visit to Germany. During his last year (1840–41) at Glasgow he communicated to the *Cambridge Mathematical Journal,* under the signature "P. Q. R.," an original paper "On Fourier's Expansions of Functions in Trigonometrical Series," which was a defense of Fourier's deductions against some strictures of Professor Kelland.

He left Glasgow University after six years of study, without even taking his degree, and on April 6, 1841, entered as a student at St. Peter's College, Cambridge. Here he speedily made his mark, and continued to contribute, at first anonymously, to the *Cambridge Mathematical Journal* papers inspired by his studies of the higher mathematics and by his love for physics. The analogy between the movement of heat in conductors along lines of flow and across surfaces of unequal temperature, and the distribution of electricity on conductors in such a way that the lines of electric force were crossed orthogonally by surfaces of equipotential, led to his paper entitled "The Uniform Motion of Heat in Homogeneous Solid Bodies, and Its Connection with the Mathematical Theory of Electricity." Here was an undergraduate of 17 handling methods of difficult integration readily and with mastery, at an age when most mathematical students are being assiduously drilled in so-called "geometrical conics" and other dull and foolish devices for calculus-dodging. It is true he followed the courses of coaching prescribed by his tutor, Hopkins, but he could not be kept to the routine of book work, and he never quite forgave Hopkins for keeping from him until the last day of his residence at Cambridge Green's rare and remarkable *Essay on the Application of Mathematical Analysis to the Theories of Electricity and Magnetism.* He also formed a close friendship with Stokes, then a young tutor, with whom, until his death in 1902, he maintained a continual interchange of ideas and suggestions in mathematical physics.

Of Thomson's Cambridge career so much has been written of late that it may be very briefly touched here. How he went up for his Tripos in 1845; how he came out second wrangler only, being beaten by the rapid Parkinson; how he beat Parkinson in the Smith's prize competition; how he rowed for his college to save Peterhouse from being bumped by Caius in the university races of 1843; how he won the Colquohoun silver sculls; how he helped to found the Cambridge University Musical Society and played the French horn in the little orchestra, which at its first concert, on December 8, 1843, performed Haydn's *First Symphony,* the

Overture to *Masaniello,* the *Overture* to *Semiramide,* the *Royal Irish Quadrilles,* and the *Elizabethan Waltzes* of Strauss! But these things—are they not written in the book of the *Cambridge Chronicle?*

Once when Lord Kelvin was in a chatty mood I asked him point-blank how it occurred that he was not senior wrangler. His blue eyes lighted up as he proceeded to explain that Parkinson had won principally on the exercises of the first two days, which were devoted to text-book work rather than to problems requiring analytical investigation. And then he added, almost ruefully:

I might have made up on the last two days but for my bad generalship. One paper was really a paper that I ought to have walked through, but I did very badly by my bad generalship, and must have got hardly any marks. I spent nearly all the time on one particular problem that interested me, about a spinning top being let fall on to a rigid plane—a very simple problem if I had tackled it in the right way—but I got involved and lost time on it and wrote something that was not good, and there was no time left for the other questions. I could have walked over the paper. A very good man, Parkinson—I didn't know him personally at the time—who had devoted himself to learning how to answer well in examinations, while I had had, during previous months, my head in some other subjects not much examined upon—theory of heat, flow of heat between isothermal surfaces, dependence of flow on previous state, and all the things I was learning from Fourier.

And then he drifted off into a talk of his early papers and to the mathematical inference (as the result of assigning negative values to the time t) that there must have been a creation.

It was [he continued] this argument from Fourier that made me think that there must have been a beginning. All mathematical continuity points to a beginning—this is why I stick to atoms . . . and they must have been small—smallness is a necessity of the complexity. They may have all been created as they were, complexity and all, as they are now. But we know they have a past. Trace back the past and one comes to a beginning, to a time zero beyond which the values are impossible. It's all in Fourier.

On leaving Cambridge Thomson went to Paris and worked in the laboratory of Regnault at the Collège de France. He was here four months. There was no arrangement for systematic instruction, and Thomson's principal occupation was to work the air pump to make a vacuum in one of two large glass globes which Regnault was weighing against one another in some determinations of the densities of gases. He made here the acquaintance of Biot and of Sturm and Foucault, of whom he spoke in terms of admiration. Returning, he was awarded a college fellowship of £200 a year.

Thomson was now 21 years old but had already established for himself a growing reputation for his mastery of mathematical physics. He had published about a dozen original papers and had gained experience in three universities. In 1846 the chair of natural philosophy at Glasgow became vacant by the death of Professor Meikleham, and Thomson at the age of 22 was chosen to fill it. His father, Professor James Thomson—he died in 1849—still held the chair of mathematics, Professor Thomas Thomson held that of chemistry, while Professor Allen Thomson occupied the chair of anatomy. William Thomson was the youngest of the five Professors Thomson then holding office in Glasgow. He chose for the subject of his inaugural lecture: "On the Distribution of Heat through the Earth."

This professorship he continued to hold till he resigned it in 1899, after continuous service of fifty-three years. Of his work as a university teacher this is hardly the occasion to say much. . . . The old college buildings where he lectured and worked for twenty-four years were ill-adapted for any laboratory facilities, yet he contrived to organize a physics laboratory—the first of its kind in Great Britain—in some disused rooms in a dark corner of one of the quadrangles and enlisted the voluntary service of a number of keen students in his early experimental researches on the electrodynamic and thermoelectric properties of matter. In the lecture theater his manifest enthusiasms won for him the love and respect of all students, even those who were hopelessly unable to follow his frequent flights into the more abstruse realms of mathematical physics. Over the earnest students of natural philosophy he exercised an influence little short of inspiration, an influence which extended gradually far beyond the bounds of his own university.

The next few years were times of strenuous work, fruitful in results. By the end of 1850, when he was 26 years of age, he had published no fewer than 50 original papers, mostly highly mathematical in character, and several of them in French. Among these researches there is a remarkable group which originated in his attendance in 1847 at the meeting of the British Association. He had prepared for reading at that meeting a paper on the exceedingly elegant process discovered by himself of treating certain problems of electrostatics by the method of electric images, a method even now not sufficiently well appreciated. But a more important event was the commencement of his friendship with

Joule, whom he met here for the first time. Joule, a Manchester brewer, and honorary secretary of the Manchester Literary and Philosophical Society, had for several years been pursuing his researches on the relations between heat, electricity, and mechanical work. Incited at first by Sturgeon into investigations on the electromagnet, and on the performance of electromagnetic engines—that is, electric motors—Joule had already in 1840 communicated to the Royal Society a paper on the "Production of Heat by Voltaic Electricity." He had also read papers at the British Association's meetings: "On the Electric Origin of Chemical Heat," at Manchester in 1842; "On the Calorific Effects of Magneto-electricity" and "On the Mechanical Value of Heat," at Cork in 1843; "On Specific Heat," at York in 1844; and "On the Mechanical Equivalent of Heat," at Cambridge in 1845. But at that date, when there was as yet no doctrine of conservation of energy, when scientific men were not accustomed to distinguish either in language or in fact between force and work, when "caloric" was classed with light and sound among the "imponderables," Joule's work was listened to with impatience, and his teachings fell upon deaf ears. Was he not an amateur, dabbling in science, and carried away with strange notions? For the Oxford meeting, too, Joule had prepared a paper. Its title was "On the Mechanical Equivalent of Heat, as Determined from the Heat Evolved by the Agitation of Liquids." It was relegated to an unimportant place and would have received as little notice as its predecessors but for Thomson's intervention.

Thomson, in fact, though he at first had some difficulty in grasping the significance of the matter, threw himself heart and soul into the new and strange doctrines that heat and work were mutually convertible, and for the next six or eight years, partly in cooperation with Joule, partly independently, he set his unique powers of mind to unravel those mutual relations. Thomson's mind was essentially metrical. He was never satisfied with any phenomenon until it should have been brought into the stage where numerical accuracy could be determined. He must measure, he must weigh, in order that he might go on to calculate.

I often say [he once remarked] that when you can measure what you are speaking about and express it in numbers, you know something about it; but when you cannot measure it, when you cannot express it in numbers, your knowledge is of a meager and unsatisfactory kind; it may be the beginning of knowledge, but you have scarcely, in your thoughts, advanced to the stage of *science,* whatever the matter may be. ... The first step toward numerical reckoning of properties of matter, more advanced than the mere reference to a set of numbered standards, as in the mineralogist's scale of hardness, or to an arbitrary trade standard, as in the Birmingham wire-gauge, is the discovery of a continuously varying action of some kind and the means of observing it definitely and measuring it in terms of some arbitrary unit or scale division. But more is necessary to complete the science of measurement in any department, and that is the fixing on something *absolutely* definite as the unit of reckoning.

It was in this spirit that Thomson approached the subject of the transformation of heat. Joule had laid down on certain lines the equivalence of heat and work and had even measured the numerical value of the equivalent. But before him, in 1824, Carnot, though he proceeded on the fallacious assumption of the material nature of caloric, had in his remarkable book, *Réflections sur la puissance motrice du feu,* discussed the proportion in which heat is convertible into work, and had introduced the very valuable notion of submitting a body to a reversible cycle of operations such that, after having experienced a certain number of transformations it is brought back identically to its primitive physical state as to density, temperature, and molecular constitution. He argued correctly that on the conclusion of the cycle it must contain the same quantity of heat as that which it initially possessed. But he argued quite incorrectly that the total quantity of heat lost by the body during one set of operations must be precisely compensated by its receiving back an equal quantity of heat in the other set of operations. We can see now that this is false, for if it were true, none of the heat concerned in the cycle would be transformed into work.

Those who were investigating the subject at this time, among them Clausius and Rankine, perceived this and noted that since the steam received into the cylinder must be hotter than that expelled from it, the degree to which the transformation is successful must depend on the respective temperatures—a fact, moreover, recognized by all engineers since the date when Watt discovered the advantage of cooling the exhaust steam by a condenser. Carnot, indeed, proved that the ratio of the work done by a perfect— that is, a reversible—engine to the heat received from the source depends on the temperatures of source and condenser only; and when these temperatures are nearly equal the efficiency is expressible by the product of their difference into a certain function of either of them, called *Carnot's function.* Rankine went further in pointing out that this function was greater as the temperature in question was lower. But here Thomson's exact mind seized upon the missing essential. Temperatures had hitherto been measured by arbitrary scales based on the expansion of quicksilver or of air or other gas, and the quicksilver thermometer scale did not agree precisely with that of the air thermometer. He was not satisfied with arbitrary scales. He had this in hand even before his first meeting with Joule, and in June 1848 communicated to the Cambridge Philosophical Society a paper "On an Absolute Thermometric Scale Founded on Carnot's Theory of the Motive Power of Heat, and Calculated from Regnault's Observations."

In this paper he set himself to answer the question: Is there any principle on which an absolute thermometric scale can be founded? He arrived at the answer that such a scale is obtained in terms of Carnot's theory, each degree being determined by the performance of equal quantities of work in letting one unit of heat be transformed in being let down through that difference of temperature. This indicates as the absolute zero of temperature the point which would be marked as — 273° on the air-thermometer scale. In 1849 he elaborated this matter in a further paper on "Carnot's Theory," and tabulated the values of Carnot's function from 1°C to 231°C. Joule, writing to Thomson in December 1848, suggested that probably the values of Carnot's function would turn out to be the reciprocal of the absolute temperatures as measured on a perfect gas thermometer, a conclusion independently enunciated by Clausius in February 1850. Independently of Joule, Mayer and Helmholtz had been considering the same problems from a more general standpoint. Helmholtz's famous publication of 1847, *Die Erhaltung der Kraft* ("On The Conservation of Force" meaning what we now term "energy"), was chiefly concerned with the proposition, based on the denial of the possibility of perpetual motion, that in all the transformations of energy the sum total of the energies in the universe remains constant.

Thomson continued to work at the subject. He experimented on the heat developed by compression of air. He verified the singular prediction of his brother, Professor James Thomson, of the lowering by pressure of the melting point of ice. He gave a thermodynamic explanation of the nonscalding property of steam issuing from a high-pressure boiler. He fomulated in the years 1851 to 1854 with scientific precision, in a long communication to the Royal Society of Edinburgh, the two great laws of thermodynamics: (1) the law of equivalence discovered by Joule, and (2) the law of transformation, which he generously attributed to Carnot and Clausius. Clausius, indeed, had done little more than put into mathematical language the equation of the Carnot cycle, corrected by the arbitrary substitution of the reciprocal of the absolute temperature; but Thomson never was grudging of the fame of independent discoverers. "Questions of personal priority," he wrote, "however interesting they may be to the persons concerned, sink into insignificance in the prospect of any gain of deeper insight into the secrets of nature." He gave a demonstration of the second law, founding it upon the axiom that it is impossible, by means of inanimate material agency, to derive mechanical effect from any portion of matter by cooling it below the temperature of the coldest of the surrounding objects. Further, by a most ingenious use of the integrating factor to solve the differential equation for the quantity of heat needed to alter the volume and temperature of unit mass of the working substance, he gave precise mathematical proof of the theorem that the efficiency of the perfect engine working between given temperatures is inversely proportional to the absolute temperature.

In collaboration with Joule he worked at the thermal effects of fluids in motion, the results appearing between the years 1852 and 1862 in a series of four papers in the *Philosophical Transactions,* and four others in the *Proceedings of the Royal Society.* Thus were the foundations of thermodynamics laid. This brilliant development and generalization of the subject (which had grown with startling rapidity from the moment when Helmholtz denied perpetual motion and Thomson grasped the conception of the absolute zero) did not content Thomson. He must follow its applications to human needs and the cosmic consequences it involved. And so he not only suggested the process of refrigeration by the sudden expansion of compressed cooled air, but propounded the doctrine of the dissipation of energy. If the availability of the energy in a hot body be proportional to its absolute temperature, it follows that as the earth and the sun—nay, the whole solar system itself—cool down toward one uniform level of temperature, all life must perish and all energy become unavailable. This far-reaching conclusion once more suggested the question of a beginning, a question which, as already remarked, had arisen in the consideration of the Fourier doctrine of the flow of heat.

In 1852, at the age of 28, William Thomson married Margaret Crum and resigned his Cambridge fellowship. The happiness of his life was, however, shadowed by his wife's precarious health, necessitating residence abroad at various times. In the summer of 1855 they stayed at Kreutznach, from which place Thomson wrote to Helmholtz, inviting him to come to England in September to attend the British Association meeting at Glasgow. He assured

Helmholtz that his presence would be one of the most interesting events of the gathering, so that he hoped to see him on this ground, but also looked forward with the greatest pleasure to the opportunity of making his acquaintance, as he had desired this ever since the "Conservation of Force" [Energy] had come into his hands. Accordingly, on July 29 Helmholtz left Königsberg for Kreutznach, to make the acquaintance of Thomson before his journey to England. On August 6 he wrote to Frau Helmholtz that Thomson had made a deep impression on him:

I expected to find the man, who is one of the first mathematical physicists of Europe, somewhat older than myself and was not a little astonished when a very juvenile and exceedingly fair youth who looked quite girlish came forward. He had taken a room for me close by and made me fetch my things from the hotel and put up there. He is at Kreutznach for his wife's health. She appeared for a short time in the evening, and is a charming and intellectual lady, but is in very bad health. He far exceeds all the great men of science with whom I have made personal acquaintance, in intelligence, and lucidity, and mobility of thought, so that I felt quite wooden beside him sometimes.

A year later Helmholtz again met the Thomsons at Schwalbach. Writing to his father, he described Thomson as "certainly one of the first mathematical physicists of the day, with powers of rapid invention such as I have seen in no other man." In 1860, after the death of Frau Helmholtz, the great German philosopher again visited Britain, staying with the Thomsons for some weeks in the island of Arran. In 1863 Helmholtz, who in the meantime had married again, came to England and visited the chief universities, and in writing to his wife gives an amusing picture of his doings:

My journey to Glasgow went off very well. The Thomsons have lately moved to live in the university buildings (the old college); formerly they spent more time in the country. He takes no holiday at Easter, but his brother James, professor of engineering at Belfast, and a nephew who is a student there, were with him. The former is a level-headed fellow, full of good ideas, but cares for nothing except engineering, and talks about it ceaselessly all day and all night, so that nothing else can be got in when he is present. It is really comic to see how the two brothers talk at one another and neither listens, and each holds forth about quite different matters. But the engineer is the most stubborn, and generally gets through with his subject. In the intervals I have seen a quantity of new and most ingenious apparatus and experiments of W. Thomson, which made the two days very interesting. He thinks so rapidly, however, that one has to get at the necessary information about the make of the instruments, etc., by a long string of questions, which he shies at. How his students understand him without keeping him as strictly to the subject as I ventured to do is a puzzle to me; still there were numbers of students in the laboratory hard at work, and apparently quite understanding what they were about. Thomson's experiments, however, did for my new hat. He had thrown a heavy metal disk into very rapid rotation, and it was revolving on a point. In order to show me how rigid it became on rotation he hit it with an iron hammer, but the disk resented this, and it flew off in one direction and the iron foot on which it was revolving in another, carrying my hat away with it and ripping it up.

But we are anticipating. Hitherto Thomson's work had been mainly in pure science, but toward the end of the fifties, while still in the midst of thermodynamic studies, events were progressing which drew him with irresistible force toward the practical applications that made him famous. Indeed, it could hardly be otherwise, seeing that he was master in whatever he touched. Early in 1853 he had communicated to the Glasgow Philosophical Society a paper "On Transient Electric Currents," in which he investigated mathematically the discharge of a Leyden jar through circuits possessing self-induction as well as resistance. Faraday and Reiss had observed that in certain cases the gases produced by the discharge of sparks through water consisted of mixed oxygen and hydrogen, and Helmholtz had conjectured that in such cases the spark was oscillatory. Thomson determined to test mathematically what was the motion of electricity at any instant after making contact in a circuit under given conditions. He founded his solution on the equation of energy, ingeniously building up the differential equation and then finding the integral. The result was very remarkable. He discovered that a critical relation occurred if the capacity in the circuit was equal to four times the coefficient of self-induction divided by the square of the resistance. If the capacity was less than this the discharge was oscillatory, passing through a series of alternate maxima and minima before dying out. If the capacity was greater than this the discharge was non-oscillatory, the charge dying out without reversing. This beautiful bit of mathematical analysis, which passed almost unnoticed at the time, laid the foundation of the theory of electric oscillations subsequently studied by Oberbeck, Schiller, Hertz, and Lodge, and forms the basis of wireless telegraphy. Fedderssen in 1859 succeeded in photographing these oscillatory sparks and sent photographs to Thomson, who with great delight gave an account of them to the Glasgow Philosophical Society.

At the Edinburgh meeting of the British Association in 1854 Thomson read a paper "On Mechanical Antecedents of Motion,

Heat, and Light." Starting with some now familiar but then novel generalities about energy, potential and kinetic, and about the idea of stores of energy, the author touched on the source of the sun's heat and the energy of the solar system and then reverted to his favorite argument from Fourier, according to which, if traced backward, there must have been a beginning to which there was no antecedent. This was a nonmathematical exposition of work which, as his notebooks show, had been going on from 1850 in a very stiff mathematical form in which Fourier's equations for the flow of heat in solids were applied to a number of outlying problems involving kindred mathematics, including the diffusion of fluids and the diffusion or transmission of electric signals through long cables. The *Proceedings of the Royal Society* for 1854 contain the investigation of cables under the title "On the Theory of the Electric Telegraph." Faraday had predicted that there would be retardation of signals in cables owing to the coating of gutta-percha acting like the glass of a Leyden jar. Forming the required differential equation and applying Fourier's integration of it, Thomson drew the conclusion that the time required for the current at the distant end to reach a stated fraction of its steady value would be proportional both to the resistance and to the capacity; and as both of these are proportional to the length of the cable, the retardation would be proportional to the square of the length. This is the famous law of squares about which so much dispute arose. This was followed by a further research "On Peristaltic Induction of Electric Currents," communicated to the British Association in 1855 and afterwards in more complete mathematical form to the Royal Society.

Submarine telegraphy was "in the air." John and Jacob Brett had pioneered the project for a Dover-Calais cable, and in 1851 Crampton successfully united England and France. In 1853 Holyhead and Howth were connected by Mr. (later Sir) Charles Bright. And these were followed by the Dover-Ostend and longer cables. Atlantic telegraphy became the dream of the telegraph engineer. Cyrus W. Field in 1856 negotiated a cable across the Gulf of St. Lawrence, thus connecting Newfoundland to the American continent. The Atlantic Telegraph Company was formed, with capital mostly subscribed in England, to promote the great enterprise to join Ireland to Newfoundland. Field, Brett, Bright, Statham, and Wildman Whitehouse were the chief promoters. Bright was engineer, Whitehouse (a retired medical man) electrician. In a pamphlet issued by the company, in July 1857, narrating the preliminary proceedings, the names of John Pender of

Manchester and Professor Thomson of "2, The College, Glasgow," are included in the list of directors; and the statement is made that "the scientific world is particularly indebted to Prof. W. Thomson, of Glasgow, for the attention he had given to the theoretical investigation of the conditions under which electrical currents move in long insulated wires, and Mr. Whitehouse has had the advantage of this gentleman's presence at his experiments, and counsel, upon several occasions, as well as the gratification resulting from his countenance and cooperation as one of the directors of the company." This is one side of the matter. The other side is that Whitehouse had at the British Association meeting in 1856 read a paper challenging the law of squares and declaring that if it was true Atlantic telegraphy was hopeless. He professed to refute it by experiments, the true significance of which was disposed of by Thomson in two letters in *The Athenæum*. He pointed out that success lay primarily in adequate section of conductor and hinted at a remedy (deduced from Fourier's equations), which he later embodied in the curb signal transmitter, namely, that the coefficient of the simple harmonic term in the expression for the electrical potential shall vanish. In December 1856 he described to the Royal Society his plan for receiving messages, namely, a sort of Helmholtz tangent galvanometer, with copper damper to the suspended needle, the deflections being observed by watching through a reading telescope the image of a scale reflected from the polished side of the magnet or from a small mirror carried by it. As we all know, he abandoned this subjective method for the objective plan in which a spot of light from a lamp is reflected by the mirror upon a scale. There is a pretty story—which is believed to be true—that the idea of thus using the mirror arose from noticing the reflection of light from the monocle which, being shortsighted, he wore hung around his neck with a ribbon.

The story of the Atlantic cable, of the failure of 1857, of the brief success of 1858, has so often been told that it need not be emphasized here. Thomson, after the failure of the first attempt, was called upon to take a more active part. He had discovered to his surprise that the conductivity of copper was greatly affected— to an extent of 30 or 40 per cent—by its purity. So he organized a system of testing conductivity at the factory where the additional lengths were being made, and was put in charge of the test room on board the *Agamemnon* in 1858. Whitehouse was unable to join the expedition, and Thomson at the request of the directors undertook the post of electrician in charge without any recompense, though the tax on his time and energies was very great.

Sir Charles Bright has given us the following little silhouette of Thomson:

As for the professor, . . . he was a thorough good comrade, good all round, and would have taken his "turn at the wheel" (of the paying-out brake) if others had broken down. He was also a good partner at whist when work wasn't on; though sometimes, when momentarily immersed in cogibundity of cogitation, by scientific abstraction, he would look up from his cards and ask, "Wha played what?"

After various disheartening mishaps, success crowned their efforts. Throughout the voyage Thomson's mirror galvanometer had been used for the continuity tests and for signaling to shore with a battery of 75 Daniell cells. The continuity was reported perfect, and the insulation had improved on submersion. On August 5 the cable was handed over to Whitehouse and reported to be in perfect condition. Whitehouse at once abandoned the Thomson mirror instruments and began working with his own patented apparatus using heavy relays and a special transmitter with induction coils. He sent in no report to the directors for a week, while he made ineffectual attempts with bigger induction coils to get his apparatus to work. After more than a week the reflecting galvanometer and ordinary Daniell cells were resumed, and then clear messages were interchanged and international congratulations. News of peace with China and the end of the Indian Mutiny was transmitted; but the insulation was found to be giving way, and on October 20, after 732 messages had been conveyed, the cable spoke no more. It had been destroyed by Whitehouse's bungling use of induction coils, some 5 feet long, working at some 2,000 volts!

Of the part played by Thomson in the next eight years in preparation for the cables of 1865 and 1866 there is not time to speak. Suffice it to say that throughout the preparations, the preliminary trials, the interrupted voyage of 1865 (when 1,000 miles were lost), the successful voyage of 1866 (when the new cable was laid and the lost one recovered from the ocean and completed), Thomson was the ruling spirit whose advice was eagerly sought and followed. On his return he was knighted for the part he played so well. He had in the meantime made further improvements in conjunction with Cromwell Varley. In 1867 he patented the siphon recorder, and in conjunction with Fleeming Jenkin, the curb transmitter. He was consulted on practically every submarine-cable project from that time forth.

Thomson's activities during the sixties were immense. Besides all

this telegraphic work he was incessant in research. He had undertaken serious investigations on the conductivity of copper. He was
urging the application of improved systems of electric measurement and the adoption of rational units. When in 1861 Sir Charles
Bright and Latimer Clark proposed names for the practical units
based on the centimeter-gram-second absolute system, Thomson
gave a cordial support; and on his initiative was formed the famous committee of electrical standards of the British Association,
which year by year has done so much to carry to perfection the
standards and the methods of electrical measurement. He was
largely responsible for the international adoption of the system of
units by his advocacy of them at the Paris congress in 1881 and
in subsequent congresses. He was an uncompromising advocate of
the metric system and lost no opportunity of denouncing the "absurd, ridiculous, time-wasting, brain-destroying British system of
weights and measures." His lecture in 1883 at the Civil Engineers
may be taken as a summary of his views, and it gives a glimpse of
his mental agility. So early as 1851 he had begun to use the absolute system, stimulated thereto by the earlier work of Gauss and
Weber. The fact that terrestrial gravity varies at different regions
of the earth's surface by as much as half of one per cent compelled
the use of absolute methods where any greater accuracy than this
is required. "For myself," he said, "what seems the shortest and
surest way to reach the philosophy of measurement—an understanding of what we mean by measurement, and which is essential
to the intelligent practice of the mere art of measuring—is to cut
off all connection with the earth." And so he imagined a traveler
with no watch or tuning fork or measuring rod wandering through
the universe trying to recover his centimeter of length and his
second of time and reconstructing thereupon his units and standards from the wave length of the yellow light of sodium and the
value of v, the velocity of light, from experiments on the oscillations in the discharge of a Leyden jar! Some of us in this very
room remember how we listened amazed to this characteristic and
bewildering excursus.

Among the activities of these fruitful years was a long research
on the electrodynamic qualities of metals—thermoelectric, ther-
moelastic, and thermomagnetic. These formed the subject of his
Bakerian lecture of 1856, which occupies no fewer than 118 pages
of the reprinted *Mathematical and Physical Papers*. He worked
hard also at the mathematical theory of magnetism. Faraday's
work on diamagnetism had appeared while Thomson was a student

at Cambridge. It established the fact that magnetic forces were not mere actions at a distance between supposed poles, but actions dependent on the surrounding medium, and Thomson set himself to investigate the matter mathematically. Faraday and Fourier had been the heroes of Thomson's youthful enthusiasm, and while the older mathematicians shook their heads at Faraday's heretical notion of curved lines of force, Thomson had in 1849 and 1850 developed a new theory with all the elegance of a mathematical disciple of Poisson and Laplace, discussing solenoidal and lamellar distributions by aid of the hydrodynamic equation of continuity. To Thomson we owe the terms "permeability" and "susceptibility," so familiar in the consideration of the magnetic properties of iron and steel. He continued to add to and revise this work through the sixties and seventies.

In 1859–60 Thomson was studying atmospheric electricity, writing on it in *Nichol's Cyclopedia* and lecturing on it at the Royal Institution. For this study he invented the water-dropping collector and vastly improved the electrometer, which developed into the elaborate forms of the quadrant instrument and other types described in the British Association report of 1867. During this work he discovered the fact that the sudden charge or discharge of a condenser is accompanied by a sound. He also measured electrostatically the electromotive force of a Daniell cell and investigated the potentials required to give sparks of different lengths in the air.

In the winter of 1860–61 Thomson met with a severe accident. He fell on the ice when engaged at Largs in the pastime of curling and broke the neck of his thigh. For several months he had to lie on his back, and it was at this time that he adopted the famous green notebooks which ever afterwards were the companions of his days. The accident left him with a slight limp for the rest of his life.

An admirable picture of Lord Kelvin as he was in the sixties, moving among his students and incessant in his researches, has been given in *The Times* of January 8, 1908, by Professor Ayrton, who was then working at Glasgow. In these years Thomson was also writing on the secular cooling of the earth and investigating the changes of form during rotation of elastic spherical shells. And as if this were not enough to have had in hand, he embarked with his friend, Professor Tait, on the preparation of a textbook of natural philosophy. There was at that date no satisfactory work to put into the hands of students, and he must supply the need. At first a short pamphlet of propositions on statics and dynamics, culled by Professor John Ferguson from mere lecture notes, was printed for the use of students. Thomson had told Helmholtz of his purpose, and in 1862 Helmholtz wrote him:

Your undertaking to write a textbook of natural philosophy is very praiseworthy, but will be exceedingly tedious. At the same time I hope it will suggest ideas to you for much valuable work. It is in writing a book like that that one best appreciates the gaps still left in science.

The first volume of Thomson and Tait's *Treatise on Natural Philosophy* was published in 1867, the second only in 1874, when it appeared that Helmholtz's hopes were just. For in approaching the subject of elasticity the gaps still left were found to be such that whole new mathematical researches were necessary before Volume I could be finished. Thomson's contributions to the theory of elasticity are no less important than those he made to other branches of physics. In 1867 he communicated to the Royal Society of Edinburgh his famous paper "On Vortex Atoms." Helmholtz had published a mathematical paper on the hydrodynamic equations of vortex motion, proving that closed vortices could not be produced in a liquid perfectly devoid of internal friction. Thomson seized on this idea. If no such vortex could be artificially produced, then if such existed it could not be destroyed. But being in motion and having the inertia of rotation, it would have elastic and other properties. He showed that vortex rings (like smoke rings in air) in a perfect medium are stable, and that in many respects they possess the qualities essential to the properties of material atoms—permanence, elasticity, and power to act on one another through the medium at a distance. The different kinds of atoms known to the chemist as elements were to be regarded as vortices of different degrees of complexity. Though he seemed at the end of his life to doubt whether the vortex-atom hypothesis was adequate to explain all the properties of matter, the conception remains to all time a witness to his extraordinary powers of mind.

In 1870 Lady Thomson, whose health had been failing for several years, died. In the same year the University of Glasgow was removed from the site it had occupied for over four centuries to the new and splendid buildings on Gilmore Hill, overlooking the Kelvin River. Sir William Thomson had a house here in the terrace assigned for the residences of the professors, adjoining his laboratory and lecture room. From his youth he had been fond of the sea and had early owned boats of his own on the Clyde. For many years his sailing yacht, the *Lalla Rookh,* was conspicuous, and he was an accomplished navigator. His experiences in cable laying had taught him much, and in return he was now to teach science in navigation. First he reformed the mariner's compass, lightening the moving parts to avoid protracted oscillations and to facilitate the correction of the quadrantal and other errors arising from the magnetism of the ship's hull. At first the Admiralty would have none of it. But the compass is now all but universally adopted both in the navy and in the mercantile marine.

Dissatisfied with the clumsy appliances used in sounding, when the ship had to be stopped before the sounding line could be let down, he devised the now well-known apparatus for taking flying soundings by using a line of steel piano wire. He had great faith in navigating by use of sounding line and once told me—apropos of a recent wreck near the *Lizard,* which he declared would have been impossible had soundings been regularly taken—how in a time of a continuous fog he brought his yacht all the way across the Bay of Biscay into the Solent, trusting to soundings only. He also published a set of tables for facilitating the use of Sumner's method at sea. He was vastly interested in the question of the tides, not merely as a sailor, but because of the interest attending their mathematical treatment in connection with the problems of the rotation of spheroids, the harmonic analysis of their complicated periods by Fourier's methods, and their relation to hydrodynamic problems generally. He invented the tide-predicting machine, which will predict for any given port the rise and fall of the tides, which it gives in the form of a continuous curve recorded on paper, the entire curves for a whole year being inscribed by the machine automatically in about four hours. Further than this, adopting a beautiful mechanical integrator, the device of his ingenious brother, Professor James Thomson, he invented a harmonic analyzer—the first of its kind—capable not only of solving differential equations of any order, but of analyzing any given periodic curve and exhibiting the values of the coefficients of the various terms of the Fourier series. Wave problems always had a fascination for him, and the work of the mathematicians Poisson and Cauchy on the propagation of wave motion were familiar studies. In his lectures he used to say, "The great struggle of 1815"—and then paused, while his students, thinking of Waterloo, began to applaud—"was not that fought out on the plains of Belgium, but who was to rule the waves, Cauchy or Poisson." In 1871 Helmholtz went with Sir William Thomson on the yacht *Lalla Rookh* to the races at Inverary, and on some longer excursions to the Hebrides. Together they studied the theory of waves, "which he loved," says Helmholtz, "to treat as a race between us." Returning, they visited many friends. "It was all very friendly," wrote Helmholtz, "and unconstrained. Thomson presumed so much on his intimacy with them that he always carried his mathematical notebook about with him, and would begin to calculate in the midst of the company if anything occurred to him, which was treated with a certain awe by the party." He possessed, indeed, the faculty of detachment and would settle quietly down with his green book, almost unconscious of things going on around him. On calm days he and Helmholtz experimented on the rate at which the smallest ripples on the surface of the water were propagated. Almost the last publications of Lord Kelvin were a series of papers on "Deep-Sea Ship Waves," communicated between 1904 and 1907 to the Royal Society of Edinburgh.

In 1874, on June 17, Sir William Thomson married Miss Frances Anna Blandy of Madeira, whom he had met on cable-laying expeditions. Lady Kelvin, who survives him, became the center of his home in Glasgow and the inseparable companion of all his later travels. He built at Netherhall, near Largs, a beautiful mansion in the Scottish baronial style; and though he latterly had a London house in Eaton Place, Netherhall was the home to which he retired when he withdrew from active work in the University of Glasgow.

Throughout the seventies and eighties Sir William Thomson's scientific activities were continued with untiring zeal. In 1874 he was elected president of the Society of Telegraph Engineers, of which in 1871 he had been a foundation member and vice-president. In 1876 he visited America, bringing back with him a pair of Graham Bell's earliest experimental telephones. He was president of the Mathematical and Physical Section of the British Association of that year at Glasgow.

Among the matters that cannot be omitted in any notice of his life was Lord Kelvin's controversy with the geologists* He had from three independent lines of argument inferred that the age of the earth could not be infinite, and that the time demanded by the geologists and biologists for the development of life must be finite. He himself estimated it at about a hundred million of years at the most. In vain did the naturalists, headed by Huxley, protest. He stuck to his propositions with unrelaxing tenacity but unwavering courtesy. "Gentler knight never broke lance" was Huxley's dictum of his opponent. His position was never really shaken,

---

* See his "Age of the Earth as an Abode Fitted for Life," *A.R.*, 1897, pp. 337–357, and T. C. Chamberlain's discussion of this view, *A.R.*, 1899, pp.

though the later researches of Perry, and the discovery by Strutt of the degree to which the constituent rocks of the earth contain radioactive matter, the disgregation of which generates internal heat, may so far modify the estimate as to increase somewhat the figure which he assigned.

The completion of the second edition of Volume I of the Thomson and Tait *Treatise*—no more was ever published—and the collection of his own scattered researches were work extending over some years. In addition he wrote for the *Encyclopædia Britannica* of 1879 the long and important articles on elasticity and heat.

In 1871 he was president of the British Association at its meeting in Edinburgh. In his Presidential Address, which ranged luminously over the many branches of science within the scope of the Association, he propounded the suggestion that the germs of life might have been brought to the earth by some meteorite.

With the advent of electric lighting at the end of the seventies Thomson's attention was naturally attracted to this branch of the practical applications of science. He never had any prejudice against the utilization of science for practical ends. He wrote:

There cannot be a greater mistake than that of looking superciliously upon practical applications of science. The life and soul of science is its 223-246.
practical application; and just as the great advances in mathematics have been made through the desire of discovering the solution of problems which were of a highly practical kind in mathematical science, so in physical science many of the greatest advances that have been made from the beginning of the world to the present time have been made in the earnest desire to turn the knowledge of the properties of matter to some purpose useful to mankind.

And so he scorned not to devise instruments and appliances for commercial use. His electrometers, his galvanometers, his siphon recorders, and his compasses had been made by James White, optician, of Glasgow. In this firm he became a partner, taking the keenest commercial interest in its operations and frequenting the factory to superintend the construction of apparatus. New measuring instruments were required. He set himself to devise them, designing potential galvanometers, ampere gauges, and a whole series of standard electric balances for electrical engineers. Lord Kelvin's patented inventions were very numerous. Without counting in those since 1900, taken mostly in the name of Kelvin and James White, they number 56. Of these 11 relate to telegraphy, 11 relate to compasses and navigation apparatus, 6 relate to dy-

namo machines or electric lamps, 25 to electric measuring instruments, 1 to the electrolytic production of alkali, and 2 to valves
for fluids. He was an independent inventor of the zigzag method
of winding alternators, which the public knew under the name of
Ferranti's machine, which was manufactured under royalties pay-
able to him. He was interested even in devising such details as
fuses and the suspension pulleys with differential gearing by which
incandescent lamps can be raised or lowered.

He gave evidence before a parliamentary committee on electric
lighting and discussed the theory of the electric transmission of
power, pointing out the advantage of high voltages. The introduction into England in 1881 of the Faure accumulator excited him
greatly. In his Presidential Address to the Mathematical and Physical Section of the British Association at York that year he spoke
of this and of the possibility of utilizing the powers of Niagara.
He also read two papers, in one of which he showed mathematically that in a shunt dynamo best economy of working was
attained when the resistance of the outer circuit was a geometric
mean between the resistances of the armature and of the shunt. In
the other he laid down the famous law of economy of copper lines
for the transmission of power.

Helmholtz, visiting him again in 1884, found him absorbed in
regulators and measuring apparatus for electric lighting and electric railways. "On the whole," Helmholtz wrote, "I have an impression that Sir William might do better than apply his eminent
sagacity to industrial undertakings; his instruments appear to me
too subtle to be put into the hands of uninstructed workmen and
officials. . . . He is simultaneously revolving deep theoretical
projects in his mind, but has no leisure to work them out quietly.
As far as that goes, I am not much better off." But he shortly
added, "I did Thomson an injustice in supposing him to be wholly
immersed in technical work; he was full of speculations as to the
original properties of bodies, some of which were very difficult to
follow; and, as you know, he will not stop for meals or any other
consideration." And, indeed, Thomson had weighty things in his
mind. He was revolving over the speculations which later in the
same year he was to pour out in such marvelous abundance in
his famous 20 lectures in Baltimore, "On Molecular Dynamics and
the Wave Theory of Light." These lectures, delivered to 26 hearers,
mostly accomplished teachers and professors, were reported ver-
batim at the time and reprinted by him with many revisions and
additions in 1904. Of this extraordinary work, done at the age of
60, it is difficult to speak. Day after day he led the 26 "coeffi-

cients" who sat at his feet through the mazes of solid-elastic theory and the spring-shell molecule, newly invented in order to give a conception of how the molecules of matter are related to the ether through which light waves are propagated. All his life he had been endeavoring to discover a rational mechanical explanation for the most recondite phenomena—the mysteries of magnetism, the marvels of electricity, the difficulties of crystallography, the contradictory properties of ether, the anomalies of optics. While Thompson had been seeking to explain electricity and magnetism and light dynamically, or as mechanical properties, if not of matter at least of molecules, Maxwell (the most eminent of his many disciples) had boldly propounded the electromagnetic theory of light and had drawn all the younger men after him in acceptance of the generalization that the waves of light were essentially electromagnetic displacements in the ether. Thomson had never accepted Maxwell's theory. It is true that in 1888 he gave a nominal adhesion, and in the preface which in 1893 he wrote to Hertz's *Electric Waves* he himself uses the phrase "the electromagnetic theory of light, or the undulatory theory of magnetic disturbance." But later he withdrew his adhesion, preferring to think of things in his own way. Thomson's Baltimore lectures, abounding as they do in brilliant and ingenious points, and ranging from the most recondite problems of optics to speculations on crystal rigidity, the tactics of molecules and the size of atoms, leave one with the sense of being a sort of protest of a man persuaded against his own instincts and struggling to find new expression of his thoughts so as to retain his old ways of regarding the ultimate dynamics of physical nature.

One characteristic of all Lord Kelvin's teaching was his peculiar fondness for illustrating recondite notions by models. Possibly he derived this habit from Faraday, but he pushed its use far beyond anything prior. He built up chains of spinning gyrostats to show how the rigidity derived from the inertia of rotation might illustrate the property of elasticity. The vortex-atom presented a dynamical picture of an ideal material system. He strung together little balls and beads with sticks and elastic bands to demonstrate crystalline dynamics. On the use of the model to illustrate physical principles he spoke as follows at Baltimore:

My object is to show how to make a mechanical model which shall fulfill the conditions required in the physical phenomena that we are considering, whatever they may be. At the time when we are considering the phenomena of elasticity in solids I shall want a model of that. At another time, when we have vibrations of light to consider, I shall want to show a model of the action exhibited in that phenomenon. We want to understand the whole about it; we only understand a part. It seems to me that the test of "Do we or do we not understand a particular subject in physics?" is "Can we make a mechanical model of it?" I have an immense admiration for Maxwell's mechanical model of electromagnetic induction.

And again Lord Kelvin says:

I never satisfy myself until I can make a mechanical model of a thing. If I can make a mechanical model, I can understand it. As long as I cannot make a mechanical model all the way through I cannot understand it.

This use of models has become characteristic of the tone and temper of British physicists. Where Poisson or Laplace saw a mathematical formula, Kelvin with true physical imagination discerned a reality which could be roughly simulated in the concrete. And throughout all his mathematics his grip of the physical reality never left him. According to the standard that Kelvin set before him, it is not sufficient to apply pure analysis to obtain a solution that can be computed. Every equation, "every line of the mathematical process must have a physical meaning, every step in the process must be associated with some intuition; the whole argument must be capable of being conducted in concrete physical terms." In other words, Lord Kelvin, being a highly accomplished mathematician, used his mathematical equipment with supreme ability as a tool; he remained its master and did not become its slave.

Once Lord Kelvin astonished the audience at the Royal Institution by a discourse on "Isoperimetrical Problems," endeavoring to give a popular account of the mathematical process of determining a maximum or minimum, which he illustrated by Dido's task of cutting an oxhide into strips so as to inclose the largest piece of ground; by Horatius Cocles's prize of the largest plot that a team of oxen could plow in a day; and by the problem of running the shortest railway line between two given points over an uneven country. On another occasion he entertained the Royal Society with a discourse on the "Homogeneous Partitioning of Space," in which the fundamental packing of atoms was geometrically treated, affording incidentally the theory of the designing of wallpaper patterns.

To the last Lord Kelvin took an intense interest in the most recent discoveries. Electrons—or "electrions," as he called them—were continually under discussion. He prided himself that he had read Rutherford's book on radioactivity again and again. He objected, however, in toto to the notion that the atom was capable of division and disintegration. In 1903, in a paper called "Aepinus Atomized," he reconsidered the views of Aepinus and Father Boscovich from the newest standpoint, modifying Aepinus's theory to suit the notion of electrons.

After taking part in the British Association meeting of 1907 at Leicester, where he entered with surprising activity into the discussions of radioactivity and kindred questions, he went to Aix les Bains for change. He had barely reached home at Largs in September when Lady Kelvin was struck down with a paralytic seizure. Lord Kelvin's misery at her hopeless condition was intense. He had himself suffered for fifteen years from recurrent attacks of facial neuralgia and in 1906 underwent a severe operation. Under these afflictions he had visibly aged, and the illness of Lady Kelvin found him little able physically to sustain the anguish of the stroke. He wandered distractedly about the corridors of his house, unable at last to concentrate his mind on the work at hand. A chill seized him, and after about a fortnight of prostration he sank slowly and quietly away. He was buried in Westminster Abbey, with national honors, on December 23, 1907.

. . .

Honors fell thickly on Lord Kelvin in his later life. He was President of the Royal Society from 1890 to 1894. He had been made a Fellow of the Royal Society in 1851 and in 1883 had been awarded the Copley medal. He was raised to the peerage in 1892. He was one of the original members of the Order of Merit, founded in 1902; was a grand officer of the Legion of Honor; and held the Prussian order Pour le Mérite; in 1902 was named a privy councilor. In 1904 he was elected chancellor of the university in which he had filled the chair of natural philosophy for fifty-three years. He had celebrated his jubilee with unusual marks of world-wide esteem in 1896 and finally retired in 1899. He was a member of every foreign academy and held honorary degrees from almost every university. In 1899 we elected him an honorary member of our institution.

In politics he was, up to 1885, a broad Liberal; but, as was natural in an Ulsterman, became an ardent Unionist on the introduction of the home-rule bill. He once told me that he preferred Chamberlain's plan of home rule with four Irish parliaments—one in each province. In religion Lord Kelvin was an Anglican—at least from his Cambridge days, but when at Largs attended the Presbyterian Free Church. His simple, unobtrusive, but essential piety of soul was unclouded. He had a deep detestation of ritualism and sacerdotalism, which he hated heart and soul in all its forms; and he denounced spiritualism as a loathsome and vile superstition. His profound studies had led him again and again to contemplate a beginning to the order of things, and he more than once publicly professed a profound and entirely unaffected belief in Creative Design.

Kindly hearted, lovable, modest to a degree almost unbelievable, he carried through life the most intense love of truth and an insatiable desire for the advancement of natural knowledge. Accurate and minute measurement was for him as honorable a mode of advancing knowledge as the most brilliant or recondite speculation. At both ends of the scale his preëminence in the quest for truth was unchallenged. If he could himself at the end of his long career describe his own efforts as "failure," it was because of the immensely high ideal* which he set before him. "I know," he said on the day of his jubilee, "no more of electric and magnetic force, or of the relation between ether, electricity, and ponderable matter, or of chemical affinity, than I knew and tried to teach to my students in my first session." Yet which of us has not learned much of these things because of his work? We of this Institution of Electrical Engineers may well be proud of him—proud that he was one of our first members, that he was thrice our president, and that as our president he died. We shall not look upon his like again.

* He conceived the possibility of formulating a comprehensive molecular theory, definite and complete, "in which all physical science will be represented with every property of matter shown in dynamical relation to the whole." Presidential Address to the British Association, 1871, reprinted in *Popular Lectures and Addresses,* Vol. II, p. 163. [Original note.]

Thomas Henry Huxley *

1825–1895

———◆———

THEODORE NICHOLAS GILL †

THE HISTORY of scientific progress has been marked by a few periods of intellectual fermentation when great bounds have been taken forward and a complete revolution ensued. Very few have been such, but in one the name of Huxley must be ever conspicuous. It was as a lieutenant of the organizer of that revolution that he appeared, but unquestionably without him it would have been long delayed, and it was through his brilliant powers of exposition that the peoples of the English-speaking lineage soon learned to understand, to some extent, what evolution was and, learning, to accept it.

On the 4th of May, 1825, was born the infant Huxley, in due course christened Thomas Henry. "It was," Huxley himself has remarked, "a curious chance that my parents should have fixed for my usual denomination upon the name of that particular apostle with whom I have always felt most sympathy." In his physical and mental peculiarities he was completely the "son of his mother," whose most distinguishing characteristic was "rapidity of thought"; that characteristic Huxley claimed to have been passed on to him "in full strength" and to have often "stood him in good stead," and to it he was undoubtedly indebted for success in the many intellectual duels he was destined to be engaged in. His "regular school training was of the briefest," and he has ex-

* A.R., 1895, pp. 759–779. Memorial address before scientific societies of Washington, Jan. 14, 1896, published with additions in Science, Feb. 21, 1896. See also John Fiske, "Reminiscences of Huxley," A.R., 1900, pp. 713–728; William Keith Brooks, "Lesson of the Life of Huxley," A.R., 1900, pp. 710–711; Thomas Henry Huxley, "Advance of Science in the Last Half-Century," A.R., 1887, pp. 57–98.
† American zoologist (1837–1914). See William Healey Dall, "Theodore Nicholas Gill," A.R., 1916, pp. 579–586.

pressed a very poor opinion of it. His early inclination was to be a mechanical engineer, but he was put to a brother-in-law to study medicine. The only part of his professional course which really interested him was physiology, which he has defined as "the mechanical engineering of living machines." The only instruction from which he thought he ever obtained the proper effect of education was that received from Mr. Wharton Jones, who was the lecturer on physiology at the Charing Cross School of Medicine. At Mr. Jones's suggestion in 1845 Huxley communicated to the *Medical Gazette* (p. 1340) his first paper "On a Hitherto Undescribed Structure in the Human Hair Sheath." Two years later he contributed to the British Association for the Advancement of Science the first paper generally attributed to him, "Examination of the Corpuscles of the Blood of *Amphioxus.*" (*Abstracts,* p. 95.) In 1845 he passed the first M. B. examination at the London University. Soon afterwards he was admitted into the medical service of the navy and was, after some waiting, assigned to the *Rattlesnake,* and for four years (1846–1850) served on her during her exploration of the Australasian seas; he was, he supposed, among the last voyagers "to whom it could be possible to meet with people who knew nothing of firearms—as [they] did on the south coast of New Guinea."

While on board Huxley zealously prosecuted zoological investigations and in 1849 and 1850 sent records of various observations, in papers which were published in the *Philosophical Transactions* and *Annals* and *Magazine of Natural History.* Most important of all was a monograph on the oceanic *Hydrozoa,* published by the Ray Society. It is amusing to find that while in Sydney he was impressed by MacLeay and led to believe that "there is a great law hidden in the 'circular system' if we could but get at it, perhaps in Quinarianism, too," but sober sense doubtless soon came to the rescue, and he appears to have been never otherwise touched by the strange monomania that had been epidemic in England during the previous quarter century. In 1851 he became a Fellow of the Royal Society. He continued in the navy three years after his return but in 1853 resigned when ordered to sea again.

In 1853 Huxley and Tyndall became candidates for professorships in the University of Toronto, but that university preferred others for the vacant places and thus missed the opportunity of an age. In 1854 Huxley was appointed to the post of lecturer on natural history in the School of Mines, which he held for the next thirty-one years. In the same year he became Fullerian Professor in the Royal Institution. "The first important audience [he] ever addressed was at the Royal Institution." In 1862 he served as president of the biological section and in 1870 of the British Association for the Advancement of Science itself; in 1869 and 1870 of the Geological and Ethnological Societies, and in 1883 to 1885 of the Royal Society. He was inspector of salmon fisheries from 1881 to 1885. In 1876 he visited the United States and delivered an address at the opening of the Johns Hopkins University.

In 1885 failing health and desire for freedom led him to retire from most of his offices, and thenceforth he devoted himself chiefly to literary work rather than to scientific investigation. On the accession of Lord Salisbury to the premiership in 1892 Huxley was made privy counselor, and with it came the title of Right Honorable, by which he was later styled. In the last years of life he resided at Hodeslea, Eastbourne, and after a long illness ("complication following influenza") died there on the 29th of June, 1895.

Such were the principal episodes in the life of Huxley. Many more details may be found in the numerous periodicals of the day, and in some of them are depicted various phases of his character and labors. The short time that is at our disposal tonight may be most profitably and entertainingly utilized in reviewing his feats as a warrior of science and estimating the measure of influence he exercised in diverting human thought from the ruts in which it had moved for centuries and directing it into a highway where increasing light from different sides could guide the wayfarer. Although this period of warfare was at its height not further back than the early afternoon of the present century, and some of us here assembled joined in the fray, to the younger naturalists it is an unknown past except through history, and to some of us who were of it, it is so strange as to recur to us rather as a dream than as a realized passage in actual life.

Doubtless man, almost from the moment of his acquisition of those characters which distinguished him as representative of the genus *Homo,* had wondered and speculated as to how he came into being and how the animals assembled round him had sprung into existence. Those early concepts must have been strange, indeed, but were doubtless transmitted from mother to child, only with some eccentricities lopped off with advancing intelligence. Gradually, among peoples of the Aryan stock at least, they crystallized into a doctrine that in the beginning there was chaos, that the three elements of air, water, and earth were differentiated, and that animals were successively created to occupy the spaces. Such were the views of the old oriental cosmologists and such of the later Romans as epitomized in Ovid's verse. These ideas were long regnant and naturalists embodied some in their schemes, most accepting the idea that animals may have been created in pairs, but a few (such as Agassiz*) urging that they must have been created in communities approximating to those still found. There were very few to dissent from these views of specific creation, and those few had little influence on the popular beliefs. But as the present century advanced, curious men delved into all the mysteries of nature; the sciences of morphology, physiology, histology, embryology, geology, and zoogeography came into being, and facts were marshaled from every side that militated against the old conceptions. Even when these sciences were inchoate or newborn, sagacious men had perceived the drift of the facts and anticipated induction by the formulation of hypotheses of evolution, but the hypotheses were too crude to insure acceptance. Meanwhile, however, the facts accumulated, and in 1859 a factor determining the course of development of species was appreciated by Darwin and Wallace and soon applied to a wide range of facts in the former's *Origin of Species by Means of Natural Selection.*

Darwin's work at once aroused great popular interest, but it was too diffuse and the intellectual pabulum it contained was too strong and indigestible for ordinary readers, and it is probable that the general acceptance of the Darwinian form of evolution would have been delayed much longer than it was had it not been for the excursions from the scientific fold into the popular arena by one having the confidence of the former and the ear of the latter, as did Huxley.

Scarcely had Darwin's work come from the press when Huxley commenced his missionary work. Almost exceptional among numerous reviews, remarkable chiefly for crudity, ignorance, and arrogance, was one that appeared in the great daily organ of English opinion, *The Times,* marked by superior knowledge, acuteness of argumentation, and terse and vigorous style. This review, which attracted general attention, was acknowledged later by Huxley. Lectures and addresses before popular audiences and even to those distinctively claiming to be "workingmen" followed, and these were published or supplemented by publication in various forms. Answers, critiques, and other articles in reply came out in rapid succession, and loud clamor was made that Huxley was an

* See Ernest Favre, "Louis Agassiz: A Biographical Notice," *A.R.,* 1878, pp. 236–261; Rufus P. Stebbins, "Louis Agassiz," *A.R.,* 1873, pp. 198–210.

infidel and a very bad man and that he falsified and misrepresented in a most villainous manner.

A memorable occasion was the meeting of the British Association for the Advancement of Science in the year 1860, following the publication of the *Origin of Species*. A discussion of the subject was precipitated by the presentation of a communication by our own Draper, "On the Intellectual Development of Europe with Reference to the Views of Mr. Darwin and Others that the Progression of Organisms is Determined by Law." The Reverend Mr. Cresswell and the Reverend Dr. Wilberforce, Bishop of Oxford, followed in opposition, and they were answered by Huxley. The scene has lately been redescribed by a great physiologist and friend of Huxley, who is one of the few witnesses who now remain:

The room was crowded, though it was Saturday, and the meeting was excited. The bishop had spoken; cheered loudly from time to time during his speech, he sat down amid rapturous applause, ladies waving their handkerchiefs with great enthusiasm; and in almost dead silence, broken merely by greetings which, coming only from the few who knew, seemed as nothing, Huxley, then well-nigh unknown outside the narrow circle of scientific workers, began his reply. A cheer, chiefly from a knot of young men in the audience, hearty but seeming scant through the fewness of those who gave it, and almost angrily resented by some, welcomed the first point made. Then as, slowly and measuredly at first, more quickly and with more vigor later, stroke followed stroke, the circle of cheers grew wider and yet wider, until the speaker's last words were crowned with an applause falling not far short of, indeed equaling that which had gone before, an applause hearty and genuine in its recognition that a strong man had arisen among the biologists of England.

The versatile bishop indulged in the *argumentum ad hominem* so very trite and familiar to us all (Who has not heard it?): he would like "to hear from Mr. Huxley whether it was by his grandfather's or grandmother's side that he was related to an ape." Huxley replied:

I asserted, and I repeat, that a man would have no reason to be ashamed of having an ape for a grandfather. If there were an ancestor whom I should feel shame in recalling it would be a man; a man of restless and versatile intellect who, not content with an equivocal success in his own sphere of activity, plunges into scientific questions with which he has no real acquaintance, only to obscure them by an aimless rhetoric and distract the attention of his hearers from the real point at issue by eloquent digressions and skilled appeals to religious prejudice.

The arguments adduced against evolution during those days were sometimes very comical, and the confident air of the up-holder of the ancient views and the assurance with which he claimed that his position was fixed and that the burden of proof rested entirely upon the advocate of the opposite view were very amusing. It was urged that no one had ever seen one species turn into another. Had anyone ever seen any animal made? Could any-one really conceive of any animal being actually made? Did an omnipotent Creator actually take the "dust of the ground" and mold it into animal shape and then breathe into its nostrils "the breath of life?" "Did infinitesimal atoms flash into living tissues?" Certainly no physiologist with a competent knowledge of histology could believe in any such mode of creation. On the other hand, everyone that could exercise the necessary skill could follow the evolution of an animal from an undifferentiated protoplasmic mass into a perfect animal. A clutch of eggs could be successively taken from a mother hen or a hatching oven, and day after day the actual evolution of the undifferentiated matter into derivative functional parts could be followed. That which is true of the hen is true of man, only in the latter case it is more difficult to obtain the requisite material, and greater skill to use it is requisite. Com-pare the embryos developing in the hen and human eggs and at first no difference except size and environment can be perceived. Compare them in successive stages, and adult animals more or less parallel to some early stages may be found still living or entombed in earlier formations of the earth in fossilized form.

It was argued that no one had ever seen one species turn into another. But is it not a matter of historical evidence that many breeds of domestic animals have actually been developed by the agency of man and propagate their kind? And how are such breeds distinguished from species except by the fact that we know their origin, and that they have come into prominence through selec-tion by man rather than by nature? Interbreeding is no criterion.

But it is unnecessary to go into details, and these hints are of-fered only because their bearings on the subject were so generally overlooked by those who opposed evolution. One opponent, so emi-nent as to be styled the "pope" of a great Protestant Church, pub-lished a work against evolution largely based on the contention that the existence of the eye, except through direct creation, was inconceivable. Yet this very evolution of the eye from simple protoplasm could have been witnessed at any time with little trouble in the hen's egg. Is evolution through great reaches of time more inconceivable than actual evolution capable of daily observation? Well and skillfully did Huxley meet the arguments against evolution. Even most of the old naturalists sooner or later recognized the force of the arguments for and the weakness of those against evolution. Those who did not in time gave up the contest with their lives. The young who later entered into the field of investigation have done so as evolutionists.

. . .

Darwin, in his *Origin of Species,* had refrained from direct allusion to man in connection with evolution and many casual readers were doubtless left in uncertainty as to his ideas on the subject. Naturally, the scientific man recognized that the origin of his kind from a primate stock followed, and believed that Darwin's reticence was probably due to a desire to disturb popular beliefs as little as possible. When we recall what strange views were held respecting man's origin and relations we can understand how the unlearned could easily fail to recognize that man must follow in the chain of his fellow-creatures. (We preserve *creature* still as a reminiscence of ancient belief, but without the primitive conception attached to the word.)

Man was claimed as a being isolated from animals generally, and naturalists of acknowledged reputation and one or two of great fame more or less completely differentiated him from the rest of the animal kingdom and even from the animal kingdom itself. As long as the isolation of man from the animal kingdom, or from the greater part, was based on metaphysical or psychological ideas, the naturalist perhaps had no cause of quarrel, although he might wonder why a morphologist should stray so far from the field of observation. But when naturalists confused morphological and psychological data, he had reason to protest. This confusion was effected by one of great eminence. There was no naturalist in Britain about the middle of the century who enjoyed a reputation equal to that of Richard Owen. An anatomist of pre-eminent skill and extraordinary industry, his merits had been appreciated by the entire world. An opinion of his had a weight accorded to no others. Consequently a new classification of the mammals, published by him in 1857, soon became popular. This classification was founded on alleged characters of the brain and on successive phases of increase in the cerebrum. Man was isolated not only as the representative of a family, but of an order and a subclass. According to Owen:

In man the brain presents an ascensive step in development, higher and more strongly marked than that by which the preceding subclass was distinguished from the one below it. Not only do the cerebral hemispheres overlap the olfactory lobes and cerebellum, but they extend in advance of the one and farther back than the other. Their posterior development is so marked that anatomists have assigned to that part the character of a third lobe. It is peculiar to the genus *Homo,* and equally peculiar is the "posterior horn of the lateral ventricle," and the "hippocampus minor," which characterize the hind lobe of each hemisphere. The superficial gray matter of the cerebrum, through the number and depth of the convolutions, attains its maximum of extent in man. Peculiar mental powers are associated with this highest form of brain, and their consequences wonderfully illustrate the value of the cerebral character.

The views thus expressed by Owen were reiterated on various occasions, but many anatomists dissented from them, and the rumbling of a future storm was betokened. At last the storm cloud broke, and Owen was overwhelmed. At a great popular assemblage at Oxford, on the occasion of the meeting of the British Association for the Advancement of Science, Owen once more urged his contention of the cerebral characteristics of man and maintained this wide difference from the apes.

Huxley immediately rose and with that cogency of reasoning which characterized him proceeded to divest the subject of the sophistries in which it had been enveloped. The question, he said, appeared to him in no way to represent the real nature of the problem under discussion. He would therefore put that problem in another way. The question was partly one of facts and partly one of reasoning. The question of facts was, What are the structural differences between man and the highest apes?—the question of reasoning, What is the systematic value of those differences? Several years ago Professor Owen had made three distinct assertions respecting the differences which obtained between the brain of man and that of the highest apes. He asserted that three structures were "peculiar to and characteristic" of man's brain, these being the "posterior lobe," the "posterior cornu," and the "hippocampus minor." In a controversy which has lasted for some years Professor Owen has not qualified these assertions, but has repeatedly reiterated them. He (Professor Huxley), on the other hand, had controverted these statements, and affirmed, on the contrary, that the three structures mentioned not only exist, but are often better developed than in man, in all the higher apes. He now appealed to the anatomists present in the section whether the universal voice of Continental and British anatomists had not entirely borne out his statements and refuted those of Professor Owen. Professor Huxley discussed the relations of the foot of man with those of the apes, and showed that the same argument could be based upon them as on the brain; that argument being that the structural differences between man and the highest ape are of the same order and only slightly different in degree from those which separate the apes one from another. In conclusion, he expressed his opinion of the futility of discussions like the present. In his opinion the differences between man and the lower animals are not to be expressed by his toes or his brain, but are moral and intellectual.

The appeal to anatomists was answered on the spot. The foremost anatomists of England there present (Rolleston and Flower) successively rose and endorsed the affirmations of Huxley. Not one supported Owen, and, brilliant as his attainments were, his want of candor entailed on him the loss of his eminent place, and Huxley took the vacated throne. But the contest that resulted in Owen's overthrow was of great service, for in the chief centers of civilization anatomists eagerly investigated the question at issue, and the consequence was that in a few years more material had been collected and studied than under ordinary conditions would have been done in five times the period. Unlike other battles, one in scientific warfare is almost always advantageous to the general cause, whatever it may be to a party.

The first important memoir by Huxley was written in his twenty-third year "On the Anatomy and the Affinities of the Family of the *Medusæ*" (*Phil. Trans.,* 1849, pp. 413–434, pl. 37–39), and contained the germ of a fundamental generalization. He therein laid "particular stress upon the composition of [the stomach] and other organs of the medusæ out of two distinct membranes, as," he says, "I believe that is one of the essential peculiarities of their structure, and that a knowledge of the fact is of great importance in investigating their homologies. I will," he continues, "call these two membranes as such, and independently of any modification into particular organs, 'foundation membranes'." In his summary he also formulates "that a medusa consists essentially of two membranes, inclosing a variously shaped cavity, inasmuch as its various organs are so composed."

I have thus given Huxley's own words, inasmuch as Professor Haeckel has asserted that Huxley therein "directed attention to the very important point that the body of these animals is constructed of two cell layers—of the ectoderm and endoderm—and that these, physiologically and morphologically, may be compared to the two germinal layers of the higher animals." (*Nature,* 1874.)

And Professor Kowalevsky has also claimed that Huxley "founded modern embryology by demonstrating the homology of the germinal layers of vertebrates with the ectoderm and endoderm of cœlenterates." (*Nature,* October 31, 1895, p. 651.) In all candor, I must confess that, important as the generalization of Huxley for the *Medusæ* was, it was only applied by him to the *Medusæ* and was not necessarily extensible with the homologies indicated, but it was pregnant with suggestiveness and to that extent may have led to the wider generalization that followed. Let all possible credit then be assigned to it.

The classification of animals generally adopted, and in this country especially, up to at least the early years of the present half-century, was based on what was called *plan* or *type* and was mainly due to Cuvier. According to this school, there were four "great fundamental divisions of the animal kingdom," and these were "founded upon distinct plans of structure, cast, as it were, into distinct molds or forms." The term generally used to designate this category was *branch* or *subkingdom,* and the subkingdoms themselves were named *vertebrates, mollusks, articulates,* and *radiates.* Various modifications of this system and more subkingdoms were recognized by many zoologists, but the one specially mentioned was in very general use in the United States because favored by Agassiz, who then enjoyed a great reputation. Almost all naturalists of other countries and many of this recognized the distinctness, as subkingdoms or branches, of the *protozoans* and *cœlenterates.* But Huxley in 1876 went still further and segregated all animals primarily under two great divisions based on their intimate structure, accepting for one the old name, *Protozoa,* and for the other Haeckel's name, *Metazoa.*

Among those animals which are lowest in the scale of organization there is a large assemblage which either present no differentiation of the protoplasm of the body into structural elements, or, if they possess one or more nuclei, or even exhibit distinct cells, these cells do not become metamorphosed into tissues—are not histogenetic. In all other animals the first stage of development is the differentiation of the vitellus into division masses, or blastomeres, which become converted into cells, and are eventually metamorphosed into the elements of the tissues. For the former the name *Protozoa* may be retained; the latter are coextensive with the *Metazoa* of Haeckel.

While not exactly original with Huxley, the recognition of these two great categories of the animal kingdom was hastened among naturalists and found place in most of the works by men of authority that followed. That such recognition greatly facilitates morphological concepts is certain. But most of the further new features of this classification have not received the approbation of naturalists generally.

Germany's great poet, Goethe, was "passionately devoted to the natural sciences," but was "induced by the habit of his mind to search for the general truths which give life to the dry bones of detail." In the Jewish cemetery of Venice a broken sheep's skull came under his notice, and he thought he recognized that it was made of modified vertebrae. Another German, Oken, in the Harz mountains "stumbled upon the blanched skull of a deer," and he was inspired with the idea that "it is a vertebral column." Oken immediately proclaimed his idea to the world. It found acceptance in many places, and England's great anatomist, Richard Owen, took it up and carefully elaborated a new form of it. Owen's modifications, dubbed the "archetype" of the skeleton, became popular in Britain and America, and elements of the skull were described in terms indicating that they were "homotypes" with appendages of vertebra, the nasals, for example, being styled the neural spines of the nasal vertebra, the premaxillary the hæmal spine of the same vertebra, and the dentary of the lower jaw the hæmal spine of the frontal vertebra. But still more fanciful was the terminology for the limbs, the anterior being allocated to the occipital vertebra, and the scapula regarded as a pleuropophysis, the coracoid as a hæmapophysis, and the limb itself as a "diverging appendage."

Strange as this conception may appear to the young who have only been educated in modern methods, it had attractions for some, as I can testify from personal experience. When a boy I made an enlarged copy of the diagram republished in Carpenter's *Physiology* and colored the neurapophyses blue and the hæmapophyses red. Later reflection led me to the conclusion that an "archetype" should be more or less realized, and if it were not, it had no place in nature. As the Owenian archetype was at most only distantly approximated by specialized fishes, it could not be a true archetype of the vertebrate skeleton as such, however near it might represent the typical fish skeleton. Doubtless others were led by similar reasoning to discard the Owenian ideas, yet they continued in favor among many.

But in 1858, in a lecture on the Croonian Foundation before the Royal Society, with Owen himself in the chair, Huxley discoursed "on the theory of the vertebral skull" and conclusively showed the inconsistency of the archetypal conception with the facts of embryology and development. After a recapitulation he confessed that he did "not perceive how it is possible, fairly and consistently, to reconcile these facts with any existing theory of the vertebrate composition of the skull, except by drawing *ad libitum* upon the *deus ex machina* of the speculator—imaginary confluences, 'connations,' 'irrelative repetitious,' and shiftings of position—by whose skillful application it would not be difficult to devise half a dozen very pretty vertebral theories, all equally true, in the course of a summer's day." He naturally reached not only "the negative conclusion that the doctrine of the vertebral composition of the skull is not proven," but "the positive belief that the relation of the skull to the spinal column is quite different from that of one part of the vertebral column to another."

The blow thus dealt against the Owenian archetype was a serious one, and it was nearly coincident with the growing adoption of the doctrine of evolution and the overthrow of the doctrine of types and patterns. At any rate, the old idea of the vertebration of the skull became an idea of the past. Owen continued to preach it, but his disciples abandoned it, and he was soon left without a single notable follower.

The designation of *Ganoidei* was originally given by Agassiz to a heterogeneous group of fishes distinguished by a covering of what were called ganoid scales and having no other common characters; some of its representatives even lacked the ganoid scales. But most of the extinct species at least were really structurally affiliated and such were segregated by Johannes Müller in a comparatively natural group distinguished by cerebral, cardiac, and intestinal peculiarities, and for this group was retained the Agassizian term *Ganoidei.* Its constituents were contrasted under two subordinate groups named *Chondrostei* and *Holostei.* The families of the latter group were evidently related in various degrees, but such degrees were not expressed in the arrangement of the families, and the families themselves were mostly defined by superficial characters of little value. The appointment of Huxley to the professorship of natural history in the Government School of Mines led him to investigations which culminated in a "Preliminary Essay upon the Systematic Arrangement of the Fishes of the Devonian Epoch" (1861), and "Illustrations of the Structure of the Crosstoperygian Ganoids" (1866). He proceeded "to reconsider the whole question of the classification of the fishes of this epoch and eventually to arrive at results which seemed to necessitate an important modification of the received arrangement of the great order of *Ganoidei.*" He recombined the *Chondrostei* and *Holostei,* and then distributed the aggregate (which he designated as an order) into five suborders in the following manner:

Ordo GANOIDEI

Subordo   I.—AMIADAE.
Subordo   II.—LEPIDOSTEIDAE.
Subordo III.—CROSSOPTERYGIDAE.
    Fam. 1.—POLYPTERINI.
            Dorsal fin very long, multifid; scales rhomboidal.
                Polypterus.
    Fam. 2.—SAURODIPTERINI.
            Dorsal fins two; scales rhomboidal, smooth; fins sub-
                acutely lobate.
                Diplopterus, Ostcolepis, Megalichthys.
    Fam. 3.—GLYPTODIPTERINI.
            Dorsal fins two; scales rhomboidal or cycloidal, sculp-
                tured; pectoral fins acutely lobate; dentition den-
                drodont.
        Sub-fam. A. with rhomboidal scales.
                Glyptolaemus, Glyptopomus, Gyroptychius.
        Sub-fam. B. with cycloidal scales.
                *Holoptychius, Glyptolepis, Platygnathus [Rhizodus,
                Dendrodus, Cricodus, Lamnodus].*
    Fam. 4.—CTENODODIPTERINI.
            Dorsal fins two; scales cycloidal; pectorals and ventrals
                acutely lobate; dentition ctenodont.
                Dipterus [Ceratodus? Tristichopterus?].
    Fam. 5.—PHANEROPLEURINI.
            Dorsal fin single, very long, not subdivided, supported
                by many interspinous bones; scales thin, cycloi-
                dal; teeth conical; ventral fins very long, acutely
                lobate.
                Phaneropleuron.
    Fam. 6.—COELACANTHINI.
            Dorsal fins two, each supported by a single interspinous
                bone; scales cycloidal; paired fins obtusely lobate;
                air bladder ossified.
                Cœlacanthus, Undina, Macropoma.
Subordo IV.—CHONDROSTEIDAE.
Subordo   V.—ACANTHODIDAE.

The chief merit in this arrangement is the appreciation of the closeness of the relations between the extinct fishes of the groups now recognized as Dipnoans and Crossopterygians, and the antici-pation, by a kind of intuition, of part of the truth as now recognized. The "suborder Crossopterygidæ" of Huxley is really a compound of the subclasses or superorders of Dipnoans and Crossopterygians. The distinctive characters of the two were not recognized, and the author even failed to appreciate the exact relations of the living and extinct Dipnoans, or that in fact many of his Crossopterygidæ are really Dipnoans. In his *Anatomy of the Vertebrates* (1871), even he retained his arrangement of the "Ganoidei," which were placed as the fourth order of fishes, and considered the "Dipnoi" after the Teleostei and as the sixth order of fishes. He failed even to find any extinct Dipnoans and concluded his observations on the group with the statement: "It is a remarkable circumstance that, while the *Dipnoi* present, in so many respects, a transition between the piscine and the amphibian types of structure, the spinal column and the limbs should be not only piscine, but more nearly related to those of the most ancient Crossopterygian Ganoids than to those of any other fishes."

Finally, in 1876 Huxley published as No. 1 of *Contributions to Morphology,* a memoir "On *Ceratodus forsteri,* with Observations on the Classification of Fishes." He still persisted in separating the recent Dipnoans from the extinct forms combined with the Crossopterygidæ, and contended that "even *Dipterus,* which approaches *Ceratodus* and *Lepidosiren* so closely in its definition and in the form of its fins, is far more similar to *Polypterus* and *Amia* in other respects; and there is at present no reason to believe that any of the Crossopterygian Ganoids possessed other than a hyostylic skull, or differed from *Polypterus* in those respects in which *Polypterus* differs from the existing *Dipnoi.* All known Crossopterygians have jugular plates, of which there is no trace in the Dipnoi."

It will be thus seen that the suborder of Crossopterygidæ was really the result of a misunderstanding and included most Dipnoans (and to such extent was a synonym for that group) as well as the Crossopterygians of later authors. It was by no means the exact equivalent of Crossopterygians, and consequently the latter name can not be considered as a synonym of Crossopterygidæ or be replaced by it. Nevertheless, the introduction of the so-called suborder was not only the expression of an advance in our knowledge of the system itself, but paved the way for future investigators.

I am even inclined to credit mainly to his sagacity the early appreciation of the affinity of the *Neoceratodus* of Australia to the mesozoic Ceratodontids with all the far-reaching consequences that appreciation involved. It was in 1870 that the living Ceratodontid was introduced to the scientific world as *Ceratodus forsteri* and thus generically associated with the mesozoic fishes. How did Krefft (or Clarke) get the idea of this association of a living fish with some known only from fossil teeth referred by Agassiz to the same family, as the Cestraciont sharks? In 1861 Huxley published his *Preliminary Essay upon the Systematic Arrangement of the Fishes of the Devonian Epoch,* and therein suggested that *Ceratodus* was a Ctenodipterine fish and ranged it (with a mark of interrogation) by the side of *Dipterus.* He also drew "attention to the many and singular relations which obtain between that wonderful and apparently isolated fish, *Lepidosiren,*" and the Ctenodipterine fishes. (The exact truth was not discovered, but was approximated.) Is it not probable that this memoir was known to Clarke, who claimed to have suggested to Krefft the systematic relations of the newly discovered Australian Dipnoan? It was creditable to both Clarke and Krefft that they did recognize this relationship and profited by their bibliographical knowledge, but it is doubtful whether they would have been able to make the identification or appreciate the importance of the discovery had not Huxley partly prepared the way. By this discovery our acquaintance with the ichthyic faunas of both the present and past was almost revolutionized.

To the casual observer none of the terrestrial backboned animals appear to be less related than birds and reptiles. As Huxley remarks, "to superficial observation no two groups of beings can appear to be more entirely dissimilar. - - - Placed side by side, a hummingbird and a tortoise, an ostrich and a crocodile, offer the strongest contrast, and a stork seems to have little but animality in common with the snake it swallows." A difference in habits appears to be associated with the difference in form. The activity and freedom of the bird contrasts with the lethargy and restriction in range of the tortoise—the warm body of the former with the cold mass of the latter. The birds are looked upon as inhabitants of the air, the reptiles as degraded to crawling on the earth. The popular conclusions were to a considerable extent adopted by the scientific, and for a long time the birds and mammals were associated together as "warm-blooded" in contradistinction to the reptiles and other vertebrates, which were designated as "cold-blooded." This classification was in vogue in England when Huxley reopened the question as to the relative affinities of the vertebrates and in 1864 claimed that the classes of that division "are capable of being grouped into three provinces—(1) the Ichthyoids, comprising Fishes and Amphibia; - - - (2) the Sauroids, - - - comprising Reptiles and Birds; and (3) the Mammals." - - - The Sauroids (afterwards called *Sauropsida*) agree in having "a single occipital condyle, a complex mandibular ramus articulated to the skull by a quadrate bone, nucleated blood corpuscles," and thus differ from the mammals, which have "a well-developed basi-occipital - - -; a simple mandibular ramus articulated with the squamosal and not with the quadratum, with mammary glands and with red non-nucleated blood corpuscles."

In 1868 Huxley directed his inquiries "on the animals which are most nearly intermediate between birds and reptiles." The differences between the recent members of the two classes are indeed many. The question, then, was, How far can this gap be filled up by a reference to the records of the life of past ages? "The question resolves itself into two: (1) Are any fossil birds more reptilian than any of those now living? (2) Are any fossil reptiles more bird-like than living reptiles?" Both of these questions Huxley found "must be answered in the affirmative."

The remains of Archæopteryx found in the "lithographic slate of Solenhofen" furnished a bird with decided reptilian characters —so prominent, indeed, that some of the paleontologists of the period claimed that the animal was a reptile rather than a bird. The remains of various Dinosaurians of Mesozoic times yielded reptiles with characteristics manifest only among the birds of the present epoch. Such characteristics were especially exemplified in details of structure of the hind limbs. One of the Dinosaurians—Compsognathus—was so much like a bird in the legs that "it is impossible to doubt that it hopped or walked, in an erect or semi-erect position, after the manner of a bird, to which its long neck, slight head, and small anterior limbs must have given it an extraordinary resemblance."

From the vantage ground of the present, with its increased stores, we may justify Huxley's "hope" that he had redeemed his "promise to show that in past times birds more like reptiles than any now living and reptiles more like birds than any now living did really exist." There is now even a tendency to regard the differences remaining between the birds and reptiles as of less than class value, and to combine both groups in one and the same class —Sauropsida. The first to propose such a union was Professor Cope, who had even to some extent anticipated Huxley in the recognition of the similarity between the Dinosaurians and birds. The fact that two such men independently arrived at similar conclusions is significant as evidence for their truth. But there is danger of pushing a truth to the extreme of itself deceiving. There is still a great gap between any known reptile and any known bird. Huxley concluded with the caution that, "as we possess hardly any knowledge of the terrestrial reptiles of [the Triassic] period, it may be regarded as certain that we have no knowledge of the animals which linked reptiles and birds together historically and genetically, and that the *Dinosauria,* with *Compsognathus, Archæopteryx,* and the struthious birds, only help us to form a reasonable conception of what these intermediate forms may have been." This cautious statement is as apt for the present time as that in which it was expressed.

One of the most persistent prejudices that has influenced the progress of zoological taxonomy has been (perhaps still is) a belief in the importance of superficial adaptation of structure for life in the water contra-distinguished from life on the land. This prejudice was long impressed on ornithology. The birds with feet adapted for swimming by the development of webs between the toes or for wading by elongation of the legs were set apart from those fitted mainly for progress on land or through the air—in other words, from those having negative characters in such respects. The major subdivisions of those groups, too, were almost solely distinguished by superficial characters of little importance, such as the form of the bill, the character of the claws, and the combinations of toes. Variations in such trivial characters, which in other classes of vertebrates would be esteemed of little systematic value, were assigned ordinal rank. Comparative anatomy, too, was almost entirely neglected in the classification of birds; even most anatomists were content to limit their observations to simple irrelative details or to interject them into the framework of existing arrangements. Such was the state of ornithology in 1867 when Huxley published, in the *Proceedings of the Zoological Society of London,* a memoir, "On the Classification of Birds, and on the Taxonomic Value of the Modifications of Certain of the Cranial Bones Observable in That Class." In this he discarded the characters generally used and allowed himself to be influenced by the modifications to be found in the skeleton without reference to the habits or habitats of the birds. He reduced the orders to three—the Saururæ (extinct), the Ratitæ, and the Carinatæ. The last, including almost all the living forms, were divided into primary groups defined by modifications of "the bones which enter into the formation of the palate." "Four different modes" were recognized and were "called, respectively, the *Dromæognathous, Schizognathous, Desmognathous,* and *Ægithognathous* arrangement." It was urged that "these cranial characters may safely be taken as indications of natural affinities," and Huxley proposed "to regard these divisions as suborders, and to name them *Dromæognathæ, Schizognathæ, Desmognathæ,* and *Ægithognathæ.*" The last three suborders were divided into groups with the termination *morphæ,* as Ætomorphæ (Raptores), Psittaco-morphæ (Psittaci), etc., not taxonomically designated, but essentially equivalent to "super-families." The Ægithognathous "Coracomorphæ" corresponded with the "Passeres" as limited by recent naturalists, and Huxley was "disposed" to divide it "into two primary groups, one containing *Menura,* and the other all the other genera." How the immense aggregate represented by all the other genera were to be subdivided Huxley did not venture to decide, but he leaves the impression that he had little respect for the numerous "families" which had been recognized by most ornithologists.

The value of this work consisted chiefly in disturbing the old classifications and calling attention to the proper method of investigation. Much of it, nevertheless, appears to have been of permanent value, and most of the superfamilies at least have been recognized as natural assemblages, although still generally given ordinal or subordinal rank and endowed with older names. The memoir at least gave an impulse in the right direction—morphological as opposed to teleological—and has incited to many elaborate investigations to the great advantage of ornithology.

Much doubt had existed respecting the nature of the non-mammalian ancestors of the mammals. It was supposed by some that they must have been reptiles related to the Dinosaurians, but the specialized characteristics and high development of that type forbade the belief that they were in the direct line of descent. Of course the birds which agreed with the mammals in the possession of a quadrilocular heart, complete circulation, and warm blood must even more positively than the Dinosaurians be excluded from the line of descent. The problem of what was the genealogy of the highest class of animals was at last attacked by Huxley. In several memoirs published in 1876, 1879, and 1880, he examined the evidence and fomulated his conclusions. Those conclusions were expressed in the following terms:

Our existing classifications have no place for [the] submammalian stage of evolution (already indicated by Haeckel under the name of *Promam-male*). It would be separated from the Sauropsida by its two condyles, and by the retention of the left as the principal aortic arch; while it would probably be no less differentiated from the Amphibia by the presence of an amnion and the absence of branchiæ at any period of life. I propose to term the representatives of this stage *Hypotheria;* and I do not doubt that when we have a fuller knowledge of the terrestrial vertebrata of the later palæozoic epochs, forms belonging to this stage will be found among them. Now, if we take away from the Hypotheria the amnion and the corpus callosum, and add the functional branchiæ— the existence of which in the ancestors of the mammalia is as clearly indicated by their visceral arches and clefts as the existence of complete clavicles in the ancestral Canidæ is indicated by their vestiges in the dog —the Hypotheria, thus reduced, at once take their place among the Amphibia, for the presence of branchiæ implies that of an incompletely divided ventricle and of numerous aortic arches, such as exist in the mammalian embryo, but are more or less completely suppressed in the course of its development.

Thus I regard the amphibian type as the representative of the next lower stage of vertebrate evolution; and it is extremely interesting to observe that even the existing Amphibia present us with almost every degree of modification of the type, from such forms as the oviparous, branchiate, small-lunged *Siredon* and *Menobranchus,* which stand in the same relation to it as *Gymnura* to the Eutheria, to the exclusively air-breathing salamanders and frogs, in which the period of intraovular development, either within the uterus itself or in special receptacles, may be as much prolonged as it is in the Mammalia.

A careful study, on full materials, of the development of the young of such forms as *Hylodes* will probably throw great light on the nature of the changes which ended in the suppression of the branchiæ and the development of the amnion and of the extra-abdominal part of the allantois in the fœtus of the higher Vertebrata.

During the intervening years no discoveries of fossil forms substantiating these inferences have been discovered. Among the ancient verterbrates now known none appear to be more nearly allied to the mammals than certain Permian animals representing a special order named by Cope *Theromorpha* or (later) *Theromora.* As early as 1878 "the order Theromorpha was regarded by Professor Cope as approximating the Mammalia more closely than any other division of Reptilia, and as probably the ancestral group from which the latter were derived." These views were subsequently developed in greater detail and appear to be entitled to much consideration. In this connection it may be added that the difference between Huxley and Cope is less than the terms in which they have been stated might seem to indicate. The gap between primitive amphibians and reptiles is by no means as great as between the modern types, and it may be doubted whether the ancestors of the mammalian stock were members of the specialized order defined as Thermorpha. Neither of the philosophers may be far out of the way.

Among the most important results of Huxley's investigations

were the discovery and approximately correct recognition of the nature of the "peculiar gelatinous bodies" found in all the seas, whether extratropical or tropical, through which the *Rattlesnake* sailed, and which were named *Thalassicola,* precursors of radiolarian hosts afterwards to be brought to light, and the perception of the comparative affinities of the southern forms of astacoidean crustaceans and their contrast as a group with the forms of the northern hemisphere. I must resist the temptation to further enumerate the great naturalist's discoveries and generalizations.

A few words on the nature of his work may be desirable. And here it may be admitted that Huxley was rather a morphologist in a narrow sense, or anatomist rather than a systematist of greatly superior excellence. Unquestionably he did much excellent work in systematic zoology, but the direct subject of investigation was perhaps treated from too special a standpoint and sometimes without an attempt to coordinate it with the results in other fields, or to measure by some given standard. He was indeed a great artist, but he used his powers chiefly to sketch the outlines of a picture of nature. This was done with the bold and vigorous hand of a master, but his productions were deficient in details and finish and were sometimes imperfect on account of inattention to perspective and perhaps deliberate neglect of the niceties of nomenclature. (And lest I may be misunderstood, let me here explain that by systematic zoology I mean the expression of all the facts of structure in a form to represent best the values of the differences as well as resemblances of all the constituents and parts of the entire organization, from the cells to the perfected organs and the body as a whole.) For example, he separated amphibians from reptiles and combined them with fishes, and yet under the last name comprised the Leptocardians and Marsipobranchs, and to his influence is doubtless due to a large extent the persistence of English (but not American) naturalists in a combination which is elsewhere regarded as contradicted by all sound morphological doctrine. The value of the characters distinctive of the Rhynchocephalian reptiles and their consequent significance for taxonomy and paleontology were also denied by him. Nevertheless, even his negative position was of use in that it incited investigation. The numerous memoirs on the anatomy and characteristics of various groups of animals, too, were always replete with new facts and the hints were almost always sagacious, even if not always in exactly the right direction.

While the contest between the old and new schools of biological philosophy was at its height, the former was almost entirely supported by the religious element, and bitter were the invectives against evolution. The opposition was almost solely based on the ground that the doctrine was in opposition to revealed religion. The naturally combative disposition of Huxley was much aroused by this opposition, and the antagonism early engendered was kept aglow during his entire life. Meanwhile it had been discovered by many of the more sagacious and learned clergymen that there was no real antagonism between the scriptural account of creation and evolution, but that the two could be perfectly reconciled. The reconciliation had been effected between Genesis and astronomy and between Genesis and geology, and was continued on the same lines for Genesis and evolution. But Huxley would have none of it. He gave expression to his convictions in the following words:

For more than a thousand years, the great majority of the most highly civilized and instructed nations in the world have confidently believed and passionately maintained that certain writings, which they entitle sacred, occupy a unique position in literature, in that they possess an authority, different in kind, and immeasurably superior in weight, to that of all other books. Age after age, they have held it to be an indisputable truth that, whoever may be ostensible writers of the Jewish, Christian, and Mohammedan Scriptures, God Himself is their real author; and, since one of the attributes of the Deity excludes the possibility of error and—at least in relation to this particular matter—of willful deception, they have drawn the logical conclusion that the denier of the accuracy of any statement, the questioner of the binding force of any command, to be found in these documents is not merely a fool, but a blasphemer. From the point of view of mere reason he grossly blunders; from that of religion he grievously sins.

But if this dogma of Rabbinical invention is well founded; if, for example, every word in our Bible has been dictated by the Deity, or even if it be held to be the Divine purpose that every proposition should be understood by the hearer or reader in the plain sense of the words employed (and it seems impossible to reconcile the Divine attribute of truthfulness with any other intention), a serious strain upon faith must arise. Moreover, experience has proved that the severity of this strain tends to increase, and in an even more rapid ratio, with the growth in intelligence of mankind and with the enlargement of the sphere of assured knowledge among them.

It is becoming, if it has not become, impossible for men of clear intellect and adequate instruction to believe, and it has ceased, or is ceasing, to be possible for such men honestly to say they believe that the universe came into being in the fashion described in the first chapter of Genesis; or to accept, as a literal truth, the story of the making of woman with the account of the catastrophe which followed hard upon it, in the second chapter; or to admit that the earth was repeopled with terrestrial inhabitants by migration from Armenia to Kurdistan, little more than four thousand years ago, which is implied in the eighth chapter; or, finally, to shape their conduct in accordance with the conviction that the world is haunted by innumerable demons, who take possession of men and may be driven out of them by exorcistic adjurations, which pervades the Gospels.

So far even Huxley was not in disagreement with some of the most eminent and learned of theologians. Those of you who are interested will be able to recall utterances of enlightened clergymen which would differ from Huxley's only in the absence of the leaven of sarcasm that permeates his lines. At a late congress of the Church of England, held at Norwich, the Reverend Canon and Professor Bonney gave voice to words that convey the same ideas as Huxley's.

I cannot deny [he said] that the increase of scientific knowledge has deprived parts of the earlier books of the Bible of the historical value which was generally attributed to them by our forefathers. The story of the creation in *Genesis,* unless we play fast and loose either with words or with science, can not be brought into harmony with what we have learned from geology. Its ethnological statements are imperfect, if not sometimes inaccurate. The stories of the flood and of the Tower of Babel are incredible in their present form. Some historical element may underlie many of the traditions in the first eleven chapters of that book, but this we cannot hope to recover.

But Huxley was not content to deny any authority to the Scriptural basis of most of the religions of Europe and America. He denied that there was any means of knowing what the future had in store. He did not deny that there was a heaven or a hell; he did not deny that in a future world man might continue in a sublimated state, and might be punished for his misdeeds or rewarded for the good deeds he had performed and for good thoughts on earth. He did not venture to express any opinion on the subject for the reason that he had no data to base an opinion upon. He called himself an agnostic and the attitude he assumed was agnosticism.

This term *agnostic,* we are told by R. H. Hutton, was suggested by Professor Huxley at a party held previous to the formation of the now defunct Metaphysical Society, at James Knowles's house on Clapham Common, one evening in 1869, and was suggested by St. Paul's mention of the altar to the unknown God— Ἀγνώστῳ θεῷ. But Huxley has explained that he assumed this term in contradistinction to the gnostic of old. The gnostic claimed to know what in the nature of things is unknowable, and as Huxley found himself with an exactly opposite mental status, he coined a word to express that antithetical state—agnostic. I have done all I conceive to be necessary in giving this statement of Huxley's attitude. Whether he was right or wrong, each one must judge for himself or herself. Believing as he did, on a bed of prolonged illness he resignedly awaited the inevitable, and desired that his sentiments be reflected in verse by his wife should be engraved on his tomb:

> And if there be no meeting past the grave,
>   If all is darkness, silence, yet 'tis rest.
> Be not afraid, ye waiting hearts that weep,
> For God "still giveth his beloved sleep,"
>   And if an endless sleep he wills—so best.

Pierre Eugène Marcelin Berthelot *

1827–1907

———◆———

CAMILLE MATIGNON †

THE ILLUSTRIOUS SCHOLAR to whom all France has paid a last solemn tribute held an extraordinary rank in the science of the nineteenth century. What he accomplished was tremendous, almost superhuman. No other man can grasp it in its entirety, for in order to comprehend it in detail one would need to have an encyclopædic knowledge such as no one in this day possesses. The scholars of the whole world bowed before this grand intellect, unanimously recognized as one of the broadest of its time. This intellect, moreover, was powerfully aided by a memory no less widely famed. It was by uniting with these natural gifts obstinate and incessant, systematic endeavor, that Berthelot was able to build up an immense life work in which is shown the universal scope of his knowledge. A man of letters, a philosopher, an historian, there was no subject with which he was not familiar; he was well and accurately informed on all topics.

Pierre Eugène Marcelin Berthelot was born in Paris, October 28, 1827, in a house on the Place de Grèves, now the Place de l'Hôtel de Ville. He studied at the Lycée Henri IV and showed from the start remarkable aptitude in the most varied directions. Fouqué, in recalling at the fiftieth anniversary of his scientific career the old fellowship at the Lycée that brought him close to Berthelot, added: "Even at that time you felt the lofty position in the science of the future which awaited you. Your professors, and even your fellow-students, were alike conscious of it, and, more than anyone else, I had faith in you." In 1846 Berthelot won the

---

* *A.R.*, 1907, pp. 669–684. Translated from *Revue générale des sciences pures et appliquées,* May 15, 1907.
† French chemist (1867–1934), Professor at Collège de France, and at one time assistant to Berthelot.

honor prize in philosophy at the *Concours général*. He devoted himself henceforth to the study of the sciences without passing through any school. He was selected as Balard's assistant in the Collège de France in January 1851, and for nine years he filled this humble office with its annual allowance of 500 francs. During this period, in April 1854 he earned the degree of doctor of sciences with a masterly thesis, *Réproduction des corps gras naturels*.

On December 20, 1859, he left the Collège de France for l'École de Pharmacie, where he had been chosen professor of organic chemistry. The following year he brought together his researches on synthetic chemistry in two important volumes entitled *Chimie organique fondée sur la synthèse*. The Academy of Sciences for his assembled works awarded him the Jecker prize. Berthelot at 33 years of age was known by name to chemists throughout the world, and his reputation had penetrated even into the Parisian salons, as is evident from letters written in 1860 and 1861 by Madame Didier to Madame Edgar Quinet:

I must not forget to have you meet a very learned scholar named M. Berthelot. They swear by him alone in the rue de l'Ouest [at Michelet's]. Madame Michelet told me that he would go down to posterity, and that he would not rest satisfied with mere genius. He is, besides, full of life and a charming fellow to be with. She drew me the picture of an accomplished man; I am curious about this wonder. I must make his acquaintance and tell you my impressions of him. [October 26, 1860.]

After having received him she wrote (January 19, 1861):

He seemed shy; he has a very sweet and interesting countenance. I greatly enjoyed the conversation of M. Berthelot. If I have one regret it is in not being able to follow him in the field of science; he has made great discoveries in chemistry and has published two volumes that are beyond me; I should not be able even to understand their language. But they say that the synopsis of the book is obtainable and it gives the conclusions of all of his works. I shall do my best to get an idea of it. Finally, there is nothing he does not know something about; he has had a thorough literary education.

At the initiative of Balard, a certain number of professors of the Collège de France and chemists of the Institut requested of the public officials the establishment of a chair of organic chemistry in the Collège de France, in order to allow Berthelot to develop his ideas. The request was favorably received by Duruy, minister of public instruction, and the chair was created August 8, 1865. Berthelot then gave up the École de Pharmacie for the Collège de France, which he was destined never to leave.

A member of the Academy of Medicine in February 1863, he did not enter the Academy of Sciences until March 3, 1873, at the age of 46 years, in the section of physics, taking the place of Duhamel. He developed at this time a whole system of calorimetric methods. He was not only a chemist of the first class, but likewise an eminent physicist, as was recognized by the Institut in giving him the first vacant place in the section of physics. Most of the foreign scientific societies and academies recognized Berthelot's fame by admitting him to their own membership. He was elected successively to the Royal Society of London, the Society of Physics of Geneva, the Society of Naturalists of Moscow, and the academies of St. Petersburg, Stockholm, Dublin, Copenhagen, Munich, Turin, Amsterdam, Hungary, Boston, Lisbon, Vienna, Berlin, etc. Designated Chevalier of the Legion of Honor August 13, 1861, he ran rapidly through the whole hierarchy until by the time of the fiftieth anniversary of the beginning of his scientific career the Government of the Republic had decreed to him the highest reward it gives, decorating him with the Grand-Croix.

The interest that Berthelot brought to bear on the reorganization of our method of education led him to the general inspection of higher educational affairs in 1876, to the permanent section of public instruction, of which he was vice-president, and to the École des Hautes Études, of which he was president for the section of physical sciences. Head of the scientific committee for the defense of Paris in 1870, he was named member of the consultation committee on powders and saltpeters in 1876 and president of the commission on explosive substances in 1878. Elected perpetual senator in 1881, he improved the opportunity by pleading on numerous occasions the cause of higher education and of scientific research. In 1886 he became minister of public instruction in the Goblet cabinet and was called later by Léon Bourgeois to the Quai d'Orsay. Berthelot succeeded Joseph Bertrand in the Académie Française and was received there by Lemaître.

.   .   .

Berthelot not only transformed and broadened the domain of chemistry, but at the same time he advanced its status among the exact sciences. Before Berthelot most chemists considered the substances which form in living organisms as impossible of reproduction in the laboratory from their constituent elements—carbon, oxygen, hydrogen, and nitrogen—by the sole play of chemical affinities. "In organic nature," wrote Berzelius in 1849, "elements appear to obey laws entirely different from the laws of inorganic nature." A mysterious force, the vital force, was judged indispensable to their elaboration. The chemist can only destroy them, separate them with the aid of appropriate reagents, and take from them certain new substances, isolated stones in the complex edifice. His rôle is therefore extremely limited, since in the field of organic compounds he has at his disposal, as objects of study, only the immediate principles elaborated by animals and vegetable growths. Berthelot took up the separated products and tried step by step to put them together again to construct the initial edifice. It was thus that in a really masterly achievement he reconstructed fats, oils, and butters out of the glycerine and the acids derived from these fatty substances. The barrier which separated the reactions of the laboratory from the reactions of living organisms disappeared from this time on and the identity of biological and physico-chemical forces was thereupon established. The significance of such a demonstration may be readily understood.

This was not all. It was at this time that the creative power of the chemist began to be manifested. As soon as Berthelot had discovered how to reproduce a fatty substance, stearine, for example, he had by the generalization of the process found the method of reproducing an infinite number of new fatty substances. Thus, while most of the animal or vegetable fats are formed essentially by the mixture of three or four well-defined chemical substances, the only ones found in nature, the chemist can make from them in his laboratory as large a number as he pleases. "The synthesis of neutral fats," said Berthelot in 1860, "permits not only the formation of some natural fats already known, but it still further permits one to foresee the formation of innumerable analogous fats, which it will be easy hereafter to produce in their entirety by virtue of the general law that governs their composition." The domain of chemistry therefore becomes unlimited. The chemist himself by synthesis creates the object of his investigation, and in the thousands of new substances that are produced each year in the laboratories of the world he distinguishes those whose properties can be used in the arts, in industry, in medicine, etc. The synthesis of fatty substances was only a partial synthesis; glycerine and the fatty generating acids were themselves produced from fats originally divided in two. In imitation of nature it was necessary to try to produce organic matters out of mineral substances. Taking carbon in the form of carbonic oxide, Berthelot combined this gas with potash and produced potassium formate. The barium formate, heated, lost methane, which by pyrogenation was able to give acetylene, ethylene, and ethane. From these

carburets thus formed Berthelot passed to the corresponding alcohols, methyl, ethyl, and their very varied derivatives.

It is not, however, under the form of carbonic oxide that charcoal enters into plants; these build up the molecules of fatty matters, the hydrates of carbon necessary to their growth, with
anhydrous carbon and water. Berthelot tried in vain to generate
a primary carburet out of these two substances, so he replaced
them with substances whose functions were most closely related
to them, sulphuret of carbon and sulphuric acid; then in making
both of these pass over copper he obtained methane. By substituting iron for copper he obtained the same reaction from sulphuret
of carbon and water.

In his work *Chimie organique fondée sur la synthèse* Berthelot
published the collective results of his researches, and at the same
time he explained the methods that should be followed in solving
the synthetic problem in the series not then studied. He presented a
general view of organic products and in order to classify them
introduced the theory of function. He had previously in the case of
glycerine shown that the molecule of that substance possesses three
times the alcoholic function and likewise introduced the idea of
polyatomic alcohols and polyalcohols.

Berthelot employed electric energy in its most varied forms to
bring about the combination or to destroy the composition of substances. The electric arc enabled him to effect the simplest, the
most unexpected, and the most fertile of organic syntheses, that
of acetylene. An arc flashing in an atmosphere of hydrogen partially
transformed this hydrogen into acetylene, for the carbonic vapor
which constituted the arc through its high temperature of 3,500
degrees united directly with the gaseous element. Carburetted
hydrogen, stable at the highest temperature reached, became on
the contrary unstable at about its ordinary temperature; it only had
to be compressed to above two atmospheres for it to decompose
with an explosion, under the influence of a spark, into its two
elements, carbon and hydrogen. If, on the contrary, it is heated
gradually toward 400 degrees, the same acetylene returns to its
stable form, carbon and hydrogen, passing through a series of
intermediate terms, benzol, toluol, naphthalene, anthracene, etc.,
carburets poorer and poorer in hydrogen, the limit of which will
be charcoal. These new carburets constitute the starting point in
preparing coloring matters, perfumes, substitutes for sugar, new
explosives, etc. It is possible to combine again with acetylene, by
the aid of simple reactions, ethylene, ethane, oxalic and acetic
acids, alcohol, etc. Thus by heating the carburet with its hydrogen,

ethylene is generated, capable of fixing water in the presence of sulphuric acid to form alcohol. The entire synthesis of this immediate threefold principle is thus realized from its three constituent elements, carbon, oxygen, and hydrogen.

The electric spark is likewise useful in synthetic chemistry. For example, the sparks produce hydrocyanic acid when nitrogen is placed in the presence of acetylene or generally of any hydrocarbon vapor whatever. The electric current passing into a conducting solution permits the obtaining of products of oxidation at the anode and products of reduction at the cathode. The sulphuric solution itself peroxidizes in giving a new substance, persulphuric acid, the existence of which was at first doubted by several chemists who had not experimented, until persulphates became industrial products. Berthelot, moreover, made an exhaustive study of all the secondary chemical reactions which were produced at or near the electrodes. Upon these complex questions no chemist had so comprehensive a knowledge founded on experiment. Thus we may understand the skepticism with which he received all mathematical theories overlooking these secondary reactions.

It was above all through the electric current that Berthelot obtained the most delicate syntheses. He showed that this current constituted the form of energy the most active and the most effective for securing the combination of substances. By its aid he was enabled to unite iodine with oxygen, to produce sulphuric anhydride from sulphurous gas and oxygen, to effect the absorption of nitrogen in considerable quantities by sulphuret of carbon, benzol, etc. Everyone still recalls the discovery of argon by Lord Rayleigh and Ramsay,* who, after a number of years of trials of different sorts, were unsuccessful in obtaining a combination with this new gas. These scholars sent Berthelot several cubic centimeters of argon, and, eight days after, the eminent chemist announced to the Academy of Sciences that he had succeeded in uniting argon with sulphuret of carbon by means of the electric current. The small quantity of resinous matter obtained under these conditions, when sufficiently heated, in decomposing, regenerated argon with its initial properties.

The contemporaries of Berthelot also did their share in developing chemical synthesis. It is sufficient to recall in particular his rival, Wurtz, to whose credit stand very important experiments on the synthesis of compound ammonias, of carburets of hydrogen, and of glycols.

---

* See pp. 601–608.

It is with respect to the synthesis of glycols [wrote Berthelot in 1884] that a productive rivalry has arisen between us, in which each of us has developed the various resources of a nature as different from that of the other in its point of view as in its operations. Works without number have sprung from these theories and in thirty years have transformed organic chemistry. Wurtz played a prominent part in this transformation.

Convinced of the unity of natural forces, Berthelot tried to adapt the laws of chemical transformations to the laws of mechanics. He devoted himself to developing a new science, thermochemistry, from which was derived chemical mechanics. Lavoisier and Laplace, Hesse, Favre, and Silbermann had already succeeded in taking several calorimetric measurements, but the principle of equivalents in the order of chemical reactions was a new idea which was to be established with precision by the researches of Berthelot. At this time Regnault had completed his numerous calorimetric experiments and had secured for this division of physics an accuracy theretofore unknown. Regnault obtained this accuracy through a more complex apparatus, by superimposing in a certain way on the principal apparatus accessory contrivances either to eliminate or to measure the different causes of error. Berthelot, however, secured accuracy by more simple methods. The experimental technique which he worked out from beginning to end for measuring different calorific factors is an admirable accomplishment which would suffice alone to make a physicist illustrious. Although I have had occasion to initiate a large number of French and other scholars into the calorimetric methods of Berthelot, I have never once done it without noting after a first experiment their astonishment and their admiration for methods so simple and accurate. These methods were afterwards to attain perfection in the use of the calorimetric bomb. Altogether, Berthelot's accomplishments in thermochemistry are marvelous. Their consequences extend into all domains of science. Engineers, experimenters, and theorists are continually using his calorimetric data.

In theory Berthelot shows that the amount of heat is the principal factor upon which depend the conditions of composition or decomposition of substances; but the mass heat of reaction is connected with these conditions by an extremely complicated relationship. Berthelot tried to disengage from this mass heat all the calories connected with reversible phenomena and obtained a quantity, "chemical heat," which approaches the heat not compensated for in the reaction. From 1865 Berthelot worked without interruption to establish and render exact the different terms for expressing chemical heat. This chemical heat, especially in solutions, is not always easily calculated, and so in the secondary schools they have let stand the old rule of maximum work, which in many cases can give an exact idea of the process of reaction.

The study of electrical piles which forms, with the working out of reactions in advance, one and the same problem, took part of Berthelot's time. As I said above, he studied very thoroughly all the secondary phenomena which occurred in connection with it in such a way as to separate from the chemical mass energy all these secondary forms of energy and to try to give, if possible, an experimental interpretation of the differences between the voltaic and chemical energies. Berthelot has frequently called attention to the importance of these secondary reactions often neglected by the theorists. For this reason the pupils of Helmholtz could verify the accuracy of the relation between voltaic and chemical energy only by measuring the chemical energy directly on the calorimeter, as Jahn did, and not, like Brauner, by calculating it from the fundamental chemical reaction occurring in the pile.

Moreover, in a general way, the study of the thermochemistry of reactions forced Berthelot to go into their slightest details, and with his talent for generalizing he knew how to draw observations of a general application. It is thus that the idea of preliminary work, necessary for bringing about reactions, corresponds in the language of this time to an elevation of temperature necessary to overcome chemical resistance. He showed likewise that it is not the reactions producing the most stable system that are found, but unstable, intermediary systems. The principle of the appearance of the unstable forms before the stable forms is found again here, a principle which has been quite accurately established in these later years. Moreover, all the modern physico-chemists have drawn from the numerous thermochemical documents accumulated by Berthelot, and some of them have even at times reproduced his researches, but in a language corresponding to the physico-chemistry of these later years. I am convinced for my part that it is particularly through thermochemistry that Berthelot acquired that truly extraordinary understanding of chemical phenomena by which he seemed almost to dominate and command them.

Thermochemistry was destined to lead Berthelot to the study of explosives. His position as president of the commission of scholars organized by those in command of the national defense during the siege of Paris had given him an opportunity to become initiated into the knowledge of these products. The various tasks that he accomplished in this field either alone or in collaboration with members of the commission on powders and saltpeters have been brought together in great part in his treatise *Sur la force des matières explosibles d'après la thermochimie*. I should like to speak here simply of his "studies of genius," to use the expression of Nernst, on the explosive wave. In a mixture of oxygen and hydrogen, for example, the combination propagates itself in the form of a wave all the factors of which can be defined in advance when the properties of the exploding mixture are known. The surface of this wave, which is the seat of the combination, propagates itself with a speed much greater than that of sound, 2,800 meters in the case of oxygen and hydrogen, so that the influence of the cooling of the surfaces has no time to become effective. Besides, the speed itself is constant and independent of the nature of the tube which contains the mixture. The surface of the wave is at an extremely high temperature and exerts a strong pressure in its passage, a pressure which may easily be registered by placing pressure gauges in the path of the wave.

The explosive wave has been the means of realizing the highest temperatures (4,000 degrees), but the products of combustion remain at this temperature for only a very short time. Berthelot and Vieille in some extremely remarkable experiments have used the explosive wave for furnishing quantitative evidence on the properties of gas at temperatures as high as 4,000 degrees. Among the numerous results which follow from this I may call special attention to the curious fact that nitrogen, oxygen, and oxide of carbon, up to 4,000 degrees, have identical molecular specific heats, which tends to prove that the molecule is not dissociated at this high temperature during the very short period of heating. Theoretical studies on explosives, on the speed of explosions, were to lead to the discovery of smokeless powder by Vieille, the pupil and collaborator of Berthelot. This was for some time to give superiority to our armament.

In collaboration with Péan de Saint Gilles, Berthelot in 1862 in a celebrated memoir defined equilibrium and at the same time showed by a full series of reactions methodically worked out the rôle of time in chemical phenomena. He endeavored to translate into mathematical formulæ the results of his experiments. He introduced the idea of active masses and established a relation which, slightly modified, was to lead Guldberg and Waage the following year, as they themselves acknowledged, to the establishment of the law of mass action. For his study on etherification the name of Berthelot deserves to be inscribed by the side of those of Saint-Claire Deville and of Raoult among the creators of physico-chemistry.

By reason of his studies of synthesis the rôle of nitrogen in the organic world always interested Berthelot. Some years ago this element was considered as an inert body incapable of entering in reaction and yet it is indispensable to the life of animals and plants. By what process does inorganic nitrogen pass into the state of organic nitrogen? The problem is today in great measure solved, thanks particularly to Berthelot's experiments.

Under the influence of electrical actions, spark or current, the nitrogen and oxygen of the air enter into combination to form, first of all, oxide of nitrogen, and then, by secondary reaction, nitrous vapors. Likewise, all active combustion, like that of charcoal, for example, quickens the combination of quantities of nitrogen and oxygen. The difference of electrical potential between two strata of air of unequal levels may be employed to effect the absorption of nitrogen by the most varied bodies. By exact quantitative experiments Berthelot showed that exterior electrical actions, storms, differences of potential, and the combustions of charcoal, going on year after year in the world, are insufficient to calculate the total quantity of nitrogen necessary for the development of plants. Other causes must be found. For this reason Berthelot devoted himself to the study of the soil. He showed that the earth was enriched in nitrogen under the influence of the tiny particles that swarm here. The organic world was no longer considered inert; it became a living entity in which a race of the tiniest midgets works to introduce the elementary nitrogen of the air into the cycle of organic reactions.

The ideas of the professor were from the first warmly opposed, but soon Hellriegel and Wilfarth, Schlœsing and Laurent, Winogradsky, brought in from every side important contributions to the question of the absorption of nitrogen and demonstrated in a startling manner the truth of the ideas put forth by Berthelot. This, moreover, was not the only occasion upon which Berthelot was actively disputed by opposing scholars. A posthumous memoir of Claude Bernard towards 1878 was the text of a most scholarly and most earnest scientific discussion between Berthelot and Pasteur. The latter held, on the basis of experiments, that the fermentation of glucose absolutely demanded the presence of leaven or barm of beer, while, according to Berthelot, the transformation of glucose into alcohol could take place through the intermediary of a ferment that was not living, of a diastase emitted by the yeast itself. The two scholars maintained their positions without reaching a common conclusion. Twenty years afterwards a German scholar, Buchner, demonstrated that yeast, sufficiently compressed, furnished a liquid without trace of living cells and capable of continuing for some time the fermentation of sugared juices. Berthelot's instinct of genius had surmounted Pasteur's experimental skill.

Having acquired a knowledge of the ancient languages, Berthelot was exceptionally well fitted to study the history of chemistry in early times. In the *Origines de l'alchimie* he shows that alchemy was founded on a doctrine of philosophy, that of the sameness of matter molded as if formed of four elements. Its practice rested upon the actual experiments performed by the Greco-Egyptian gold- and silversmiths and metallurgists. This the author indisputably established by the comparative study of a papyrus found in Thebes and some receipts of the pseudo-Democritus, in a second work entitled *Introduction à l'étude de la chimie des anciens et du moyen-age.*

Berthelot was led in this connection to publish the Greek, Syriac, and Arabic alchemic texts, which up to this time had remained unpublished, with the collaboration of distinguished linguists— Messrs. Rouelle for the Greek, Rubens Duval for the Syriac, and Houdas for the Arabic. Thus was again built up an entire branch of the science of early times, theretofore almost unknown. Furthermore, he pursued his studies up to the fourteenth century, in order to ascertain by what means the science of alchemy had penetrated into the Occident. He found that these means were two: first, by the handing down of the arts and industries which had up to that time been almost completely ignored and which nevertheless had subsisted continuously since the fall of the Roman Empire, and second, by the Syriac translations of the Greek alchemists, equally ignored, which were the sources of Arabic works. These latter were translated into Latin in the twelfth and thirteenth centuries.

Profoundly patriotic, Berthelot always considered it the duty of every scholar to place at the disposal of his country the results of his experience and of his learning. He never refused his services, when asked in the name of public interest, in any of the most varied directions, especially in matters relating to industry or to the public defense, public instruction, or general governmental policy. He was attached to all the technical commissions connected with the several government departments and applied to the solution of the problems presented all the talents employed in work in his own laboratory. This multiple activity of Berthelot furnished occasion for various articles or discourses, combined in four volumes: *Science et philosophie, Science et morale, Science et éducation, Science et libre pensée.*

Like all creators, Berthelot had a powerful faith, a faith which served him as director and guide both in his private and public life, faith in science and its methods. For Berthelot science dominated everything. It alone rendered definite services, and its domain was not restricted to the study of positive facts. Material progress due to science was the least important product of his work. Science included a higher and broader field, that of the ethical or spiritual and the social world.

In his letter to Renan on the ideal science and the positive science, after having explained in a masterly way by a concrete example how positive science proceeds in establishing facts and in attaching one to another by immediate relations, Berthelot extended the same method to the study of the domain outside the material world:

In the domain outside the material world, as in the material order of things, it is necessary at the start to establish the facts and to control them by observation, then to marshal them by constantly bringing to bear this same observation. All reasoning which tends to deduce them *a priori* from some abstract axiom is chimerical. It is the observation of the phenomena of the world outside the material, revealed either by psychology or by history and political economy, it is the study of their relations gradually generalized and at each step verified, that serves as a basis for a scientific understanding of human nature. The method by which each day are solved the problems of the material and industrial world is the only method by which can be solved and will be solved sooner or later the fundamental problems relative to the organization of society.

Berthelot, moreover, recognized that truth could not be attained with such a degree of certainty in the ideal science as in positive science. "It is in a way like a building hidden behind a cloud, of which only some outlines are visible." The farther up you go in the order of consequences, the farther away you get from real observations and the more does certainty, or rather probability, diminish. A system is true not in proportion to the logic of its reasoning, but to the sum of positive facts introduced into it.

It is to these philosophical conceptions that may be attributed to a certain extent Berthelot's opposition to constitutional formulæ. A slave to facts, he would not admit these systematized signs to which some went so far as to attach an objective reality.

The symbols of chemistry present in this respect some strange allurements by the algebraic ease of their combinations and by the tendencies of the human mind. They naturally lead to the substitution, in the place of a direct conception of things, never absolutely determined, the more simple and apparently more comprehensive view of their representative signs. It would be a strange misconception of the philosophy of the natural and experimental sciences to attribute to such mere machinery for working a fundamental importance. In fact, in the study of the sciences, all depends on the discovery of general facts and of the laws that bind them one to another.

Berthelot saw in these formulæ only a chemical language, and it meant no more to him than that the facts could be translated into one or another language.

I may be permitted to recall that on reaching the college laboratory at the close of a lecture, when Berthelot had explained his ideas on notations and chemical formulæ, I respectfully suggested to him that it would be more logical for him to use a language adopted by the majority of chemists. It was following this conversation that I presented to the Academy of Sciences the first work from the laboratory of Berthelot with atomic formulæ. Some time after, in a work performed in collaboration with my teacher, on the chlorine derivatives Berthelot definitely gave up notation in equivalents for atomic notation (1890).

Berthelot, at least at the time that I knew him, attached only a secondary importance to theories. This, moreover, is a trait common to nearly all learned men who have pursued a long scientific career. They have seen so many systems rise and fall that they arrive in the end at skepticism. I presented to him one day a short paper containing some theoretical ideas to which I attached some degree of importance and I carried it to him proud of my theoretical explanation of the facts observed. Glancing rapidly over my paper, Berthelot seized a pencil and quickly crossed out all that part on which I expected to be complimented. I was still a beginner, and notwithstanding all the admiration that Berthelot commanded from those about him, I confess that I consoled myself for my disappointment by considering the act as that of a scholar grown too old. This little incident springs to my mind whenever I come across an old memoir from which I have to draw any references and find the facts swamped in the theories of the period, today of such mediocre value. I am irritated at the author who makes me lose time in this way, and I understand fully the justice of Berthelot's action.

It is, moreover, a characteristic of youth, ignorant, inexperienced, and presumptuous, to hold decided opinions on everything and not to acquiesce on many points in the opinions of experienced persons and authorities. Age cures this fault quickly, but the memory of it comes back all the stronger when we find it again in succeeding generations.

Berthelot leaves a number of French and foreign pupils, many of whom are among those who most honor the chemical profession. To speak only of the oldest ones, I may mention the following: Jungfleisch, his collaborator in his *Traité de chimie organique* and in his researches on the coefficient of distribution, of which Nernst more recently published a valuable generalization; Barbier, who gave proof of great experimental ability in assisting the professor in delicate researches on the reductive properties of hydriodic acid; Sabatier, the learned teacher, well known for his works, already classic, on catalyzers of hydrogen gas; André, Berthelot's devoted collaborator in his researches on organic chemistry; Joannis, whose works on soda ammonium constitute good experimental models; de Forcrand, the distinguished director of the chemical institute of Montpellier, whose thermic data form a table of figures of undisputed accuracy; Guntz, who had the honor of separating barium and strontium in a pure state and of discovering subsalts of silver; Recoura, whose thesis was one of the most remarkable ever presented before the Faculty of Sciences of Paris, etc. In other countries a number of Berthelot's pupils teach in universities: Louguinine, Croustschoff, Ossipoff, Timoféieff, Werner, etc., in Russia; A. Werner in Switzerland; Fogh in Denmark; Hartog in England; Bredig in Germany; Paul Henry in Belgium, etc.

Berthelot's activity never waned a single instant. Last year he published a very extensive volume on the analysis of gases. He wrote out before his death a fifth volume on organic chemistry. At the same time he kept up his laboratory researches, which, by the way, were uninterrupted for fifty-five years. Berthelot could, like Hofmann or Bæyer, have realized a considerable fortune, but he never took out a patent nor derived any material profit from his discoveries. Offers made by groups of financiers to turn into money the results of his researches were in every case declined. Very sparing of his time, it was not always easy to hold a desired conversation with him. In order not to rob him of his leisure moments, it was best to meet him coming out of his laboratory toward noon and accompany him from the Collège de France to the Institut. How many times have we thus walked together down the rue de l'École de Médécin and the rue Mazarin while he chatted with me on the results of his researches or explained to me his ideas on the latest sensational discovery! But it was principally at the station de Chimie végétale de Bellevue-Meudon, where he came each year in April or May and installed himself and his family, that he willingly received his pupils on Sunday mornings. Thus, during his last sojourn at Meudon, I was chatting with him one October morning just before his return to Paris. Very busy with his researches on radioactivity, he showed me all the specimens of quartz he had colored in violet under the influence of radium, thus producing for the first time the synthesis of the amethyst. Then we passed to an examination of experiments he was conducting, of which he was destined never to know the results. Small glass tubes filled with different substances had for several days been ranged about a central tube containing a piece of radium. No transformation was yet apparent, but he was awaiting some interesting modifications by the time he should return the following spring, if, however, he added, he were still alive.

Berthelot's conversation was never trivial; his phrases were always correct, accurate, and simple, as those of a scholar and thinker should be. He gave immediately the impression of a superior man. He was, moreover, a man of delicate temperament. "There never was between us," said Renan, "I will not say a moral relaxation, but a plain vulgarity. We always acted toward one another as toward a lady we respect."

It was a genuine treat to listen to him at the private receptions presided over with such distinction by Madame Berthelot. He would then lay aside his thoughts of science to devote himself entirely to the interests of his wife and his friends. The Goncourts have described in their *Journal* the dinners at the home of Magny, where Berthelot was listened to with keen interest by everyone. "Renan," says Goncourt, "followed the trend of his thoughts without failing, and I am certain that many of the ideas afterwards uttered by the philosopher in his volumes were collected in the course of conversations with the chemist." Berthelot had, in fact, a powerful influence on the greatest minds of his time. Both Renan and Taine had a deep admiration for the learned man. It would be interesting some day to say more about the share of collaboration in Renan's work that can be traced back to the man of science.

Berthelot had six children—four sons and two daughters. He had the misfortune to lose one of his daughters and more recently a grandson, who was tragically killed in an accident on the Chemin de Fer du Nord. "No loss," he wrote, "can be compared to the loss of a child who has grown up under the eyes of its parents, surrounded and sustained by their love, and who is taken away in the flower of its youth, leaving in the depths of the hearts of its near relatives an inconsolable grief."

The dramatic death of the great man of science was a startling proof of the deep love that bound him to his wife. There was between these two souls such a close union, such mutual adaptation, that their existence made a veritable symbiosis. When we saw him come to the laboratory in those last days, his appearance told us of the condition of health of Madame Berthelot. Pale and worn during the critical periods, he walked with a step more alert during the periods of improvement. We knew that the days of her illness were numbered and we had no doubt but that her death would shortly be followed by that of her husband. Their mutual affection was even deeper than we supposed it to be, for Berthelot was unable to survive his worthy companion. [Berthelot died at Paris, March 18, 1907, in the Palais de l'Institut, very shortly after his wife had drawn her last breath.]

In all the realms where the activity of a human being could be exercised, Berthelot had performed his whole duty. He was a scholar, a citizen, a husband, a father, a teacher, without an equal. It would seem that such a fine nature should never encounter difficulties in its career. But this would be attributing to men a rapidity and accuracy of judgment to which they are hardly accustomed. Two months ago I confided to him some personal troubles. He placed himself, as always, at my disposal to help me overcome them. Then he added: "I was talking last night of the past, with Madame Berthelot, and we arrived at the conclusion that I had not lived a year without having a struggle to keep up." Sincerity always ends in triumph. On November 24, 1901, in that memorable meeting on the fiftieth anniversary of the professor's scientific career, the scholars of the whole world came to pay their respects in recognition and admiration of Berthelot. After having listened to several of the two hundred addresses coming from all corners of the civilized world, Berthelot arose and in the midst of the general emotion, in a clear and distinct voice, made a memorable speech, of which I shall try here to recall the beginning:

I am profoundly touched and completely overcome by the honors that you bestow upon me at this moment. These honors, I know, are not due alone to your personal regard for me; I should attribute them also to my age, to my long labors, and to such services as I have been able to render to our country and our fellow-men.

.   .   .

If any of us add anything to the common good in the realm of science, of art, or of morality, it is because a long line of generations has lived, toiled, thought, and suffered before us. It is the patient efforts of our predecessors that has created this science that you honor today.

Each one of us, whatever has been his individual initiative, should likewise attribute a considerable part of his success to contemporary scholars competing with him in the great common task.

In fact, for the brilliant discoveries of the past century, for these discoveries, let us proclaim it boldly, no one person has at all the right to claim exclusive merit. Science is essentially a collective work, pursued during the course of time by the efforts of a multitude of workers of every age and of every nation, succeeding themselves and associating by virtue of a tacit understanding for the search for pure truth and for the applications of that truth to the continuous betterment of the condition of all mankind.

Samuel Pierpont Langley *

1834–1906

———◆———

CYRUS ADLER †

SAMUEL PIERPONT LANGLEY, the third secretary of the Smithsonian Institution, astronomer and physicist, famed the world over for epoch-making contributions to our knowledge of the sun and the establishment of the principles of aerial flight, passed away in his seventy-second year, at Aiken, S. C., on the 27th of February, 1906.

Langley was descended of families who came to Massachusetts in the early part of the seventeenth century and to a great extent remained in the colony and even in the State itself. In a biography prepared by the late George Brown Goode eleven years ago it was pointed out that an unusual number of his ancestors were skilled mechanics and artisans, while on the other hand a group of them were of the most intellectual men of early New England—clergymen, schoolmasters, and indeed one of them, Increase Mather, a president of Harvard College and the author of the first American work on astronomy. His immediate forebears were especially characterized by great physical and intellectual vigor, wide cultivation, and a staunch sense of duty; and if to these distinguishing characteristics of a long line of ancestors there be added mechanical skill, high moral ideals, and a restless, all-consuming pursuit of new truth, in season and out of season, by skillful methods, upon original lines, we have a picture of the intellectual and moral make-up of the man whose life I am now attempting, inadequately, to portray.

He beguiled the tedium of his last illness by beginning the

* *A.R.,* 1906, pp. 515–533. From *Bulletin of the Philosophical Society of Washington,* vol. 25, pp. 1–26. Read before the Society Nov. 24, 1906.
† Historian, orientalist, educator (1863–1940), for some years librarian of the Smithsonian Institution.

preparation of his memoirs, which I have been permitted to see. They are so fragmentary that they can never be published, but from them I have been able to learn a few incidents of his early life which it is not improper to recite. He was born on the 22d of August, 1834, in Vernon street, Roxbury, to Samuel Langley and Mary Williams; attended various private schools, and later entered the Boston High School. His education was of the type then prevalent, and much of his time was devoted to Latin grammar. On the moral side the two strongest impressions which he recollected of this period were being taught a horror of debt and through it a sense of duty, and these two traits were firmly present to the last. Yet another fact taken from these very interestingly written pages shows that his father, himself a wholesale merchant in Boston, possessed a telescope with which the small boy watched the building of Bunker Hill monument.

As a child he was an omnivorous reader, had a reflective mind, an interest in art and in foreign lands, and a very strong bent toward mathematics, all of which grew to importance in later life. Not being sent to college, his choice of a profession fell upon civil engineering and architecture, which were primarily chosen because they would afford a livelihood and at the same time keep him near to several of the studies that interested him most.

In 1857 he went to the West and spent the next seven years mainly in Chicago and St. Louis, engaged in the practice of his profession and in business, acquiring a mercantile training and skill as a draftsman, which were of high importance in his later scientific and administrative career. In 1864 he definitely abandoned his profession and returned to New England, spending some time with his brother, John Williams Langley, in building a telescope, and the brothers afterwards had a year or more of European travel, visiting art galleries and observatories and indeed all scientific institutions. This European journey had another notable influence in familiarizing him with the continental languages, especially French, in which he acquired great proficiency.

Upon his return to Boston the then director of the Harvard College Observatory, Professor Joseph Winlock, invited him to become an assistant in that Observatory; and so at the age of 30, without any previous preparation, but with an accurately trained eye and hand and experience in observation, both in his native country and in Europe, at that time by no means usual, he was enabled to realize the dream of his early life and devote himself to scientific pursuits in that department which had most strongly interested him. His work with Professor Winlock was of brief duration, though even after leaving Cambridge he continued the association with him for some time. The attachment formed then was a strong one, and he bore in grateful remembrance the man who had given him his first opportunity to realize his early ambitions. In after years, when he came to Washington, he chose as one of his principal assistants here a son of Joseph Winlock, William Crawford Winlock, also an astronomer and for a number of years the secretary of this society, and to the end of his life he held these two men in affectionate memory.

In 1866 he went to the United States Naval Academy at Annapolis, with the title of assistant professor of mathematics, but with the understanding that his duties would lie principally in the reorganization of the small observatory, whose work had been interrupted by the Civil War. There he remounted and put into service the instruments and equipped the observatory for practical and scientific work. His stay in Annapolis, though fruitful in this regard, was a brief one, for at the end of the same year he was called to the Western University of Pennsylvania, where he became professor of astronomy and physics and director of the Allegheny Observatory. This position he held for twenty years, and here it was that he carried on scientific labors of such importance and originality as to have won the international scientific reputation and recognition which caused Professor Baird to invite him to the Smithsonian Institution as assistant secretary, and the Regents to elect him later as its chief executive officer.

His early years at Pittsburgh were spent largely in securing the proper instrumental equipment for the observatory, which upon his arrival was one only in name. It consisted of "a building in which was mounted an equatorial telescope of 13 inches aperture, bought by the university of a local club of amateur astronomers. Besides this there was no apparatus whatever, not even a clock, and the equatorial itself was without the necessary accessories." This was before the period of great endowment for astronomical or indeed, other scientific research in America, and the group of men whose wealth has since enriched Pittsburgh and many other places in this country and elsewhere were with a single exception either at the beginnings of their fortunes or without perception of the needs of science. It was imperatively necessary that money be secured for the purchase of apparatus if the Allegheny Observatory were to do proper work and its director have the opportunity of pursuing his own investigations.

Many affairs of ordinary life, but more especially the growth of railroads, demanded that the common clock, upon which every dweller of a civilized land depends, should be correct and that some plan be devised whereby other than solar time should serve over considerable areas. Tentative efforts in this direction had been made by the Greenwich Observatory, by the Naval Observatory, by Harvard College, at Albany, at Brussels, and at other places, but nowhere systematically nor upon any really practical or useful plan. To the needs of the Allegheny Observatory and the fruitful mind of Langley we owe the establishment of the time service and its outgrowth, the standardization of time in the United States and in other countries, and through its financial returns the instrumental equipment of Allegheny Observatory was rendered possible and likewise the great discoveries in astrophysics by its director.

At the age of 35, in 1869, Langley published his first two papers, the very first being a report of two pages on the observation of the total eclipse of August 7, 1869, at Oakland, Kentucky, and the second, "a proposal . . . for regulating from this observatory the clocks of the Pennsylvania Central and other railroads associated with it." When we recall the intolerable inconvenience which attached to the changing of time in every 40 or 50 miles of travel, and the empirical method by which clocks and watches were set, resulting in annoyance, confusion, delay, and disappointment, these early labors of Langley, resulting in our standard time system and in the almost universal regulation of public clocks through electrical signals from observatories, must be counted, if not an important advance in knowledge, a really great contribution to the convenience, comfort, and welfare of mankind.

While these practical efforts to secure a fund for the equipment of the Observatory were maturing, Langley had the opportunity of carrying on astronomical work under other auspices. In 1869 he took charge of a coast survey party to observe the total eclipse of August 7 of that year at Oakland, Kentucky, resulting in the brief paper above referred to, and in 1870 he accompanied a Government eclipse expedition to Jerez de la Frontera, which was under the general direction of Professor Joseph Winlock, and included on its staff besides Mr. Langley, Professors [Charles A.] Young and [Edward C.] Pickering, both of whom have since become among the foremost of American astronomers.

He had meanwhile not lost his interest in the time service, the methods of which he described in an article in the *American Journal of Science* in 1873, proposing, in addition to transmitting time to railroads, to supply it to watchmakers and jewelers and to cities in general for their public clocks.

Almost from the beginning of his astronomical work he had

devoted his attention to the sun, his investigations being chiefly astrophysical in character, and among his earlier observations in this field were his sunspot studies, carried on about 1873. From that time on until 1880 he was engaged in minute telescopic study and drawing the details of the surface of the sun and especially of sunspots. Photography had not begun to be used for such purposes, and his skill and accuracy in making drawings of observations of these phenomena were particularly valuable. Indeed, it is declared by astrophysicists that his sunspot drawings made at Allegheny prior to 1875 are even yet to be regarded as the best recorded evidence of their structure. I learn from [Charles Greeley] Abbot, of the Astrophysical Observatory, that "Professor George E. Hale, who has enjoyed the choicest opportunities for examining the sun, both with the 40-inch reflector of the Yerkes Observatory and with the horizontal telescope on Mount Wilson, and also during various expeditions to high mountain peaks, says that in the best views of sunspots he has ever had, the better they were seen the more nearly have they appeared as shown in Langley's drawings." In spite of this great power of direct personal observation, he was quick to appreciate and to employ the aids which photography lends to this research, though it should be said that the standard illustration of a sunspot which appears in most of the textbooks and works on astronomy of the present time is one drawn by Langley with his own hand at Allegheny in December 1873. The following state-ment of his continued work in this field during his Allegheny period was prepared recently for publication in a general encyclopedia, and, having had the advantage of his own revision, it is taken as an authoritative statement of his researches:

About 1875 he began to devote much attention to the measurement of the heat spectra of the sun and other sources of radiation. Convinced after long experience with the thermopile of the futility of attempting to discriminate the effects of narrow portions of the spectrum by means of any heat-measuring apparatus then employed, he sought to devise some-thing more satisfactory, and in 1879 and 1880 was successful in the in-vention of the bolometer. This instrument has found high favor for a wide range of experimental work, but in his hands it has been used from 1880 to the present time to open up a great new field of investigation in connection with the invisible long wave length rays proceeding from all heated bodies and to change many of the older ideas concerning them.

The more important of his many researches published during this period were upon the energy spectrum of the sun, the transmission of the earth's atmosphere and the solar constant, the behavior of prisms toward long wave-length radiators, the energy spectra of heated terrestrial bodies, and the energy spectrum of the moon, the moon's heat hitherto having been recognized with difficulty even in gross by the thermopile, but now, by the bolometer, being analyzed in minute detail in a lunar heat spectrum. More recently a comparison of the proportions of luminous and nonluminous heat in the spectra of the sun and artificial light sources with the corresponding proportions of the light and heat in the radiations emitted by the glowworm gave important economical results.

In 1881, previous observations at Allegheny having led him to believe that there was a great and then unappreciated selective absorption both in the sun's and in the earth's atmosphere, which rendered in the latter case Pouillet's methods inapplicable, and which when recognized tended to give a far larger value to the solar constant, he, with the aid of the Government, organized an expedition to the top of Mount Whitney, the loftiest mountain in southwestern California, whose abrupt precipices permitted observations to be made from two neighboring stations, yet with a distance of more than 2 miles of altitude between them. These observations were published by the United States Government in a volume entitled *Professional Papers of the Signal Service, No. XV. Researches on Solar Heat and its Absorption by the Earth's Atmosphere.* Perhaps the most important result of the expedition was the entire change in the hitherto accepted value of the solar constant, while incidentally these and others carried on at Allegheny led to the displacement of the old assumption in favor of the present view, namely, that the general absorption is largest as we approach the violet end of the spectrum.

By 1885 the solar spectrum had been followed by him to wave lengths ten times as great as those of the visible spectrum, and radiations from terrestrial sources even farther, thus overthrowing the ideas previously held of a natural limit to the infrared wave lengths at about 1 μ. His extended bolometric researches on the heat spectrum of the moon led him to fix the maximum lunar temperature at little above 0° C. In his researches on these long wave-length spectra Mr. Langley developed the optical possibilities and determined the constants of rock salt, a substance already employed by Melloni, but whose range of usefulness was now very greatly extended.

But he did not confine himself during this time either to his labors in the observatory or to making their results known to scientific men through contributions to societies and journals. He had a decided opinion of the right of the world to know what scientific men were doing and a remarkable gift of presenting such knowledge to the man of average intelligence. He occasionally delivered lectures in the city of Pittsburgh, which were reported for one or another of the Pittsburgh papers, and wrote letters to the *Pittsburgh Gazette* when any unusual astronomical phenomenon which might be of public interest presented itself. By 1875 his reputation had grown to such an extent that he was invited to lecture at Stevens Institute, and his papers, which had heretofore been published only in American journals, commenced to appear abroad in English and Italian periodicals and in the *Transactions of the Academy of Sciences of the Institute of France,* this, be it noted, within five years from the date of his first publication.

The trend of his mind toward the popularization of science may be judged from a paper which appeared in the *Popular Science Monthly* in 1877, entitled "The First Popular Scientific Treatise," in which he declared that "science is not for the professional student only, but everyone will take an interest in its results if they are only put before the world in the right way." The treatise was Fontenelle's *Conversations on the Plurality of Worlds,* and the article, while holding strictly to its subject, showed something of that intimate knowledge of French history to which I shall allude later on.

The question of the personal error or personal equation, which has attracted so many astronomers, also had his attention, and he described in a communication to the *American Journal of Science* in 1877 a machine whereby this personal error could be entirely eliminated.

In 1878 he took charge of a party sent out by the United States to witness the total eclipse of that year from Pikes Peak, at an elevation of 14,000 feet, and besides the scientific memoirs which resulted therefrom and through which he was able to follow the corona to a hitherto unsuspected distance from the sun he wrote pleasant, chatty letters describing the more personal side of the work of the party. In the winter of 1878, during the course of a visit to Europe, he spent some time upon Mount Etna, and made observations there which resulted in the production of scientific papers and a very interesting article entitled "Wintering on Etna," which was contributed to the *Atlantic Monthly.* In 1881, through the generosity of the citizens of Pittsburgh and with the cooperation of the United States Signal Service, he conducted an expedition to Mount Whitney, to which reference has already been made.

Langley's general reputation shortly after this became greatly enhanced by a series of popular lectures delivered at the Lowell Institute and at the Peabody Institute at Baltimore, afterwards published in the *Century Magazine,* and later still in the form of a book, which has gone through several editions, under the title of *The New Astronomy.* These lectures and this work set clearly before educated people the results of his own labors and of others in that branch of astronomy which, dealing not with the questions of longitude and latitude, or the discovery of planets, asteroids, or comets, or the other problems of the older astronomers, had to do with the physics of the heavenly bodies—the study through patient observation and numerous ingenious devices not of the mere existence of the heavenly bodies, but of their constitution.

The spirit in which this work is written can be gleaned from its very brief preface:

I have written these pages [he says] not for the professional reader, but with the hope of reaching a part of that educated public on whose support [I am] so often dependent for the means of extending the boundaries of knowledge.

It is not generally understood that among us not only the support of the Government, but with scarcely an exception every new private benefaction is devoted to "the old" astronomy, which is relatively munificently endowed already; while that which I have here called "the new," so fruitful in results of interest and importance, struggles almost unaided.

We are all glad to know that Urania, who was in the beginning but a poor Chaldean shepherdess, has long since become well-to-do, and dwells now in state. It is far less known than it should be that she has a younger sister now among us, bearing every mark of her celestial birth, but all unendowed and portionless. It is for the reader's interest in the latter that this book is a plea.

Of the scientific importance of this book and of the other work of Langley I am naturally dependent for my opinion upon others, but I may be permitted to say that its literary character is unsurpassed—indeed, probably unequaled—by the scientific work of any other in America, and deserves to rank among the popular scientific expositions of Darwin, Wallace, Huxley, and Tyndall. Even prior to this Langley had been invited to lecture at the Royal Institution of Great Britain; his fame was growing and recognition was coming to him from many sources.

In the autumn of 1886 Professor [Spencer Fullerton] Baird,* after a personal conference with Langley, wrote him inquiring whether he would enter the service of the Smithsonian Institution as an assistant secretary in charge of foreign and domestic exchanges, including the international service, the library, and the publications, with the understanding that not more than half of his time should be given to the Institution and the remainder could, as Professor Baird said, be employed in

keeping up those original researches at Allegheny University which have already secured for you so much distinction in the scientific world. The Smithsonian Institution does not desire in any way to interrupt the progress of your investigations; on the contrary, it will be most happy

* For Baird, see *A.R.*, 1888, pp. 703–744.

to facilitate them as far as lies in its power, with the hope, at some future day, of being able to give, in Washington, facilities equal, or superior, to those that you can have elsewhere.

The reply of Langley, a portion of which I quote, throws an interesting side light upon the character of the man utterly unsuspected by the world at large and known to only a few of his intimates—that is, a strong craving for real society, by which he meant intercourse with people of diverse minds and knowledge, all of whom might give him that intellectual companionship for which he hungered. Langley, on November 27, 1886, wrote from Allegheny to Professor Baird:

I am obliged by your official letter of the 22nd instant, inviting me to accept the assistant secretaryship of the Smithsonian Institution, and by its kind allusion to those relations of mine to physical science, which have influenced you in making the proposal.

The opportunity for usefulness in that direction is a strong motive to me for acceptance, as I mentioned in the conference to which you refer; but I find from your letter that I did not then make my actual position plain, as I intended to do. To repeat what I then meant to say, I have no wish or ambition to tempt me from giving most of my time to physical investigation—at least now, while I enjoy exceptional facilities for this, together with a freedom which I could not expect in any subordinate position.

My professional life here is, through the kindness of those to whom I owe more than official duty, a very pleasant one, in most respects, nor have I any occasion to leave the work of my predilection to increase my income.

At the same time both my professional and domestic life here are exceptionally isolated, and I have felt the need of some change which would bring with it, along with society, new occupation, if that could be of a kind not wholly dissociated from my accustomed pursuits.

His loneliness in the Allegheny Observatory can well be imagined. Pittsburgh of that day was largely engaged in adding to the wealth of the State of Pennsylvania and, indeed, of the entire country, and this astronomer and physicist, student of art and literature, philosopher and dreamer, was there almost as isolated as though upon the top of a lonely peak. He told me once that he attended the meetings of the medical society of the city of Pittsburgh in order that he might have contact with professional and scientific men, and that he walked down and toiled up Observatory Hill once a week to spend Sunday evening in a room back of a drug store, in which four or five men would assemble to discuss the great things of the mind and the scientific problems of the day.

It was a revelation to me, as I assume it will be to others, to learn from the letter of Langley quoted above, that it was principally the desire to associate with others of his kind, and not ambition or opportunities for work, which brought him to Washington.

On January 12, 1887, Langley was appointed Assistant Secretary of the Smithsonian Institution. In August of the same year Professor Baird died, and in November Langley was elected Secretary by the Board of Regents. During his brief term as Assistant Secretary he had given much thought to the departments with which he was especially charged, the exchange service, the library, and the publications, and in these important agencies he retained a deep interest. The exchanges he regarded as one of the principal means for carrying out the terms of Smithson's bequest "for the diffusion of knowledge among men," and to the publications he gave an ever-increasing amount of thought, especially those which could be, to use his term, "understanded of the people," developing the *Smithsonian Report* to such a point that today it appeals to every man of ordinary education and intelligence and is in many places where books and libraries are inaccessible, the sole and yet the entirely satisfactory means of keeping people abreast of the scientific advancement of the world.

The hope held out in the letter to Professor Baird that some opportunity would be afforded here for the continuance of Langley's original researches was made good, first through the generosity of the late Jerome H. Kidder and Alexander Graham Bell and later through appropriations by Congress for the establishment of an astrophysical observatory under the direction of the Smithsonian Institution. The Observatory,* housed in a modest frame structure on the Smithsonian grounds and entailing an annual cost upon the Government of a very inconsiderable sum, made it possible for Langley not only to continue his researches, but to reach new and even more valuable results than had been obtained heretofore.

It is due to his initiative and energy that the people of this country have the National Zoological Park. He specialized in astronomy, but his interest in nature was not confined to it. He had an eager curiosity about animal life and a great love for natural scenes, and so it fell to him, the astronomer, to move successfully in the establishing of the Park, which, besides having high scientific possibilities for usefulness and instruction, is one of the great pleasure grounds of the people who live in this capital and

* See Bessie Z. Jones, *Lighthouse of the Skies: The Smithsonian Astrophysical Observatory, Background and History, 1846–1955* (Washington, 1965).

to those hundreds of thousands of American citizens who annually make a pilgrimage to it.

Shortly after Langley's accession to the secretaryship, and aside from his work in the establishment of the Observatory, he strongly desired to create a new activity for the Smithsonian Institution, and his first choice would have been that of extending its scope in the direction of the fine arts. But the time was not then ripe. He met opposition and foresaw insuperable difficulties, and so he reluctantly abandoned this field and put his persevering energy into the other just mentioned, the establishment of the Park. But he always had the feeling that the Smithsonian Institution should act for the nation in the matter of art. He caused to be collected such art objects as belonged to it and were deposited elsewhere, and reimplanted, as it were, the idea of the fine arts in the Institution by setting aside a room in the Smithsonian building which should be devoted to these collections. His death came at a time when the realization of this idea of his was about to have fruition.

He had for many years been in the habit of going annually to Europe, and this personal contact with the scientific men of England and of the Continent and the reputation that his researches had brought to him and to the Institution, and his increased zeal in pushing forward the exchange service, led to a great enhancement of the international reputation of the Institution.

It was my rare good fortune to accompany Langley upon two of his European trips—first in 1894 and again in 1898. Upon the first occasion I heard him read before the physical and astronomical sections of the British Association for the Advancement of Science a paper describing his work on the infrared spectrum. The meeting was held at Oxford, and the hall, holding some 250 persons, was crowded. He spoke very simply and without notes, describing the apparatus that he had devised and brought together and the results that had been attained; and so vivid was his statement and so forceful that at the conclusion of his remarks the supposedly stolid Englishmen who composed the audience arose almost in a body and cheered. At a meeting of the physical section on the same occasion he discussed the future of aerial navigation. The session was held under the chairmanship of the late Lord Salisbury, premier of Great Britain, and that year president of the association, and the discussion that followed was participated in by Lord Kelvin, Lord Rayleigh, and Sir Hiram Maxim, none of whom dissented from the views which Langley expressed.

None regretted more keenly than he that of the many great

benefactions which came to American science few, if any, found their way to the funds of the Smithsonian Institution; so that relatively the activities of the Institution proper were not increased in the United States commensurate with the growth of other scientific organizations, though it should be said that after the original foundation the only important addition to the Smithsonian funds, that received from Thomas G. Hodgkins, came during the administration of Langley.

Among his many notable addresses was that delivered in 1888, as the retiring president of the American Association for the Advancement of Science, under the title of "A History of a Doctrine," this doctrine being the views concerning radiant energy. The address is a charming one in every respect—as an historical investigation, as a summing up of results obtained, as a literary document, and as a prophecy. Some of the phrases are worthy of a great philosophic mind. "We have perhaps seen," he declared, "that the history of the progress of this department of science is little else than a chapter in that larger history of human error which is still to be written." And yet there is no pessimistic note in it, for he asks the question, "Shall we say that the knowledge of truth is not advancing?" and he replies to this query, "It is advancing, and never so fast as today; but the steps of its advance are set on past errors, and the new truths become such steppingstones in turn." To this same time belong other papers of great general interest, notably that on "The Observation of Sudden Phenomena," which will have a certain value even for the physiological psychologist, although designed for the astronomer primarily and containing descriptions of the personal-error machine invented by Langley; and also another paper on "The Cheapest Form of Light," this study being based upon an examination of the radiation of the firefly, and showing that it is possible to produce light without heat other than the light itself, and that this is actually effected now by nature's processes.

I am brought, however, to another field of scientific work in which Langley engaged and with which his name has been identified during the past fifteen years, the subject popularly known as flying machines, and which he denominated *aerodynamics*. Langley came before the scientific world and the public generally on this subject first in a very brief communication to the Academy of Sciences of the Institute of France in July 1890; second, by the publication of an extended memoir in the *Smithsonian Contributions to Knowledge;* and third, through a brief popular article on the possibility of mechanical flight in the *Century Magazine.* I alluded above to one of the group of what would now be called "captains of industry" in Pittsburgh who had sympathized with Langley and his work and had aided him in its prosecution. The name of this man, William Thaw, was commemorated in the preface to "Experiments in Aerodynamics" in the following phrase: "If there prove to be anything of permanent value in these investigations, I desire that they may be remembered in connection with the name of the late William Thaw, whose generosity provided the principal means for them," though it should be said that Thaw's aid in this direction was not to be measured alone by money contribution to the experiments, for it meant much at that time that as eminently a practical man as he should have believed in what was then considered a wild idea and have supported a scientific man in it both by money and by moral encouragement. This memoir, "Experiments in Aerodynamics," was at once republished in full in French and attracted widespread attention. Langley persevered in the study, and in 1893 he issued a second memoir, "The Internal Work of the Wind." This also appeared in English and French and was designed to prove that aerial flight had an aid, described as the potentiality in the internal work of the wind, which would be of great moment in the practical solution of the problem.

But the painstaking experiments with the whirling table and with other forms of apparatus devised by Langley for the study of the question of aerial navigation did not content him, and although not himself a mechanical engineer, and with very inferior appliances, he took up the building of a machine driven by a steam engine, which he hoped would practically demonstrate the possibility of mechanical flight. There were innumerable mechanical difficulties in its construction and also in its launching, and after failures which would have disheartened an ordinary man success came in the spring of 1896 when a steam-driven aerodrome, constructed under Langley's direction in his own shops, engine and all, actually flew for three-quarters of a mile or more over the Potomac River. This remarkable success had world-wide recognition. It was communicated to learned bodies, was the talk of the newspapers, and in a specially written article in *McClure's Magazine* Langley himself described this trial and how he came to enter upon the subject. From his own words we learn that this was a problem with him from childhood days; that he used to lie in a New England pasture and watch the hawks soaring far up in the blue and sailing for a long time without any motion of their wings, and this question he thought of in mature life and set himself to inquire whether the problem of artificial flight was as hope-less and as absurd as it was thought to be. "Nature," he says, "has solved it, and why not man?" And with this question he described the experiments with the whirling table down to the actual flight. As was his wont, he discussed the attempts of those who came before him and in simple language explained the theory upon which mechanical flight would be possible. This article, printed in 1897, closed with the following paragraph:

I have thus far had only a purely scientific interest in the results of these labors. Perhaps if it could have been foreseen at the outset how much labor there was to be, how much of life would be given to it, and how much care, I might have hesitated to enter upon it at all. And now re-ward must be looked for, if reward there be, in the knowledge that I have done the best I could in a difficult task, with results which it may be hoped will be useful to others. I have brought to a close the portion of the work which seemed to be specially mine—the demonstration of the practicability of mechanical flight—and for the next stage, which is the commercial and practical development of the idea, it is probable that the world may look to others. The world, indeed, will be supine if it do not realize that a new possibility has come to it, and that the great universal highway overhead is now soon to be opened.

Immediately after the success of these experiments and shortly before the article was written, Langley passed through a most depressing period of his official and personal life, and his feelings then were no doubt reflected in its closing words. In the month of September 1896 his two principal associates in the Smithsonian Institution, George Brown Goode, a distinguished naturalist who was in charge of the Museum, and William Crawford Winlock, already alluded to, had prematurely passed away, and their loss was a serious blow to Langley, whose friendships were deep ones. Of both these men he wrote memoirs—in fact, of Goode two, the longer of which, presented to the National Academy of Sciences, is at once a discriminating and affectionate tribute to a great man and a dear friend.

For the next few years Langley's time was not so productive; his physical health was good, but the severe strain of his scien-tific labors and his personal losses tended to a depression of spirits which caused him to shrink from new work. In spite of his almost definitely announced intention no longer to carry on the work in flying machines, he was led in 1898, through circumstances not clearly known but which had to do to a certain extent with the Spanish-American war, to take up the building of a flying machine large enough to carry a man, this work being undertaken under the Board of Ordnance and Fortification of the United States Army, and with an allotment made by that board for the purpose. He had meanwhile, after a little lapse of time, renewed his astrophysical work, which, through the improvement of the instruments he had invented, produced new and valuable results. The bolometer was brought to a greater degree of refinement than had ever been attained. The researches of the Astrophysical Observatory had progressed to such a point as to justify the publication of a remarkable volume of *Annals,* and an expedition made by him, to observe the solar eclipse of 1900 at Wadesboro, N. C., was signally successful.

A half dozen or more papers illustrating the various advances made in the study of the spectrum were also issued about this time. The building of the large aerodrome and of models to aid in its construction was rapidly being pushed ahead. Since the successful flight of the first aerodrome in 1896 a further possibility of increased power with comparative lightness had come with the employment of the gas engine, and this was experimented upon with a view to determining its feasibility for the purpose.

In the midst of these labors, either of them enough to engross the thought of an ordinary man, carried along as they were in addition to the management of the Institution and its correspondence and the interviews and the appearances before committees which this work entailed—in the very midst, I say, of these labors there appeared an article, of all places, in the *Saint Nicholas Magazine,* describing the Children's Room of the Smithsonian, prefaced by a letter written by Langley himself, in which he appears as the attorney for the children and pleads their cause with a grown-up museum man, and almost at the same time he wrote a curious and interesting paper describing the fire-walk ceremony in Tahiti, where Langley spent part of the summer of 1901, and where he hoped to find a miracle but witnessed instead an interesting ceremony, which, almost to his own regret, he was able to explain by natural law.

A brief popular account of the subsequent experiments with the Langley aerodrome was published in 1905, an extended memoir on the subject being yet unpublished, though left in such shape as to render its publication certain.* He describes in the briefer paper the attempt made to purchase a suitable engine or to secure its building by contract elsewhere; the acceptance of such a contract

* See *The Langley Memoir on Mechanical Flight,* vol. 27 of *Smithsonian Contributions to Knowledge* (Washington, 1911).

by a mechanical engineer, and the failure, after two years, to deliver the engine in accordance with the agreement; the consequent necessity of building it at the Institution; the innumerable details of construction that had to be considered, and, finally, the trials, first of the test models, which proved successful. Twice, on the 7th of October, 1903, and again on the 8th of December of the same year attempts were made to launch the large machine, and in both cases, according to the observation of numerous reliable engineers, members of the Board of Ordnance and others, it was the launching that proved a failure, and the words of Langley, in closing this statement, seemed to be justified: "Failure in the aerodrome itself," he declared, "or its engines there has been none; and it is believed that it is at the moment of success, and when the engineering problems have been solved, that a lack of means has prevented a continuance of the work."

There can be no doubt but that this failure to launch the big machine was a serious blow to Langley. Not so much the failure itself, for he was a philosopher and a scientific man who knew that success came only after repeated defeat. Had it meant unsuccessful experiment in his laboratory or shop it would have daunted him not in the least. It was necessary to make these experiments in the open air before the eyes of the world, while his arrangements with the Board of Ordnance and Fortification rendered it imperative that the details of the construction should not be made public. The newspaper press of the country, misunderstanding his motives and angered possibly at the large expense connected with maintaining special correspondents at an inconvenient place on the Potomac River, united in a chorus of ridicule and attack which in time made itself felt in the national legislature. At his years—for he was then nearly 70—the attitude assumed by the public press broke his spirit at this, the first, indeed the only, defeat in his career.

The lack of means of which he speaks was only a lack of funds from the source from which he thought he was entitled to obtain it. One or more private individuals offered him the opportunity to continue. Several years before he had been offered a considerable sum for this work if he would but place it upon some commercial basis and take out patents on such portions of the machinery as were patentable in order that commercial reward might come to the persons furnishing the money, but he steadfastly refused either to secure a patent or to accept money from private persons. He declared that this work was solely in the interest of the Nation, and if the Nation was not prepared to support it he was not willing to proceed with it As far as I can learn, he never wavered in his belief that success would result from his work. Aerial navigation was in his opinion sure to come, and the very machine which was declared by the public press to have been wrecked beyond hope he had repaired in absolute condition for another trial.

It is a gratification to be able to record that the last paper that he ever read was a series of resolutions adopted by the Aero Club at New York City expressing appreciation of his work in behalf of aerial navigation and confidence in the directions which it had taken, and any reader of the current magazines or the daily press can see for himself that in spite of criticism and ridicule the principles which he discovered are more and more gaining recognition. The future of aerial navigation lies not in the direction of the balloon, which is being abandoned even by its most ardent votaries, but in that of the aeroplane; and whatever form this may take or whatever modifications may be made as the result of experiment, the laws of aerodynamics will be the laws which Langley discovered, and the aeroplane or other form of machine heavier than the air will be based upon the models which he made and which actually flew.

The tributes in recognition of his work are almost too numerous to recite. He received the degree of D.C.L. from Oxford, D.Sc. from Cambridge, and, among numerous others, the degree of LL.D. from the universities of Harvard, Princeton, Michigan, and Wisconsin. He was awarded the Henry Draper medal by the National Academy of Sciences, the Rumford medal by the Royal Society of London, and the Rumford medal by the American Academy of Arts and Sciences, as well as the Janssen medal from the Institute of France, and the medal of the Astronomical Society of France. He was a foreign member of the Royal Society of London, a correspondent of the Institute of France, a fellow of the Royal Astronomical Society of London, member of the Royal Institution of London, member of the Academia dei Lincei, of Rome, of the National Academy of Sciences, and of many others.

Langley, although a member of very many scientific and other societies, was not a regular attendant at any of them. He systematically avoided holding any office in any society, the only exceptions that I know of being his presidency of the American Association for the Advancement of Science, his acceptance of the vice-presidency for a brief time of the American Philosophical Society, and membership in the council of the National Academy of Sciences. It was not that he failed to recognize the importance of scientific societies, but rather that he felt confident that others could attend to their management, and that his time must be guarded for his official duties and for his scientific work.

Among the many societies to which he belonged he had an especial affection for this Philosophical Society. He was elected to membership in it in 1887, the year in which he came to Washington, and with hardly any exception read before it the scientific papers that he presented in this city. Many of you will probably remember his various papers on the infrared spectrum and that on mechanical flight, and I may be permitted to say in passing that no novice ever prepared a paper or lecture more carefully than he did, for while he always spoke with great directness and simplicity and clearness, apparently without effort and usually without notes, his communications were always written carefully in advance, every slide gone over, and an actual rehearsal made, and this method was one that he carried into his scientific work as well. I remember that before going on the eclipse expedition to Wadesboro there was a rehearsal almost daily for a period of nearly three months on both his own part and that of every other person in the party as to the duties which each one would be expected to perform during the very few moments when the phenomenon was observable.

One would naturally suppose that what has gone before at least fully describes a single man. Indeed, it relates enough to fill the lifetime of two or three men, yet it by no means adequately goes to make the full picture. I have alluded above to his having been an omnivorous reader, but this is too general an expression to give any idea of the extent of his literary cultivation. He knew the German classics but had, like many men of his generation, an especial fondness for Heinrich Heine. It is not too much to say that he knew everything good in English, though he had some special interests and had become an ardent Borrovian. He personally owned a considerable selection of the original manuscript of George Borrow and aided in the preparation of the *Life of Borrow* by Knapp, visiting him at Oxford and furnishing suggestions and information for this interesting work. The history of England and even more the history of France engaged his attention. He was at one period of his life an ardent admirer of Thomas Carlyle, whose personal acquaintance he enjoyed, and it is not impossible that from him he acquired a sort of method of historical reading, for he looked to men rather than to documents of the periods as furnishing the keynotes for the progress of nations. Leonardo da Vinci, and Cromwell, and Frederick the Great, and Louis XIV, and Napoleon, and Lincoln were some of the men about whom he had read everything available to the student, and he had gone deeply into the memoirs of their respective periods, more especially, however, the French memoirs, with which he had an acquaintance that might have been envied by a professional historical student. He was especially interested in the problems of the soul and studied the metaphysicians and the modern psychologists, and was himself associated with societies for psychical research, and personally engaged in the examination of spirit mediums, though never with satisfaction to this keen observer. He knocked hard and loud at the door which leads to knowledge of the soul, for it seemed to have been one of the necessities of this great mind that it should attempt all the difficult problems which were offered to human observation or curiosity. He loved to talk with men possessed of positive religious views upon their own beliefs and had a deep interest in a Jesuit, or a Jew, or a Buddhist, or a Mohammedan, or, indeed any man who thought he had secured the truth and knew the way of life in this world and the world to come. His paper, "The Laws of Nature" is a very significant contribution from this point of view.

He was probably less understood upon his personal side than any other. When I came here to live in 1892 I remember that Goode said to me once that Langley was a very reserved man and a very lonely one, and that though it might be difficult to gain his friendship the effort was well worth the making. I do not know that I did make a conscious effort. In my then position as librarian I came into official contact with him because of his very great interest in and constant demand for books of every nature. By chance I found that he was a collector of translations of the *Arabian Nights* and had read all the editions in English and French available. I happened to tell him of my own interest in the subject and the fact that as a student I had read portions of the *Arabian Nights* in the original. There then began a closer acquaintanceship which, I am proud to say, resulted in a friendship which has been to me one of the most profoundly valuable and touching experiences of my life. He was a very shy man and greatly feared that he might obtrude himself upon others or that an advance that he might make would prove unwelcome. He was also, like some other mathematicians and astronomers, at times very much abstracted and with a painfully bad memory for names, or rather an inability to associate faces and names—a difficulty which he told me had nothing to do with his scientific studies but was inherited and belonged to his father, who was a merchant. This difficulty he attempted to hide as far as possible, producing upon the average man the conviction that he was dealing with a very haughty and distant individual—a deduction which was very far from the truth.

Living here without family ties, coming in his fifty-third year, almost after the period when men make close friendships, his hunger for real friendship and affection was pathetic. Most of the men with whom he came into contact were of another generation, and it was a genuine revelation to see him, as I sometimes did, with a friend of his youth, a man of his own age whom he had known for many years. He was a most rigidly truthful man—not truthful in any ordinary sense, but in that extraordinary Puritan New England sense, which did not even permit him to subscribe himself as being "very sincerely yours," if he was not.

I have alluded above to the fact that he himself ascribed his interest in aerial navigation to a childish wonder as to how the great heavy birds which he used to watch in a New England pasture could fly and maintain themselves in the air, and in another place he has told us that his work on the sun also grew out of a childish interest in this great center of our system upon which life on this planet depends. I think that these two ideas of his were not fancies, but that it was a fact that in his case especially the child was father to the man. One of his favorite quotations was the initial stanzas of the poem of Wordsworth:

> Who is the happy warrior? Who is he
> That every man in arms should wish to be?
> It is the generous spirit, who, when brought
> Among the tasks of real life, hath wrought
> Upon the plan that pleased his boyish thought.

But this memorial, inadequate as it may be, must draw to a close. I have been able to faintly trace the lines of a great mind and a great soul, one that left a powerful impress upon the knowledge and thinking of the country in which he was born and the time in which he lived, and his name and his fame are bound to be handed down through all posterity. Yet he valued these labors and the results which sprung from them but little when compared with the affection of his kin and of his friends—affections not many in number nor easily obtained, for he was, as I have said, a shy man; but he gave in full measure his confidence and his love to those whom he called friend.

A long life filled with many perplexities left his soul white. This Nation and the world at large are the richer for the life of this great man.

David Gill *

1843–1914

───────◆───────

ARTHUR STANLEY EDDINGTON†

BY THE DEATH of Sir David Gill astronomy has lost one of its ablest figures and best-known leaders. By his widespread activity, his close association with all the great enterprises of observational astronomy, and by the energy and enthusiasms of his character, he had come to hold an almost unique position in astronomical councils; and the withdrawal of his great motive power leaves a universal sense of loss. By his individual achievements and by his leadership he has exerted an incalculable influence on the progress of all that pertains to precision of observation. It will be our task in this notice to give an outline of his work as an astronomer, but to understand his immense influence it is necessary also to realize the personal character of the man. Those who came in contact with him felt the charm of his personality. In some indefinable way he could inspire others with his enthusiasm and determination. Enjoying a life crowded with activity, surrounded by an unusually wide circle of friends, he was ever ready and eager to encourage the humblest beginner. It was no perfunctory interest that he displayed. He was quick to discern any signs of promise and no less outspoken in his criticism; but whether he praised or condemned, few could leave him without the truest admiration and affection for his simple-hearted character.

David Gill was born at Aberdeen on the 12th of June, 1843. His family had long been associated with that city, where his father had an old-established and successful business in clocks and watches of all kinds. In due course he entered the Marischal College and University, Aberdeen. At that time J. Clerk Maxwell was

* *A.R.*, 1915, pp. 511–522. From *Monthly Notices of the Royal Astronomical Society,* London, Feb., 1915.
† Noted British astronomer and physicist (1882–1944).

a professor there, and his teaching had a great influence on the young student. Judged by ordinary standards, Maxwell was not a successful lecturer; but there were some students who could catch a part of his meaning as he "thought aloud" at the blackboard and feel the impression of his personality in after-lecture conversation, and these found him an inspiring teacher. Gill was among these, and he became imbued with a zeal for experimental science which soon manifested itself in his setting up a small laboratory in his father's house.

Up to the age of 20 Gill's scientific interests appear to have had no particular inclination to astronomy, but in 1863 he became desirous of securing an accurate time service at Aberdeen. Encouraged by a visit to Professor Piazzi Smyth at Edinburgh Observatory, he succeeded in interesting Professor David Thomson in his efforts. There was at that time an old observatory at King's College, Aberdeen. Together the two men unearthed and set up in adjustment a portable transit instrument which had long been disused; the sidereal clock was overhauled and fitted with contact springs for the electrical control of other clocks, and the observations for time determination now became the chief occupation of Gill's leisure evenings.

It was not long before he began to seek for an instrument which would give him a wider scope for astronomical work. He met with a second-hand silver-on-glass mirror of 12 inches aperture and 10 feet focal length. The task of mounting this equatorially gave him the first opportunity of displaying that skill in instrumental designing for which he afterwards became so famous, and the whole mounting was made from his working drawings. He made the driving clock with his own hands. Among the chief results obtained with this telescope were some excellent photographs of the moon. At that time Lord Lindsay (son of the Earl of Crawford) was planning to erect an observatory at Dun Echt, 13 miles from Aberdeen. Having seen these photographs, he visited Gill in order to see his instruments and methods of work. The acquaintance thus formed led to Gill's receiving early in 1872 an invitation to take charge of the Dun Echt Observatory that was about to be erected.

At this time Gill was actively at work all day, his father having retired, leaving the business in his hands; it was only his evenings that could be devoted to scientific pursuits. He had married in 1870 and was living in Aberdeen near his little observatory. To accept Lord Crawford's offer meant the giving up of a flourishing business and a heavy pecuniary sacrifice; but by now astronomy was claiming him irresistibly, and he made the choice without hesitation. The business that he now relinquished had never been congenial to him, but the time he had devoted to the clockmaker's art had not been wasted, for it is reasonable to believe that his natural mechanical genius was in no small measure fostered by this early training.

Gill's direction of the Dun Echt Observatory lasted from 1872 to 1876. It was his task to design and install the fine equipment that was rapidly acquired—for him a foretaste of the similar work he was afterwards to carry out at the Cape. But this period of his life is chiefly remembered not for observations made at Dun Echt but for an expedition to the island of Mauritius on the occasion of the transit of Venus, 1874. It was in preparation for the work at Mauritius that he first began to use the heliometer, an instrument with which his most celebrated researches were afterwards made. The 4-inch heliometer of the Dun Echt Observatory (afterwards purchased for the Cape) was made under Gill's superintendence by Repsold; and whilst it was in the course of construction he took the opportunity to visit Hamburg for the meeting of the Astronomische Gesellschaft in 1873. Besides attending this congress, Gill visited several of the continental observatories, and in this way made the acquaintance of the leading European astronomers and also obtained an insight into the organization of the large observatories.

The Mauritius expedition introduced him to two of the great problems which more especially he made his life's work—the determination of the solar parallax and the problems of geodetic measurements. Deferring, for the present, consideration of the scientific results of this expedition and of another expedition to Ascension Island in 1877, we pass on to the next great step in his career.

Early in 1879 David Gill was appointed by the admiralty to be Her Majesty's astronomer at the Cape of Good Hope, in succession to E. J. Stone. Before sailing for the Cape he made another tour of the European observatories, visiting Paris, Leiden, Groningen, Hamburg, Copenhagen, Helsingfors, and Poulkovo. Perhaps the most important fruit of these visits was his acquaintance with Dr. Auwers and Dr. Elkin, which led to much valuable cooperation between them.

On the 29th of May, 1879, he arrived at Cape Town and took up his duties at the observatory. The only instruments which he found in use were the Airy transit circle, a 7-inch equatorial, and a photo-heliograph. The observatory, founded in 1820, had fulfilled a useful duty by the regular work of meridian observation, the early Cape catalogues being a most valuable source for the positions of the southern stars. Its history had also been marked by one conspicuous achievement—Henderson's detection of the parallax of α Centauri, the first proof that the parallax of a fixed star could amount to a measurable quantity. Whilst the instruments and observations might be open to many criticisms, the work was for that period fairly efficient. But the standard of precision was being raised, and Gill's standard was the highest of his time. To his mechanical insight the faulty design and unsatisfactory repair of the old instruments was apparent, and he would not rest until the defects were remedied. He was no believer in the Airy type of transit circle, incapable of reversal, but it was many years before he could obtain an instrument according to his ideals. Meanwhile it was necessary to make the best of the existing telescope. The object glass was deteriorated, the micrometer screws were worn, and the whole instrument was in need of a thorough overhaul. He at once set to work upon it with his usual energy and so transformed it that for differential work it left little to be desired. The Airy transit circle performed useful service until 1901, when it was replaced by the new reversible transit circle. It is still used at times for special researches. The 7-inch equatorial was likewise submitted to a thorough overhaul.

The only immediate addition to the equipment was the 4-inch heliometer which was secured by Gill by private purchase. With this provision he was content to spend the first few years of his directorship until he should be in a stronger position to press his claims on the treasury. The principal additions made during the subsequent years that he spent at the Cape were the 6-inch Dallmeyer lens used for the photographic *Durchmusterung,* acquired in 1884; the 7-inch heliometer in 1887, the astrographic refractor erected in 1890, the Victoria telescope (a 24-inch photographic refractor with guiding telescope and spectroscopic equipment) in 1898, and the reversible transit circle in 1901. He was thus for his first researches limited to instruments of very moderate size and cost, and the success with which he afterwards obtained an adequate provision for the observatory was due both to the confidence inspired by his brilliant early work and to his pertinacity in pressing the needs of astronomy.

If from his many and varied services to astronomy we were asked to pick out the one in which he arrived at the most striking and complete success, there is little doubt that the answer would be his determination of the solar parallax. At the time when Gill, by accepting the charge of the Dun Echt Observatory, definitely embarked on an astronomical career a celestial event of the first magnitude was approaching—the transit of Venus of 1874. Great expectations were entertained that this would afford an improved determination of the solar parallax, a fundamental constant which was at that time involved in unsatisfactory uncertainty. Preparations were made by the leading observatories and astronomical societies on an unprecedentedly lavish scale, and expeditions were dispatched to different parts of the world. Lord Lindsay was co-operating in the work, and the Dun Echt expedition took up a station at Mauritius. Gill had already formed the opinion (which he afterwards conspicuously advocated) that there were other and better methods of finding the sun's parallax involving far less expense. He believed that the observations of the transit were of such a nature that the results would be inaccurate and capable of more than one interpretation; for too much depended on the arbitrary judgment of those who had to discuss the observations. He determined therefore to use the opportunity of the expedition to make trial of another method, namely, morning and evening observations of the minor planet Juno, which was then favorably situated. He considered that a single observer could by heliometer observations of a minor planet obtain results comparable in accuracy with those derived from all the transit of Venus observations together. Unfortunately, the heliometer was delayed in arrival at Mauritius, and the first half of the opposition of Juno was lost. Observations in the latter half were secured on 12 evenings and 11 mornings, but the parallax factor was then small. The result, $8.77'' \pm 0.041''$, though disappointing owing to the causes mentioned, gave a clear indication of the value of the method, and this pioneer effort served its purpose as a preliminary to a more ambitious attempt. From that time onwards Gill had a strong conviction of the value of the heliometer for work of the highest refinement, and he acquired his remarkable skill in using it. The transit of Venus was observed by the party, but Gill appears to have formed so low an opinion of the trustworthiness of the measures that he took little interest in their subsequent use.

In 1877 an exceptionally favorable approach of Mars to the earth offered a good opportunity for a renewed attack on the problem of the solar parallax. Gill, who had resigned his position at Dun Echt, began to prepare for an expedition to Ascension Island for this purpose. He fully expected that Mars would, owing to its large disk, prove to be a less satisfactory subject for heliometer observation than a minor planet, which is practically indistinguishable in appearance from the comparison stars; but the parallax factor was so much more favorable than for any minor planet then known that the opportunity was not to be missed. His anticipations proved correct. The value of the solar parallax now found showed a great improvement on any previous determination. The result, 8.78″, with a probable error of ±0.012″, marks a new stage of advance. But Gill by this work became more than ever convinced that the definitive determination of the constant must rest on minor planets.

For his third and final attempt, in 1888–9, the minor planets Iris, Victoria, and Sappho were chosen. Instead of measuring the diurnal parallax, he proceeded this time by the combination of observations made at widely separated stations. This involved a great scheme of co-operation in which many observatories and individuals took some part. The actual heliometer measures of the planets were made mainly by Gill and Finlay at the Cape, by Elkin and Hall at Yale, and by Peter at Leipzig. Of the many other co-operators Dr. Auwers in particular took a large and important share in the work. Accurate places of the comparison stars were needed, and meridian observations of these were made at a large number of places. In the case of Victoria this was supplemented by a heliometer triangulation in order to avoid the various systematic errors that affect meridian observations. The whole discussion, which forms two large volumes (vi and vii) of the Cape *Annals,* is a remarkable record of a thorough and laborious undertaking. It was particularly the kind of investigation to bring out the characteristic qualities of Gill's genius. To plan the work required that perfect understanding of instruments and observations in which he was unrivaled; and to carry it through in its completeness required a dogged persistence which overcame all obstacles, an enthusiasm which shirked nothing, and a power of leadership which inspired all his helpers. There have been other great and successful co-operative schemes since then, but we miss in them the unity of execution which the immense driving force of Gill's leadership supplied.

The final result gave for the solar parallax 8.804″ ± 0.0046″, and in due course this value was adopted (as 8.80″) in the Ephemerides. Insofar as a single investigation can be held to settle so important a constant, the solar parallax was now known with all the accuracy required for the calculations in which it plays a part. Subsequent researches have all tended to confirm Gill's value; the discordant results found by other methods are disappearing, whilst the superiority of the minor planet method has become more and more manifest. In the Eros campaign of 1900–1901 the

Cape Observatory took no share, owing to the northern declination of the planet, but Gill followed the investigation with keen interest and took part in the arrangement of the work. The results from Eros, whilst diminishing the range of uncertainty so far as accidental errors are concerned, have not appreciably altered the value. Shortly before leaving the Cape, Gill initiated a determination of the same constant by means of spectroscopic observations, the line-of-sight velocity of the earth relative to a star being measured at opposite seasons, so that the earth's orbital velocity is found. These observations are now yielding excellent results.

We have seen that his measurements during the observations of Juno at Mauritius convinced Gill of the value of the heliometer as an instrument of research. In his hands it was capable of remarkable accuracy. The instrument is peculiarly difficult to use, and the number of those who observe with it has always been few. At the time when the 4-inch instrument was constructed for him the heliometer was usually regarded in England as an exercise for the textbook or the examination question. Even now that its possibilities have been demonstrated it has not been taken up widely. At the present day it is natural to prefer photographic methods, which give equal or perhaps slightly superior accuracy, whilst making far less demands on the observer. Perhaps, too, the prospect for future progress and development is more obvious in the case of photographic than of heliometer observations. Certainly Gill's success with the heliometer never blinded him to the advantages of the long-focus refractor, and he fully shared the modern tendency to depend more and more on photography. But there is one advantage of the heliometer over the photographic refractor, both for solar and stellar parallaxes, on which Gill strongly insisted—the heliometer measures are independent of the color of the object under observation. He maintained and confirmed by experimental observations that the skilled observer, in making coincidences of the images, matches the colors and not the most intense points of the minute spectrum caused by atmospheric dispersion. This is a refinement obviously impossible in photography, and, for example, it is well known that the doubtful effect of atmospheric dispersion leaves a little uncertainty in the solar parallax deduced from the photographic observations of Eros.

So early as 1872 Gill had begun to plan a series of determinations of stellar parallax with a micrometer attached to his reflector —an investigation which was interrupted by his removal to Dun Echt. On his appointment to the Cape he began to apply his 4-inch heliometer to this work. In this he was joined by Elkin, as a volunteer observer, and they set to work on a program of 9 stars, including Sirius, Canopus, α and β Centauri, with some stars of exceptionally large proper motion. The most important outcome of this work was the parallax of α Centauri, 0.75″, with a probable error of only a hundredth of a second of arc. The desirability of a larger instrument with some alterations of design soon became apparent, and in 1887 a 7-inch heliometer was constructed at a cost of £2,200. With this Gill and Finlay, and afterwards De Sitter, measured 17 stars, including 12 of the brightest in the southern sky, in most cases with a probable error as low as ±0.01″. These results were of great interest, establishing the remoteness and intense luminosity of some of the brightest stars, such as Canopus and Rigel. Whenever they have been put to the test Gill's values have always been confirmed. Spurious parallaxes are a great bane in stellar investigation, and at least until recently few observers have escaped an occasional bad error; but Gill's parallaxes can always be relied on. His general accuracy has been equaled, perhaps a little surpassed, by some modern photographic determinations; but when we compare the sizes of the instruments —the 40-inch telescope at Yerkes or the 26-inch at Greenwich with his 7-inch heliometer—we must marvel at the precision he could obtain. The following table (given by him) will show the comparative accuracy of his work. It gives the probable error of the measured position of a parallax star:

Cambridge refractor (19.3 feet focus), 4 exposures .... ±0.048″
Yerkes refractor (63 feet focus), 3 exposures .... ±0.026″
Heliometer, one complete observation, i. e., 16 pointings ... ±0.036″

Another application of the heliometer was made in his determination of the elements of Jupiter's satellites and of the mass of Jupiter. The longitudes of the satellites can be found very accurately from the usual observations of eclipses, but the latitudes are more difficult to derive. Heliometer measures had been made before by Bessel and others, but in all cases the satellite had been referred to the limb or center of the disk. Gill's method was to measure the distances and position angles of the satellites relative to one another; for, as he had found in his observations of Mars, the best results are possible only when the objects to be measured have no sensible disks. The observations were carried out in 1891. On each night the measures were reduced to a constant scale by referring them to the distance between two standard stars. The absolute distance between the standards was determined by a lengthy comparison with the distances of stars employed in the

Victoria triangulation, whose definitive coordinates had been found with an accuracy quite exceptional. These observations were the beginning of a very thorough investigation of the whole problem; but the further observations and the discussion of the results were placed by Gill in the hands of younger men, who could give a more undivided attention to the problem. The nature of the investigation required a repetition of the observations at a subsequent date. This was made by the late Bryan Cookson at the Cape in 1901–2. Photographic observations were made concurrently in 1891 and 1902 and again in 1903–4. The whole material thus collected formed an exceedingly valuable source for improving the accuracy of our knowledge of Jupiter's system. The detailed discussion was taken up by De Sitter at Gill's suggestion; he reduced Gill's own observations during a visit to the Cape (1897–99) and worked out the elements and masses derivable from the whole work. It is evident that Gill attached the greatest importance to this work, and though the later stages were in the charge of other workers he followed its progress to the minutest detail. His stimulating influence carried it to a successful conclusion, if conclusion it can be called, for in his summary of the work in the *History of the Cape Observatory* he urges the need for an extended program of future work and appeals to astronomers to carry it out. His last scientific effort, on the day the fatal illness began, was to write an introduction to De Sitter's discussion.

Gill's detection of the existence of magnitude equation in observations of right ascension with the meridian circle was an incidental result of his heliometer observations at Ascension. This definitive discovery of a systematic personality, by which faint stars are regularly observed too late relatively to bright stars, has been of fundamental importance in meridian work. He took great interest in the problem of eliminating this peculiarly difficult source of error by screens and other methods, and it was a source of great satisfaction to him that the traveling-wire micrometer seems to have successfully accomplished this object.

Reference has already been made to Gill's early photographs of the moon. These were of course not by any means the first lunar photographs, but in 1882 Gill made a notable advance in celestial photography by successfully photographing the great comet of that year. Several pictures of this comet had already been obtained with fixed camera, and the knowledge thus obtained that the light was sufficiently intense encouraged Gill to attempt to obtain images of greater scientific value by guiding the camera in the modern way. He was assisted by Allis, a local photographer, from whom he borrowed a doublet of 2½ inches aperture and 11 inches focal length. He mounted this doublet on the 6-inch equatorial, which he used as guiding telescope. Excellent representations of the comet were obtained with exposures of from 30 minutes upwards; but, a fact of still greater importance, it was found that notwithstanding the insignificant size of the apparatus a great many stars were shown whose images were well defined over a large field. This suggested the practicability of using similar but more powerful instruments for mapping the sky and for other astronomical purposes to which photography is now applied.

We now know how this result has revolutionized the methods of observational work. Gill led the way in turning the new possibilities to a practical account. The immediate outcome was the Cape Photographic *Durchmusterung,* started in 1885. The survey covers the region of the sky from the South Pole to Dec. − 18°, and is complete so far as photographic magnitude 9$^{m.}$2 (on the C.P.D. scale). A rapid rectilinear Dallmeyer lens of 6 inches aperture and 54 inches focal length was used for the photography. The work was completed in 1890. Very soon after the start Professor Kapteyn's* offer was received to devote himself for some years to the arduous labor of the measurement and reduction of the plates, a work for which the Cape Observatory was unable to provide. This is a further instance of Gill's success in attracting for his helpers the men best capable of carrying out the work desired. The association of Gill and Kapteyn, which began now, has proved a most powerful influence in the advance of stellar investigation, and, to quote Gill's own words, "probably the most valuable result of the C.P.D. to science is the fact that it first directed Kapteyn's mind to the study of the problems of cosmical astronomy and thus led him to the brilliant researches and discoveries with which his name is now and ever will be associated."

We can only mention briefly the other photographic work with which Gill was associated. When the history of the inception of the International Astrographic Chart and Catalogue comes to be written it will probably be found that much was due to Gill's initiative. It may be difficult to trace whence the first suggestion arose, but at least we know that he was in its councils from the very beginning and gave his whole-hearted support to the great enterprise. His measuring machine for photographic plates, designed by him and constructed by Repsold, has been very gen-

* See A. Van Maanen, "Jacobus Cornelius Kapteyn," *A.R.,* 1923, pp. 555–562; J. C. Kapteyn, "Researches in the Structure of the Universe," *A.R.,* 1908, pp. 301–319.

erally copied in its main features. Another work of great value which owes much to his counsel and assistance is the chart of the sky made by the late J. Franklin-Adams. Mr. Franklin-Adams, an enthusiastic amateur, who had only recently applied himself to astronomy, came to the Cape at an early stage of the work to photograph the Southern Hemisphere. It needs little imagination to realize how Gill, by his experienced advice and his insistence on a high standard of quality, helped to make of this the valuable work that it became.

In 1897 the necessary expenditure for a new reversible transit circle at the Cape was at length sanctioned. Since his first appointment Gill had lost no opportunity of urging the need for an instrument which should be free from the defects which were obvious in the old design. For the determination of fundamental right ascensions and declinations the chief requirements are an extreme stability of the instrument, means of eliminating or determining the flexures of the various parts, and of guarding against the effects of temperature changes both in the instrument and in the surrounding air. The problem of equalizing the distribution of temperature was most carefully thought out. The piers were made hollow, covered externally with nonconducting material, and filled with water. The telescope tube was surrounded by a double envelope of copper to minimize the effects of local heating, and the graduated circles were similarly protected by copper disks. Of special interest was Gill's method of obtaining fixed meridian marks for maintaining the azimuth of the transit circle. Four deep pits, reaching down to the unweathered rock, were constructed underneath the long-focus collimating lenses and the marks respectively, and a simple method was devised by which the apparatus above ground could be readily set in a definite position with respect to the vertical collimating lines of object glasses fixed in the rock below. So perfect is the stability of these marks that it has been found possible to measure the movement of the North Pole over the earth's surface by the apparent change of azimuth. It is certain that the device will be widely imitated in future.

On his appointment as H. M. Astronomer in 1879, Gill began to consider the question of a geodetic survey of South Africa. His previous experience of such work had been obtained on the occasion of his visit to Mauritius. In connection with the transit of Venus expeditions of 1874 numerous longitude determinations were made by the various parties of observers, and indeed these geodetic results proved to be the most important outcome of the whole work. Gill's share was a chain of telegraphic longitudes connecting Berlin with Malta, Alexandria, Suez, and Aden. Before returning home he proceeded to Egypt in response to an invitation from General Stone, chief of the military staff of the Khedive, in order to measure a base line for the proposed survey of the country. This work made slow progress at first, as Gill had no trained assistance on which he could rely; but in the end, with the help of Professor Watson, he carried it through satisfactorily. No permanent outcome of this work has survived, for the defining marks of the base line were afterwards destroyed by Arabs.

It would serve little purpose here to enter into the details of the work which Gill succeeded in accomplishing in South Africa. Besides the more practical uses of an accurate survey, Gill kept ever in view the object of the ultimate measurement of the great arc of the meridian of 105° from the North Cape to Cape Agulhas—the longest measurable arc of the meridian in the world. Colonial and foreign governments, the chartered company, and the scientific societies were all in turn pressed and persuaded. Difficulties of funds, of personnel, of war, interposed obstacles, but there was no resisting Gill. His indomitable persistence always won in the end. Worried ministers would ultimately come to terms with their genial persecutor. Still active in this great cause after retirement from the Cape, he had the satisfaction of getting the last link of the South African chain filled in. The great measured arc along the meridian of 30° E. now extends from Cape Agulhas to within a short distance of Lake Tanganyika, near the boundary of British territory, a length of 24°, at which point it awaits the other chain of triangulation that will some day be pushed down from Egypt.

We have now passed in review the most important of Gill's scientific investigations. To these may be added some miscellaneous contributions, of which we cannot here give any detail. A triangulation by heliometer of the southern circumpolar stars was made under his direction in 1897–1900, but he was not very satisfied with the consistency of the observations. A series of meridian observations of the lunar crater Mösting A, organized by him jointly with Sir William Christie at Greenwich, led to a good determination of the lunar parallax and figure of the earth. The arrangements for a catalogue of zodiacal stars were placed in his hands by the International Astrographic Congress.

In October 1906 Sir David Gill left the Cape. Owing to ill health he had anticipated by rather more than a year the date of compulsory retirement. But there were no signs of failing vigor when he returned to England; on the contrary, he plunged into a strenuous life of scientific activity in London. He became president and afterwards foreign secretary of the Royal Astronomical Society, president of the British Association at Leicester, and on the councils of the Royal and Royal Geographical Societies as *président d'honneur* of the committee of the astrographic chart, and in numerous other duties he was a center of energy and initiative. For several years he worked at his *History and Description of the Cape Observatory,* published in 1913. Amid our sorrow at his death, when still in the full vigor of scientific activity, there is cause for thankfulness that he was spared to complete and to see the reception of this retrospect of the work to which he had devoted his life.

To this record of strenuous work in the cause of science must be added some allusion to the other side of his life. There was an ideal background to his public life in the quiet home, always characteristically Scotch wherever he lived. In Lady Gill he found a sympathizer in all his sacrifices and devotion to astronomy. She did not become an astronomer, but she shared all his desires, and it was ever her care to aid him to fulfill his great calling. She was of Scotch birth, like himself, and their home was bright with an indescribable spirit of open-heartedness which seemed to come from his loved Highlands.

In December 1913 he was seized with double pneumonia, and from the first the gravity of the illness was realized. His magnificent constitution carried him bravely through a long fight with the disease, but heart failure supervened, and on the morning of January 24 he died peacefully. There is no need to enumerate the honors conferred on him by the British, French, and German Governments, and by numerous academies and universities. Official recognition was generously bestowed; even richer was the tribute of admiration and affection of his world-wide circle of friends.

Henry Augustus Rowland *

1848–1901

———◆———

THOMAS CORWIN MENDENHALL †

IN REVIEWING the scientific work of Professor Rowland one is most impressed by its originality. In quantity, as measured by printed page or catalogue of titles, it has been exceeded by many of his contemporaries; in quality it is equaled by that of only a very, very small group. The entire collection of his important papers does not exceed 30 or 40 in number, and his unimportant papers were few. When at the unprecedentedly early age of 33 years he was elected to membership in the National Academy of Sciences, the list of his published contributions to science did not contain over a dozen titles, but any one of not less than a half-dozen of these, including what may properly be called his very first original investigation, was of such quality as fully to entitle him to the distinction then conferred.

Fortunately for him, and for science as well, he lived during a period of almost unparalleled intellectual activity, and his work was done during the last quarter of that century to which we shall long turn with admiration and wonder. During these twenty-five years the number of industrious cultivators of his own favorite field increased enormously, due in large measure to the stimulating effect of his own enthusiasm, and while there was only here and there one possessed of the divine afflatus of true genius, there were many ready to labor most assiduously in fostering the growth, development, and final fruition of germs which genius stopped only to plant. A proper estimate of the magnitude and extent of Rowland's work would require therefore a careful examination, analytical and historical, of the entire mass of con-

* *A.R.*, 1901, pp. 739–753. From *Johns Hopkins University Circulars,* vol. 21, December, 1901.
† American physicist and educator (1841–1924).

tributions to physical science during the past twenty-five years, many of his own being fundamental in character and far-reaching in their influence upon the trend of thought in theory and in practice. But it was quality not quantity that he himself most esteemed in any performance; it was quality that always commanded his admiration or excited him to keenest criticism. No one recognized more quickly than he a real gem, however minute or fragmentary it might be, and by quality rather than by quantity we prefer to judge his work today, as he would himself have chosen.

Rowland's first contribution to the literature of science took the form of a letter to the *Scientific American,* written in the early autumn of 1865, when he was not yet 17 years old. Much to his surprise this letter was printed, for he says of it, "I wrote it as a kind of joke and did not expect them to publish it." Neither its humor nor its sense, in which it was not lacking, seems to have been appreciated by the editor, for by the admission of certain typographical errors he practically destroyed both. The embryo physicist got nothing but a little quiet amusement out of this, but in a letter of that day he declares his intention of sometime writing a sensible article for the journal that so unexpectedly printed what he meant to be otherwise. This resolution he seems not to have forgotten, for nearly six years later there appeared in its columns what was, as far as is known, his second printed paper and his first serious public discussion of a scientific question. It was a keen criticism of an invention which necessarily involved the idea of perpetual motion, in direct conflict with the great law of the conservation of energy which Rowland had already grasped. It was, as might be expected, thoroughly well done and received not a little complimentary notice in other journals. This was in 1871, the year following that in which he was graduated as a civil engineer from the Rensselaer Polytechnic Institute, and the article was written while in the field at work on a preliminary railroad survey. A year later, having returned to the Institute as instructor in physics, he published in the *Journal of the Franklin Institute* an article entitled "Illustrations of Resonances and Actions of a Similar Nature," in which he described and discussed various examples of resonance or "sympathetic" vibration. This paper, in a way, marks his admission to the ranks of professional students of science and may be properly considered as his first formal contribution to scientific literature. His last was an exhaustive article on spectroscopy, a subject of which he, above all others, was master, prepared for a new edition of the *Encyclopædia Britannica,* not yet published. Early in 1873 the *American Journal of Science* printed a brief note by Rowland on the spectrum of the aurora, sent in response to a kindly and always appreciated letter from Professor George F. Barker, one of the editors of that journal. It is interesting as marking the beginning of his optical work. For a year, or perhaps for several years previous to this time, however, he had been busily engaged on what proved to be in its influence upon his future career the most important work of his life. To climb the ladder of reputation and success by simple, easy steps might have contented Rowland, but it would have been quite out of harmony with his bold spirit, his extraordinary power of analysis, and his quick recognition of the relation of things. By the aid of apparatus entirely of his own construction and by methods of his own devising, he had made an investigation both theoretical and experimental of the magnetic permeability and the maximum magnetization of iron, steel, and nickel, a subject in which he had been interested in his boyhood. On June 9, 1873, in a letter to his sister, he says: "I have just sent off the results of my experiments to the publisher and expect considerable from it; not, however, filthy lucre, but good, substantial reputation." What he did get from it at first was only disappointment and discouragement. It was more than once rejected because it was not understood, and finally he ventured to send it to Clerk Maxwell in England, by whose keen insight and profound knowledge of the subject it was instantly recognized and appraised at its full value. Regretting that the temporary suspension of meetings made it impossible for him to present the paper at once to the Royal Society, Maxwell said he would do the next best thing, which was to send it to the *Philosophical Magazine* for immediate publication, and in that journal it appeared in August, 1873, Maxwell himself having corrected the proofs to avoid delay. The importance of the paper was promptly recognized by European physicists, and abroad, if not at home, Rowland at once took high rank as an investigator.

In this research he unquestionably anticipated all others in the discovery and announcement of the beautifully simple law of the magnetic circuit, the magnetic analogue of Ohm's law, and thus laid the foundation for the accurate measurement and study of magnetic permeability, the importance of which, both in theory and practice during recent years, it is difficult to overestimate. It has always seemed to me that when consideration is given to his age, his training, and the conditions under which his work was done, this early paper gives a better measure of Rowland's genius than almost any performance of his riper years. During the next year or two he continued to work along the same lines in Troy, publishing not many, but occasional, additions to and developments of his first magnetic research. There was also a paper in which he discussed Kohlrausch's determination of the absolute value of the Siemens unit of electrical resistance, foreshadowing the important part which he was to play in later years in the final establishment of standards for electrical measurement.

In 1875, having been appointed to the professorship of physics in the Johns Hopkins University, the faculty of which was just then being organized, he visited Europe, spending the better part of a year in the various centers of scientific activity, including several months at Berlin in the laboratory of the greatest Continental physicist of his time, Von Helmholtz. While there he made a very important investigation of the magnetic effect of moving electrostatic charges, a question of first rank in theoretical interest and significance. His manner of planning and executing this research made a marked impression upon the distinguished director of the laboratory in which it was done and, indeed, upon all who had any relations with Rowland during its progress. He found what Von Helmholtz himself had sought for in vain, and when the investigation was finished in a time which seemed incredibly short to his more deliberate and painstaking associates, the director not only paid it the compliment of an immediate presentation to the Berlin Academy, but voluntarily met all expenses connected with its execution.

The publication of this research added much to Rowland's rapidly growing reputation, and because of that fact, as well as on account of its intrinsic value, it is important to note that his conclusions have been held in question, with varying degrees of confidence, from the day of their announcement to the present. The experiment is one of great difficulty, and the effect to be looked for is very small and therefore likely to be lost among unrecognized instrumental and observational errors. It was characteristic of Rowland's genius that with comparatively crude apparatus he got at the truth of the thing in the very start. Others who have attempted to repeat his work have not been uniformly successful, some of them obtaining a wholly negative result, even when using apparatus apparently more complete and effective than that first employed by Rowland. Such was the experience of Lecher in 1884, but in 1888 Röntgen confirmed Rowland's experiments, detecting the existence of the alleged effect. The result seeming to be in doubt, Rowland himself, assisted by Hutchinson, in 1889 took it up again, using essentially his original method, but employing more elaborate and sensitive apparatus. They not only confirmed the early experiments, but were able to show that the results were in tolerably close agreement with computed values. The repetition of the experiment by Himstedt in the same year resulted in the same way, but in 1897 the genuineness of the phenomenon was again called in question by a series of experiments made at the suggestion of Lippmann, who had proposed a study of the reciprocal of the Rowland effect, according to which variations of a magnetic field should produce a movement of an electrostatically charged body. This investigation, carried out by Crémieu, gave an absolutely negative result, and because the method was entirely different from that employed by Rowland and therefore unlikely to be subject to the same systematic errors, it naturally had much weight with those who doubted his original conclusions. Realizing the necessity for additional evidence in corroboration of his views, in the fall of the year 1900 the problem was again attacked in his own laboratory, and he had the satisfaction, only a short time before his death, of seeing a complete confirmation of the results he had announced a quarter of a century earlier, concerning which, however, there had never been the slightest doubt in his own mind. It is a further satisfaction to his friends to know that a very recent investigation at the Jefferson Physical Laboratory of Harvard University, in which Rowland's methods were modified so as to meet effectively the objections made by his critics, has resulted in a complete verification of his conclusions.

On his return from Europe in 1876 his time was much occupied with the beginning of the active duties of his professorship, and especially in putting in order the equipment of the laboratory over which he was to preside, much of which he had ordered while in Europe. In its arrangement a great many of his friends thought undue prominence was given to the workshop, its machinery, tools, and especially the men who were to be employed in it. He planned wisely, however, for he meant to see to it that much, perhaps most, of the work under his direction should be in the nature of original investigation, for the successful execution of which a well-manned and equipped workshop is worth more than a storehouse of apparatus already designed and used by others.

He shortly found leisure, however, to plan an elaborate research upon the mechanical equivalent of heat, and to design and supervise the construction of the necessary apparatus for a determination of the numerical value of this most important physical constant, which he determined should be exhaustive in character and, for some time to come at least, definitive. While this work lacked the elements of originality and boldness of conception by which many of his principal researches are characterized, it was none the less important. While doing over again what others had done before him, he meant to do it, and did do it, on a scale and in a way not before attempted. It was one of the *great* constants of nature, and, besides, the experiment was one surrounded by difficulties so many and so great that few possessed the courage to undertake it with the deliberate expectation of greatly excelling anything before accomplished. These things made it attractive to Rowland.

The overthrow of the materialistic theory of heat, accompanied as it was by the experimental proof of its real nature, namely, that it is essentially molecular energy, laid the foundation for one of those two great generalizations in science which will ever constitute the glory of the nineteenth century. The mechanical equivalent of heat, the number of units of work necessary to raise 1 pound of water 1° in temperature, has with much reason been called the golden number of that century. Its determination was begun by an American, Count Rumford, and finished by Rowland nearly a hundred years later. In principle the method of Rowland was essentially that of Rumford. The first determination was, as we now know, in error by nearly 40 per cent; the last is probably accurate within a small fraction of 1 per cent. Rumford began the work in the ordnance foundry of the Elector of Bavaria at Munich, converting mechanical energy into heat by means of a blunt boring tool in a cannon surrounded by a definite quantity of water, the rise in temperature of which could be measured. Rowland finished it in an establishment founded for and dedicated to the increase and diffusion of knowledge aided by all the resources and refinements in measurement which a hundred years of exact science had made possible. As the mechanical theory of heat was the germ out of which grew the principle of the conservation of energy, an exact determination of the relation of work and heat was necessary to a rigorous proof of that principle, and Joule of Manchester, to whom belongs more of the credit for this proof than to any other one man, or perhaps to all others put together, experimented on the mechanical equivalent of heat for more than forty years. He employed various methods, finally recurring to the early method of heating water by friction, improving on Rumford's device by creating friction in the water itself. Joule's last experiments were made in 1878, and most of Rowland's work was done in the year following. It excelled that of Joule, not only in the magnitude of the quantities to be observed, but especially in the greater attention given to the matter of thermometry. In common with Joule and other previous investigators, he made use of mercury thermometers, but this was only for convenience, and they were constantly compared with an air thermometer, the results being finally reduced to the absolute scale. By experimenting with water at different initial temperatures he obtained slightly different values for the mechanical equivalent of heat, thus establishing beyond question the variability of the specific heat of water. Indeed, so carefully and accurately was the experiment worked out that he was able to draw the variation curve and to show the existence of a minimum value at 30° C.

This elaborate and painstaking research, which is now classical, was everywhere awarded high praise. It was published in full by the American Academy of Arts and Sciences with the aid of a fund originally established by Count Rumford, and in 1881 it was crowned as a prize essay by the Venetian Institute. Its conclusions have stood the test of twenty years of comparison and criticism.

In the meantime Rowland's interest had been drawn, largely perhaps through his association with his then colleague, Professor Hastings, toward the study of light. He was an early and able exponent of Maxwell's magnetic theory, and he published important theoretical discussions of electro-magnetic action. Recognizing the paramount importance of the spectrum as a key to the solution of problems in ether physics, he set about improving the methods by which it was produced and studied, and was thus led into what will probably always be regarded as his highest scientific achievement.

At that time the almost universally prevailing method of studying the spectrum was by means of a prism or a train of prisms. But the prismatic spectrum is abnormal, depending for its character largely upon the material made use of. The normal spectrum as produced by a grating of fine wires or a close ruling of fine lines on a plane reflecting or transparent surface had been known for nearly a hundred years, and the colors produced by scratches on polished surfaces were noted by Robert Boyle more than two hundred years ago. Thomas Young had correctly explained the phenomenon according to the undulatory theory of light, and gratings of fine wire, and later of rulings on glass, were used by Fraunhofer, who made the first great study of the dark lines of the solar spectrum. Imperfect as these gratings were, Fraunhofer succeeded in making with them some remarkably good measures of the length of light waves, and it was everywhere admitted that for the most precise spectrum measurements they were indispensable. In their construction, however, there were certain mechanical difficulties which seemed for a time to be insuperable. There was no special trouble in ruling lines as close together as need be; indeed, Nobert, who was long the most successful maker of ruled gratings, had succeeded in putting as many as 100,000 in the space of a single inch. The real difficulty was in the lack of uniformity of spacing, and on uniformity depended the perfection and purity of the spectrum produced. Nobert jealously guarded his machine and method of ruling gratings as a trade secret, a precaution hardly worth taking, for before many years the best gratings in the world were made in the United States.

More than thirty years ago an amateur astronomer in New York City, a lawyer by profession, Lewis M. Rutherford, became interested in the subject and built a ruling engine of his own design. In this machine the motion of the plate on which the lines were ruled was produced at first by a somewhat complicated set of levers, for which a carefully made screw was afterwards substituted. Aided by the skill and patience of his mechanician, Chapman, Rutherford continued to improve the construction of his machine until he was able to produce gratings on glass and on speculum metal far superior to any made in Europe. The best of them, however, were still faulty in respect to uniformity of spacing, and it was impossible to cover a space exceeding two or three square inches in a satisfactory manner. When Rowland took up the problem, he saw, as indeed others had seen before him, that the dominating element of a ruling machine was the screw by means of which the plate or cutting tool was moved along. The ruled grating would repeat all of the irregularities of this screw and would be good or bad just as these were few or many. The problem was, then, to make a screw which would be practically free from periodic and other errors, and upon this problem a vast amount of thought and experiment had already been expended.

Rowland's solution of it was characteristic of his genius; there were no easy advances through a series of experiments in which success and failure mingled in varying proportions; "fire and fall back" was an order which he neither gave nor obeyed, capture by storm being more to his mind. He was by nature a mechanician of the highest type, and he was not long in devising a method for removing the irregularities of a screw, which astonished everybody by its simplicity and by the all but absolute perfection of its results. Indeed, the very first screw made by this process ranks today as the most perfect in the world. But such an engine as this might only be worked up to its highest efficiency under the most favorable physical conditions, and in its installation and use the most careful attention was given to the elimination of errors due to variation of temperature, earth tremors, and other disturbances. Not content, however, with perfecting the machinery by which gratings were ruled, Rowland proceeded to improve the form of the grating itself, making the capital discovery of the concave grating, by means of which a large part of the complex and otherwise troublesome optical accessories to the diffraction spectroscope might be dispensed with. Calling to his aid the wonderful skill of Brashear in making and polishing plane and concave surfaces, as well as the ingenuity and patience of Schneider, for so many years his intelligent and loyal assistant at the lathe and workbench, he began the manufacture and distribution, all too slowly for the anxious demands of the scientific world, of those beautifully simple instruments of precision which have contributed so much to the advance of physical science during the past twenty years.

While willing and anxious to give the widest possible distribution to these gratings, thus giving everywhere a new impetus to optical research, Rowland meant that the principal spoils of the victory should be his, and to this end he constructed a diffraction spectrometer of extraordinary dimensions and began his classical researches on the solar spectrum. Finding photography to be the best means of reproducing the delicate spectral lines shown by the concave grating, he became at once an ardent student and shortly a master of that art. The outcome of this was that wonderful "Photographic Map of the Normal Solar Spectrum," prepared by the use of concave gratings 6 inches in diameter and 21½ feet radius, which is recognized as a standard everywhere in the world. As a natural supplement to this he directed an elaborate investigation of absolute wave lengths, undertaking to give finally the wave lengths of not only every line of the solar spectrum, but also of the bright lines of the principal elements, and a large part of this monumental task is already completed, mostly by Rowland's pupils and in his laboratory. Time will not allow further expositions of the important consequences of his invention of the ruling engine and the concave grating.

Indeed, the limitations to which I must submit compel the omission of even brief mention of many interesting and valuable investigations relating to other subjects begun and finished during these years of activity in optical research, many of them by Rowland himself and many of them by his pupils, working out his suggestions and constantly stimulated by his enthusiasm. A list of titles of papers emanating from the physical laboratory of the Johns Hopkins University during this period would show somewhat of the great intellectual fertility which its director inspired, and would show especially his continued interest in magnetism and electricity, leading to his important investigations relating to electric units and to his appointment as one of the United States delegates at important international conventions for the better determination and definition of these units. In 1883 a committee appointed by the Electrical Congress of 1881, of which Rowland was a member, adopted 106 centimeters as the length of the mercury column equivalent to the absolute ohm, but this was done against his protest, for his own measurements showed that this was too small by about three-tenths of 1 per cent. His judgment was confirmed by the chamber of delegates of the International Congress of 1893, of which Rowland was himself president, and by which definitive values were given to a system of international units.

Rowland's interest in applied science cannot be passed over, for it was constantly showing itself, often perhaps unbidden, an unconscious bursting forth of that strong engineering instinct which was born in him, to which he often referred in familiar discourse, and which would unquestionably have brought him great success and distinction had he allowed it to direct the course of his life. Although everywhere looked upon as one of the foremost exponents of pure science, his ability as an engineer received frequent recognition in his appointment as expert and counsel in some of the most important engineering operations in the latter part of the century. He was an inventor and might easily have taken first rank as such had he chosen to devote himself to that sort of work. During the last few years of his life he was much occupied with the study of alternating electric currents and their application to a system of rapid telegraphy of his own invention. A year ago his system received the award of a *grand prix* at the Paris Exposition, and only a few weeks after his death the daily papers published cablegrams from Berlin announcing its complete success as tested between Berlin and Hamburg, and also the intention of the German postal department to make extensive use of it.

But behind Rowland, the profound scholar and original investigator, the engineer, mechanician, and inventor, was Rowland the man, and any estimate of his influence in promoting the interests of physical science during the last quarter of the nineteenth century would be quite inadequate if not made from that point of view. Born at Honesdale, Pennsylvania, on November 27, 1848, he had the misfortune, at the age of 11 years, to lose his father by death. This loss was made good, as far as it is possible to do so, by the loving care of mother and sisters during the years of his boyhood and youthful manhood. From his father he inherited his love for scientific study, which from the very first seems to have dominated all of his aspirations, directing and controlling most of his thoughts. His father, grandfather, and great-grandfather were all clergymen and graduates of Yale College. His father, who is described as one "interested in chemistry and natural philosophy, a lover of nature and a successful trout fisherman," had felt, in his early youth, some of the desires and ambitions that afterwards determined the career of his distinguished son but yielding no doubt to the influence of family tradition and desire, he followed the lead of his ancestors. It is not unlikely, and it would not have been unreasonable, that similar hopes were entertained in regard to the future of young Henry, and his preparatory school work was arranged with this in view. Before being sent away from home, however, he had quite given himself up to chemical experiments, glass blowing, and other similar occupations, and the members of his family were often summoned by the enthusiastic boy to listen to lectures which were fully illustrated by experiments, not always free from prospective danger. His spare change was invested in copper wire and the like, and his first five-dollar bill brought him, to his infinite delight, a small galvanic battery. The sheets of the *New York Observer,* a treasured family newspaper, he converted into a huge hot-air balloon, which, to the astonishment of his family and friends, made a brilliant ascent and flight, coming to rest at last and in flames, on the roof of a neighboring house and resulting in the calling out of the entire fire department of the town. When urged by his boy friends to hide himself from the rather threatening consequences of his first experiment in aeronautics, he courageously marched himself to the place where his balloon had fallen saying, "No, I will go and see what damage I have done."

When a little more than 16 years old, in the spring of 1865, he was sent to Phillips Academy at Andover to be fitted for entering the academic course at Yale. His time there was given entirely to the study of Latin and Greek, and he was in every way out of harmony with his environment. He seems to have quickly and thoroughly appreciated this fact, and his very first letter from Andover is a cry for relief. "Oh, take me home," is the boyish scrawl covering the last page of that letter, on another of which he says, "It is simply horrible; I can never get on here." It was not that he could not learn Latin and Greek if he was so minded, but that he had long ago become wholly absorbed in the love of nature and in the study of nature's laws, and the whole situation was to his ambitious spirit most artificial and irksome. Time did not soften his feelings or lessen his desire to escape from such uncongenial surroundings, and at his own request Dr. Farrand, principal of the Academy at Newark, New Jersey, to which city the family had recently moved, was consulted as to what ought to be done. Fortunately for everybody, his advice was that the boy ought to be allowed to follow his bent, and at his own suggestion he was sent in the autumn of that year to the Rensselaer Polytechnic Institute at Troy, where he remained five years, and from which he was graduated as a civil engineer in 1870.

It is unnecessary to say that this change was joyfully welcomed by young Rowland. At Andover the only opportunity that had offered for the exercise of his skill as a mechanic was in the construction of a somewhat complicated device by means of which he outwitted some of his schoolmates in an early attempt to haze him, and in this he took no little pride. At Troy he gave loose rein to his ardent desires, and his career in science may almost be said to begin with his entrance upon his work there and before he was 17 years old.

He made immediate use of the opportunities afforded in Troy and its neighborhood for the examination of machinery and manufacturing processes, and one of his earliest letters to his friends contained a clear and detailed description of the operation of making railroad iron, the rolls, shears, saws, and other special machines being represented in uncommonly well-executed pen drawings. One can easily see in this letter a full confirmation of a statement that he occasionally made later in life, namely, that he had never seen a machine, however complicated it might be, whose working he could not at once comprehend. In another letter written within a few weeks of his arrival in Troy he shows in a remarkable way his power of going to the root of things, which even at that early age was sufficiently in evidence to mark him for future distinction as a natural philosopher. On the river he saw two boats equipped with steam pumps, engaged in trying to raise a half-sunken canal boat by pumping the water out of it. He described engines, pumps, etc., in much detail, and adds, "But there was one thing that I did not like about it; they had the end of their discharge pipe about 10 feet above the water, so that they had to overcome a pressure of about 5 pounds to the square inch to raise the water so high, and yet they let it go after they got it there, whereas if they had attached a pipe to the end of the discharge pipe and let it hang down into the water, the pressure of water on that pipe would just have balanced the 5 pounds to the square inch in the other, so that they could have used larger pumps with the same engines and thus have got more water out in a given time."

The facilities for learning physics in his day at the Rensselaer Polytechnic Institute were none of the best, a fact which is made the subject of keen criticism in his home correspondence, but he made the most of whatever was available and created opportunity where it was lacking. The use of a turning lathe and a few tools being allowed, he spent all of his leisure in designing and constructing physical apparatus of various kinds, with which he experimented continually. All of his spare money went into this and he always wished he had more. While he pays without grumbling his share of the expense of a class supper, he cannot help declaring that "it is an awful price for one night's pleasure; why, it would buy another galvanic battery." During these early years his pastime was the study of magnetism and electricity, and his lack of money for the purchase of insulated wire for electro-magnetic apparatus led him to the invention of a method of winding naked copper wire, which was later patented by someone else and made much of. Within six months of his entering the Institute he had made a delicate balance, a galvanometer, and an electrometer, besides a small induction coil and several minor pieces. A few weeks later he announced the finishing of a Ruhmkorff coil of considerable power, a source of much delight to him and to his friends.

In December 1866 he began the construction of a small but elaborately designed steam engine which ran perfectly when completed and furnished power for his experiments. A year later he is full of enthusiasm over an investigation which he wishes to undertake to explain the production of electricity when water comes in contact with red-hot iron, which he attributes to the decomposition of a part of the water. Along with all of this and much more he maintains a good standing in his regular work in the Institute, in some of which he is naturally the leader. He occasionally writes: "I am head of my class in mathematics," or "I lead the class in natural philosophy," but official records show that he was now and then "conditioned" in subjects in which he had no special interest. As early as 1868, before his 20th birthday, he decided that he must devote his life to science. While not doubting his ability "to make an excellent engineer," as he declares, he decides against engineering, saying:

You know that from a child I have been extremely fond of experiment; this liking instead of decreasing has gradually grown upon me until it has become a part of my nature, and it would be folly for me to attempt to give it up; and I don't see any reason why I should wish it, unless it be avarice, for I never expect to be a rich man. I intend to devote myself hereafter to science. If she gives me wealth, I will receive it as coming from a friend; but if not, I will not murmur.

He realized that his opportunity for the pursuit of science was in becoming a teacher, but no opening in this direction presenting itself, he spent the first year after graduation in the field as a civil engineer. This was followed by a not very inspiring experience as instructor in natural science in a western college, where he acquired, however, experience and useful discipline.

In the spring of 1872 he returned to Troy as instructor in physics, on a salary the amount of which he made conditional on the purchase by the Institute of a certain number of hundreds of dollars' worth of physical apparatus. If they failed in this, as afterwards happened, his pay was to be greater, and he strictly held them to the contract. His three years at Troy as instructor and assistant professor were busy, fruitful years. In addition to his regular work he did an enormous amount of study, purchasing for that purpose the most recent and most advanced books on mathematics and physics. He built his electro-dynamometer and carried out his first great research. As already stated, this quickly brought him reputation in Europe and, what he prized quite as highly, the personal friendship of Maxwell, whose ardent admirer and champion he remained to the end of his life. In April 1875 he wrote: "It will not be very long before my reputation reaches this country"; and he hoped that this would bring him opportunity to devote more of his time and energy to original research.

This opportunity for which he so much longed was nearer at hand than he imagined. Among the members of the visiting board at the West Point Military Academy in June 1875 was one to whom had come the splendid conception of what was to be at once a revelation and a revolution in methods of higher education. In selecting the first faculty for an institution of learning which within a single decade was to set the pace for real university work in America, and whose influence was to be felt in every school and college of the land before the end of the first quarter of a century, Dr. Gilman was guided by an instinct which more than all else insured the success of the new enterprise. A few words about Rowland from Professor Michie of the Military Academy led to his being called to West Point by telegraph, and on the banks of the Hudson these two walked and talked, "he telling me," Dr. Gilman has said, "his dreams for science and I telling him my dreams for higher education." Rowland with characteristic frankness writes of this interview: "Professor Gilman was very much pleased with me," which, indeed, was the simple truth. The engagement was quickly made. Rowland was sent to Europe to study laboratories and purchase apparatus, and the rest is history already told and everywhere known.

Rowland's personality was in many respects remarkable. Tall, erect, and lithe in figure, fond of athletic sports, there was upon his face a certain look of severity which was in a way an index of the exacting standard he set for himself and others. It did not conceal, however, what was after all his most striking characteristic, namely, a perfectly frank, open, and simple straightforwardness in thought, in speech, and in action. His love of truth held him in supreme control, and, like Galileo, he had no patience with those who try to make things appear otherwise than as they actually are. His criticisms of the work of others were keen and merciless, and sometimes there remained a sting of which he himself had not the slightest suspicion. "I would not have done it for the world," he once said to me after being told that his pitiless criticism of a scientific paper had wounded the feelings of its author. As a matter of fact, he was warm-hearted and generous, and his occasionally seeming otherwise was due to the complete separation, in his own mind, of the product and the personality of the author. He possessed that rare power, habit in his case, of seeing himself not as others saw him, but as he saw others. He looked at himself and his own work exactly as if he had been another person, and this gave rise to a frankness of expression regarding his own performance which sometimes impressed strangers unpleasantly, but which to his friends was one of his most charming qualities. Much of his success as an investigator was due to a firm confidence in his own powers and in the unerring course of the logic of science which inspired him to cling tenaciously to an idea when once he had given it a place in his mind. At a meeting of the National Academy of Sciences in the early days of our knowledge of electric generators he read a paper relating to the fundamental principles of the dynamo. A gentleman who had had large experience with the practical working of dynamos listened to the paper and at the end said to the Academy that unfortunately practice directly contradicted Professor Rowland's theory, to which instantly replied Rowland, "So much the worse for the practice," which, indeed, turned out to be the case.

Like all men of real genius, he had phenomenal capacity for concentration of thought and effort. Of this, one who was long and intimately associated with him remarks, "I can remember cases when he appeared as if drugged from mere inability to recall his mind from the pursuit of all-absorbing problems, and he had a triumphant joy in intellectual achievement such as we would look for in other men only from the gratification of an elemental passion." So completely consumed was he by fires of his own kindling that he often failed to give due attention to the work of others, and some of his public utterances give evidence of this curious neglect of the historic side of his subject. As a teacher his position was quite unique. Unfit for the ordinary routine work of the classroom, he taught, as more men ought to teach, by example rather than by precept. Says one of his most eminent pupils, "Even of the more advanced students only those who were able to brook severe and searching criticism reaped the full benefit of being under him, but he contributed that which, in a university, is above all teaching of routine—the spectacle of scientific work thoroughly done and the example of a lofty ideal."

Returning home about twenty years ago, after an expatriation of several years, and wishing to put myself in touch with the development of methods of instruction in physics and especially in the equipment of physical laboratories, I visited Rowland very soon after, as it happened, the making of his first successful negative of the solar spectrum. That he was completely absorbed in his success was quite evident, but he also seemed anxious to give me such information as I sought. I questioned him as to the number of men who were to work in his laboratory, and although the college year had already begun, he appeared to be unable to given even an approximate answer. "And what will you do with them?" I said. "Do with them?" he replied, raising the still dripping negative so as to get a better light through its delicate tracings, "Do with them? I shall neglect them." The whole situation was intensely characteristic, revealing him as one to whom the work of a drillmaster was impossible, but ready to lead those who would be led and could follow. To be neglected by Rowland was often indeed more stimulating and inspiring than the closest personal supervision of men lacking his genius and magnetic fervor.

In the fullness of his powers, recognized as America's greatest physicist, and one of a very small group of the world's most eminent, he died on April 16, 1901, from a disease the relentless progress of which he had realized for several years and opposed with a splendid but quiet courage. It was Rowland's good fortune to receive recognition during his life in the bestowal of degrees by higher institutions of learning; in election to membership in nearly all scientific societies worthy of note in Europe and America; in being made the recipient of medals of honor awarded by these societies, and in the generously expressed words of his distinguished contemporaries. It will be many years, however, before full measure can be had of his influence in promoting the interests of physical science, for with his own brilliant career, sufficient of itself to excite our profound admiration, must be considered that of a host of other younger men who lighted their torches at his flame and who will reflect honor upon him whose loss they now mourn by passing on something of his unquenchable enthusiasm, something of his high regard for pure intellectuality, something of his love of truth and his sweetness of character and disposition.

Antoine Henri Becquerel *

1852–1908

———◆———

ANDRÉ BROCA †

It is no small or easy task to retrace the life of Henri Becquerel, unveiling his inner life and showing how in a life consecrated to daily labor, moment by moment, he accumulated the great mass of scientific material which in his thirtieth year opened to him the doors of the Académie des Sciences, and how finally, through the logical development of his train of thought, he reached the discovery which has immortalized his name.

It was an instructive spectacle to see Becquerel in his laboratory arranging his apparatus with consummate skill, often constructing it from odd pieces of card or of copper wire, which seemed alive under his fingers and with which he made the discoveries that form his memoirs. Foreign scientists who came in throngs to see each new experiment could scarcely believe a laboratory so barren could yield so abundant a harvest. They were astonished and charmed at their reception, so simple and cordial, where they had expected formal dignity of a man so eminent. The laboratory seemed his normal place. Experimental research, in the accomplishment of which he braved every difficulty, seemed to be in him a veritable physiological function.

Becquerel made physics from all that fell under his hands. He was raised for physics and by a physicist. The most precious memories, with which he often entertained his friends, were of his father and grandfather, whose discourse and example had helped to shape his mind. In his youth the great reward for his vacation days was to enter the laboratory of his father and see the old or new experiments, to perform those within his ability, fashioning the apparatus

* A.R., 1908, pp. 769–785. Translated with some condensation from *Revue générale des sciences pures et appliquées,* Oct. 30, 1908.
† French scientist (1863–1925), specialist in medical sciences and optics.

with his own hands. One of his most vivid recollections was seing his father come in one noon from his laboratory to announce to his grandfather the invention of the phosphoroscope, discussing it and its results, which the following day more than verified.

Becquerel recounted these circumstances in no boastful spirit, but rather to attribute to his upbringing much of his success. He had the joy of seeing his son enter with distinction the same career and to be able to transmit what had been his own heritage. Although trained in science, his artistic tastes were not undeveloped. In painting he was an enlightened connoisseur, owing this trait to his ancestor, Girodet, of whom he possessed some masterpieces, among others, admirable drawings which he liked to show to his friends and whose beauty he appreciated.

His morals were of the highest, and he had a horror of all duplicity and deceit. He had for all questions the broadest and most-enlightened tolerance. That spirit whose every effort strove for the attainment of scientific truth knew how to avoid the lure of insufficient evidence. While holding a clear-cut personal opinion, he was always tolerant of any opinion of others having for its purpose the elevation of morals.

This explains how he entered the École Polytechnique at 19, in 1873; how from there he entered the Ponts-et-Chaussées and published his first work at 22 years of age, in the year following his graduation from the École Polytechnique. From then until his death he never ceased to publish works more and more remarkable. The École Polytechnique made him a lecturer in physics while he was yet only an engineering student in order to give him the place as professor upon the retirement of Potier, and the museum judged him worthy of holding the chair already made illustrious by his father and grandfather and held before them by Gay-Lussac. Merited honors have never ceased to be his recompense; he was a member of the more renowned foreign scientific bodies, the Royal Society of London, the Academy of Berlin, the Académie Royale dei Lincei, the National Academy [of Sciences] of Washington. He received the medals and prizes held in the highest esteem—the Rumford prize of London in 1900, the Helmholtz medal of Berlin in 1901, the Nobel prize in 1903, the Barnard medal of the United States in 1905. The Académie des Sciences made him its president in 1908, and at the same time the Société Française de Physique bestowed upon him the widely coveted title of "honorary member," and at the death of Lapparent he was almost unanimously named its permanent secretary. He was but 55 and seemed destined to long hold this worthy honor when death cruelly snatched him away but a few weeks after he received it.

Before a blow so cruel it is useless to express our regrets. The homage due such a man and worthy of the memory which his own family, his friends, scientists, and the whole world will retain is to retrace as fully as possible the history of his scientific achievements.

The problems which preoccupied Becquerel during his entire life related to the constitution of matter and the manner in which this reacts upon the magnetic and optical properties of bodies. He approached the problem through rotary magnetic polarization and his theories led him to laws of primordial importance. He was the first to admit that in molecular phenomena there must be a partial carrying along of the ether by matter, and from this hypothesis he deduced the formula

$$\frac{R}{n^2 \, (n^2 - 1)} = \text{constant},$$

where R is the rotation of the plane of polarization and n the index of refraction. Experiment showed this true for bodies, group by group, and while not wholly verifying the theory yet it indicated that he was on the right path and pointed the way for further progress.

The next step was the study of rotary magnetic dispersion. Verdet had shown that the rotation is nearly proportional to the square of the wave length and that the product of the rotation by the square of the wave length slowly increases from the less to the more refrangible radiations. Becquerel divided these results by the factor $n^2 \, (n^2 - 1)$, and the result became very nearly constant, indicating how closely his theory as to the connection of ether and matter was connected with these phenomena.

Verdet noted that in magnetic media the rotation of the plane of polarization is inverse to that in diamagnetic bodies, and that consequently there is a difference between magnetism and diamagnetism. For Edmond Becquerel it did not seem so; he believed, rather, that diamagnetic bodies were less magnetic than the vacuum, magnetic ones more so. Henri Becquerel tried to show that the phenomena supported his father's views. He verified the observations of Verdet, but he showed further that magnetic and diamagnetic solutions behave very differently. In the latter case the action of the diamagnetic molecules is so weak that the rotation is proportional to the concentration. With the former, however, the magnetic action is so strong that the reaction of the molecules upon each other is noticeable. For instance, with the perchloride of iron the rotation increases faster than the concentration when the latter becomes great enough. Becquerel verified again the experiment that with mixtures of iron filings and an inert powder the magnetic field increases more rapidly than the number of iron filings.

Becquerel now asked whether a gas should not have a measurable magnetic rotary power. All the earlier attempts to show this had been unsuccessful. Before making the apparatus adapted to show it he needed an idea of the size of the effect which he might expect. The preceding law, $\dfrac{R}{n^2 (n^2-1)} = 0.2$, approximately, used with gases of which the refractive indexes are known, shows that the amount of rotation should be very different from one end of the spectrum to the other and of the order of 0.0001 of that due to carbon bisulphide. So with an apparatus having a magnetic field 30 meters in length he expected a rotation of five to ten minutes of arc. Faraday had proved that the effect may be increased by repeated reflections of the light across the magnetic field. Becquerel employed this device in an apparatus about 3 meters in length to measure the rotary power of gases and their relatively great rotary dispersion.

Oxygen was found to be abnormal. Its rotary dispersion is extremely small and perhaps anomalous, the green giving less rotation than the red. This behavior may be compared with the well-known magnetic properties of oxygen. Carbon bisulphide furnishes strong evidence in support of the law, for in the liquid state the constant is 0.231, in the gaseous, 0.234. Becquerel naturally searched for applications of his theory in the world about him. He looked for the action of the terrestrial magnetic field upon light, and with carbon bisulphide observed deviations of the plane of polarization of about half a degree. But a new question arose: Does the terrestrial magnetic field deviate the plane of atmospheric polarization, which, according to theory, must pass through the center of the sun? This study, requiring measurements of high precision, showed that the plane of polarization undergoes a daily oscillation about the theoretical plane, due for the most part to diffuse light, but there is a small residual variation caused by the earth's magnetism, 150 kilometers of air giving a rotation of about 20' of arc.

This elaborate series of experiments would not have been complete had the practical side been neglected. At the congress of electricians in 1881 Becquerel proposed to measure electric currents in absolute units by means of the rotation of the plane of polarization by carbon bisulphide. He showed that this method is free from the perturbation at the ends of the magnet, the rotation formula being $R = K.4\pi NI$. By various experiments, made by the deposit of silver, the constant, K, was found equal to 0.04841' at 0°. This gives a method of constructing a secondary scale for the ampere, precise though difficult in practice.

To return to the theories which had furnished motive for all these experiments, Becquerel combined his ideas in a theory of the magnetic rotary polarization and showed how analogous results could be reproduced mechanically if a transparent body could be turned at a speed of millions of turns per second.

In this complete series of researches, conducted by Becquerel between his twenty-second and thirty-fifth years, we see the development of all the qualities of a true investigator—the directing theoretical ideas, the consummate experimental skill, the discussion of all the interesting results, those which concern the cosmical conditions of our existence together with their practical applications, and, finally, the theoretical co-ordination. This work, completed at 35, ranked Henri Becquerel as a master and justified the glorious career which opened before him. At the time of these recondite researches he was preparing others, all tending toward the study of the constitution of matter. They were to treat of the absorption of light and of phosphorescence. These led him to the discovery of the new rays.

Let us examine next his work on crystalline absorption. While examining the absorption spectra of various crystals he noted that the bands disappeared for certain orientations of the luminous vibration. Pushing further the study of this phenomenon, he saw that in all double-refracting crystals having absorption bands similar phenomena occur, and that the absorption in general is symmetrical about three principal axes; the more complicated the crystalline structure, the more complicated the law of absorption. There is, however, one general law binding them all. The bands observed through the same crystal have invariable positions in the spectrum; their intensity alone varies.

In uniaxial crystals the phenomenon is symmetrical about one axis. The absorption spectrum, in whatever direction observed, is formed by the superposition of two series of bands, one corresponding to the vibration normal to the axis, the other to those parallel to it. For every ordinary ray—that is, for every ray normal to the axis—the absorption spectrum is the same for the same length of path. For every extraordinary ray of which the vibration is oriented in the plane of the ray and the axis the absorption spectrum is as if the two components of the ray normal and parallel to the axis individually suffered absorption and then united upon emerging.

In biaxial crystals one law is common to both orthorhombic and clinorhombic crystals. Each band has three axes of rectangular symmetry. When the Fresnel vibration coincides with one of them, the absorption band is at a maximum; with another, it has a mean value; and with the third it is generally invisible. In orthorhombic crystals the three directions of absorption coincide with the directions of symmetry of the crystal. In clinorhombic crystals the phenomena are more complex and interesting. The axis of symmetry is always a direction of principal absorption common to all the bands, but the other two principal rectangular directions of diverse bands of absorption may be variably orientated with the plane of symmetry, g_1. In certain crystals these directions depart very little from the principal axes of optical elasticity, in others they may make with these axes very great angles, reaching sometimes 45°. Becquerel gave to these directions the name *principal directions of anomalous absorption,* and inferred from them important consequences.

These phenomena occur in crystals containing the rare earths and are probably due to the complexity of the bodies which form the crystals. De Sénarmont had already shown that if we crystallize mixtures in variable proportions of the component substances, geometrically isomorphic but with the optic axes differently orientated with reference to geometrically like directions, we can obtain a crystal having any optical properties whatever, the resultant emergent vibration being due to the resultant of the partial vibrations traversing the various crystals, the symmetry of the total system depending upon the portions of each component. So in apparently like crystals the absorption may be wholly different, each component crystal absorbing certain radiations independent of its neighbors and there may be no relation between the axes of absorption corresponding to these bands and the directions of symmetry of the crystals. If certain crystals have principal directions of anomalous absorption, it is because they are such mixtures of crystals. Crystals containing didymium show the necessity of admitting its division into neodidymium and præsodidymium. Demarcay was able to separate the distinct elements in præsodidymium, the existence of which Becquerel had thus shown the necessity. In neodidymium there are bands which characterize complex crystals.

This method of analysis can indicate bodies existing in a crystal which are destroyed by its solution. If, having noted all the absorption bands in a crystal of sulphate of didymium, we dissolve it, the spectrum of the solution is notably different, certain bands have disappeared, others have suffered displacement, while yet others have remained unchanged. The bands modified are those which in the crystal were marked by these anomalies and the variations may be explained if we admit that there exists in the crystal such a mixture which is completely destroyed and transformed by the water.

The separation of the rare earths is very difficult. They are very numerous and distinguished from each other only by extremely small variations in their physical and chemical properties. It is generally almost impossible to purify them. It would be very valuable to be able to seize, by some optical process, in the heart itself of a mixture, a crystalline body which shows this anomalous absorption and which, the moment the body is dissolved, disappears to take place as another compound. It would be a true method of spectrum analysis which could be employed in researches relative to the rare earths.

After having shown upon many crystals the fruitfulness of his method, Becquerel closed his research in this line by, as usual, reuniting into a theory the facts observed. The intensity of a ray after having traversed a unit thickness of a crystal must be $i = (a \cos^2 a + b \cos^2 \beta + c \cos^2 \gamma)^2$ for a given wave length, the ray making the angles a, β, and γ, with the principal absorption axes, the intensity observed along the three axes being a, b, and c. But there are cases where two absorption bands are superposed in the same part of the spectrum having different principal directions of absorption. Then the photometer measures must be represented by the product of two expressions of the same form. Thus we may have an asymmetric curve for the intensity as a function of the angles a, β, γ. This takes place in epidote, and Becquerel was able to explain the apparently paradoxical results of Ramsay in making photometric measures for various orientations of the plane g_1 of epidote.

We see in this series of researches the same qualities of mind present in the earlier one—extremely delicate experiments directed by theoretical ideas and the final embodiment in a theory rendering numerical account of the observed facts. The problem brought to this point had no further interest for Becquerel; he left to others the patient work of applying his methods. He himself started on a new path, one already laid out for him, which in a sense was a heritage. Edmond Becquerel had already made discoveries upon it of the first order. In phosphorescence Henri Becquerel found a subject well adapted to his trend of mind and where his radical ideas could bear full fruit. We find again the double line of work, the theoretical and the practical, side by side. He showed the first in establishing a new method for the spectroscopic analysis of flames, the other in discovering two distinct laws: first, the law connecting the radiation engendering phosphorescence and that emitted from the phosphorescing body; second, the law connecting the diminution of the emitted energy with the time. This series of experiments is also of the first rank, for the study of the constitution of matter for phosphorescence is certainly intimately connected with molecular resonance. Phosphorescence results from selective absorption, but the nature of the radiation is such that a purely thermal connection between the phosphorescent emission and the nature of the body's absorption is an insufficient explanation of the emission, which is itself selective. These phenomena seem related to those of the selective emission of incandescent vapors, and so it was natural to look for laws analogous to those governing the luminous emission of gases and vapors. It is true that the molecules are less free in solid phosphorescing bodies than in gases and the light emitted is less simple; yet Becquerel was able to unravel definite relations.

Edmond Becquerel had already shown that if the infrared rays strike an excited phosphorescing body the phosphorescence is destroyed, just as it would have been had the temperature of the body been raised. The extinction is preceded by a temporary increase of the phosphorescence, as if the stored-up energy was given out at a greater intensity during a shorter time. Generally the two phases occur so rapidly that the final extinction alone is appreciable. Edmond Becquerel had thus commenced the study of the infrared of the spectrum. Henri Becquerel resumed this study, making many important advances. He studied the solar spectrum by means of phosphorescence and described in this infrared portion unknown or little-known bands between the wave lengths 0.76μ and 1.9μ. Abney, by direct photography, had gone as far as 0.98μ. Langley with the bolometer had explored a much greater region and had recognized the more interesting of these bands of Becquerel. But in the region, relatively small to be sure, where the phosphorescent method is applicable, it could then detect finer lines than the bolometer. Becquerel studied new absorption and emission spectra; he showed that the liquid-water absorption nearly coincides with that of atmospheric water vapor; that the compounds of didymium and samarium have characteristic lines in the infrared which may serve as standard marks; finally, he mapped the characteristic lines of the infrared of the incandescent vapors of potassium, aluminum, zinc, cadmium, lead, bismuth, silver, and tin.

While some substances lose their phosphorescence nearly uniformly over the infrared, with others the extinction is unequally rapid in different regions. The extinction is produced under the influence of definite radiations, often to the exclusion of the neighboring regions, so that the spectrum consists of one or more bands where the extinction has been active, separated by regions where it has been either much smaller or nil. Under the influence of the infrared radiations the phosphorescence varies in color with the time. This may be noted in the phosphoroscope. So even in the various infrared bands in the same substance it was found that the color cannot always be the same. It is interesting to correlate these facts with the very similar behavior in the violet and ultraviolet. The ensemble of the bands of excitation of emission, and of extinction must be connected by analogous formulæ with the various radiations emitted by incandescent vapors, for both are intimately connected with the vibration periods of the molecules.

The most remarkable phenomena are shown by the compounds of uranium, and it was the study of these which led to Becquerel's discovery of radioactivity. Uranium forms two distinct series of salts. Edmond Becquerel had shown the phosphorescence of one set. The second does not phosphoresce. Henri Becquerel soon noted that the latter salts have characteristic bands of absorption in the visible and the infrared spectrum. Studying further the compounds of the first class, he noted that most of them phosphoresce as had already been shown and that they have in general a discontinuous spectrum of seven or eight bands or groups of bands between the C and the F lines; these bands vary according to the nature of the compound. The compounds have selective absorption bands which correspond to all the radiations which will excite the phosphorescence. If the body is excited by the light of the wave length of any one of these latter bands it will give out its total emission spectrum of all the wave lengths proper to its phosphorescence. Becquerel formulated this law: The difference in the oscillation frequencies in passing from one band to another is a constant, the bands of absorption continuing the series formed by those of emission. The latter seem to be the subharmonics of the former. Often one or two of the less refrangible absorption bands coincide with the more refrangible ones of emission. It seems probable that the absorption forms some kind of synchronism with the periods of the emission, but it is not expected that they will be found to be subharmonics. They are essentially distinguished from incandescent vapors in absorption. The ordinary theories of resonance are incapable of explaining them, but the simplicity of the law which binds them gives hope some day of the possibility of a mechanical explanation.

It is remarkable that the second series of uranium salts which do not phosphoresce but seem to degrade into heat the selectively absorbed radiation, should have bands which follow with a notable regularity the same law which holds for the emission bands of the other series. The bands have not, however, the same relative intensities.

We have just seen the theoretical difficulties offered by these phenomena. Edmond Becquerel had already studied and formulated the variation of the intensity of the phosphorescent emission with the time. His formula, however, held only for very short periods of time. Nor was the one derived by Wiedemann sufficient. The formula, $i = i_0 e^{-at}$, was deduced theoretically from the hypothesis that the molecular degradation of energy is proportional to the velocity of what we will now call electrons. Becquerel thought it better to make this degradation proportional to the square of the velocity and so obtained the formula $i = i_0 \left\{ \dfrac{1}{a + bt} \right\}^2$. As the photometric measures of the total phosphorescence intensity did not agree with this, Becquerel, remembering the changes of color, thought it possible that a similar term ought to be used for each band, so that if there are two bands in the spectrum the formula becomes $i = i_0 \left\{ \left(\dfrac{1}{a + bt} \right)^2 + \left(\dfrac{1}{c + dt} \right)^2 \right\}$. He verified this formula in several cases, so that it seems proved that the phosphorescent phenomena follow a law probably adaptable to some mechanical explanation but much more complicated than acoustical resonance or other analogue to which we are at present accustomed. From that moment for Becquerel, phosphorescence became a source offering mysterious properties, the unraveling of the secret of which would embrace a multitude of new discoveries.

When the discovery of Röntgen was announced, Becquerel, like many others, at once tried to see whether phosphorescent bodies emitted photographic or phosphorogenic radiations that would traverse opaque bodies. And here we may still better appreciate the subtlety of Becquerel's mind. In the midst of a maze of seemingly contradictory facts, he knew by his marvelous intuition how to avoid the paths to error and to take that which would lead him by infinitely small manifestations to the fundamental phenomena of radioactivity, that immortal discovery which has already revolutionized modern physics and promises to lead the physics of the future into fields as yet unrealized.

The biography now becomes difficult. It could be made nothing more than the enumeration of Becquerel's astonishing discoveries without explaining the extraordinary conditions under which they were produced. Those physicists who may read this will recall that fever of excitement among men of science which followed in 1896 the announcement of Röntgen's discovery. They will recall, too, the first experiments of Becquerel, which raised the doubts of the older school and the curiosity of the younger. Then Becquerel, aroused by the daily disclosure of new truths and by the increased publication of his works, accumulated in three years a mass of results that confounds us. And we should also note at this time the devoted collaboration of his assistant, Matout, in whom he inspired admiration as a man of science and an unlimited personal attachment.

Ordinary phosphorescent substances give off no emanation capable of traversing black paper. But it is not so with the compounds of uranium, whose peculiar properties Becquerel had already recorded. By first covering a photographic plate with black paper and placing over the latter a salt of uranium excited by direct sunlight, he succeeded in obtaining an impression upon the plate. But one day the sunlight disappeared a moment after the exposure had been started and the apparatus was left in the dark. Later the plate was developed and the impression was found as strong as if the sunlight had struck the salt. Upon trying the experiment again without sunlight the same result was reached as if the sun had been used. Although this uranium compound, which had been prepared some time, was now kept in the darkness in a lead box, yet it still continued to give the same results.

The discharge of an electrified body under the influence of the uranium emanation was next tried. This was at that time the only process known which would give quantitative measures of this strange power. Then it was necessary to see if the phosphorescent state was necessary for the newly found emanation. A nitrate of uranium crystal, whether in solution or melted in its water of crystallization, gave the same effect as when in the solid state, although in neither of the liquid states would it phosphoresce. An attempt to see whether bodies near such active compounds became active by a phenomenon analogous to phosphorescence was unsuccessful. It was several years later that the power of radium enabled M. and Mme. Curie to show this and the profound difference between this new phenomenon and luminous phosphorescence.

Some odd results, not yet understood, led Becquerel for a moment to believe erroneously that the new rays were ordinary radiation. But he soon saw his error, noting that the propagation of this new emanation took place as well across pulverized matter as across solid, continuous bodies. Since all the compounds of uranium, whatever their chemical or physical state, showed these phenomena, it was therefore natural to attribute them to the uranium itself. Pure uranium was tried and gave more intense results than the salts. It was now made evident that neighboring bodies became the source of a secondary emanation as long as they were struck by the uranium discharge, but that the phenomenon ceased as soon as the body was removed from the presence of the uranium.

By pushing the experiments with the electrical discharge still further it was shown that the air is rendered conductive and remains so a few moments and that this plays an essential rôle in the phenomenon. Air, active under the influence of the uranium and blown upon an electroscope, actively discharges the latter. If ordinary, inactive air is blown between the uranium and the ball of the electroscope, the latter is discharged more slowly. The emission seems independent of the temperature of the uranium. The temperature of the gas, however, modifies the discharge.

In order to regulate this method of measuring the emanation it was necessary to find some law governing the discharge under the varying potential. Becquerel established a limit of the velocity of discharge for potentials above 300 volts; Rutherford later called this the "saturation current." Finally, by studying the modification of the velocity of discharge produced by the interposition of lamina of different substances, Becquerel showed the complexity of the emanation emitted by the uranium. From now on these radiations were called "Becquerel rays."

All these results were verified by Rutherford, who extended them, characterizing by their absorption two classes of rays: the α rays, very active and greatly absorbed by the air; the β rays, less active and much less absorbed. He applied to gases, rendered conductive by these rays the theory of ionization which J. J. Thomson was then developing, and showed the identity of the phenomena produced in the air by the Becquerel rays and the Röntgen rays.

While Becquerel's results were being verified in England, M. and Mme. Curie in France and Schmidt in Germany were searching for this emanation from other bodies. Mme. Curie and Schmidt discovered it simultaneously in thorium. Mme. Curie found that all active bodies contained either uranium or thorium. She determined by the quartz-piezoelectrical method of Curie that each compound of uranium, whatever its history, possessed the same power of discharging—the same radioactivity—using the name adopted by Curie. The two Curies then tried to isolate the body endowed with the property of radioactivity; and by an immense amount of work, using Becquerel's rays and Curie's piezoelectrical method in their analyses, they finally discovered polonium and then radium. Using pure uranium as the unit of radioactivity, radium chloride has an activity of 1,800,000.

Becquerel could now continue his researches with the extremely active products placed at his disposal by the Curies. His earlier experiments he repeated with polonium and radium and showed by his absorption tests that polonium emits an emanation different from that of radium. Utilizing the admirable collection of phosphorescent compounds left by his father, Becquerel did not delay in establishing several new properties of the emanation from the new products, showing that each of them emitted a complex bundle of rays exciting in a special manner the diverse phosphorescent substances. By his absorption method he showed that the very penetrating rays excite the double sulphate of uranium and polonium and that the most penetrating rays excite the diamond. Finally, he noted that the radium emanation can give back to bodies the property which they may have lost of becoming phosphorescent by being heated. This may also be accomplished by means of the electric discharge.

Becquerel noted that the radium emanation gives to chlorine a phosphorescence much more persistent than that produced by ordinary light, and compared this with the similar result produced by the cathode rays as shown by Sir William Crookes* and Edmond Becquerel. He compared the chemical phenomena produced by the cathode rays and those which the Curies had observed with the action of radium upon glass.

It was but a step to Becquerel's examination of the effect of the

* Papers by Crookes appeared in *A.R.*, 1897, pp. 219–235; 1899, pp. 143–153; 1903, pp. 229–241.

magnetic field upon the emanation. Giesel, Meyer, and Schweidler had already obtained some results along that line, but they were unknown to Becquerel. Becquerel's observations when completed were more profound, more fertile than those of his predecessors. He observed the important fact that the radiation, deflected like the cathode rays by the magnetic field, suffers a dispersion. This showed that the emanation is composed of electrons having different velocities. At the same time, working with an electrometric method, the Curies showed that in the emanation from radium there is an undeviated part much more absorbed than the other rays, thus giving a new distinction between the a and β rays of Rutherford. Polonium according to Becquerel gives only the nondeviable rays. But at the same time Villard showed that in the nondeviable bundle there exists, besides the very absorable a rays, a set, extremely transmissible, which he called the "γ rays," and which are identical with the Röntgen or X rays.

The remarkable studies of J. J. Thomson[†] on the cathode rays recorded that from the trajectories of the electrons in a known magnetic field we may determine the quantity $\dfrac{mv}{e}$, where m is the mass of the electron charged with a quantity of electricity e, and having the velocity v. The trajectory of the rays discharged normal to the field should be a circle whose radius $R = \dfrac{mv}{He}$, where H is the intensity of the field. It was necessary to see if the radium rays gave trajectories whose radius equaled $\dfrac{mv}{e}$, analogous to cathode rays. Experiments showed this to be true and that all the preparations of radium or its salts gave the same kinds of rays. It served also to show that the dispersion in the magnetic field could serve for the study of the penetrability of the various emanations, for the more deviable the more penetrating are the rays. The images obtained by placing various screens separating a photographic plate from a morsel of radium in the bottom of a lead trough, and all placed in a magnetic field, allowed, by means of the images upon the plate, a determination of the limits to which the emanations penetrated the screens. Moreover, the radii of curvature were easily calculated. Knowing the field H, the products RH could be easily deduced. These products, equal to $\dfrac{mv}{e}$, lay be-

† Thomson's paper, "Cathode Rays," appeared in *A.R.*, 1897, pp. 157–168, and other studies by him were published in *A.R.*, 1892, pp. 229–254; 1901, pp. 231–243; 1903, pp. 199–201; 1908, pp. 233–244; 1909, pp. 185–205.

tween 637 for copper and 3082 for lead. Admitting veloci-
ties analogous to those of the cathode rays, the values, $\frac{m}{e}$, could
be approximately found, showing whether the emanation should
have a sensible electric deviation. Becquerel made the calculations
and prepared the experiment at the same time that the Curies
demonstrated directly that the deviable rays of radium carried
negative charges. On March 26, 1900, at the Académie des Sciences he published the confirming results. Dorn independently
published the same results, depending on the calculations of
Becquerel.

Knowing the radius of curvature for a cathode ray in a known
magnetic field and its electrostatic deviation, we may calculate $\frac{e}{m}$
and v. When his discovery was well assured Becquerel published figures obtained from the absorption in black paper, giv-
ing $v=2.37\times10^{10}$ and $\frac{e}{m}=1.32\times10^{7}$, very close to the last given
by Kaufmann.

While Becquerel struggled against his insufficient means for
constructing the necessary *in vacuo* apparatus, Kaufmann completed experiments with sufficient accuracy to conclude that $\frac{e}{m}$
varies with the velocity—that is to say, that mass, the constant
which has seemed so well established since the time of Newton,
has no absolute existence and that we can consider its coefficient as
constant only with velocities infinitely small compared with the
velocity of light. We will say nothing further on this aspect of
radioactivity. It now passes out of Becquerel's domain. Indeed before the flood of foreign investigations which furthered his results
and before the new results secured every day, he had to leave to
others the experiments for which he had neither the material nor
the means.

After the α and the β rays had been clearly distinguished by
the experiments already stated, it was questioned whether the
former are only slightly deviable or not deviable at all. Rutherford
performed an experiment from which he concluded that they are
slightly deviable, but his conclusion was too involved to carry conviction. Becquerel took up the question, using accurate measures
made upon his photographic plates, and was able to establish a
weak deviation undoubtedly, the α rays forming a pencil clearly
defined and not showing any sensible magnetic dispersion. These
rays are analogous to the canal rays of Goldstein. The curvature

of the α rays seemed to augment with the length of path in the air. Although the great absorption of the rays by the air made difficult the simultaneous study of the magnetic and electric deviation, the problem was solved by Des Coudres. The experiments of Becquerel and of Rutherford proved that the change of curvature in traversing a thin sheet of aluminum is due to a noticeable retardation of the charged corpuscles. To Becquerel it seemed due to an augmentation of the mass, to Rutherford to a diminution of the velocity. Becquerel found that polonium gives rays that are identical with the α rays of radium. An exhaustive study of uranium, even *in vacuo*, disclosed no α rays, but it was found to emit very deviable β rays—that is, rays of small velocity.

The beginning of these studies had shown the existence of secondary rays produced by the bombardment of another body by the Becquerel rays. Further study showed that all radium rays do not possess this property. The most rapid corpuscles traverse aluminum and suffer no modification. Those for which $RH=3.436$ are the first to suffer change and produce the secondary rays after passing through the aluminum. When $RH<1.500$ they are completely absorbed by the aluminum and give no emission. The secondary rays are deviated like the primary in an electric field.

It was these secondary rays which produced the intense impression on the photographic plates of Becquerel. The very penetrating emanation traversed the lead, producing the secondary rays which then affected the plate. These rays produce the augmentation of the impression along the screen hit by the Becquerel rays. These experiments repeated with polonium showed that in time the secondary rays due to mica indicate a much more penetrating emanation than that ordinarily noted from polonium.

Becquerel studied the transformation of white into red phosphorus under the influence of these emanations and showed that the slightly penetrating rays produced the essential part of the action. The α rays could not be tried because of the necessity of protecting the radium.

The fertile success of the ionization theory made it interesting to see whether analogous phenomena took place in solid dielectrics. J. J. Thomson showed that it occurred with the X rays. Becquerel showed that liquid or solid paraffin became conducting under the action of the rays. That the action continued constant in the same apparatus during a year indicated that it took place even when the paraffin had reached its permanent state. At the time of these discoveries the Curies were bringing to notice induced radioactivity, and Rutherford, the emanation of radium with its curious properties, the exhaustion of the solution which gave the emanation, and the recovery of the radioactivity after a certain time. Thorium had an emanation of its own. None could be isolated for uranium, and yet Becquerel showed that certain phenomena appeared to indicate one. Sir William Crookes showed that by fractional crystallization of the nitrate of uranium in ether the foreign matter became reactive, the nitrate less and less so. He attributed this to a new body which he called uranium-X. Becquerel showed that these phenomena follow the same laws as those of the salts of radium in solution and that the nitrate crystallizes reactive after a time. It seemed then that uranium has an emanation. He showed that the double sulphate of uranium and potassium is spontaneously luminous in the dark like the radium salts, only the effect is far smaller than was expected. Becquerel proved that the phenomenon of Crookes's spinthariscope is due to the cleavage of the hexagonal blende under the bombardment of the α rays.

Becquerel considered with Curie that the radioactive phenomena are due to a constant evolution of the atom, the atoms of the active bodies being variable and constantly destroyed by explosions. The debris may be in part inert matter, partly groups of electrons or single electrons which constitute the various emanations, the α and the β rays, and communicating to the ether concussions (γ rays). The corpuscles remain scattered in matter or in space. According to this theory the emanation may be regarded as a group of electrons carried by gases or matter. Perhaps, as Filippo Re believes, we may consider the radioactive atom as a condensing solar system; perhaps with Perrin, as a solar system from which the exterior planets are escaping. Becquerel said of these hypotheses: "Re's may be considered of equal worth with the inverse hypothesis; they both deserve the interest due attempts to connect by common laws the infinitely small atom with the infinitely great universe."

Along with these great problems, in which Becquerel held such a leading position, he worked on certain other problems which the greater ones had temporarily replaced: his research with Edmond Becquerel on the temperature of the sun; then in 1879, on the magnetic properties of nickel and cobalt; then he showed by interference methods that in the propagation of radiations across rotary-polarizing magnetic fields the right and the left circularly polarized components travel with different velocities. Later, when the Zeeman effect was discovered, he took up his latest ideas relative to the action of the magnetic field upon light and showed the connection between the Faraday and the Zeeman phenomena. Then, in collaboration with Deslandres, he studied these phenomena experimentally, particularly with iron. They showed that in this case certain rays are unaffected, some give triplets, others quadruplets. The ray 0.3865 μ is anomalous; the two extreme rays are perpendicularly polarized to the lines of force, the other two parallel.

Becquerel also showed in a beautiful way the anomalous dispersion of sodium vapor by the classic method of crossed-prisms spectroscopes, but with a very original disposition of the apparatus. He produced a prism of sodium vapor by means of a small platinum trough held over a yellow sodium Bunsen flame. He received the spectrum of white light formed by this upon the slit of his grating spectroscope, and the hyperbolic form of the D lines indicated the phenomenon of the anomalous dispersion.

We will close this short notice of Becquerel with recalling that both he and M. Curie were the first to experience the painful effects of radium upon the human body. Becquerel, by carrying in his armpit for several hours a preparation of radium, contracted an ulceration in his side which was very long in healing, and at another time he received a noticeable pigmentation. With Curie he published his observations at about the same time that Curie had suffered the effects upon himself. These two great men were thus victims of the discovery which led them both to glory, and perhaps the weakness caused by their injuries was partly to blame for their premature end.

And now that I have so hastily reviewed these great accomplishments, may I be permitted, as a friend of Becquerel and of France, to express a heartfelt regret. Since Henri Becquerel built his work with the poorest of scant material, the regret which I wish to express is that so great a man had not at his hand the credit, the equipment, and assistants found in so many foreign laboratories, which would have more often allowed Becquerel to arrive ahead of others at the goal of the fertile paths which he disclosed.

William Ramsay *

1852–1916

———◆———

CHARLES MOUREU †

ALTHOUGH THE progress of science is continuous, it is neither uniform nor regular. From time to time this progress is suddenly accelerated, leaving strewn along the route the successive limits and creating thus a sort of discontinuity in the continuity. These sudden forward leaps are the work of a small number of geniuses whose discoveries guide the countless efforts of experimenters. When Dalton conceived the atomic hypothesis, he opened up and made fertile the entire domain of chemistry. When Davy isolated the alkaline metals he revealed to astonished chemists a whole new world. The idea of chemical function, the law of substitution, the law of homology, the atomic theory, are fundamental additions to knowledge derived from the works of Dumas, Laurent, and Gerhardt, who have transformed and rejuvenated chemistry, opening to it wider horizons. In opening synthesis as a channel for organic chemistry, Berthelot rolled back its frontiers immeasurably. It is in the ranks of these great chemists, worthy followers of Lavoisier and of Priestley, that belongs the brilliant investigator, the fertile inventor, the hardy pioneer whose work, so deeply original, and whose powerful personality, the counselor of the Chemical Society has given me the flattering mission of reviewing before you.

The name of Sir William Ramsay calls to mind at once, with all their meaning, two capital discoveries, to some extent paradoxical: On the one hand, the existence in the atmospheric air of a series of gaseous elements, which their chemical inertness relegates to the very borderland of chemistry; on the other hand, the production of one of these gases, helium, by the spontaneous

* *A.R.*, 1919, pp. 531–546. An address delivered to La Société Chimique de France, June 5, 1919, published originally in *Revue Scientifique*, Oct. 1919.
† French chemist (1863–1929).

disintegration of the radium atom, two classes of facts essentially new and of fundamental importance, whose discovery was possible only to an investigator of the highest rank, capable through exceptional ability, natural or acquired, of bringing light into the darkness of the unknown.

Of Scotch origin—he was born in Glasgow in 1852—Ramsay's hereditary influences were most favorable. In his family were chemists and doctors of note, and one of his uncles, Sir Andrew Ramsay, was a well-known geologist. Thus, as he himself liked to recall, Ramsay was descended from ancestors well above the average intellectually and in scientific pursuits, and he was well aware that he owed to them his calling and his ability as a chemist.

Having begun his studies in his native city, Ramsay went to complete them in Germany at first at Heidelberg, with Bunsen, and afterwards in Tübingen in the Fittig laboratory, where after some researches on the ammonia compounds of platinum, he studied the toluic acids. Organic chemistry attracted him by the flexibility of its combinations and the ingeniousness of its structural theories. On his return to Glasgow, where he secured a post as assistant, he studied specially the pyridic group, doubtless attracted by the problem of the synthesis of the cinchona alkaloids. Let us recall the synthesis of pyridine itself by the direct union of cyanhydric acid with acetylene, the production of the different pyridinic acids by the oxidation of the bases of Anderson, the production of the same acids (in collaboration with Dolbie) from quinine, from cinchonine, etc., an important observation which directly related these alkaloids to pyridine.

In 1880 at the age of 28, given the title of professor of chemistry at the University of Bristol, Ramsay began, in collaboration with his assistant, S. Young, a series of works on physicochemistry which were not slow in being noticed. They had for an object the revision of the physicochemical properties of a certain number of liquid types, water, alcohols, ethers, hydrocarbons, etc., with a view especially of determining exactly the relation of these properties to the atomic or molecular weights. A vast field was thus explored: the densities of steam, the tensions of steam, thermic constants, dissociation, critical points were studied, and many new and interesting observations were made. For the execution of so many delicate researches all kinds of new apparatus had to be designed and constructed with the result, extremely fortunate for the following of his career, that Ramsay became a very adroit blower of glass. Many of these contrivances are today in every-day use in laboratories.

It was in 1887 that Ramsay was called to the University College at London to succeed Williamson in that chair of chemistry already renowned, which he was by his efforts to make shine with a great light. For 30 years, in fact, Ramsay was to display in this post of honor the most fertile and brilliant activity. His peculiar qualities as an experimenter and his originality stood out in striking relief in a work which he published in 1893 in collaboration with Shields. Following a remarkable series of researches on surface tensions and densities at different temperatures, Ramsay gave to science the first experimental method of determining the molecular weights of substances in a liquid state.

We will leave here various other works, of a special nature, in order to come without more delay to those researches which were to immortalize the name of Ramsay. In 1894 Ramsay was 42 years of age. His work was already considerable in amount and his reputation solidly established, but he could not yet be called a celebrity. In possession of scientific knowledge as profound as it was extensive and varied, a penetrating mind with broad vision, a philosopher mindful of the general movement of the sciences, and eager to solve the mysteries of nature, free from all dogmatism and with mind open to even the most daring conceptions, an experimenter of finished technique, an enthusiastic spirit, Ramsay was ready for epoch-making discoveries. Given a favorable occasion, his genius would be fully equal to the task. Here is the occasion.

As often happens in scientific research, a chance observation may lead to the most unexpected results. Lord Rayleigh, who for several years had pursued with meticulous care the determination of the density of the principal simple gases (hydrogen, oxygen, nitrogen), noticed that the density of the nitrogen extracted from the air through absorption by other known gases was always greater than that of "chemical nitrogen," coming from different sources—oxides of nitrogen, ammonia, urea, etc. The difference affected the third decimal and did not exceed one-half per cent, but it was certainly more than experimental error.

Three hypotheses could explain this irregularity. The atmospheric nitrogen might be constituted in part of complex molecules of nitrogen comparable to the oxygen compound called ozone. Conversely, in the chemical nitrogen a certain proportion of the molecules might be dissociated into free atoms. But the density of neither of the gases, after being kept for eight months, underwent any change, and the permanent existence of condensed nitrogen or of dissociated nitrogen (atomic nitrogen) would scarcely be likely. Lord Rayleigh, who had at first accepted these explanations, rejected them to adopt the third hypothesis, according to which the atmospheric nitrogen is constituted of a chemical nitrogen mixed with an unknown gas of greater density. Being consulted by Lord Rayleigh, Ramsay was of the same opinion, and the two scholars at once united their efforts to isolate the mysterious gas whose existence was thus revealed.

It is interesting to recall here that in the fundamental experiments in which Cavendish a century before had established the formation of nitric acid by the prolonged action of electric sparks on a mixture of oxygen and nitrogen in moisture, the celebrated English chemist had noted that even after a very long time there always remained after absorption of the oxygen in excess a small gaseous residue representing about one one-hundred-and-twentieth of the volume of nitrogen. But the observation had passed unnoticed, and until the researches of Lord Rayleigh the nitrogen in the air had been considered as a simple gas identical with "chemical nitrogen."

While Lord Rayleigh, taking up again the experiments of Cavendish, verified the fact that atmospheric nitrogen does indeed leave, after the action of the oxygen and the spark, a residue which could not be overlooked, Ramsay attacked the problem by a purely chemical method, that of absorbing the nitrogen by magnesium at red heat. The repeated action of this metal increased the density of the gas. From 14, its weight in relation to hydrogen, the density increased little by little to become fixed in the neighborhood of 20. What remained was a new gas, absolutely distinct from nitrogen, characterized, aside from its density, by a peculiar spectrum very rich in lines in all regions and, a fact without precedent, by absolutely no ability to combine with any other substance whatsoever.

At the British Association meeting at Oxford in 1894, at the memorable session of August 13, Lord Rayleigh and Ramsay announced in turn that the nitrogen of the air is not pure nitrogen and that it contains a small proportion of a gas more dense and much more inert, to which they gave, on account of its chemical inertness the name of argon (α priv.; εργοσ, energy). This communication caused a great sensation among the audience, and the daily press took up the matter at length.* But chemists are generally conservative, and although the discovery was affirmed by two

---

* The discovery won for the two collaborators the Hodgkins Prize of $10,000 awarded by the Smithsonian Institution.

scholars so well qualified, many remained incredulous. It was not certain that argon was a simple substance. The molecular weight, according to the density, being 40, it might be a form of nitrogen cyanide CN_2; it was noticed also that a triatomic molecule of nitrogen N_3 would have a weight of 42, a figure not far from the one given above. A few months sufficed for Ramsay to clear up the question and dissipate all doubts. The comparison of the specific heats at a constant volume and at constant pressure shows an equally unexpected fact—that the molecule is monatomic, and consequently the new gas can only be an element.

There is never anything fundamentally new except that which could not be foreseen; that which is foreseen is implicitly contained, like the corollaries of a theorem, in that which is already within the domain of knowledge. To find in the air a new gas and in addition one of absolute chemical inertness is indeed a truly great discovery. It brought at once to the authors a deservedly great renown. Ramsay was not slow in adding to it through other researches not less surprising. And it was here again that a fortunate opportunity presented itself to him; he exploited it with admirable and masterful decision.

Early in 1895 Ramsay learned through a letter from Sir Henry Miers, that [William Francis] Hillebrand, chemist in the United States Geological Survey, had observed, while treating a uraniferous mineral, cleveite, with boiling sulphuric acid, the giving off of a gas which appeared to him to be nitrogen. The effect produced on Ramsay by this news was entirely characteristic of his scientific temperament. Many chemists, while finding the observation interesting, would have put off the study of the subject until later, when they might have more leisure. Ramsay, on receipt of the letter from Sir Henry Miers, called the laboratory aid and dispatched him immediately to the shops of the mineral merchants of London to buy all the cleveite that he could find. The cleveite arrived toward noon; before night it had been treated and the gas collected. During the two following days the known gases, except argon, which it had been expected would be found, were eliminated and the residue introduced into a spectrum tube. The spectrum of argon was not observed. There were few lines; one of these—yellow—was very brilliant. It was thought at first to be the line of sodium, present perhaps in the corroded electrodes. But Ramsay laughed at the idea; he was not in the habit of using dirty spectrum tubes, and, besides, he had made the tube himself. A comparison spectrum of sodium was observed simultaneously. The two lines were distinct and in no way superposed. It was then beyond doubt that it was a new gas, and the hypothesis was advanced that it might be helium.

Helium was that element, still unknown on the earth, whose existence in the sun was known through a spectroscopic observation carried out by the French astronomer Janssen at the time of the solar eclipse of the year 1868 and the subsequent suggestions of the English physicists Frankland and Lockyer. Was this new gas of Ramsay's helium or was it not? The answer was not long in coming. The spectrum tube was sent to Sir William Crookes, who measured with great care the wave length of the yellow line and found it identical with that of the solar line of helium. Scarcely a week had passed since Ramsay had received the letter from Sir Henry Miers. At the general meeting of the Chemical Society in March 1895 the discovery of terrestrial helium in the gases from cleveite was announced. Its molecular weight was 4, and a study of the specific heat indicated that the molecule was monatomic, like that of argon, which it also resembled through its complete chemical inertness.

During the two following years Ramsay hunted carefully for other sources of argon and helium. Argon and helium were found in certain mineral waters, those of Cauterets among others; today we know that they exist in all subterranean waters and gases. Furthermore, helium can be derived from a series of rare minerals. This observation was of great interest in what followed, after it was discovered that the same gas was given off in the disintegration of radium, as we shall see later on.

Their resistance to any combination assigned to argon and helium a place apart among the elements, and they did not fit in any of the groups of Mendeleyeff's table. Ramsay boldly suggested that they constituted the first two known terms of a new group, characterized by a valence of zero. Secure in observed analogies in the other groups of the periodic system, Ramsay, in a communication to the meeting of the British Association in Toronto in 1897 with the suggestive title, "An Undiscoverd Gas," predicted the existence of at least one other inert element, situated between helium and argon, near fluorine and having an atomic weight not far from 20. Before another year had passed, not only had Ramsay's prediction been realized, but more, in collaboration with Morris Travers, two other elementary inert gases had been discovered whose places he also fixed in the periodic system, near bromine and iodine, with the neighboring atomic weights of 82 and 130.

Ramsay submitted to a close examination different thermal

waters, such as those of minerals and of meteorites, without being able to discover any of the gases which he sought. Their presence in all the subterranean gases was to be demonstrated later, thanks to the use of a method of fractionating by means of cooled charcoal inaugurated by Sir James Dewar.* But if the three gases to be discovered really existed, ought they not to be found in considerable proportion in the atmospheric nitrogen along with argon?

One hundred cubic centimeters of liquid air having been reduced through spontaneous evaporation to several cubic centimeters, Ramsay vaporized them in a gasometer, then eliminated from it the oxygen and nitrogen by appropriate means. The gaseous residue thus prepared furnished the spectrum of argon with, in addition, a yellow line and a very brilliant green line. Besides, the density was a little greater than that of pure argon; the residue examined was then argon mixed with a certain proportion of a heavier gas. In order to isolate this gas, Ramsay, aided by Travers, prepared 15 liters of argon, a task requiring several months, and liquefied it by cooling with liquid air. The clear liquid obtained was submitted to a fractional evaporation very skillfully conducted, with the purpose of separating the gases more or less volatile than argon. The success was complete.

The first fraction yielded a light gas, about ten times more dense than hydrogen and characterized by a magnificent spectrum with brilliant lines in the red and the yellow. Ramsay called it neon. It is moreover accompanied by a certain proportion of helium, present also in the air, and from which it can be separated by the use of liquid hydrogen (—253°) which solidifies the neon and leaves the helium in a gaseous state. The end products of the distillation of liquefied argon were two other new gases, which could, however, be separated by liquefaction and fractionating. Ramsay called them krypton and xenon; their densities in relation to hydrogen were 41 and 65. For the three new gases, neon, krypton, and xenon, the study of the specific heats led, as for helium and argon, to a monatomic molecule. They are likewise chemically inert. Their atomic weights—20, 82, and 130—were found to occupy exactly the places indicated by the classification of Mendeleyeff.

* See James Chrichton-Browne, "Sir James Dewar," *A.R.*, 1923, pp. 547–553; Dewar, "History of Cold and the Absolute Zero," *A.R.*, 1902, pp. 207–240; "Liquefaction of Hydrogen and Helium," *A.R.*, 1898, pp. 259–266; "Liquid Hydrogen," *A.R.*, 1899, pp. 131–142; "Magnetic Properties of Liquid Oxygen," *A.R.*, 1893, pp. 183–187; "New Researches on Liquid Air," *A.R.*, 1896, pp. 135–148; "Solid Hydrogen," *A.R.*, 1901, pp. 251–261.

Thus, in the atmospheric air, which during more than a century had been believed to be perfectly known, Ramsay had succeeded in the four years from 1894 to 1898 in isolating a complete natural group of simple gases.* Indeed a splendid achievement! Striking proof of the fundamental truth comprehended in the periodic law! Witness, just as noteworthy, of the scientific faith and the ability in experimentation of this master! Nearly all the apparatus had to be invented, and Ramsay also had to construct most of it himself. Only those who have handled small quantities of gas and have prepared absolutely pure gases, giving spectra entirely free from foreign lines, are able to understand all the technical difficulties of such a work.

A little before the discovery of krypton, Ramsay thought he had isolated another element in the atmospheric argon; it had the same density as argon, but its spectrum was entirely different. He called it metargon and described several principal lines. Metargon was not, however, a new element; it was recognized that the lines indicated were due to traces of carbonic oxide, which occurs as an impurity in argon. Other chemists were working on the same problem, and Ramsay, too much hurried, had insufficiently purified his argon. I will cite Ramsay himself in this connection:

Should we under such circumstances regret the publication of an error? It seems to me that an occasional error should be excusable. No one can be infallible; and besides, in these conjectures one has always a large number of good friends who promptly correct the inaccuracy.

It is certain that anyone may be deceived; but it is not anyone indeed who would have been capable of discovering krypton and xenon in the air, which contains in volume 1 in 20,000,000 of the first and 1 in 170,000,000 of the second. This research on the rare gases of the atmosphere will remain a perfect model of original research. And if there was anything to be admired more than the ability in experimentation and the scientific penetration displayed, it was the energy and perservering ardor, qualities doubtless less brilliant, but which in this kind of work were absolutely indispensable.

Another question, in this connection, could not fail to present

---

* See his "Liquids and Gases," *A.R.,* 1892, pp. 303–312; "Undiscovered Gas," *A.R.,* 1897, pp. 247–258; "Kinetic Theory of Gases and Some of its Consequences," *A.R.,* 1898, pp. 277–287; "Recently Discovered Gases and Their Relation to the Periodic Law," *A.R.,* 1898, pp. 267–276. Other articles by Ramsay appeared in *A.R.,* 1900, pp. 233–257; 1904, pp. 207–220; 1911, pp. 183–197; 1912, pp. 219–229.

itself to Ramsay's mind. Are there not in the same group of inert gases, noble gases, as he liked to call them, other elements, heavier than xenon as predicted by the periodic system, or lighter than helium, such as nebulium, whose presence is probable in the nebulæ, and coronium, which appears to exist in the solar corona? We will recall in passing that besides the inert gases, Armand Gautier recognized in the atmospheric air an appreciable proportion of a gas lighter than helium, which was in fact hydrogen, whose production posed a most suggestive geochemical problem. Ramsay busied himself then in the search for new rare gases. With Watson he examined the lightest gases in the atmosphere in the hope of obtaining a gas less dense than helium, but without success. He was not more fortunate in the systematic study, undertaken with Richard Moore, of the distillation products of an enormous mass of liquid air (120 tons), put at his disposal by George Claude. Ramsay arrived at the conclusion that if the air contains gases heavier than xenon, the proportion of them is extremely small and does not exceed one twenty-fifth of one-billionth.

The discovery of the rare gases had excited universal enthusiasm. Physicists and chemists far and near wished to study these new elements; and it is interesting, for the glory of Ramsay, to indicate briefly the principal results that have issued from this study. Some, interested especially in the problem of affinity, sought, but in vain, to arouse chemical activity which they supposed to be dormant in the rare gases. Others, on the other hand, sought for them in natural media. Following a systematic study of a great number of subterranean gases (gas from thermo-mineral sources, volcanic gas, fire-damp), some simple conclusions have been formulated:

(1) All the natural gaseous compounds contain the five rare gases, and certain of them contain appreciable quantities of helium, some as much as 6 per cent (thermal gas of Maizières, Côte-d'Or), and even 10 per cent (thermal gas of Santenay, Côte-d'Or). (2) The krypton-argon ratio has practically the same value in all natural mixtures, including the atmospheric air; the krypton-xenon ratio differs from the preceding, but is likewise constant, as is also that of xenon to argon. This is also true of the ratio of these three gases to neon. The chemical inertness and other analagous properties of rare gases explain the constancy of the ratios. They have come through all the cataclysms of astronomy and geology without alteration of their relative proportions from those of the original nebulae. (3) Helium, it is true, accompanies the other members of the group on all their voyages,

but it escapes all proportionality; and it could not be otherwise, inasmuch as only helium is produced continually from radioactive substances, and these are unequally divided in the different strata.

You see, what unexpected and weighty problems have been brought up by Ramsay's discovery. What an exceptional destiny is that of these five gases, whose chemical inertness has assured to them, since the beginning of time, an eternal inviolability, and has thus made of them, like the demigods, immortal witnesses of all the physical phenomena of the earth and of the evolution of the spheres!

For what practical applications are the new elements destined? Lighting tests in neon have proved very encouraging. Argon is used in incandescent lamps. And above all—Ramsay himself made the proposition—balloons have been inflated with helium, and by this means made noninflammable.

What a prospect for aeronautics! How far we are from the famous solar spectrum line of Janssen, found again by Ramsay in the gas from cleveite! Other uses will follow for helium as well as for the related gases; their career is still only at the beginning. New example, among a thousand, of the value of purely speculative research! All scientific discoveries, however exclusively contemplative their concern at first might appear, cannot fail to lead sooner or later to practical applications. Would that the directors of our affairs could realize this fact which carries with it so much benefit and so much hope, and which also holds for them duties and responsibilities in the eyes of the country which has put its future in their hands. Could they but understand that science is power, that science is wealth! Let them encourage with all their power scientific research. Let them understand that learned men cannot live differently from other men and that they also have the right to a normal and honorable existence. Let them generously endow laboratories. Let them grant means for specially interesting studies which may be indicated to them. Let them take under their protection the young men of talent whose gifts should belong to the nation and whose development would bring to it glory and prosperity. Let them be able, in a word, to see in the budget for science a productive expenditure, a veritable investment with large returns. Then will they assure to research workers the means for their study, to learned men the possibility of giving their lives to science.

We now come to the year 1902. Pierre Curie and Mme. Curie had just obtained radium, the magnificent completion of an admirable work begun by Mme. Curie in 1897, a little after the discovery of radioactivity by Henri Becquerel in 1896. It was a logical outcome that Ramsay was attracted toward these most interesting researches. The new domain thus opened to science had as yet been explored only by physicists; it seemed to him immediately that chemistry also could and ought to enter on the scene. He entered boldly on the subject; he was to make conquests in it of vast importance.

Frederick Soddy had come from Montreal, where he had been assisting Sir Ernest Rutherford in his beautiful work on thorium. The curious fact had been discovered that a material substance was continually given off from thorium; it was given the name of *emanation*. Actinium and radium also gave off an emanation. These new substances were evidently of a gaseous nature. With all the skill already acquired in the manipulation of small quantities of a gas Ramsay found himself very well fitted to make a study of them. In collaboration with Soddy he tried to obtain the spectrum of the emanation of radium. As the amount of emanation which comes from even a relatively large quantity of radium is extremely small it was necessary to devise a special spectrum tube. It consisted of a thermo-metric capillary tube with an electrode made of a platinum wire soldered at the end, the second electrode being mercury, which was put in in advance with the very small quantity of emanation with the aid of a pump. Traces of impurities prevented seeing the spectrum of the emanation, which was not expected to be visible until later; but what was the surprise of Ramsay and Soddy when, after the passage of sparks through the gas for some time, they saw appear, little by little, the lines of helium!*

Helium! Still helium, a kind of *leit motiv* in the scientific life of Ramsay. And an element produced by another element! The magnitude of the discovery immediately appeared. For the first time was beheld the transmutation of one element to another! It was entirely revolutionary. Is it necessary to add that the scientific public did not at first believe and that it would continue to doubt for a long time? The helium had come from anywhere except from the emanation: from the glass, from the mercury, from the platinum, from the walls of the pump. Was not the indestructibility of atoms the dogma of dogmas? Since the time of the alchemists no one has believed in transmutation. Transmutation was the most extravagant of utopias. And yet today, but a few years later, who doubts that the atom has contradicted its etymology and disowned

* See William Ramsay and Frederick Soddy, "Experiments in Radioactivity and the Production of Helium from Radium," *A.R.*, 1903, pp. 203–206.

its name? Who doubts that the atom of radium disintegrates spontaneously and that the emanation and helium are the products of this disintegration? Who doubts that there is a complete genealogy of radium, going from uranium to lead, and that the differences in mass are due definitely to the expulsion of particles of helium gas thrown out like ballast in order to lighten the atoms for the beginning of a new existence? Who doubts finally, since the beautiful work of Sir J. J. Thomson, Sir E. Rutherford, and some other physicists, that the atom with its electrons and other constituent elements, is a very complicated organism, in fact, an entire world? It is no use for people to erect barriers between the known and the unknown; they will fall some day under the continuous pressure of original research; and happily there are many that have already thus been overturned on the paths of science.

The discovery of Ramsay and Soddy was not slow in being taken up. The formation of helium was demonstrated as coming from actinium by Debierne, from thorium and uranium by Soddy, from polonium by Mme. Curie and Debierne, and from ionium by Boltwood. It is fitting to recall, before leaving this subject, that Rutherford had previously expressed the idea that the particles "given off by the radioactive elements ought to be made up of atoms of helium."

This destruction of radioactive atoms, from which Ramsay was the first to see helium atoms arise, had the effect of liberating an enormous quantity of energy, capable of effecting immediately varied chemical reactions—the breaking up of water, of carbonic gas, of hydrochloric acid gas, of ammonia gas, of the substance of glass, etc. The emanation from radium in its disintegration gives off for each cubic centimeter a quantity of heat equal to that furnished by the explosion of 3½ cubic meters of the explosive mixture of oxygen and hydrogen gases. Ramsay supposed that if a sufficient amount of emanation of radium was put in actual contact with atoms, the energy liberated by the decomposition of the emanation would be able to break off some of them. In common with Cameron, he announced that he had thus obtained lithium, starting with copper, and carbon, starting with thorium and other elements of the same group. There has been and still is a great deal of skepticism regarding these transmutations. Mme. Curie and Mlle. Gledisch having repeated the experiments with copper, the results were negative. On the other hand, Ramsay carried out experiments without the use of emanation and they gave no trace of lithium. Continued researches ought to settle the debate.

The experiments of Ramsay and Cameron had been carried out

on aqueous solutions of metallic salts. In the case of copper, the gases derived from the liquid after the elimination of the oxygen and hydrogen coming from the decomposition of the water, gave the spectrum of argon, without any line of helium. On the other hand, in treating distilled water with the emanation, neon was obtained, with a trace of helium, but no argon. These results also were contested.

Ramsay, asked one day by Richard Moore if he would try the experiments again, made a typical response: "No," he said, "I do not believe it worth while. I can only again find lithium and neon, and for me to obtain the same results again would not be a confirmation. I will leave to others the task of repeating the researches." The extreme interest of the subject led him to expect that new studies would be undertaken by skilled experimenters having at their disposal sufficient quantities of radium.

Another problem, in some degree the reciprocal of the preceding, naturally presented itself: If the disintegration of heavy elements can lead to light elements, would it not be possible, by an inverse method, to condense light atoms into heavy atoms and thus realize in all its fullness the dream of the alchemists? Ramsay was not afraid to take up the subject. Collie and Patterson, having submitted the glass of an ordinary empty tube to cathodic bombardment, had announced the production of helium, which had been formed by the condensation of four atoms of hydrogen. Ramsay confirmed this result and, going further, found that if the hydrogen is moist—that is, if it is accompanied by oxygen—there will be, moreover, formation of neon, created by the addition of the atom of helium (4) to the atom of oxygen (16). It seemed to him therefore that under analogous conditions sulphur would lead to argon and selenium to krypton. Here, as well, the question should be taken up again. Its breadth perhaps surpasses that of all the others. Ramsay will have the honor of having opened up the new field, thanks to his incomparable talent in experimentation, as well as to his boldness and the independence of his scientific conceptions.

These are, in fact, Ramsay's most pronounced characteristics. They are shown again and in a most brilliant manner in another work on the radium emanation which he carried out in 1910 with the assistance of Whitlaw Gray. According to the theory of disintegration, the atom of emanation results from the loss of a helium atom by an atom of radium. If the atomic weight of radium is 226 and that of helium 4, the weight of an atom of emanation ought theoretically to be 222. Emanation, whose resistance to all combination had, moreover, been shown, came thus to occupy in the column of rare gases in the periodic system the place predicted for a homolog of xenon. Ramsay wished to prove this by experiment. And what an experiment! The volume of emanation at his disposal at any one time never exceeded five one-thousandths of a cubic millimeter (much less than the smallest head of a pin), and to determine the atomic weight it was necessary to weigh this infinitesimal volume of gas. A modification of the microbalance of Steel and Grant was constructed, whose sensitiveness attained several millionths of a milligram. The skill shown in preparing, purifying, and weighing the minute quantities of emanation was truly wonderful; and it was this work more than all the others which showed Ramsay's marvelous experimental talent. The result justified the effort. The mean of five determinations gave the number 223 for the atomic weight of radium emanation—a full and complete verification of the theoretical predictions, which Debierne also confirmed by an entirely different method (diffusion).

The brilliance of his work had brought to Ramsay the highest distinctions not only in his own country but all over the world. Academies and learned societies hastened to open their ranks to him. Our Academy of Sciences, which had elected him a correspondent in 1895, named him an associate in 1910. He was also an associate member of our Academy of Medicine. In the year 1904 the Academy of Stockholm awarded him the Nobel prize in chemistry.

One of the characteristic traits of Ramsay's personality was his enthusiasm, which he communicated to all those who worked under his direction, and the impression which he produced on his students, even during a very brief contact, remained ineffaceable. Friendly and patient with all, to "do well," according to his own expression, was all that was necessary to become his friend. Ramsay was a remarkable teacher with an elegant and picturesque manner of expressing himself, impulsive, clear, concise, and with the great charm of simplicity. In his lessons he did not hesitate at times to use the most advanced teachings; he was the first in England to introduce the works of Raoult, Arrhenius,* and van't Hoff.†

Everything which lives is in process of evolution. The real life of an experimental science like chemistry is in progress and discovery. On this subject Ramsay was of the opinion that he wanted original research to occupy early as great a place as possible in the work of a student. He distrusted examinations such as are usually

---

* See pp. 638–659 of the present volume.
† See G. Bruni, "Work of J. H. van't Hoff," *A.R.*, 1913, pp. 767–789.

held to judge candidates, which were too often dependent on chance. He feared especially that they might result in unjust and unfortunate eliminations capable of discouraging a student in his choice of a vocation. The professor who has followed the student during several years in the course and especially in the laboratory seemed to him to be better fitted than anyone to appreciate his true value. Ramsay always forcefully maintained these ideas and their logical consequences.

. . .

Ramsay wrote but few didactic works. His little treatise on *Modern Chemistry,* which has been translated into French, is a brief but substantial account of the principles of chemical philosophy. The same qualities are found in the highest degree in all Ramsay's writings. They are noted especially in several dissertations in which he developed his own ideas, and whose titles alone are enough to indicate their originality: "The Electron Considered as an Element," "Element and Energy," "Helium in Nature," "Problems Presented by Inorganic Chemistry," etc.

Ramsay was a polyglot and spoke fluent French and German. At the International Congress of Applied Chemistry held in Rome in 1906 he gave in French a lecture on "The Purification of Drain Water," a subject far enough away from the matters of pure science with which he was supposed to be entirely occupied. He came willingly into our country. He loved it and counted there many friends who have many charming letters from him full of a natural simplicity. We have also the remembrance of the excellent lectures which he gave here on his discoveries. Before the war he had also many connections in Germany and was there the object of many flattering attentions. During the celebration of the centenary of the University of Berlin in 1910 the delegates of the universities of the whole world were invited for the principal ceremony. Ramsay represented the University of London. When the Kaiser entered the room with his whole following, having perceived Ramsay, he stopped the cortege and went out of his way to take his hand.

. . .

At the beginning of the war, during the tragic days of 1914, Ramsay was at Le Havre, where he attended with Lady Ramsay and his son the Congress of the French Association for the Advancement of Science, presided over by Armand Gautier. He delivered a discourse at the opening session and was present at the first session of the section of chemistry. But, visibly, his thought was absent. The news each day became more alarming. After Wednesday, the 29th, when he perceived war imminent, . . . he was not seen again at the Congress. From the beginning of hostilities Ramsay with his ardent patriotism threw himself into the conflict. He fought with all the means in his power, through research in the laboratory and through his original suggestions, by pen and word, which he made the auxiliaries of his most indisputable authority. Of him also could be employed the famous phrase, "Je fais la guerre." It was through his persevering efforts chiefly that cotton was, too late perhaps, declared contraband of war. He died at 63 while his genius was still so rich in promise for science and for humanity, brought down by an incurable disease that carried him off in a few months. . . . The premature death of Ramsay is for science an irreparable loss by which a powerful beacon light is extinguished. This great investigator explored chemistry as a conqueror, and the progress which it owes to him comes from the strides of a giant. Ramsay served and was an honor to humanity, and he has brought to his native land incomparable renown. He was great not only in his genius and scientific enthusiasm, but also in the elevation of his soul, absorbed in the ideal, and in the greatness of his character. He will live in the memory of mankind, and posterity will keep aloft the name of Ramsay.

Jules Henri Poincaré *

1854–1912

———◆———

CHARLES NORDMANN †

WITH THE sudden death of Henri Poincaré a great sadness came to all lovers of idealism and of science. Among all classes it was felt that a great light had been extinguished in the firmament of thought. But that feeling was nowhere so poignant or so lasting as among those who in their silent arsenals slowly forge their weapons for the struggle against the unknown, in the workshop of the physicist, beneath the dome of the astronomer, or in the bare room which the philosopher so richly furnishes with his meditations.

Henri Poincaré was not only the uncontested master of natural philosophy, the intellectual beacon whose penetrating rays could pierce all the regions of science. It was not for such qualities alone that we admire him, for he had also those characteristics which made us love him. That is why for a century he, more than any other philosopher, has had "that personal influence which he alone can exercise whose heart has not ceded to his brain."

And now, when death takes from us this master whose task is done, it is the man alone whom we mourn. In the work which he left was the best part of himself. When a man passes from us while yet young, yet full of creative activity, of mental vigor, of moral force, the weight of whose authority was constantly re-

* *A.R.,* 1912, pp. 741–763. Translated from *Revue des Deux Mondes,* Sept. 15, 1912, pp. 331–368. Since this memoir deals mainly with Poincaré's scientific work and philosophy, it assumes biographical information. Poincaré was born in Nancy, France, April 29, 1854, and died in Paris, July 17, 1912. See his "Connections between Ether and Matter," *A.R.,* 1912, pp. 199–210; "Future of Mathematics," *A.R.,* 1909, pp. 123–140; "Light and Electricity, According to Maxwell and Hertz," *A.R.,* 1894, pp. 129–139.
† French astronomer (1881–1940), an authority on star photometry, director of the Paris Observatory.

newed, then our regrets are beyond bounds. In our sadness we are angry at fate, for what we lose is the unknown, the hopes without limit, the discoveries of tomorrow which those of yesterday promised.

Other nations regret the loss of Henri Poincaré no less than we. He was received with unbounded admiration in Germany where, on the invitation of their universities, he several times lectured so brilliantly on his work. Such intellectual crusades were among his greatest joys, for he felt that he was not only carrying conviction but friendship as well. Philosophers, mathematicians, astronomers, all spoke of him as the greatest authority of our time ("Die erste Autorität von dieser Zeit"). And just recently one of the most eminent of American astronomers, Professor [Forest Ray] Moulton, a member of the National Academy of Sciences of the United States, wrote of him that "although France had the honor of giving birth to this admirable man yet he may be regarded as a genius of the whole world. On his tomb should be engraved, those words which the English have put on that of Newton, 'Mortals, congratulate yourselves that so great a man has lived for the honor of the human race.' "

.   .   .

With his ruddy face, his beard turning a little gray and not always geometrically arranged, his shoulders bent as if under the ever-present weight of his thoughts, the first impression of Henri Poincaré was one of singular spirituality and notable gentleness. But two traits were particularly characteristic: his voice, deep and musical and remarkably animated when speaking of problems which greatly moved him, and his eyes, rather small, often agitated by rapid movements, under irregular eyebrows. In his eyes could be read the profound interior life which unceasingly animated his powerful brain. His glance was absent and kind, full of thought and penetration, his glasses scarcely veiling its depth and acuteness. His shortsightedness, poorly corrected by his glasses, added to his absent look and made one say of him, "He is on the moon." Indeed, he was often very far away. Legend began to form about him long before his death and attributed to him numerous traits, many of which for half a century have been attributed to Ampère, some erroneous, some indeed true.

It has been said that he was absent-minded; absorbed in thought would be more exact. Great thinkers, as well as all who are intense, are slaves of the interior tyrant which usurps their souls. When thought assumes control of a man it holds him under its claws as the vulture of Prometheus. The profound visions which possessed the soul of Poincaré left him no rest. Often he lost sight of the near-at-hand objects and the petty things of daily life, for his vision was closely focused on the infinite. It was when he was troubled with the immediate and ordinary things of life (and his judgment was then as sound as in regard to weightier matters), that he was ever really distracted, if we use the word in its true etymological sense.

In the discourse in which he was honored at the Académie Française Frédéric Masson wittily narrated several anecdotes of this absent-mindedness. Especially amusing was the carrying off one day unconsciously by Poincaré of a willow cage from the front of the shop of a basket-maker. The incident was true, but upon inquiry we find that Poincaré was only four years old when it happened. How many men of genius, indeed, how many men of no genius, are there at whom no one has ever been astonished that at that age they did not show the prudence of Nestor in their conduct on some stroll? Nor is this at all for the purpose of weakening our skepticism at that "little science of conjecture" which we call history. Poincaré was himself amused at all such anecdotes. . . . Moreover, he has very well explained that

if we meet so many geometricians and naturalists who in the ordinary doings of everyday life show a conduct at times astonishing, it is because, made inattentive by their meditations to the ordinary things which surround them, they do not see what is about them; it is not because their eyes are not good that they do not see; it is because they are not seeing with them. That in no way hinders them from being capable of using keen discernment toward those objects which are of interest to them.

The psychological characteristics of Poincaré were made the object of an interesting and very full study by Dr. Toulouse, of which certain conclusions should be noted. This study was made especially as an experimental test of the celebrated statement of Moreau of Tours that "genius is a nervous disease." We know how Lombroso took up and amplified that idea and that he thought that he could conclude from his researches that genius is inseparably connected with nervous troubles, especially with epilepsy. Yet, despite all those researchers and from whatever side they conducted their attack, Dr. Toulouse and his collaborators were unable to find in Poincaré the least trace of neuropathy. All their measures, all their tests, showed them a man perfectly normal psycho-physiologically, possessing in every way the most harmonious and perfect equilibrium. Thus he demonstrated at its proper value one of the most brilliant, one of the most sensational errors of Professor Lombroso.

.   .   .

The instability of attention in Poincaré was one of the characteristics which most struck Dr. Toulouse. Indeed, Poincaré had a habit of jumping from one subject to another entirely unconnected, of jumping, if I may employ a slang phrase, "from a cock to a donkey." In keeping with this was his habit, which often astonished strangers, of rising brusquely in the middle of a conversation, walking briskly for a moment, and then reseating himself. "Those are ideas," he would say, "which come and go." . . .

Poincaré, retired within the ivory towers of his thoughts, was insensible to all that disturbs the hearts of ordinary men. He himself used a somewhat lofty phrase full of a sad stoicism which would confirm that impression, when he said: "The sole end which is worthy of our labor is the search for truth. There is no doubt that first we must set ourselves to ease human suffering, but why? Not to suffer is a negative ideal and one which would be most certainly attained by the annihilation of the world." If in the eyes of the world he thus seemed to resist his own feelings, we ought not to believe them the less sensitive. But to goodness no less than to beauty belongs the quality of modesty. Poincaré was adverse to the familiarity of special friendships, because, with Renan, he felt that they made one unjust and were unfavorable to larger interests. Nevertheless, his kindness was perfect, even with those who importuned him for advice or praise. Within those two concentric circles, the family and the fatherland, modern society has accustomed us to limit our altruistic affections. He loved them dearly. He was too good a son of Lorraine not to feel hurt when he thought of mutilated France; in what sad and troubled accents he knew how to speak of that great grief which has left us twice inconsolable even though our sons seem to forget. But it was especially in his family that he showed without constraint his charming tenderness of heart. He himself taught his four children to read, and I have known aspects of his romps with them which would recall Henry IV, but it would be imprudent to describe them here. How far removed he seems in these from that abstract mind in which they would have us see him, retired like some monstrous snail within the inaccessible convolutions of his thoughts. Moreover, he had the good fortune to live in surroundings the most favorable to creative work, in an atmosphere of silent affection and discreet quiet which the gentle hands of the women of his household knew how to create around him.

Poincaré was attracted by beauty in all its forms provided only it was noble. Music, painting, poetry, were his preferred relaxations. Even in science we will see that he loved it above all for the esthetic pleasure it brought to him. . . . We should also recall his brilliant school days, his wonderful faculty for assimilation. He followed all the mathematical courses of the École Polytechnique without taking a single note, not because he remembered the demonstrations but because he could reason them out at will. We should recall that he was very skilled in reasoning, but what does that prove? The greater portion of the teachers of mathematics have left no trace of themselves in the world. For it is one thing to assimilate, another to invent . . .

To be complete, we should conclude by speaking of his career, his rise to the very highest rank, to the greatest honors given by society. But that matters little. . . . Poincaré never attached much weight to such honors. He was deeply and sincerely modest, hesitating always to announce definite conclusions, and his intellectual attitude was constantly one of doubt. It is perhaps for that reason that among a dozen great scientists who have lived during the last century, he accomplished the miracle of never having made a single enemy, a single one hostile to him in science.

In his scientific work Poincaré touched all the great mathematical questions. He did not merely touch them as, from the multiplicity of problems examined, one might suppose, just skimming over them. . . . Mathematician above all, he could clear fields for himself in those studies which transcend reality and where the pure geometrician, lost completely among his harmonious abstractions and pure deductions, constructs at his will, immaterial, impeccable beings of strange beauty. The pure mathematician has at his beck intimate delights of such esthetic quality that, lost in a kind of grand mysticism, he no longer finds interest in the exterior world. Poincaré, however, was not of that kind, although his researches in geometry and analysis made him the greatest mathematician of our times. "Experience," he said, "is the sole source of all truth." And those words acquired a singular force coming from the mouth of the greatest theorist of our epoch. That was why among mathematical problems Poincaré attacked especially those which physics brought before him. That was why he passed so readily from pure analysis to mathematical physics and then to celestial mechanics. And, finally, that was why he came to reflect upon the very foundations of our knowledge, upon the past and the future of our world, upon the value of our thoughts as we pass to the limits of what we can know to the borders of that abyss separating physics and metaphysics, into which most of us cannot glance except with dizziness. It wrung from Pascal many sighs, yet he could look at such matters as he looked at all other things, not with a useless despair, without prejudice and foolish illusions, but with simple, clear, and profound good sense. He knew how to look at them and after a glance with his eagle eye to sum up all in a word.

"My daily mathematical studies," said Poincaré—"how shall I express myself?—are esoteric and many of my hearers would revere them more from afar than close to." That is what he said one day to excuse himself for speaking on a mathematical subject. Whenever he commenced one of his profound lectures, in which he charmed his listeners, he felt the need of thus excusing himself. Thus by his modesty he knew how to make us pardon his genius. . . . Were I to characterize in a few words what Poincaré brought new into the divers processes of calculus, which won for him the title "Princeps Mathematicorum," by unanimous consent given to no other man since Gauss, I would proceed thus: In algebra and in arithmetic, where he introduced the new and fertile idea of arithmetical invariants and in the general theory of functions, his discoveries were numerous and would have sufficed for the glory of several mathematicians.

It was especially in the theory of differential equations that the genius of Poincaré showed itself. If he spent on them the greater part of his intellectual resources it was without doubt because most of the problems offered in the physical study of the universe led to just such equations. Newton was the first to show that the state of a moving system, or, more generally, that of the universe, depends only on its immediately preceding state, and that all the changes in nature take place in a continuous manner. True, the ancients in their adage, *Natura non fecit saltus,* had an inkling of it. But Newton was the first, with the great philosophers of the seventeenth century, to free the idea from the scholastic errors which perverted it and then to assure its development. A law, then, is only the necessary relation between the present state of the world and that immediately preceding. It is a consequence of this that in place of studying directly a succession of events we may limit ourselves to considering the manner in which two successive phenomena occur. In other words, we may express our succession by a differential equation. All natural laws which have been discovered are only differential equations. Looking at it slightly differently, we may say that such equations have been possible in physics because the greater part of physical phenomena may be analyzed as the succession of a great number of elementary events, "infinitesimals," all similar.

The knowledge of this elementary fact allows us to construct the differential equation, and we have then to use only a method of summation in order to deduce an observable and verifiable complex phenomenon. This mathematical operation of summation is called the "integration" of the differential equation. In the greater number of cases this integration is impossible, and perhaps all progress in physics depends on perfecting the process of integration. That was the principal work of Poincaré in mathematics. And in that line his work was amazing, especially in the development of those now famous functions, the simplest of which are known as the Fuchsian functions (named after the German mathematician Fuchs, whose work had been of aid to Poincaré). We may represent by these new transcendental functions, which are also called automorphic, curves of any degree and solve all linear differential equations with algebraic coefficients. Poincaré thus gave us, using the apt expression of Humbert, his colleague in the Académie des Sciences, "the keys of the algebraic world." Poincaré himself used these algebraic tools in his researches in celestial mechanics.

To tell the truth, the Newtonian idea of the continuity of physical phenomena has of late been somewhat battered in several places by the new and odd theory of "quanta," to the construction of which several physical discoveries have led. This supposes a certain physical discontinuity in the atomic phenomena which produce radiation. Not wishing to go too much into detail on this subject, I am going to make a somewhat bold comparison, one perhaps not wholly void of meaning: The hypothesis of quanta has grown up side by side with that of continuity, just as in biology the Lamarckian and Darwinian theories of slow and imperceptible evolution have come recently face to face with those of sudden and discontinuous mutation advanced by the Dutch naturalist, De Vries. The latter, by the new evidence brought forward, has not destroyed the older theory. He has merely enlarged it, shown its limitations, and left it intact in its essentials. Similarly, the theory of quanta, it is probable, will not prevent the greater part, if not all, of physical phenomena from being capable of representation by differential equations. The progress which the latter have brought, the physical discoveries to which they have led, notably in optics, in electricity, and in astronomy, are their guaranty. Accordingly, the new functions discovered by Poincaré will always remain one of the most brilliant contributions of pure theory to the study of external phenomena.

If we study the characteristics of Poincaré's method and of his mathematical genius, we find especially a wonderful faculty for generalization. Instead of starting, as do most students, with a study of the minor details, he jumped to the very heart of his problem, neglecting the intermediate details, like an audacious conqueror, who, without preliminary skirmishing, makes his first onslaught upon the master difficulty, the most impregnable fortress, inventing on the spot the instruments for subduing it and then forcing its surrender without striking a blow. Then he would leave to others the investigation and organization of the new province which he had just won and pass immediately to other conquests. In that sense we may speak of him as being "more a conqueror than a colonizer." There resulted that peculiar method of thought so noticeable in his philosophical writings, so disconcerting at times to the novice, one which brought upon him the reproach of being disconnected. True, Poincaré's process of reasoning was not smooth and continuous. He proceeded by successive bounds which had more the effect of a broken line. . . .

.   .   .

Contrary to our expectations, conscious work, voluntary and logical, did not with Poincaré play the most important part. Nothing is more amusing in that respect than the manner in which he has told us of his discovery of the Fuchsian function. This idea, which struggled vaguely in his brain one evening after he had drunk an unaccustomed cup of coffee that kept him awake, took shape little by little under the strangest of circumstances. Everyone has read his account in which he told how he saw in due proportion all the chief difficulties but did not consider them further, and then how, long afterwards, in a flash the solutions he wished appeared to him when he was putting his foot on the step of an omnibus, at another time when crossing a street, and yet again in the midst of a trifling conversation during a geological stroll.

The "subconscious self," or, as some have put it, "the subliminal self," plays in mathematical invention a supreme part. There where we believe reason and will ruled alone we find something appearing analogous to the inspiration which custom attributes to poets and composers. And it is a troublesome circumstance that this subconscious self succeeds in solving problems and overcoming difficulties that the conscious self could not. Is then the subconscious not superior to the conscious self? Have we not here something within, greater than ourselves, a sort of divine essence superior to our will and reason that makes us capable of tasks greater than ourselves? We can understand the importance of such a question and the spiritual significance of a positive reply. The positive mind of Poincaré, however, would not admit supernatural explanations unless absolutely necessary, and in a penetrating and accurate investigation he has shown a way to escape such a conclusion. He makes us see how the automatism of the subliminal self works only upon material which the conscious self prepares for it and then explains how, among the great number of combinations which the subliminal self forms, only those come into our consciousness which are apt and elegant and consequently affect our senses and attract our attention. The simple and most harmonious construction turns out to be precisely the most useful, as experience and reason repeatedly teach. The esthetic sentiment for the harmony of form and number and geometrical elegance dominates the thought of the mathematician. His soul is first of all that of an artist and a poet. These views, so deep and true, are somewhat at variance with the classic idea of a mathematician, respectable, exact, but rather ludicrous, with his mechanical brain and an eye which the traditional glasses have rendered blind to all beauty and in whose heart nature has placed, instead of feeling, a table of seven decimal-place logarithms.

In unveiling to us in a man of science worthy of the name, a sensitive and esthetic being, Poincaré has again yielded to his innate modesty. The limitations of our brain have made us exalt its merits in our modern society where the "cult of intelligence" rules. We have had and perhaps still have a tendency to exalt the virtues of the will at the expense of those which come from the heart. We hold as superior to all else the attributes of the thinking man, and so our system of justice has a deep disdain for those who are irresponsible, though indeed we do not always judge that they merit punishment. In thus showing us that his logical development for science was due largely to his subconscious and involuntary and only partly to his conscious faculties, Poincaré doubtless somewhat diminished his own glory, perhaps even of all scientists in the eyes of some. As to that I imagine that he would be easily consoled. His marvelous autopsychological study has explained one thing which seemed at first very surprising: how working only four hours, or rather consciously working only four hours a day, Poincaré was able to produce a scientific contribution perhaps greater than that ever made by any other mathematician. Uncontrolled by his will, his cerebral machine worked by itself night and day, without stopping. Perhaps otherwise he might not have died so young. That interior flame, which without rest shone so brightly, burned up too soon the lamp which held it.

In astronomy the work of Poincaré was gigantic. That science could not have failed to attract him from the very first. . . . The study of the stability of our universe has been for two centuries the fundamental problem of celestial mechanics for the solution of which the genius of mathematicians has striven. This portion of space wherein we are placed, the solar system, is it stable? Will those planets which we have observed from time immemorial continue to describe invariably the same immense orbits with only a few periodic oscillations from their mean positions, will they continue thus indefinitely in the future? Or will this machine so harmoniously contrived, wherein we at present see no apparent sign of possible destruction, become unstable and disappear some day? That is the problem.

When Newton demonstrated that gravity acted not only between the sun and the planets but also between the planets themselves, it was seen that there must result irregularities in the harmony of the solar system, that the reciprocal attraction of the planets must slightly deform the perfect ellipses which the attraction of the sun alone would have made them describe. Truly these deformations are small because of the smallness of the masses of the planets compared with the central sun. (Jupiter's mass is 300 times that of the earth but only one one-thousandth that of the sun.) But might not these planetary perturbations, accumulating through centuries the effects already observable in the time of Newton, finally destroy the Kepler ellipses? At any rate, the simple harmony of the world of Kepler no longer is real. Newton, strongly disturbed by the possibility of the impending catastrophe, made, in his optics, this allusion to the planetary inequalities, "which probably," he says, "will become so great in the long course of time that finally the system will have to be put in order by its Creator."

In 1772 Laplace believed he was able to demonstrate that these fears were groundless. He showed that the secular inequalities of the planetary elements compensated themselves periodically at the end of a sufficiently long period and the terms of the first order of the perturbations would disappear in the calculations. That implies a stability of our system at least for a very long time, thousands of secular periods. Consequently, Laplace criticized the *deus ex machina* concept invoked by Newton and somewhat haughtily believed he could affirm, arguing from his results, that the machinery of our world had had no need of the initial fillip, that it would go ahead indefinitely without outside assistance. Is it necessary to note that there must be some fault in logic on the part of one who could suppose that when the solar system had so beautifully evolved from a nebula the process of evolution would stop and become fixed in eternal immobility or perhaps better in invariable mobility? But even great men sometimes make slips in their logic. Men have always made them.

Later, two celebrated mathematicians, Lagrange and Poisson, considerably extended the system of Laplace. The indefinite stability of the planetary elements seemed assured forever. The address delivered by the astronomer De Pontécoulant (by no means one of the least) before the Académie des Sciences when the statue of Poisson was dedicated, shows well the state of belief of the world upon this matter then, and it was scarcely altered at the end of the nineteenth century.

For his masterpiece [he said] Poisson had the honor of solving that most important problem, the stability of the solar system, of which, after the works of Laplace and Lagrange, doubts still existed in the most judicial minds. In the future the harmony of the celestial spheres is assured. Their orbits will never depart from the almost circular form which they have today and their respective positions will make only slight departures from a mean position in which the succession of centuries will finally see them revolving. The physical universe was therefore built upon indestructible foundations, and God, in order to conserve the human race, will not be obliged, as Newton wrongly believed, to retouch his work.

So matters stood when Poincaré attacked the problem. Soon discoveries succeeded discoveries. The problem set is this: Being given several bodies of known masses in given places and with given velocities at some known moment, to determine what these places and velocities will be at any future time t. For a single planet and the sun the problem is completely solved by the laws of Kepler. But when *two* planets and the sun are considered, the reciprocal attraction of the planets upon each other must be considered. Then we have the celebrated problem of *three bodies*. The difficulties of this latter problem are such that it can be solved only by the method of successive approximations. In the equations which led Laplace and his successors to their conclusions as to the stability, the coordinates of the planets were developed in a series whose terms were arranged in powers of the masses. Poincaré first showed that we could not thus obtain an indefinite approximation and that the convergence of the series had been assumed without proof by those who employed them, and that it is probable that in the terms of higher order, t, the time, enters not only with the sine and cosine, which would lead to periodic compensations of the irregularities, but also outside of the trigonometric functions, so that certain of the terms, at first negligible, may possibly increase indefinitely with the time. Here with one blow he reduced to naught the conclusions of Laplace and his successors.

Poincaré found later that certain new methods would allow him to express in every case the coordinates of the planets in a purely trigonometric series, avoiding the inconveniences of the former methods, and he proved for the purpose a brilliant series of new theorems of great generality. The rigorous proof of the stability now depended only on knowing whether the new series would be convergent. This was the nub of the problem, for before Poincaré all astronomers had supposed a trigonometric series to be absolutely convergent. Poincaré showed that that opinion, despite the fact that it was classic, was erroneous, and indeed that, when we have represented the coordinates of the planets by a convergent series which is not very different from that employed by Laplace, we will not have demonstrated the stability of the solar system. Because of these great results which are like the crowning of three centuries of incessant research, posterity will certainly place this new treatise on celestial mechanics (*Les Méthodes nouvelles de la mécanique céleste*) by the side of the immortal *Principia* of Newton. All future researches on this subject must be built upon the solid foundations laid by Poincaré.

Celestial mechanics in general considers the planets only as if all their matter were concentrated in mathematical points. It leaves out of consideration the other properties of these objects, evidently generally negligible in comparison with the Newtonian attraction, but whose effects with time may become of importance relative to the stability of the systems. Attacking the question from a new side, Poincaré showed that there are three preponderant forces tending to modify the orbits: the resistance, weak though it may be, of the interplanetary medium; the tides that the planets and the sun produce upon each other; and the magnetism of the planets. The accumulated effects of these will finally precipitate the planets into the sun. That will be the end of our system of planets. Will that be the end of the human race? Certainly not, for it is very probable that other changes will have ended terrestrial life long before the day of that final catastrophe. The day? No, I should not say day, for there will no longer be day and night—our earth will then forever present the same side toward the sun! Many reasons lead us to believe that in the future as well as in the past the duration of human life upon this globe will be infinitely small compared to the age of our earth. So those who fear that their end will be hastened by that of the solar system may be reassured. The retinue of the sun once having disappeared, does that mean that other analogous and distant systems, scattered here and there like living dust, will not exist indefinitely? That is a question much discussed at present, but one we cannot answer.

The problem of the shape of a star resolves itself into that of a fluid mass rotating and subject to various forces. Next to the problem of three bodies it is the most important one of celestial mechanics. Here, too, Poincaré made remarkable discoveries. They mark an epoch in the study of the subject, as Sir George Darwin noted the day he presented to Poincaré the gold medal of the Royal Society of London. Formerly but two figures of equilibrium were known for rotating fluids, the ellipsoid of revolution and that of Jacobi with three unequal axes. Poincaré found through his calculations an infinite number of others which are stable and shaped like pears, whence the name apiodes given to this class of bodies. The pear-shaped bodies discovered by Poincaré appear to have an important place in nature, as proved by the evidence from certain nebulæ and close double stars. They enable us to get some idea of the mechanism of that bipartition, somewhat analogous to that of organic cells, which may have given birth to a great number of binary systems and which successively separated the earth from the sun and then the moon from the earth.

Finally, Poincaré showed that no form of equilibrium is stable when the velocity of rotation exceeds a certain limit. He at once applied this fact to that enigmatic marvel, the ring system of Saturn. Maxwell showed that the rings could not be solid and that, if fluid, their density could not exceed three one-hundredths the density of Saturn. Poincaré proved that if the rings are fluid they could not be stable unless their density is greater than one-sixtieth that of Saturn. He concluded as the only alternative the supposition that they are formed of a multitude of small satellites, gravitating independently. We know how spectrum analysis subsequently proved his marvelous deduction.

A small portion only of Poincaré's scientific work is included in that just described. Even a superficial description of all would require volumes, it is so vast. Before turning to another branch of his work, that which will reveal his philosophy, I feel almost a kind of remorse as I find myself obliged by the limitations of this tribute to pass over in silence all those great discoveries which he has so generously, almost indifferently, if I may use that word, worked out, always with the same mastery, in such different branches of science, in optics, in thermodynamics, in electricity, or in astronomy. Sometimes with daring strokes he treated of the relations between matter and the ether. Again, he compared the thousands of suns of the Milky Way to the molecules of a bubble of gas, applying to them kinetic theory and revealing such astonishing aspects of the stellar universe. Then from a ray of light sent from one of the planets he teaches us to learn at the same time the motion of the sun which sends the ray, of the planet which reflects it, and of the earth which receives it. . . .

From science to philosophy there is but a step to take, they so bound and penetrate each other. The Greeks had but one word to express each. Even today the English call the physical study of the universe natural philosophy. Poincaré could not escape the attraction which has forced all the great workers in the exact sciences from Democritus to d'Alembert, toward the end of their lives, to reflect upon the primorial mysteries of the strange universe wherein our ephemeral thoughts live and die. . . . The philosophical ideas of Poincaré have deeply impressed all those who think and have given to our generation its intellectual profile. By singular chance they have stirred the most adverse camps. Each one has wished to use them for their weapons—vain desires, for these ideas soar far above them, and, indeed, such ideas sometimes seem to unchain and reanimate quarrels of other ages. Whence does this man get this strange power of thus moving by his thoughts alone a realistic epoch in which the conflicts of everyday life press harder than ever upon the world of ideals? This power is due to Poincaré's intellectual superiority and especially to his thorough sincerity. In what way are these new points of view so suggestive, so useful, so convincing?

If we exclude the bitter, everpresent struggle for better living, which does not gain in dignity as we pass from animal to man, it seems as if all man's striving has arisen from his thirst for both truth and justice. And we always find, save with Dr. Pangloss, a dead mythological figure without descendants, that in reality justice is not always the rule. The two words, truth and justice, which we are accustomed to couple, correspond in a certain way to states which the very nature of things renders mutually exclusive. Some men, whom truth, the desire for knowledge above all else, attracts, follow to their last consequences the dictates of reason even though they drown in the bitterness of their dearest illusions. The others, ever protected by that magic potion called justice, and which some intuition, whence I know not, assures them must exist, deliberately turn their eyes from exterior reality which at every step spoils their dream. To them it is enough that a thing be just in order that it be the truth. Their inner ideals are a superior guide to outside reality.

The first mode serves as a mantle for diverse forms of materialism, rationalism, positivism, scientism; the second rules as mistress to various spiritual doctrines of which the most recent and suggestive is pragmatism in its various forms. Contrary to its various predecessors, pragmatism pretends not to ignore science. With varied shades and pretenses, often modified by circumstances, these two tendencies have separated men as far back as we go in history. Nor can it be otherwise in the future. As long as our nature is what it is are we condemned to toss between these two extremes, which are called intelligence and sentiment, reasoning and dreaming, the reality and the ideal. We may sum up all history of the torments of human thought by that name which Goethe gave to one of his most beautiful books, *Dichtung und Wahrheit* (Truth and Fiction).

The conflict becomes especially bitter and irritating when it no longer takes place between schools of thought but between individuals. Sometimes one sect seems to be supreme. Oftentimes both lose. The love for the ideal and the taste for the real, lost in the bitter contest, leave the soul empty and lifeless. Poincaré's philosophy shows how we may challenge both of these dogmatic extremes. Nor does he do this with arms rusted and stacked in idle repose. He has nothing in common with a vague eclecticism. . . . He attacks the problem at its very foundation, assigning to each step its definite limitations. He gives us reasons for doubt, but at the same time reasons for action, for loving the beautiful and the true, even though they may not be accessible. . . .

To a superficial observer scientific truth is beyond the pale of doubt; scientific logic is infallible; if sometimes a scientist is deceived it is because he has overlooked some conditions.

Mathematical truths are derived from a few self-evident axioms by an unimpeachable chain of reasoning. They rule not only over us but over nature herself. They limit in a way even the Creator. He can choose only between a few possible solutions. We need, then, only a few trials to know what choice He made. From every experiment many consequences may follow through a series of mathematical deductions, each one leading into knowledge of some new corner of the universe.

Note the significance of these facts for the good of the people; the importance to those colleges which first discover the physical basis of some scientific truth. But note how they have misunderstood the relation of experiments and mathematics; for hundreds of years philosophers have made worlds of dreams based as little as possible upon facts.

Poincaré first undertook to show the weakness of that creed which refers all phenomena to time, number, and space, and which was left to us by the traditions of the seventeenth and eighteenth centuries. The "mathematical universe," that dream sketched by Descartes and elaborated by the great encyclopædists, expressed the very essence of everything in an absolute, definite geometrical form. According to the Cartesian conception, all the properties of matter are reducible to extension and movement. Matter hid nothing further. This ambitious dream was indulged in not only by the people and the colleges, as Poincaré has stated, but even in our day by scientists of considerable repute, notably in the work of the celebrated German naturalist Haeckel, who developed such a system and with naïve arrogance believed he had solved the "riddle of the universe."

There has been quite a little doubt since Kant whether these notions of time and space upon which this metaphysical structure is based, this absolute pragmatism, if I may use that term, are not a little subjective. That at once renders the very foundations of their structure insecure. But it was Poincaré's task to show in a not easily refutable, scientific manner what was to be thought of these fundamental ideas. For that he examined in turn the various sciences based upon geometrical form, first, geometry itself, then mechanics, and finally physics.

Mathematics was first tried. Complete rationalism, after having first pursued dogma and the absolute into their ancient fortress, by a strange and somewhat paradoxical turn restored them to mathematics. He believed that mathematics could not be what it seemed. There seemed to be something of fatality, necessity, from which there is no escape. . . .

Now, if with Poincaré we examine the sciences of number and extension, especially the first principles, we find this: The postulate of Euclid, upon which all geometry is based, states that "through

a point we can pass but one line parallel to a given right line."
For centuries the greatest efforts have been made to demonstrate
that postulate, and then during the last century the Russian Lobatschefski and the Hungarian Bolyai almost simultaneously
showed that such a demonstration is impossible. Yet the Académie
des Sciences each year receives a dozen or so pseudo-demonstra-
tions of that postulate.

Lobatschefski did even better: supposing that several parallel
lines can be drawn through a point parallel to a given right line,
retaining the other axioms of geometry, he proved a succession of
strange theorems, between which it was impossible to find any
inconsistency, and built a new geometry, no more unimpeachable
logically than the ordinary Euclidean geometry. Then Riemann
and yet others came who showed that we could construct as many
more geometries as we wished, each perfectly logical and coherent.
The theorems of these new geometries are sometimes very odd.
For instance, the following one, imagined by Poincaré himself,
has been demonstrated: A real right line can be perpendicular to
itself.

I imagine that architects and engineers would scarcely admit
such deductions, although they are in no way logically contradictory. That brings us to the kernel of our discussion. If, as
results from what has preceded, the axioms of geometry are only
conventions, or, as Poincaré has expressed them, "definitions in
disguise," and if the Euclidean gometry is no more absolutely true
than any other, why have men chosen and used it? Because it is
better adapted to our needs, to our daily life, to the exterior world
in which we live; because in this world its theorems reduce to the
simplest possible form the relationships between things. A meas-
urer could express just as accurately by means of a Lobatschefskian geometry the relation between the volume and the sides of a
cube of wood. But it happens from the nature of a cube of wood,
or rather from the way our senses comprehend it, that those relations would be more complex than with the ordinary Euclidean
geometry. It is possible to imagine a world so constructed physically that men having our brains—that is, our kind of logic—
would not find Euclidean geometry the simplest.

Geometry, then, is no longer the inner temple of the absolute.
It is an arbitrary creation of our intellect. It can inform us only
relatively to the corresponding logical developments. However, in
a certain sense geometry depends also on experience, since, as
we have just seen, the exterior world appears simplest in the
Euclidean aspect. That does not mean that geometrical truths can

be proved or invalidated by experiment. Our instruments and our senses are imperfect, whereas a geometrical theorem which is not exactly true is false. If we measure with our instruments the sum of the angles of a triangle drawn upon paper, we shall never find them exactly equal to two right angles. Sometimes we will find the sum smaller, by perhaps a millionth, as much smaller as you please, but nevertheless smaller, which would verify a theorem of the Lobatschefskian geometry, sometimes a little greater but sufficient to conform to a Riemann geometry. Experiment, then, does not show the exclusive truth of Euclidean geometry, which, like the others, is at bottom an edifice formed by logic. If the Euclidean method is innate to us, it is doubtless because of ancestral experiences, because the brain of man has little by little been adapted to the exterior world by natural selection and because Euclidean geometry has proved to be "the most advantageous to mankind; in other words, the most fit."

If in mathematics deduction is almost all, fact almost nothing, we find the reverse in the observational sciences. Pure deduction can teach us very little about nature except in an indirect way, and then only because our brain has little by little become harmonized to the exterior world with the fewest clashes possible. In that sense, certainly, the study of our intellect teaches us indirectly of the universe itself just as the appearance of a mortal wound indicates to the medical expert the instrument employed and the stroke of the assassin. But that evidence is not only indirect, it is incomplete, for it tells us nothing of those external conditions not involved in the adaptation of the species. These latter are the more numerous. Accordingly, the discoveries due to the experimental sciences are unlimited, whereas those from pure deduction are doubtless limited. It is better to observe than to reason, and doubtless in that sense Poincaré is to be understood when he wrote in regard to the methods of the physical sciences: "Experience is the sole source of all truth. It alone can teach us new things. It alone can give us certainty."

But then, should not the theorems of mathematical physics, which are but the synthesis and expression of physical experiences, furnish us with a definitive, although in a way dogmatic, image of the universe such as certain philosophies have promised? We once believed so. But having observed how precarious was the fortune of such theories and how rapidly and repeatedly the most brilliant gave way to others, some have been pleased to call science futile and only a source of error. Poincaré, however, has shown that physical theories deserve such excesses neither of honor nor of indignity and has brought their blind adorers as well as their systematic detractors to a more sane view.

Observation and experience furnish the physical facts to the physicist. Should he be content merely to accumulate them? No, for "he must coordinate them. Science is built with facts as houses are with stones; but an accumulation of facts is no more a science than a heap of stones a house"; and, further, a physicist must "predict" phenomena. So he generalizes what he has observed, interpolating, connecting by a line the isolated facts; then he prolongs that line, extending it into a region not yet observed where the coordinates of his curve indicate to him new phenomena. Then by further experiments he may test these predicted phenomena to see whether or not he has truly predicted. If truly, then his extrapolation was justified and expresses real relationships; if not, then he must try again.

Unless I have been deceived, the picture just sketched indicates just exactly the purpose of mathematical physics and the part it plays both in synthesis and in prediction. The mathematical expressions of physical theory are algebraic translations of the curves such as I have just described and which the physicist mentally draws. The better a physical theory expresses the real relationships between the phenomena, the better will it predict hidden relations verifiable by trial and the more useful it will be, the more fit, the more true.

But the truth of a theory must not be misunderstood. No theory could be more useful than Fresnel's in attributing light to movements of the ether. Today we prefer that of Maxwell, which supposes light is due to oscillating electric currents. Does that mean that the theory of Fresnel was erroneous? No, for the object of Fresnel was not to prove the existence of the ether or whether or not it is formed of atoms, whether these atoms move this or that way. His object was to predict optical phenomena. For that the theory of Fresnel serves today as well as it did before Maxwell. What changes is only the picture by which we represent the objects between which the physicist has discovered and proved relationships. Various reasons make us from time to time change these pictures which otherwise are unimportant. But it is these pictures alone which change; the relationships always remain true, provided they rest upon well-observed facts.

It is because of this common foundation upon truth that the most ephemeral theories do not die in every part. But like the torch which the couriers of ancient times passed on from hand to hand, each theory transmits to its successor that which is the only accessible reality, namely, the group of laws expressing the relationships existing between things. These conclusions reached by Poincaré relative to physics hold as well for the other branches of science, chemistry, the biological sciences, even for those sciences which are yet young and classed as moral or social, since they all branch out from physics, and according to their nature have for their final object the foundation of their more or less complex laws upon those of physics. Accordingly, upon the latter will be based all of our knowledge of the world.

It is clear that the conclusions of Poincaré reduce to its proper value, which is a minimum, a certain common materialism that dreams of attaining the absolute and inclosing it in several differential equations. There is not, there cannot be, a metaphysical conception of science.

Those who, in the name of Poincaré, have proclaimed anew the failure of science have not understood him. Otherwise they would have seen that he battered down only a certain interpretation of science made by men who did not know it at all. The attitude of Poincaré has nothing in common with that of the men of the rank and file whose agnosticism ill conceals their ignorance and upon whom he sometimes liked to use his indulgent irony. "It is not enough to doubt indiscriminately; we must know why we doubt."

The fragile nature of scientific theories proves nothing against science. They are only show cases, shop windows, frames wherein we arrange more or less conveniently our treasures. It is just the same as when for our world's fairs we gather together all the most marvelous products of our industries in ephemeral palaces built of mill boards but of the most brilliant designs, and then, because the wind and the rain demolish these structures of boards, if we try to keep them too long, or because we demolish them ourselves to build again others yet differently to expose anew our products, who would dare to say that our human industries had failed? But that is just the way these men reason, who, may I so call them, are the perpetual assignees of the failure of science. Is it not just as a blind man would reason if it occurred to him to disparage the light of the stars?

But, side by side with these simple and ingenious detractors, there has recently arisen a new class which criticizes and diminishes the value of science. They uphold a body of doctrine due to a very intelligent, educated, subtle set of men belonging more or less to the new school of pragmatic philosophy. They pretend to draw arguments from the ideas of Poincaré. What would he think of them?

What gives pragmatism its absorbing interest is that while not ignoring science, arguing indeed from its results, it appeals to other criteria than reason. But this is not the time to examine these doctrines. In order to know what Poincaré himself thought of them let us ask him. There at once arises an essential antinomy. The aim of pragmatism, whence its name, is action, practical service, and if science has a value it is as a means of action and because it furnishes us with practical and useful rules. To Poincaré, on the other hand, it is knowledge which is the end of action. If he was glad of industrial development, it was not only because it furnished a ready argument to the defenders of science, but also because, by freeing men more and more from material cares, it would some day give to all the leisure to work for science.

This point of view is not only full of nobleness and beauty, it is indeed richer in useful consequences than utilitarian pragmatism itself. For a century and a half the pragmatists as well as the positivists (how can we refrain from wondering at the strange bond which unites two such different schools?) looked upon the discoveries which Galvani and Volta made upon the frogs as perfectly idle and useless. These men of science with a wholly disinterested curiosity ardently pursued their researches. It is from these little experiments, more or less then a plaything for the idle hours, that all our electrical industries with their innumerable practical consequences have sprung.

To many pragmatists science is only a nominal thing. The scientist creates the fact through experiment, then he denatures the rough facts, transforming them into "scientific facts." Poincaré replies, showing that "all a scientist creates in the fact is the language by which he expresses it." If some day we find that the statement of a physical law is incomplete or ambiguous, we have merely to change the language by which it was expressed. Because the language by which each one expresses the deeds of daily life is not free from ambiguity, should we conclude that these happenings of daily life are only the work of grammarians?

Finally, and this is the culminating point, the pragmatists consider science an artificial creation, contingent, uncertain, and teaching us nothing of objective reality. Has not Poincaré shown, indeed, that the mathematical sciences are contingent and that physical theories express only the relations between things and not the objects themselves? But here Poincaré calls, "Halt, there!" He shows that the only objective reality is precisely these relations between things.

The first condition of the objectivity to us of exterior objects is that they are common to other thinking beings, which fact we may know by comparing their impressions with our own. Perhaps, in my opinion, Poincaré goes a little too far when he affirms that this guarantees the existence of the exterior world, that this suffices to distinguish the real from a dream. We could, indeed, imagine our whole life a dream, with beings similar to ourselves telling us of sensations analogous to our own in regard to objects, so that the fiction of our dream seemed outside of ourselves. But this is not the place to discuss the reality of the exterior world, since its existence is postulated both in the scientific and in the opposing theories. The existence of what we call the external world being placed beyond doubt both by the scientists and by the pragmatists, it results clearly from what has just been said that since it is through "discourse," language, that men exchange sensations, there is no objectivity without "discourse." Discourse which, according to certain nominalists, creates nonexistent facts and is a veil before objectivity, becomes, on the contrary, its necessary condition. But on the other hand, "the sensations of others are for us an eternally closed world." I shall never know whether the color sensation produced upon me by a bluet and by the first and third stripes of the French flag are the same as yours. All that I know is that, with you as with me, the bluet and these stripes produce a similar sensation which we call blue, or otherwise, and that the third stripe, with you as with me, produces a different sensation from the first. Thus what is "pure quality" in sensations is nontransmissible and impenetrable. Only the relations between the sensations are transmissible, and consequently may have an objective value. And that is why science, which furnishes us with the relations existing between phenomena, tells us of all that is purely objective.

The profound and subtle criticism which Poincaré has made of scientific theories leads us in no way to agnostic conclusions. Those who have tried to use it to contest the value of science have reasoned wrongly.

. . .

A great inventor, a great philosopher, Poincaré was also a great writer. If it were for literary merit alone he would deserve study. His language was vigorous and vivid, with a conciseness and clearness peculiarly French. He did not disdain to clothe any profound thought in the garb of a pretty phrase, wherein he grouped himself with the encyclopædists who, like d'Alembert, believed a precious liquor yet finer when served in a finely cut glass.

The last century has produced experimenters of genius like

Pasteur, men of astonishing intuition like Maxwell. It has not produced men who have done as much as Poincaré for the progress of the purely deductive sciences and for mathematical discipline, or who like him could "think science" and place it exactly. The picture which he has left us is at the same time sad and encouraging. Science has its limits. It can know only the relative, but in that it is supreme. As to wishing to penetrate into what is called the absolute—the "things in themselves"—these questions are not only insoluble but illusory and void of sense. Science is an asymptote to the total truth as is the hyperbola an asymptote to its directrices, and further, like the hyperbola, it extends without end.

In the somber forest of mystery, learning is like a glade. Men enlarge continuously the circle which borders the clearing. But at the same time it continuously touches the shades of the unknown at a greater number of points. No one on the borders of this glade has known how to gather newer and more magnificent flowers than has Henri Poincaré. So, as long as there are men who think that it is noble to live at the summit where harsh truth is enthroned, his Lorraine name will tremble on their lips. If I may paraphrase a famous saying, he was one of the essential elements of human thought.

Svante Arrhenius *

1859–1927

———◆———

JAMES WALKER †

A LITTLE over 40 years ago the conjunction of the ideas of osmotic pressure and of electrolytic dissociation ushered in a new era in the development of the physical chemistry of solutions—an era of unexampled fertility. Van't Hoff and Arrhenius, the originators of these new ideas, have now both passed away. It is 16 years since I was charged by the society to deliver the van't Hoff memorial lecture. Today it is my task to discharge a similar duty in honor of Arrhenius. My relations to these men were altogether different; Arrhenius was a close friend, van't Hoff a remote immortal. The sketch of the life and work of Arrhenius which I present is therefore not that of a completely detached historian, but is shaped by personal reminiscence and tinged with personal affection.

I well remember when I first encountered his name. It was in the autumn of 1887 in the small departmental library of Baeyer's laboratory in Munich. On a shelf there lay the loose numbers of the first volume of the *Zeitschrift für Physikalische Chemie,* newly founded by Ostwald. Turning over the pages of this interesting new journal, I saw what seemed to me the very odd name of Svante Arrhenius as author of a paper on the influence of neutral salts on the velocity of saponification of ethyl acetate. I did not find this paper of more than moderate interest, but later in the year there was published another by the same author on the dissociation of substances dissolved in water. This was plainly a novel and striking conception, and although I was not altogether convinced by the arguments it contained I marked it for closer study at a later time. In the spring of the following year I left Munich for Leipzig and

* *A.R.,* 1928, pp. 715–735. Memorial lecture, delivered May 10, 1928. From *Journal of the Chemical Society* (London), 1928.
† Scottish chemist (1863–1935).

was caught in the wave of Ostwald's enthusiasm for the new doctrines of osmotic pressure and electrolytic dissociation. In Ostwald's laboratory I used to work in a small room with Wilhelm Meyerhoffer, who afterwards collaborated with van't Hoff in his phase-rule investigations. One day Meyerhoffer burst into the room, and pointing excitedly along the corridor, said, "Arrhenius is there." I peered out and saw a stoutish fair young man talking to Ostwald near the entrance hall. It was Arrhenius. We were made acquainted by Ostwald, but at that time I saw little more of him. Next year he came to work in Leipzig, and I had the opportunity of meeting him daily. He was one of the simplest and least assuming of men. He gave himself no airs and treated us young fellows as if we were his scientific equals, although at that time he was becoming recognized in Germany as a leading spirit in physical chemistry. In his own country he was still unregarded.

Svante Arrhenius came of Swedish farmer folk, a remote ancestor being one Lasse Olofsson, who in 1620 moved to the village of Årena, from which the family derived its surname in the Latinized form of Arenius, the spelling being changed in the early part of the nineteenth century to Arrhenius by the uncle of Svante, Professor Johan Arrhenius, a botanist and secretary of the Academy of Agriculture. Johan and his younger brother, Svante Gustav Arrhenius (1813–1888), the father of our Svante, went as students to the University of Upsala, and the latter subsequently established himself in that town as a land surveyor. He was appointed collector to the university, but the emoluments of the post were so meager that he was forced to undertake in addition the management of the estate of Wijk on Lake Mälar, which belonged to Count von Essen. He married in 1855 Caroline Thunberg, and at Wijk there was born on February 19, 1859, a son whom they called Svante August Arrhenius. Owing to improved prospects the family moved to Upsala in the beginning of 1860. Young Svante was educated at the cathedral school of Upsala and was fortunate in the fact that the rector of the school was a good teacher of physics. He left at the age of 17 with a good record in mathematics and physics to enter the University of Upsala, where he soon passed the candidate's examination, admitting to study for the doctorate. It seems to have been his original intention to take chemistry as his main subject under Cleve, well known for his investigations on the rare earths and on complex ammoniacal compounds. Cleve, however, was apparently an uninspiring teacher and neglected the theoretical side of chemistry. Arrhenius records that he never heard any mention from the rostrum of the periodic law, although it was already

10 years old, nor when he came to write his thesis had he any knowledge of the existence of the law of Guldberg and Waage, which was even older. In 1881 he definitely turned to physics, although the conditions for its study in Upsala were far from ideal. Thalén was at that time professor of physics there. His reverence for his master and predecessor Angström was so great that, beyond the apparatus for elementary students, there was little else in the department but instruments for exact measurements of wave lengths, a subject for which Arrhenius had no liking. Thalén did not encourage independent work in his laboratory, and Arrhenius was forced to look about for some other opportunity to begin physical research. He, with a fellow student, repaired in September 1881 to Stockholm with the intention of working in the laboratory of Erik Edlund, professor of physics to the Swedish Academy. Edlund gave them a hearty welcome, and they began by assisting him in his work on electromotive forces in the spark discharge. In the spring of the following year Arrhenius started his first independent research on the decay of galvanic polarization with time, an account of which was published in the *Bihang* of the Swedish Academy of 1883. From this he passed to the measurement of the conducting power of electrolytic solutions.

It is of interest to inquire into the reasons which induced Arrhenius to take up this line of work. The pursuit of science, like other human activities, is not exempt from the prevalence of fashions. At the period under consideration the study of the properties of solutions was in the air. Van't Hoff was busy tracing the analogy between dilute solutions and gases; Raoult was developing empirical methods for the determination of the molecular weights of dissolved substances; Kohlrausch had just perfected his telephone method for determining electrolytic conductivities; Ostwald was working at reaction velocities and the affinities of acids and bases in aqueous solution. Arrhenius yielded to the same influence, but curiously enough what led him to the investigation of electrolytic solutions was not directly concerned with the conducting substances themselves. He tells us that Cleve in his lectures had emphasized the impossibiltiy of ascertaining the molecular weights of substances, such as sugar, which could not be volatilized without decomposition. Arrhenius rightly recognized that this was a great drawback, by the removal of which a considerable advance in chemistry would be rendered possible. He was unaware of Raoult's work and thought that some light might be thrown on the molecular weight of dissolved substances by measurements of electrolytic conductivity. He knew that when some of the water of a conducting solution was replaced by more complex nonconducting substances, such as alcohol, the conductivity was lowered, and he thought it might be feasible to deduce the molecular weight of this added substance from its effect on the conductivity. He had not proceeded far with his measurements, however, when he recognized that the state of the conducting salt was the matter of primary importance.

The theory of electrolysis and electrolytic solutions was also decidedly in the air at the same period. The chains of Grotthus, the hypothesis of Clausius on continual momentary separation of ions, Hittorf's work on migration, Helmholtz's conception of the atomic nature of electricity, the work of Kohlrausch on conductivity, were all leading up to some definite comprehensive theory which in the end was furnished by Arrhenius.

Arrhenius completed his experimental work in the spring of 1883 and wrote the theoretical part at his home in the summer of the same year. The memoir containing the results of his conductivity experiments and the conclusions he deduced from them was submitted to the Swedish Academy of Sciences in June 1883, and published in the following year (*Bihang*, vol. 8, Nos. 13 and 14). It is in French and is entitled "Investigations on the Galvanic Conductivity of Electrolytes. Part I. Determination of the conductivity of extremely dilute solutions by means of the depolarizer; Part II. Chemical theory of electrolytes." Arrhenius undertook the experimental investigation of dilute solutions himself, for although Kohlrausch had made similar measurements and had quoted some numerical data, the final publication of his results was delayed till 1885. The depolarizer which Arrhenius used was an apparatus devised by Edlund in 1875 and corresponds roughly to a hand-driven rotating commutator. It is of interest to note that the conductivity cell which bears Arrhenius's name is described in this paper.

Arrhenius measured the resistance of a considerable number of salts, acids, and bases at various dilutions, sometimes as high as $v = 10,000$. Unfortunately the actual dilutions are not given, so that it is difficult to correlate the data of Arrhenius with those of other authors. He tabulated his results so as to show in what ratio the resistance of an electrolyte is increased when the dilution is doubled. This ratio, as Kohlrausch had found earlier, is nearly equal to 2 for most salts, i.e., specific conductivity is nearly proportional to concentration. Departure from this ideal value he took as a basis for classification of the dissolved electrolytes and showed that chemically similar substances fell into the same category when classified according to dilution ratios. A discussion of the data led Arrhenius to the conclusion that "if on dilution of a solution the conductivity does not change proportionally to the amount of electrolyte, then a chemical change has occurred on addition of the solvent." He exemplifies this by the consideration of potassium cyanide with the abnormally high dilution ratio of 2.14, which he attributes to the partial splitting of the salt into acid and base on dilution with water. The abnormal values obtained for soluble hydroxides and dilute solutions of acids he attributes to the presence of small quantities of ammonium carbonate in the solvent water.

The importance of this paper, however, does not lie in the experimental measurements or in the detailed deductions, but in the general ideas which Arrhenius developed in the second part. Instigated and encouraged by Otto Pettersson, then professor of chemistry in Stockholm, Arrhenius greatly expanded this theoretical section, which contains the germ of the later theory of electrolytic dissociation. He bases his theoretical treatment on the hypothesis of Williamson and Clausius. How this hypothesis presented itself to a clear and critical contemporary mind, unacquainted with the work of Arrhenius, may best be gathered from the admirable report on electrolysis presented by Oliver Lodge to the British Association in 1885. Lodge writes:

No polarization exists inside a homogeneous electrolyte; there is no chemical cling of the atoms there, but only a frictional rub. Such a fact as this, if well established, renders necessary some form of dissociation hypothesis. The form of dissociation hypothesis suggested by Clausius and Williamson is well known. It supposes that the vast majority of molecules in an electrolyte are quite insusceptible to the influence of electrodes, but that a few of them (the number being increased by complexity of composition and rise of temperature) are, by collision or otherwise, dissociated and exist in the free atomic state, each atom with its appropriate charge. These alone feel the influence of the electrodes. ... Individual atoms, although permitted to combine as soon as they like, on this theory, are commonly thought of as existing in the dissociated state for a finite time. If there are chemical or other objections to such a view, it need not be held; all that the facts of electrolysis require is the most momentary dissolution of partnership—temporary but quite perfect freedom . . . Provided a sufficient supply of such temporary severances occurs throughout the liquid, no individual atom need remain uncombined for a thousandth of a second, so far as the phenomena of electrolysis are concerned.

Arrhenius derives from the hypothesis the notion of closed circular currents in the electrolytic solution in its normal state (i.e., when not undergoing electrolysis) which are due to the separation of the ions and their recombination with other than their original partners. This notion he uses in dealing with the equilibrium between electrolytes in aqueous solutions. But by far the most important original idea, on which he bases his further treatment, is that of the distinction of the dissolved molecules into active and inactive. He arrives at it in the following way. A solution of ammonia exhibits a feeble molecular conductivity which increases with dilution. This Arrhenius attributes to the progressive conversion of the nonelectrolytic NH_3 into the electrolytic NH_4OH as dilution is increased. He proceeds:

It has been shown that pure anhydrous hydrochloric acid is a nonconductor, that is, a nonelectrolyte. If water is added to it, it is converted into an electrolyte, naturally in a progressive manner. It is impossible to deny the complete analogy of this phenomenon with that occurring on the dilution of ammonia or acetic acid, although it takes place much more rapidly.

He sums up in the following statement:

The aqueous solution of any hydrate [i. e., acid or base] is composed, in addition to the water, of two parts, one active (electrolytic), the other inactive (nonelectrolytic). These three substances (viz, water, active hydrate, and inactive hydrate) are in chemical equilibrium, so that on dilution the active part increases and the inactive part diminishes.

Arrhenius gives nowhere in this memoir a precise account of the nature of the active and inactive portions. He indicates and illustrates what they might be, but that is all; he does not define. The most important special feature of the paragraph is the statement that the active part increases on dilution. He continues:

In what respect these two parts differ remains to be elucidated. Probably the active part (as with ammonia) is a compound of the inactive part and the solvent. Or possibly inactivity may be caused by the formation of molecular complexes. Or again the difference between the active and inactive parts may be purely physical. The same statement applies to bases, and we may also speak of the inactivity of dissolved salts, in which case the notions of inactivity and complexity completely coincide.

With regard to solutions of normal salts he makes the following statements:

(1) Aqueous solutions of all electrolytes contain the dissolved electrolyte at least in part in the form of molecular complexes. (2) If the at-

tenuation of the solution of a normal salt is continued, the complexity approaches asymptotically an inferior limit. (3) The limit to which the complexity of a normal salt at extreme dilution tends to approach is of the same degree for all normal salts. Probably this limit will not be attained before all the salts are split up into simple molecules, represented by the chemical molecular formula.

To fix our ideas, I have introduced the notion of coefficient of activity defined as follows: The coefficient of activity of an electrolyte is the number expressing the ratio of the number of ions actually contained in the electrolyte to the number of ions it would contain if the electrolyte were completely transformed into simple electrolytic molecules.

Before going on we shall describe more precisely the notion of coefficient of activity by the aid of the hypothesis of Williamson and Clausius. According to section 2 this coefficient is defined by the number of ions present in a solution. But to each pair of ions there corresponds an electrolytic molecule which can take part in the production of a circular current; that is to say, its ions are endowed with the movement assumed by the hypothesis. If, now, an electrolyte is constituted in such a manner that only a certain fraction $1/n$ can at the same time take part in such a movement, it is evident that its coefficient of activity is $1/n$. It is not necessary, however, that a chemical difference should exist between the active and inactive parts. For greater clearness we choose an ammoniacal solution as example. In this solution there are two different parts, one active NH_4OH, the other inactive NH_3. If the latter is transformed into the former, the sum of the molecules of the two species is not augmented. Thus if m and n are the numbers of molecules of NH_4OH and NH_3, the first factor of the coefficient of activity will be $\dfrac{m}{m+n}$. Now several of the NH_4OH molecules may be associated with each other, so that the number of physical molecules of NH_4OH is p, of $(NH_4OH)_2$ q, of $(NH_4OH)_3$ r, etc., where evidently $p + 2q + 3r + \ldots = m$. Again of the molecules NH_4OH only a fraction $1/\lambda$ presents a simultaneous movement of ions. The corresponding numbers for $(NH_4OH)_2$ and $(NH_4OH)_3$ are $1/\mu$ and $1/\nu$. In this case the coefficient of activity of the ammonia will be equal to

$$\frac{m}{m+n}\left(\frac{p}{m\lambda}+\frac{q}{m\mu}+\frac{r}{m\nu}+\ldots\right)=\frac{1}{m+n}\left(\frac{p}{\lambda}+\frac{q}{\mu}+\frac{r}{\nu}+\ldots\right)$$

It is intresting to compare with this coefficient of activity the "dissociation ratio" of Lodge, which is defined in the report from which I have already quoted. Lodge writes:

mn^3 is the number of grams of the electrolyzed or dissociated substance in a unit cube, and this we may write $N\mu$ where N stands for the number of monad gram-equivalents of the really electrolyzed substance per cubic centimeter and μ is its molecular weight compared with hydrogen. [Considering the case of two electrolytes dissolved in the same solution, he proceeds:] . . . there will be N_1 and N_2 to represent the amount of dissociated substance present, reckoned in gram-equivalents per cubic centimeter of solution. We come to the conclusion that we do not know the absolute velocity of any ion, and cannot know it without further information regarding the dissociation ratio (that is, N_1/N' or N_2/N') of each substance present, where N' is the total number of monad gram-equivalents of the dissolved substance in a cubic centimeter of solution.

To Lodge the "dissociation ratio" is in all probability small. Arrhenius, on the other hand, contemplates the variability of the "coefficient of activity" with dilution and the likelihood of its being large in very dilute solutions. So far the considerations are purely theoretical; now comes an important step, their union with experimental data. Kohlrausch had shown that the molecular conductivity of an electrolyte was additively composed of two terms, one depending on the positive radical and the other on the negative radical. But in extremely dilute solutions of salts the value for negative radicals was nearly the same; therefore, according to Arrhenius, "the molecular conductivity of the active part of an acid (in dilute solution) is constant and independent of the nature of the acid," and as a corollary from this "the better the (dilute) solution of an acid conducts electricity, the greater is its active part." For want of precise data for calculating the absolute value of the coefficient of activity, Arrhenius takes it as proportional to the molecular conductivity. Thus he is enabled to compare the activities of acids amongst themselves, and of bases amongst themselves. He finds at once that the activities of acids as thus determined from their conductivities agree well with our general notions regarding their strengths, and is led to the statement that "for acids and bases galvanic activity is accompanied by chemical activity." He proceeds to discuss double decomposition in electrolytic solutions, on somewhat hypothetical grounds, and arrives at a formula (containing coefficients of activity) which he applies practically to many important reactions. If in the general equation of double decomposition

$$AB + CD \rightleftharpoons AC + BC,$$
$$1 - x \quad n - x \quad p + x \quad q + x$$

are the molecular proportions at equilibrium, and a, δ, β, γ are the coefficients of activity of the various substances, then at equilibrium $(1 - x)(n - x) \, a\delta = (p + x)(q + x)\beta\gamma$. If the action considered is Acid + Base ⇆ Salt + Water, the product of the co-efficients of activity on the left is, when acid and base are strong, enormously greater than the product of those on the right, and salt-formation is, therefore, practically complete. If acid or base is weak, the two products are comparable, and in consequence, entire neutralization will not take place, notable quantities of acid and base remaining free. If the activity coefficient of one of the substances (say alcohol regarded as acid) is smaller than that of water, only traces of the salt are formed. Here we find a definite treatment of salt hydrolysis based on the following principle: "What is common to all these cases is the necessity of regarding water as an acid (or as a base) which competes with other acids (or bases) present in the equilibrium." Arrhenius states further the proposition, which requires some restriction, that "at a dilution not excessively great the quantity of salt decomposed is approximately proportional to the square root of the quantity of the solvent water."

The theory is then applied to the displacement of one acid by another, to the influence of acid salts, and to equilibrium in heterogeneous systems. The consequences of the variation of the coefficient of activity in homogeneous and in heterogeneous systems are considered, and sections are devoted to the behavior of molten electrolytes and to thermochemistry. He deduces the following important principle: "The heat of neutralization evolved by the transformation of a base and an acid, both perfectly active, into water and a simple salt, is nothing but the heat of activation of water."

After a review of anterior theories Arrhenius summarizes his work thus:

We have first shown the probability that electrolytes can assume two different forms, one active, the other inactive, such that the active part is always, in the same external circumstances (temperature and dilution), a certain fraction of the total quantity of the electrolyte. The active part conducts electricity, and is thus in reality electrolytic; not so the inactive part. Moreover we have proved that the necessary consequence of the hypothesis of Clausius and Williamson is that there exist continuous circular currents, in which the active parts alone participate. The molecules participating in such currents are necessarily decomposed according to the scheme of double decomposition, new electrolytes being thereby formed. On this basis we have founded a chemical theory of electrolytes, which, being deduced from very probable sources, possesses also a high degree of probability. This theory leads to formulæ valid for chemical processes, formulæ very conformable to those proposed by Guldberg and Waage, which have been verified in a great number of instances. . . . As a provisional approximation we have assumed the coefficient of activity to be equal to the molecular conductivity. The numbers calculated on this hypothesis and the reactions thus foreseen, agree very well with experimental facts. . . . These propositions and these laws are taken from the most different parts of chemical science; but as the theory agrees so well with reality on these different points, it seems probable that it ought to do so also in intermediate regions. . . . The theory is completely free from any hypothesis of an affinity different from physical forces, and in this respect is preferable to all prior theories. . . . True, it may be objected that the theory is only valid for electrolytes, while previous theories have embraced all substances. Against this we remark that chemical knowledge is mainly based on the reaction of electrolytes . . . Reactions in general seem to manifest a considerable analogy to those of electrolytes, so that one could perhaps in the future enlarge the theory until it becomes, with some modification, applicable to all substances.

Nowhere does Arrhenius mention the word dissociation, although, as we have seen, the word is currently used by Lodge. The idea is of course there, but there is no identification of the "active part" of the electrolyte with free ions acting as separate molecules. The theory of electrolytic dissociation is as it were in solution in this memoir; it has yet to be crystallized out.

This comprehensive paper, which runs to 150 printed pages, was presented to the University of Upsala as a dissertation for the doctorate of the university. Its somewhat strange form is no doubt due to the use thus made of it. At the ends of sections and paragraphs there are numbered and italicized propositions, of widely different degrees of probability, and deduced by arguments of very different degrees of cogency. The paper then on a cursory inspection might convey an unfavorable impression if only the italicized portions were attended to. These propositions were probably the theses which were to be defended by the candidate in public debate with an opponent appointed by the university. The disputation passed off successfully, and it must have been a bitter disappointment to Arrhenius when his dissertation was awarded a fourth class (*non sine laude approbatur*) and his defense a third (*cum laude approbatur*). After every allowance has been made for the novel and unusual character of the dissertation, it is difficult to see how the University of Upsala, the university of Bergman and Berzelius, should have condemned a brilliant thesis on the very subjects of affinity and electrochemistry associated with these names. For the award amounted to a condemnation; in view of it

Arrhenius could not normally become a docent in the University of Upsala.

Arrhenius sent copies of his paper to Clausius, Lothar Meyer, Ostwald, and van't Hoff. "These celebrated men," he says, "with whom the Upsala professors were not to be compared, treated me as a colleague and not as a stupid schoolboy." Ostwald was eminently friendly. He himself in his work on chemical dynamics was being drawn to the conclusion that velocities of reactions in which acids participate are connected with the electric conductivities of the acids. He writes (*J. pr. Chem.*, 1884, 30, 93):

To test the idea I have during the past six months made preliminary experiments, which however have often been interrupted by other work. Meanwhile Svante Arrhenius, working in another range of ideas, undertook similar experiments and has published them in two memoirs, which also contain a very notable theory of chemical affinity developed from them. To the author of these memoirs, which belong to the most important ever published on the subject of affinity, there must be accorded not only priority of publication but priority of the idea.

Oliver Lodge was impressed by the paper and wrote for the *Reports* of the British Association in 1886 an abstract and critical analysis of it extending to 30 closely printed pages. "The paper seems to me a distinct step toward a mathematical theory of chemistry. The title affixed to it is 'The Chemical Theory of Electrolytes,' but it is a bigger thing than this: it really is an attempt at *an electrolytic theory of chemistry.*"

In August 1884 Ostwald visited Arrhenius in Upsala, and his visit had a marked effect on Arrhenius's future. Ostwald undertook to get Arrhenius appointed as a docent in Riga, and the offer no doubt led to the favorable reception of an application by Arrhenius for a similar post in physical chemistry at Upsala. The two men had while together projected a scheme of research on physical chemistry to be undertaken in Ostwald's laboratory in Riga, but the illness and subsequent death of Arrhenius's father kept him in Upsala. Through Edlund's influence he received in December 1885 a valuable traveling scholarship from the Academy of Sciences which enabled him to work in continental laboratories at discretion. The next five years were *Wanderjahre.* In 1886 he was with Ostwald in Riga and Kohlrausch in Würzburg, during 1887 with Boltzmann in Graz, during 1888 with van't Hoff in Amsterdam, and again with Ostwald, now in Leipzig. In 1889 and 1890 he worked in the laboratories of Ostwald and Boltzmann. When in Sweden he lectured on physical chemistry in Upsala or worked in

Edlund's laboratory in Stockholm. It was during this journeyman's period of his life that the theory of electrolytic dissociation was finally developed.

His original papers left the nature of the difference between the active and the inactive portions of the electrolyte unsettled, and the absolute value of the dissociation vague. As I have said, the theory was still in solution. The nucleus which determined its crystallization came through van't Hoff's theoretical work on osmotic pressure and his interpretation of Raoult's experimental results.

Van't Hoff, in a memoir presented to the Swedish Academy on October 14, 1885, showed that it was possible to write for solutions an equation $PV = R'T$, analogous to the gas equation, where P, however, is the osmotic pressure instead of the gaseous pressure. The constant R' was in many cases equal to the gas constant, but in many others differed from it. Van't Hoff then wrote the general equation for dissolved substances in the form of $PV = iRT$, where R is the gas constant and i a coefficient sometimes equal to unity, but sometimes assuming values much greater, in particular for aqueous salt solutions when the results are calculated from Raoult's experiments. For example, i is 1.98 for hydrochloric acid, 1.82 for sodium nitrate, and 1.78 for potassium chlorate. Van't Hoff contented himself with these empirical values and made no attempt at an explanation. His paper was published in 1886, but Arrhenius did not receive a copy until March, 1887. On the 30th of that month he wrote to van't Hoff from Würzburg:

Your paper has cleared up for me to a remarkable degree the constitution of solutions. If, for example, sodium chloride were normal in its behavior, i. e., if it consisted of simple molecules, its coefficient i would be equal to unity. But since i is much greater than unity, the natural explanation is to say that NaCl is partially dissociated, just as we say that at high temperatures I_2 is dissociated. Now this assumption might be deemed very rash, were it not that on other grounds we are led to look upon electrolytes as partially dissociated, for we assume that they decompose into their ions. But as these ions are charged with very great quantities of electricity of opposite sign, conditions are such that we cannot in all cases treat a solution of NaCl as if it simply consisted of Na and Cl. The pressure on the walls cannot, however, be appreciably affected, so that in this case the solution acts as if Na and Cl were free. And when we consider which substances (according to Raoult's experiments) are abnormal, it is not the inorganic (e. g., not $HgCl_2$, CO_2, H_2S, etc.), but the electrolytic substances (i. e., substances which are conductors of the same order as salts) even when they are organic, e. g., oxalic acid. Trichloroacetic acid and sulphonic acids must show this still more clearly when they come to be investigated. Since according to the above assumption electrolytes decompose into their ions, the coefficient i must lie between unity and the number of the ions. This in reality holds good; for example, the coefficient nearly reaches 2 for NaCl, KCl, KNO_3, NaOH, etc., which have two ions; for $Ba(OH)_2$, $CaCl_2$, K_2SO_4, etc., which have three ions, it almost approaches 3, and so on. . . . From the above assumption we can even calculate the value of i from the conductivity, and this I shall probably soon carry out; till now time has failed me. What I called in my paper "Sur la conductibilité" active molecules, are thus the same as dissociated molecules. One of the propositions which I then put forward would now be written: In all probability all electrolytes are completely dissociated at the most extreme dilution.

Here we have the first appearance of the theory of electrolytic dissociation. If we cannot fix its birthday at least we can its birth month. It is clear, definite and concise, and all Arrhenius's previous theoretical treatment can easily be translated into terms of it. Van't Hoff accorded the new idea a favorable reception. He replied on April 7: "Your statement that the number of ions roughly keeps pace with the values of i, and that the conductivity also increases with i, agrees with most of the cases known to me." . . . He remarks that he had always thought of the dissociation into ions as being confined to an extremely small portion of the salt, but confesses that he sees no grave difficulty in assuming a greater dissociation. Arrhenius in a letter dated April 13 is pleased to learn that this is van't Hoff's view and states that Emil Fischer, with whom he had discussed the matter in Würzburg, although he was friendly to the idea, was of opinion that most chemists would be opposed to such far-reaching dissociation. Arrhenius continues:

It is true that Clausius had only assumed that a minute quantity of a dissolved electrolyte is dissociated, and that all other physicists and chemists had followed him; but the only reason for this assumption, as far as I can understand, is a strong feeling of aversion to a dissociation at so low a temperature, without any actual facts against it being brought forward. In my paper on the conductivity of electrolytes I was led to the conclusion that at the most extreme dilutions all salts would consist of simple conducting molecules. But the conducting molecules are, according to the hypothesis of Clausius and Williamson, dissociated; hence at extreme dilutions all salt molecules are completely dissociated. The degree of dissociation can be simply found on this assumption by taking the ratio of the molecular conductivity of the solution in question to the molecular conductivity at the most extreme dilution.

These two short excerpts give the gist of the complete theory.

Van't Hoff and Arrhenius now made their ideas available to a wider public by publishing them in the first volume of the *Zeitschrift für physikalische Chemie* in the latter half of 1887. Van't Hoff accepts Arrhenius's theory for electrolytes and adds finally Avogadro's Law to those of Boyle and Charles as being applicable to dilute solutions. Arrhenius gives the relationship between van't Hoff's constant i and the degree of dissociation a in the form $i = 1 + (k - 1)a$ where k is the number of ions into which the molecule of the electrolyte dissociates, e.g., 2 for KCl, 3 for K_2SO_4. He compares the values of i calculated from Raoult's freezing-point data on the one hand, and from the molecular conductivity on the other, for some 80 different substances, and finds a very satisfactory accordance. In the second part of his paper he discusses the properties of electrolytes in aqueous solutions from the point of view of their additive character, which he attributes to the independence of their ions.

The theories of osmotic pressure and of electrolytic dissociation were now fairly launched, and, propelled by the driving power of Ostwald through the waters of scientific opinion, they soon attained a world-wide recognition, though often meeting very heavy weather. That their reception was so favorable is indeed somewhat surprising, for it must be remembered that in those days the marvels of X rays, of radioactivity, of wireless transmission, had not prepared the way for that loosening and abandonment of fixed physical ideas to which we are today accustomed, if not altogether reconciled. Their general acceptance was largely due to their comparative simplicity. They could be easily tested practically, and little mathematics was required in their development, so that experimental work, centered originally in Ostwald's laboratory but gradually spreading to others in Germany and abroad, was in the next decade assiduously carried out by a new generation of physical chemists. Their application by Nernst (1889) to electromotive force was an advance of the first order. Arrhenius himself played a principal part in the development. Amongst his important contributions to the subject published in Ostwald's *Zeitschrift* may be mentioned the theory of isohydric solutions (1888), the heat of dissociation of electrolytes and the influence of temperature on the degree of dissociation (1889), the conditions of equilibrium between electrolytes (1890), the determination of electrolytic dissociation of salts from solubility experiments (1893), the hydrolysis of salts of weak acids and weak bases (1894), the alteration of the strength of weak bases by the addition of salts (1899).

At this point it may be well to refer to Arrhenius's position with regard to the problem of the abnormality of strong electrolytes, which, unlike the weak electrolytes, do not conform to Ostwald's dilution law. Naturally this puzzling exception to the theory he had put forward constantly claimed his attention. Although he did not succeed in accounting for it, he had arrived at a clear conception of the lines along which a solution might be sought, as may be seen from his book, *Theories of Solution,* published in 1912 from the Silliman lectures delivered at Yale in 1911. He groups the theories which might be brought forward to explain the anomaly under four headings:

1. Change of ionic friction with dilution.
2. Electric attraction of the charges of the ions.
3. Influence of foreign substances on the osmotic pressure (so-called salt-action).
4. Hydration of the ions.

The second of these, with its effect on the first and third, is now recognized as the chief cause of the abnormality. Arrhenius's original theory is sometimes spoken of as entirely obsolete. But it is well to remember that if the younger men of today see a little further into the nature of electrolytic solutions than Arrhenius, they do so by standing on Arrhenius's shoulders.

During these years Arrhenius also worked on other physico-chemical subjects, for example, on viscosity of pure liquids and solutions, on conduction in hot gases and flames, on diffusion in aqueous solution, on the velocity of hydrolysis of ethyl acetate and on the inversion of cane sugar in acid solutions. In a paper on the last subject (1889) Arrhenius makes another theoretical contribution of great significance. He is discussing the effect of temperature on reaction velocity which amounts at the ordinary temperature to an increase of 10 to 15 per cent for 1° rise. This is much too great to be accounted for by increase of molecular velocity or diminution of viscosity. Besides, the nature of the increase is altogether different from that exhibited in the temperature coefficient of ordinary physical properties. For equal increments of temperature the increase is not approximately arithmetical, but geometrical. This circumstance indicates that the increase in reaction velocity with temperature is not due to change in physical properties of the reacting substances. A similar very rapid change in reaction velocity is observed when ammonium salts are added to ammonia which is saponifying ethyl acetate. Here the explanation is that the ammonium salts greatly reduce the concentration of the free hydroxide ions which really determine the reaction. May we not then surmise that in the inversion of cane sugar the amount of the really active substances is increased by temperature? The amount of hydrogen ion, one of the active substances, is little affected by temperature. We must, therefore, assume that the other really active substance is not cane sugar, as this is not changed in amount by temperature, but another hypothetical substance, which is produced from cane sugar as fast as it is removed by inversion. Arrhenius here reverts to his old distinction between "active" and "inactive" molecules. The hypothetical substance is "active cane sugar" formed from the inactive substance. It is present at all available temperatures in very minute amount, and the quantity of it in equilibrium with the inactive cane sugar increases about 12 per cent per degree. We are therefore dealing principally with the effect of temperature on an equilibrium, namely, that between the active and the inactive substance, and can apply van't Hoff's equilibrium equation $d \log_e k/dT = q/2T^2$, where k is the equilibrium constant and q is the heat of activation. For a small range of temperature this leads to $\log k = C - A/RT$, i. e., a straight line should be obtained on Arrhenius's assumption if we plot the logarithm of the velocity coefficient against the reciprocal of the absolute temperature, the slope of the line measuring the heat of activation. Arrhenius's equation actually applies to many homogeneous and heterogeneous reactions, and although there is much that is arbitrary in its derivation, it is in its general character quite in accordance with modern ideas.

Returning once more to his personal fortunes, we find that after 1887 he was recognized abroad as one of the chief figures of physical chemistry, but the death of Edlund in 1888 deprived him of his stoutest champion at home and greatly reduced his chances of obtaining suitable academic employment in Sweden. Abortive negotiations to establish him in a chair of physics at Utrecht and of chemistry at Graz were succeeded by a definite call to the chair of chemistry at Giessen in 1891. Arrhenius, however, notwithstanding the *invidia inter suos* to which he had been subjected, was intensely patriotic and declined the offer on the chance of being appointed chief of the laboratory of physics in the Högskola (University College) at Stockholm, a post which at this time had become vacant. Arrhenius was successful in his candidature and obtained this lectureship, which was in 1895 converted into a professorship, although once more against formidable opposition, only overcome by the strong backing of German physicists. This chair Arrhenius held till 1905. During the years 1896–1902 he was rector of the Högskola, and through his personality did much to stabilize and develop the struggling institution, notwithstanding that he had no fondness for administrative tasks. Although his laboratory was small and poorly equipped, the name of Arrhenius was sufficient to attract foreign workers, among whom may be mentioned Abegg, Bredig, Cohen, and Euler, who afterwards succeeded him in the chair. Foreign distinctions also began to come his way. He was elected an honorary fellow of this society in 1898, and was awarded the Davy Medal of the Royal Society in 1902. At last he received recognition, and that of the most handsome description, from his own countrymen by the award of the Nobel prize for chemistry in 1903.

His interest had meanwhile been diverted from the study of solutions to other fields of science, at first to cosmic and meteorological problems. One of his very early papers (1883) dealt with an observation of globe lightning near Upsala, and his work on conducting gases had led him to study electrical phenomena in the earth's atmosphere. With his friend the meteorologist, Nils Ekholm, he investigated the influence of the moon on the electric state of the atmosphere, on the aurora, and on thunderstorms. In a long memoir (1896) he attempted to account for the onset and passing of glacial periods by the variation in the amount of carbon dioxide in the atmosphere. This gas exerts a selective absorption, allowing the solar radiation freely to pass inwards, but to a great extent stopping the lower-temperature radiation from the earth outwards. Arrhenius calculated that from this greenhouse effect the temperature in the Arctic regions might rise 8° C if the carbon dioxide content of the atmosphere increased to somewhat more than double its present value, and that in order to get the temperature of an ice age between the fortieth and fiftieth parallels, the value would have to sink to about half. The variation in the carbonic acid content he attributed chiefly to variation in volcanic activity. The problem of the ice ages is still a vexed question amongst geologists, but Arrhenius made a notable contribution to its discussion.

Another important paper on a geological subject was a theory of vulcanicity based on physico-chemical principles (1900). According to it the sea floor acts as a kind of semipermeable membrane, permitting water molecules to pass but not silicate molecules. Water at no very great distance under the surface of the crust would be at a temperature above its critical point, and therefore a gas, and would be absorbed by the fluid magma under the great pressures existing. But by extrapolation from known data it may be shown that, although at room temperature water is a much weaker acid than silicic acid, yet at high temperatures the reverse is the case, water at 1,000° being probably 80 times stronger than silicic acid. In the magma, then, water will attack and decompose silicates and thus be potentially stored up in the form of acid and base. When the magma on rising is cooled, the reverse process takes place; water is liberated and at a certain height will overcome the pressure of the column above it, eject the superincumbent fluid, and cause a volcanic eruption. A volcano thus acts in much the same way as a geyser. The theory aims at explaining the proximate cause of eruptions and has met with wide acceptance.

In 1898 Arrhenius wrote a remarkable paper on the action of cosmic influences on physiological processes, and in 1903 he surprised his chemical friends by publishing his *Lehrbuch der kosmischen Physik,* a work of extraordinary learning and scholarship. In it he passes under review an extensive collection of observational material and deals with it according to his own methods. The most striking novelty of treatment is the use he makes of radiation pressure, the existence of which had been predicted by Clerk Maxwell. It was applied by Arrhenius to various cosmic phenomena even before its experimental confirmation in the laboratory by Nichols and Hull and by Lebedev. Arrhenius calculated that at the surface of the sun the repulsive force of the radiation would balance the sun's gravitational attraction on black particles of diameter about 1.5μ, and specific gravity 1, and that smaller particles than these would be repelled. Schwarzschild made some necessary corrections and showed that the maximum repulsion would be for completely reflecting particles (sp. gr. 1) if their diameter was about 0.16μ, and it would then be 10 times the gravitational attraction. From the sun then we might expect streams of such minute particles to be shot out in all directions. Many of these particles would be electrically charged from the ionization existing in the sun's gaseous atmosphere. Arrhenius shows how the phenomena of the solar corona, comets, the aurora, and the zodiacal light may be caused or influenced by these particles.

With the beginning of the present century Arrhenius's thoughts took a new turn. Thorvald Madsen had succeeded in arousing his interest in the application of physico-chemical ideas to serum therapy. In 1900 and 1901 he did some experimental work with Madsen in Copenhagen and later in Ehrlich's laboratory in Frankfort. In 1902 he published jointly with Madsen a memoir on the occasion of the opening of the Danish State Serum Institute, of which Madsen had been appointed director. It was entitled "Physical Chemistry Applied to Toxins and Antitoxins." Madsen was responsible for the experimental methods, Arrhenius for the theoretical treatment. They maintained that the toxin-antitoxin combination (held by Ehrlich to be a firm chemical union) was in reality reversible and governed by the ordinary mass action law. The immunological phenomenon of antitoxin action was likened to the interaction of a weak acid and a weak base, such as boric acid and ammonia, which only partly neutralize each other. The work constitutes a classical study among the early researches into the underlying nature of immunity phenomena and contributed to laying the foundation of "immunochemistry," a term first applied by Arrhenius himself to a branch of biological research in which reactions of markedly specific character occur between biological principles of unknown chemical nature. Arrhenius pursued this type of research for a decade and published two books dealing with it, *Immunochemistry* in 1908, and *Quantitative Laws in Biological Chemistry* in 1915.

In the year 1905 Arrhenius happened to be in Berlin and was asked by the university adviser of the Prussian Ministry of Education if he would be inclined to accept a position in the Prussian Academy similar to that held by van't Hoff. This was a very tempting proposal, but Arrhenius with his usual patriotism requested time to consider it and asked and was granted permission to speak of it to the Minister of Education in Sweden. It had been the intention of the Academy of Sciences to found a Nobel institute for chemistry and one for physics, but the wish having been expressed by King Oscar II that Arrhenius should not be allowed to leave Sweden, the academy resolved to found forthwith, instead of the two proposed institutes, a Nobel Institute for physical chemistry, and of this new foundation Arrhenius was appointed director. It was housed at first in temporary quarters in Stockholm, but at Experimentalfältet, a pretty park in the neighborhood of the town, a small laboratory was erected with an official residence attached. The laboratory was inaugurated in 1909. Here, with an assistant and a few research workers as guests, Arrhenius could work and write under ideal conditions on such problems of physical chemistry, physiological chemistry, immunochemistry, meteorology, and cosmic physics as might please him.

The stormy period of Arrhenius's career was now definitely over, and from the time of his appointment to the Nobel Institute life went very smoothly for him. From being a scientific outcast in Sweden he became a scientific oracle, known and respected by all classes of the people. He himself did little practical work in the new laboratory but stimulated and encouraged others. One of his chief pleasures was to attend conferences in all countries for the purpose of meeting his scientific colleagues and discussing with them their special problems. He often visited England and was elected a foreign member of the Royal Society in 1911. In the same year he lectured in America and was presented with the Willard Gibbs Medal of the American Society. In 1914 he gave the Faraday lecture to our own society, and the Tyndall lecture to the Royal Institution. Arrhenius liked to acquire knowledge at first hand and visited many laboratories for this purpose. He spent, for example, three weeks in Rutherford's laboratory in Manchester, working at a practical course in radioactivity under Geiger. At the end of a week he had started a research on the solubility of active deposits and was with difficulty dragged away from his electroscope to witness some of Jacques Loeb's starfish experiments at the marine biological station.

He devoted a large part of the later years of his life to popularizing science. A firm believer in progress through enlightenment, he sought to bring a knowledge of scientific fact and method before the general public. His clear and easy style made his books attractive, though the matters dealt with were often in themselves difficult. The first of these books, *Världarnas Utveckling (Worlds in the Making),* which treats in a popular manner some of the subjects of his *Kosmische Physik,* had an immediate and world-wide success, being translated into all the important European languages.

Happy in his work and happy in his family life, Arrhenius during his later years radiated contentment. He was twice married— in 1894 to Sofia Rudbeck, and in 1905 to Maria Johansson. By the first marriage he had one son, Olov Vilhelm Arrhenius, who is known for his work in soil science and agricultural botany, and by the second a son and two daughters. His health remained good until the aumumn of 1925, and although he recovered in a remarkable way from the first seizure, he retired from the directorship of the Nobel Institute in February 1927, when he was granted a full pension and the right to remain in the official residence. On October 2, 1927, he died after a week's illness and was buried in Upsala on the 8th day of that month after a solemn service in Stockholm on the previous day.

Arrhenius was of the old breed of natural philosophers, a true polyhistor, devoted to science at large. Being endowed with a memory both tenacious and accurate, he had a marvelous command of scientific fact. He was, however, no unimaginative empiric; his synthetic fancy played over the vast store of knowledge and sought relations between apparently isolated regions. In consequence, his original ideas were concerned with borderland sciences —physical chemistry, cosmic physics, geophysics, immunochemistry. The conjunction in him of two special faculties explains the character of much of his work—his aptitude for scientific speculation and an extraordinary facility in dealing with figures. He loved statistics, and it is recorded of him that as a very small boy he delighted to sit beside his father and help him in casting his laborious accounts. Arrhenius might begin a new line of work by the consideration of tables of numerical data collected by himself or others. He would frame a formula to fit them—an exercise at which he was uncannily expert—and then evolve a physical hypothesis to account for the formula. Or he might start with a bold speculation as to how two entities were related, formulate this relation, and check the formula by means of data of observation or experiment. There was constant interplay between the speculative and the quantitative sides of his mind. I recollect that one day in the laboratory at Leipzig, after a long spell of very arduous experimental work, he downed tools, saying, "I have worked enough; now I must think," and did not reappear in the laboratory for a fortnight. Extreme experimental accuracy he never aimed at, considering it rather a disadvantage in the search for a general law, and he used to boast that he had never performed an exact experiment in his life. But this statement must be taken with a grain of salt. I know that his work at Leipzig was certainly more accurate than that of most of his fellow workers in the laboratory, although carried out with the simplest possible apparatus.

Arrhenius had nothing academic about him save learning. In person he was stoutly built, blond, blue-eyed, and rubicund, a true son of the Swedish countryside. His nature was frank, generous, and expansive. He was full of robust vitality and primitive force. He had hearty likes and dislikes, and beneath his inborn geniality and good humor was a latent combativeness, easily aroused in the cause of truth and freedom. He was not politically active, but he was fond of discussing the large questions of world politics. He spoke very bitterly of Norway when she broke the union with Sweden, but later admitted that the separation had been best for both countries and expressed to me the hope that Britain would give Ireland similar complete freedom. The World War he regarded as essentially a struggle between Germany and Britain, and although his greatest scientific friends belonged to the Central Powers, his sympathy was definitely with the Allies.

A word may be said about Arrhenius as a linguist. He held that to speak a foreign language what one wanted was not so much knowledge as courage. Being liberally endowed with this latter quality, he spoke and wrote many languages with ease and confidence, if not with accuracy. Indeed he considered it a waste of time to acquire the niceties of a language and was of opinion that there should be a universal language—he suggested a simplified English. Any shortcomings of accent or idiom in his own English were amply compensated by a Shakespearean richness of vocabulary, which gave extraordinary pith to many of his sayings. He paid little regard to literature or art, but keenly appreciated natural beauty, especially the gladdening phenomena of spring. His life-long interest in the lovely northern dancers and in comets that "brandish their crystal tresses in the sky" had most likely an æsthetic as well as a scientific basis.

Sweden can boast of many eminent names in science, of which two are by common consent of the first magnitude—Linnæus and Berzelius. Since the death of Berzelius she has had no name to rank with these save the name we commemorate to-day—Arrhenius. Yet withal Svante Arrhenius was so simple, so genuine, so human a personality that those who had the privilege of his intimacy always forgot the great scientific master in the genial companion and the kindly, lovable friend.